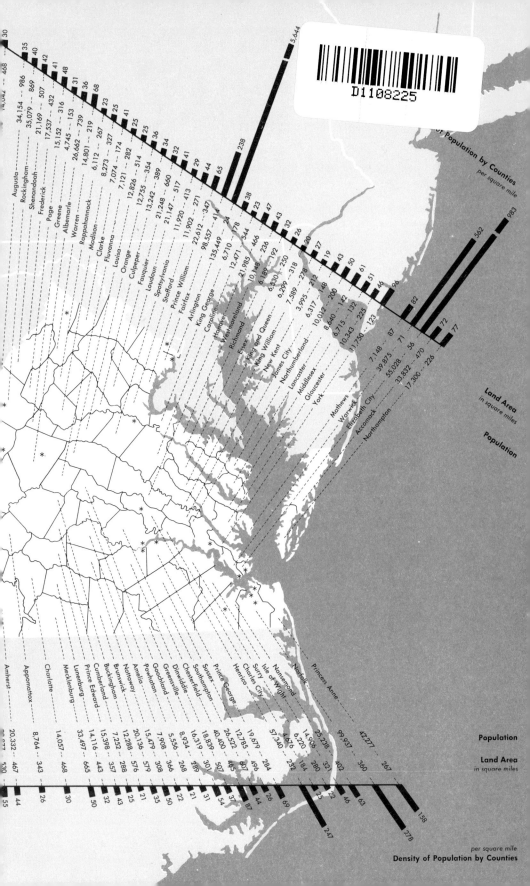

of Population by Counties
per square mile

Land Area
in square miles

Population

Population

Land Area
in square miles

per square mile
Density of Population by Counties

To Mr. Frederick G. Heymann
with my compliments
and best regards,

Jean Gottmann

Princeton, June 5, 1957.

Virginia at Mid-Century

JEAN GOTTMANN

Institute for Advanced Study, Princeton

WITHDRAWN

HENRY HOLT AND COMPANY · New York

23215-0315

Printed in the United States of America

Foreword

THIS VOLUME attempts to describe the Commonwealth of Virginia as it is today and to examine objectively its resources, its problems, and its potentialities. It is perhaps in order to explain briefly how a French geographer chances to be its author.

On an afternoon in June, 1952, while working in my office at the Institute for Advanced Study, I received a telephone call from my friend Dr. Abraham Flexner, formerly director of the Institute. It was an invitation to an informal meeting at his office a few days later. There I met Mr. Paul Mellon, a resident of Virginia and the founder and president of the Old Dominion Foundation. Through Dr. Flexner, Mr. Mellon had become acquainted with my book on Europe, in which I set forth the results of a similar study of the various European countries. I was asked whether I would be interested in taking stock, so to speak, of Virginia.

As I had for some years been familiar with the eastern section of the United States, the suggestion strongly appealed to me. The French school of geography during the first half of the present century has produced a substantial number of regional monographs on various parts of the world. To my knowledge, that method of study has not heretofore been applied to any of the American states. I was told that a pilot work of this kind, if well done, might lead other states to undertake similar assessments.

The fieldwork began in July, 1953, and has occupied about eighteen months. I have seen Virginia for myself, visiting every county and city in the state; and I have consulted scores of persons throughout the United States, and a few from abroad, who I felt could contribute to this study.

Among these I may mention a few: Professor Edward C. Higbee of Clark University, Monsieur Henri Morel of the French National Forest Service, officials of the National and State Forest Services, Professors Thomas J. Wertenbaker and Frank Notestein of Princeton University, and Professor George Boas of the Johns Hopkins University. To these and to many others associated with the University of Virginia, the Virginia Polytechnic Institute, and the staff of the Division of Planning and Economic Development of the Virginia Department of Conservation and Development, to the Henry E. Huntington Library at San Marino, California, and to many, many others—farmers, lawyers, officials, teachers, merchants, physicians, journalists—I am deeply indebted for willing and enthusiastic cooperation.

I am grateful to the Director and faculty of the Institute for Advanced Study for permitting me to carry out a part of the Virginia survey while a member of the Institute, and for much helpful advice. I wish to thank the Old Dominion Foundation and its officers, both for their material help and for their interest and encouragement. I was given a completely free hand to carry out the study in whatever manner seemed best to me and to reach whatever conclusions the facts seemed to me to warrant. While the Foundation made this study possible, neither it nor any of the persons who have assisted me are responsible for the result.

This project has been to me a delightful experience. Seldom have I enjoyed the privilege of working in such a beautiful environment, under such perfect material conditions, with such cordial, cooperative, hospitable people. Perhaps it is well that my inquiries have been concluded; had I prolonged them, I might have become prejudiced in my views of my subject.

J. G.

Princeton, New Jersey
January, 1955

Contents

Maps and Graphs

INTRODUCTION

The Significance of Virginia

VIRGINIA has probably been studied and described more often than any other state in the Union. Entire libraries of books have been devoted to various episodes or periods in the history of the Old Dominion. The part played by Virginia and Virginians in the history of America and of the world for three centuries easily explains the abundance of these works. Because Jamestown became the first permanent English settlement on the shores of the North American continent, the origins of the stupendous development of Anglo-America, this masterpiece of colonization, must be traced to Virginia in the seventeenth century.

Through the eighteenth century, Virginia remained the most important of the British colonies in America and easily assumed a leading role among the states during the early period of the Union. It had lost this leadership by the middle of the nineteenth century, but still it assumed the direction of the Confederacy in many respects during the War Between the States. No territory was more stubbornly and ardently disputed during that struggle than the area lying between the Potomac and James Rivers: Appomattox stands in the center of the Piedmont section of Virginia and Yorktown in the center of its Tidewater. Virginia occupied a strategic position indeed in the Eastern United States, and its geographical location remains today extremely important, in the middle of the Atlantic façade, at the entrance of Chesapeake Bay, and in the immediate vicinity of the national capital. Nevertheless, the relative importance of Virginia declined considerably during the nineteenth century and the first third of the twentieth. Substantial progress in recent years has fallen far short of returning the commonwealth to the position of eminence it occupied in days of yore.

Among the Southeastern states Virginia has been a leader in every period of its history, at least in some respects, but since the 1830's the Old Dominion has not dominated the national scene either politically or economically. In the great economic expansion of the United States after 1870, demonstrating the most spectacular development of resources in modern times, Virginia was satisfied with a modest part.

A region that blossomed in such remarkable fashion for two centuries and then experienced an equally remarkable slowing up of its growth over the next century cannot help creating problems for the scholar who wishes to understand what makes countries flourish or decline. To some extent Virginia's problem is that of the whole Southeast, but to some extent only. The whole Southeast did not share, even in the heyday of the plantation society, in the brilliant role of the Old Dominion from 1750 to 1830. Virginia is not, and probably never was, a completely "Southern" area. Although it led the South in fighting the Civil War, Virginia was classified by such outstanding scholars in geography as Guyot and Commodore Maury as the "southernmost of the Middle Atlantic states." While history seems to have bestowed upon Virginia the role of the northernmost of the southern states, a reverse definition could hold true in terms of physical geography. Indeed, the commonwealth occupies the very middle section of the east coast. Its territory is deeply penetrated by bays and creeks, which bring the ocean tide inland and are navigable by seagoing vessels. Further south the shores of the continent are much less chiseled by the ocean waves; and the interpenetration of land and sea, which remains characteristic of the American coast from Virginia northwards as far as Nova Scotia, disappears. To the south, Albemarle Sound, denting the coast of North Carolina, and the string of islands forming Cape Hatteras provide the transition towards the continuous, low, regular seashore, an immense mud bank, that neatly divides the realms of the ocean and of the continent in terms of geography as well as of transportation.

Since it surrounds the lower reaches and the gates of Chesapeake Bay, Virginia seemed oriented by the outline of its coast, at a time when water provided the easiest kind of transportation possible, towards greater links with the areas to the north. Nor are communications difficult towards the west, for several rivers in the western section of the commonwealth flow towards the Ohio River, to the valley of which Virginia's territory reached until the separation of West Virginia from the Old Dominion in 1863. The great thoroughfare of the Valley of Virginia, which led from the north to the southern sections that could not be easily reached from the sea, was early used by people coming from Pennsylvania and farther north and might have served as an additional argument in favor of Virginia's becoming the "southernmost of the northeastern states." Endowed with such a central and indeed commanding position, with such wide possibilities of choice, the Virginians chose to stay with the South. They contributed, nevertheless, perhaps even because of their stubborn choice, an important and original element to the shaping of the American national pattern.

Ever since the seventeenth century there has been a Virginia tradition, a Virginia mode of life, a Virginia spirit that permeates the whole history of the United States. These traditions and this mode of life are distinctly different from those of New England or of the "Middle States" of New York and Pennsylvania, which deserve to be called "Middle Atlantic" mainly because they are between Virginia and New England, the two principal springboards of early American settlement and cultural development.

Few modern nations were founded as late in history as the United States; few have had their growth and evolution as fully recorded; it would still be difficult to define plainly on the map one area that could be called "the nation's cradle." Chronologically, Jamestown was the first permanent settlement, but traditionally the tremendous process started when and where the Pilgrims alighted from the *Mayflower*. In fact the upbuilding of what is today the United States was started in many places along its present periphery at different moments during the seventeenth century. Virginia was one of these springboards, and it was able to grow through the eighteenth century into the largest, best-organized part of the new nation. It had at the time of the Revolution such a strong and original personality as a region within the United States, such a numerous and advanced *élite,* that it assumed almost naturally a temporary leadership. *How* this happened has been studied by many historians and is described in an abundant literature. The explanation of the events recorded by most of these works was seen in terms of the actions of a few exceptional individuals or in terms of a series of documents. Those writers, few in number, who paid some attention to the location, the environment, the differentiation from neighboring communities, usually alluded to some easy and simple cause inherent in certain physical traits of the area. The questions that still remain unanswered and little considered concern *what* the original nature of Virginia's contribution to the shaping of America was, and *why* this particular region provided this particular contribution. To anyone who attempts to better understand the past and the present of the United States these questions are well worth some exploration.

The case of Virginia is of course just one regional case. Whatever its past glory, the present commonwealth is only one of the forty-eight states, ranking thirty-fifth in area with its 39,893 square miles, fifteenth in population with its 3,318,680 inhabitants in 1950, and sixteenth in the amount of its income payments to individuals, 4,099 million dollars in 1951. A country's resources, however, are not all of a material nature, nor are they all statistically measurable. Resourcefulness is not a function of nature but a quality inherent in people, individuals as well as nations, in variable forms and degrees. To use whatever resources the accessible potential can provide, people need knowledge, ability, organization and the will to apply these; any analysis of the quantitatively measurable potential that neglects the resources of the mind and of the spirit will never arrive at a realistic or true picture. The part played by Virginia in shaping the modern American spirit and the modern American economy and way of life cannot be estimated or even described by a series of statistical tables or scholarly graphs, although all such data may be useful in the progress of the research. The role of Virginia consists of all these measurable material factors and of all the great men the commonwealth gave to the nation, but also of much more. There exists a Virginian mode of life of which the local people are proud and which has attracted many wealthy Northerners to the area. There is an attitude towards life that seems thoroughly American without some of the elements that cause strain in many other sections of the country. Life in Virginia has a definite charm that makes it different from other parts of the East. To feel those things is much easier than to describe them; to explain them is hazardous, although some elements of an explanation may appear in the factual analysis of the mode of life.

The Old Dominion has of course the advantage of chronology. As an area settled by people of European origin or descent it is the oldest in Anglo-America. It is therefore the part of the United States where the association between local natural conditions and local people has had most time to mature: the organization of a land by its inhabitants is a continuous process and a work in craftsmanship; as such it requires time to take its best forms; in that great art of country-making—rarely recognized although so important for all of us—wear makes for lasting qualities. The beauty of Virginian landscapes, plantations, and towns is the product of a long association between a certain kind of nature and a certain kind of people. It is not without importance and interest that in

Virginia the people have changed relatively little during the last two centuries. Basically the population of the Old Dominion has been much less affected by migration since 1750 than Massachusetts, Pennsylvania, Maryland and most of the other seaboard states.

On the vast lands of our globe there can be found no two inhabited areas that are entirely similar. There are always some features that differentiate any one of them from all the others, that make it in some respect unique. One of the factors that diversifies the world so much is that regions differently located will always be found to have, over a period of time, somewhat different histories; they were not inhabited nor administered by the same people. The past cannot be entirely erased. Most communities work hard to preserve it because they are proud of it, for it contributed to their formation. Virginia is surely one of the parts of America where this role of the past is best recognized and most highly valued.

A study of Virginia as a region must therefore give constant attention to the historical past of every section of the land, every community, every activity. Many Virginians pride themselves on belonging to a "conservative" state or group. This adjective has much more than a political connotation: it hints at a state of mind in matters of daily life that is somewhat related to the professional attitude of a museum's curator. Such a psychology is seldom found in whole areas in America, though it is much more common in the Old World. The fondness for the local past and the desire to make it survive within the present are parts of Virginia's tradition; these trends helped shape the "personality of the commonwealth." They will make historical inquiry essential to many parts of this study.

The knowledge of all this background is all the more important as today Virginia is changing fast. The rhythm of evolution may appear rather slow to an observer used to Californian or Texan rhythms, but it is an accelerated one compared to what has been customary in Virginia since the 1800's. Here again the progress of Virginia may be described as part of the general economic uplift of the southeastern states. In some respects, Virginia does not seem to be developing new resources as rapidly as some of the states to its south. It does not appear to reap all the advantages that its position as northernmost of the southern states should, in theory, confer upon its territory. Economic change is of course best measured by statistics, and statistics do not always put Virginia in the lead. Furthermore, to be effective and lasting, change must come first to the people's minds; and in this respect, it may be a long and difficult endeavor to convince Virginians. Whatever its pace according to statistics, present changes affect Virginia's attitudes and problems more and more deeply: the whole "personality" of the commonwealth may well be in the balance. This is a momentous time: it makes our study less simple but even more interesting, as we attempt to inquire into the dynamics of the transformation.

Finally the case of Virginia is a manifold one. Few other parts of the United States can display as much variety within an equivalent area. The commonwealth presents an actual mosaic of different regions; this mosaic appears on the topographic map, on the map of agricultural activities, on the map of geology and the distribution of soils, and in any attempt to describe the various kinds of people, resources, and industries. There are few crops grown in the United States that are unknown in Virginia. There are few major marketing systems that are not of concern to producers in Virginia. While various corners of the commonwealth have definite and various specializations, the whole of Virginia is not particularly specialized in any well-defined kind of activity. We shall, therefore, when examining the use of its diverse resources, touch upon a great many economic problems of national size and scope.

This remarkable variety of Virginia results to a large extent from its geographical position: to the east its lands border on the wide open spaces of the Atlantic Ocean but are also cut up into a great many scalloped peninsulas, and a few islands, by the powerful advance into the continent of the Chesapeake Bay; to the west the lands are broken up by ridges of mountains of varying size and height that partition the area into ridges, hollows and wider valleys, one of the latter being appropriately called the Great Valley of Virginia because of its breadth and length. The classical division of Virginia is thus into three parts at least: the Tidewater, the Ridges and Valleys, and, in between these two, the Piedmont. This is a sound way of subdividing it, as it encompasses both some natural features, resulting from geology and topography, and some historical features, each of these three sections having been settled at different periods and by somewhat different kinds of settlers under different economic circumstances.

The classical tripartite division can be applied also to several states lying south of Virginia, although these regional divisions do not play the same part in the other states that the three parts of Virginia play. The internal variety does not, however, stop there, for each of the three main parts has been divided up either by physical forces (such as bays, rivers, or ridges) or by historical environments. The fact that Virginia's Piedmont, for instance, is the northernmost section of the whole southeastern Piedmont naturally causes the occurrence of a whole gamut of different regional shades from North to South from the vicinity of the national capital to the tobacco and cotton belt. Some parts of mountainous western Virginia are akin to the section of Pennsylvania that stretches north-ward from them, others are akin to the ridges of West Virginia to the west, others to regions of Kentucky and Tennessee to their southwest. Virginia participates daily in the life of the eastern seaboard as well as in that of the tobacco- and peanut-growing South, in that of the crowded and suburbanized Northeast, in that of the mountainous Appalachian area, and even at times in the life of the coal-mining and heavily indus-trialized Middlewest. Truly, Virginia seems situated at the crossroads of the eastern United States. Such a position makes for a variety of local as-pects as well as for a catholicity of interests. The local tradition, however, enforces some isolation from that part of the neighborhood that is not truly Virginian.

The interplay of influences from the inside and from the outside again adds to the complexity of the case of Virginia. Some such interplay exists in any region, with the seldom occurring exception of areas completely isolated from the rest of the world. The factors that make the variety and the regional personality of Virginia offer a particularly striking illustra-tion of a rather universal phenomenon. Because so many different sec-tions of the United States are thus brought to participate in the Virginian framework, many of the problems or situations we shall be faced with in the commonwealth may take on national importance. In a study of this kind there are many ways indeed of looking at the case of Virginia: none of them can be said to have only local significance. Through either his-torical or present-day considerations, such a study ought to be of some interest to many people beyond the frontiers of the commonwealth. So vital a part of the United States is this region, and so great today are the role and responsibilities of the American people in the world arena, that some of the forthcoming chapters may be of import to sections remote from Virginia itself. Just as most of what occurs today within Virginia cannot be explained in terms of local factors only, the consequences of these occurrences do not stop either at the eastern capes or the western gaps.

It depends primarily on the Virginians themselves how far in space and in time the significance of what happens in Virginia reaches. The variability of their impact on history at different periods is demonstration enough. It depends also on the relative importance of Virginia as a whole within the economic and cultural life of the time; but this is largely de-termined by the activities of the Virginian population and by the interest aroused by the achievements of this population at home. Thus any study of Virginia as a case in history and in geography ought to begin with at least a brief description of what are and have been the land and the people; then the resources will be surveyed and their present use and trends scrutinized.

The careful examination of the problems of any region in the world may teach some lessons of general interest; few regions today, however, offer as many opportunities in this respect as does the commonwealth of Virginia.

PART ONE

The Land and the People

Making a country to live in, for a people who have come to it from elsewhere, always requires time, great patience, and many gradual changes. As new generations follow one another the relationship between the people and the land they occupy grows more intimate and comes to look natural. Men forget easily about the toil and sorrows of the past and about the treasures of skill, ingenuity and stubbornness that made the things of the present, even the landscape and the quality of the soil and water.

What is to be surveyed in Virginia nowadays has neither always been there nor always appeared the same. For three centuries and a half Virginia has been changing, and many of those changes were recorded in some way. But the whole territory did not go through the same process and did not undergo the same changes. Before we remind ourselves of the many changes, and begin to look at the present distribution throughout the commonwealth of people and things, let us be introduced to the variety of Virginia and particularly to the principal factors that make for such variety.

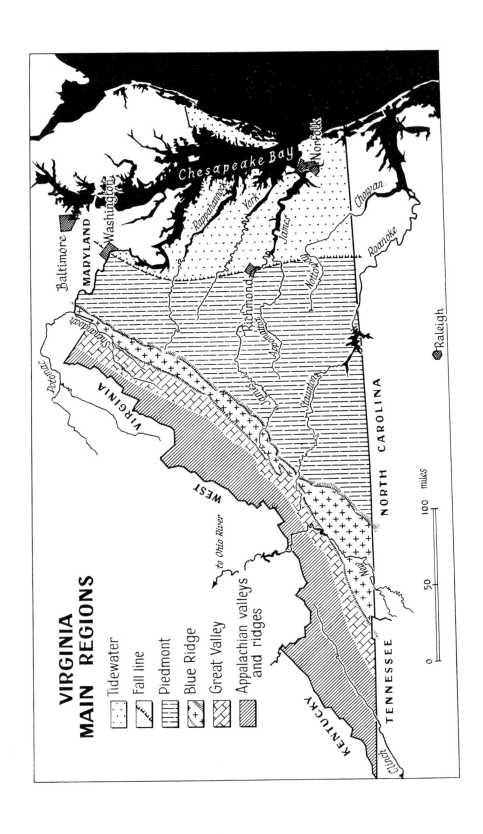

VIRGINIA
MAIN REGIONS

Tidewater
Fall line
Piedmont
Blue Ridge
Great Valley
Appalachian valleys
and ridges

1. *The Variety of Virginia*

HE FACTORS that shaped Virginia as it is today can be grouped in two main categories: physical and biological factors, all encompassed within the expression *natural conditions*, on the one hand, and the factors inherent to or resulting from human action on the other. A third category of factors intervenes in a subtler way and can be easily overlooked: both natural conditions and human activity have variable meanings according to the frame of relationships in which they are set; every isolated piece of data must be considered in the light of what happens in that field in the neighboring areas, and in the light of what kind of curve, upward or downward, that data has been following. Evolution in time and relationships in space are essential in the understanding of the facts describing a given situation.

The three main divisions

The basic and most evident differences within Virginia are between its western and eastern parts. The West is mountainous and continental, and here the main axis of topography and of early transportation or migration is oriented northeast-southwest. The East is a low flat plain deeply penetrated by the sea, and the main axis of the rivers and of traffic is east-west, with another axis, important in some areas, oriented straight north-south. The establishment of English settlers, beginning with 1607, started along the shores first reached by the vessels coming from Europe, that is, in the east or Tidewater; the western "Valleys and Ridges" section was settled later, after a delay of about a century. Thus both natural and historical conditions of development have been different in the Tidewater and in western Virginia. Moreover, Tidewater activities were too close to the Atlantic system of navigation not to be constantly influenced by economic

Shirley Plantation on the James River
Virginia Chamber of Commerce Photo by Flournoy

and political developments in Europe and the West Indies, while the
Valleys and Ridges people were, once they were settled, more isolated
from those systems of relations and more concerned with internal problems of the American continent, with regional marketing, Indian troubles, and connections with Pennsylvania to the north and the Carolinas
and Tennessee to the south. These differences in the local horizons contributed to the differentiation of Tidewater from Valley.

The Tidewater does not advance westward as far as the foot of the
Blue Ridge, the easternmost line of mountains. It is limited in its inland
expansion by the *fall line,* which follows the contact of the low, flat,
recent sedimentary deposits of the coastal plain and the mass of old, hard,
rolling, crystalline rocks that outcrop over most of the territory of Virginia. The *fall line* is of decisive importance in several respects: it accurately defines the Tidewater, as it creates on all the rivers that cross it a
zone of rapids which limit the possible surge inland of ocean tides and
brackish water; it separates two areas of different geological ages and
textures, therefore of different landforms and soils; the rapids on the
streams created opportunities for setting up mills, and the settlers knew

Cattle in Halifax County
Library of Congress Photo by Marion Post Wolcott

well how to utilize waterfalls; the river banks just downstream from the rapids became sites where sea-going navigation contacted whatever mode of transportation existed farther inland. The fall line thus rapidly became a favored location for towns where merchants congregated and mills could be advantageously built. A string of cities follows the fall line from the vicinity of New York down to the deep South, crossing Virginia, where it includes Fredericksburg, Richmond, Petersburg.

From this important line westward to the first rise of the Blue Ridge extends an area called the Piedmont, a low rolling plateau that slopes gently eastward until its hard crystalline rocks plunge deep under the mantle of sediments of the coastal plain. This plunge occurs precisely at the fall line. The Piedmont is closer geologically to the Appalachian ridges than to the coastal plain, but it is kin to the plain by its relative flatness and lack of elevation; it was also colonized chiefly from the Tidewater and in part before the main waves of settlement reached the valleys beyond the Blue Ridge. Nevertheless, it constitutes a third major division of Virginia, quite different from the two others, between which the Piedmont provides a gradual transition. A variety of local shades develops

Ida Valley Farms, part of the Shenandoah Homesteads, a Farm Security Administration project near Luray
Library of Congress

from the fact that the Piedmont is also a transitional area from north to south. In this respect the transition owes little to natural diversity, although the soil map is a variegated but most irregular one, and although the climate warms up slowly and the rainfall increases toward the south. The Piedmont changes more rapidly and extensively than the other sections because its northern reaches have been for some time under predominantly northern influences, from Pennsylvania or from Washington, while the area south of the James River remained predominantly under the influence of the Tidewater and more associated with areas to its south.

Such are the three main divisions of the commonwealth: the Tidewater or coastal plain, the Piedmont, and the Valleys and Ridges section or western Virginia. Each of them corresponds to a physiographic province, but each also has had a somewhat different history. The basic differentiation is due to the geological pattern—that is, to both the kind of materials that form the depth of the land and to the forces of erosion which, during a long past, have shaped the forms now appearing in the scenery of our area.

The geological past

It is necessary to go back to a very remote past to visualize the process that led to the present main lines of Virginia's landscapes and landforms. A very long and eventful story led to the present lie of the land. As the earth's crust was undergoing many pressures, foldings and other movements, the present area of the Atlantic Ocean sank and the section of the Appalachian Mountains was uplifted. Mountains and seas have not always occupied the same areas as at present. Geologists and physiographers have studied in great detail this long and complicated past. Our intention here is only to recall briefly the main points material to the purpose of this chapter—that is, to the understanding of the sources of Virginia's singular variety.

To a geologist the territory of Virginia must come rather close to a mixture of both paradise and hell. It could be a geologist's paradise because of the wide range of outcropping rocks that vary from very old crystalline and igneous materials to quite recent sediments and alluvial deposits, and because of the gamut of forms in which these rocks are arranged, all the way from the regular stratification of the coastal plain to the involved and highly irregular patterns of the eroded folded ridges. On the other hand, this layout is so involved and the variety so great that geologists get into increasing difficulties as they endeavor to classify, describe, and explain all the surveyed landforms and strata. Many aspects of this research remain a matter of debate between specialists, and it is for this reason that the area is not paradise alone to many scholars in the field. A few broad generalizations, summing up the generally accepted ideas, will be helpful to our purpose.

The most complicated past of the area belongs to western Virginia, with its puzzle of Appalachian ridges and valleys. This is a very old chain of mountains that rose for the first time in a remote era and were then folded and faulted under the pressure of orogenic forces. The general axis of folding outlined the alignment of the whole range as well as the present parallelism of the main valleys and of the high crests. The original topography of the ranges when the whole system first arose might have been substantially different from its present appearance, for the whole area was slowly planed by erosion. At first it seems that the level of planation or *peneplain* thus created by erosion must have been established just about above what was the sea level at that time: entire ranges of mountains were carried down by erosion to fill in the depressed areas, first the valleys within the ranges and then some of the depressions under the waves offshore. In more recent geological times, the western part of

The Great Falls of the Potomac, as photographed in 1909
Bureau of Public Roads, U. S. Department of Commerce

Virginia was twice uplifted, and each time erosion again started to plane down the whole area. In this process of planing, before an average level is reached over most of the area so that the peneplain stage is again achieved, erosion digs quickly and deeply into the softer layers and sets up the more resistant strata as towering ridges or hills. Any uplifted area is constantly being sculptured in between two stages of planing by the rejuvenated forces of activized erosion into a more diversified topography with many ups and downs.

The general northeast to southwest axis of the Appalachian folds is strongly impressed upon all of western Virginia. As the old stratification was folded under strong internal pressures at the beginning, most of the strata of various rocks were fixed in a position nearly vertical or at least endowed with a steep slope. The horizontal levels of the surfaces obtained or aimed at by erosion cut these sloping strata at a sharp angle, so that often they stand almost perpendicular to the plain. The result was to make long and relatively narrow ribbons of various rocks appear on the geological map, oriented predominantly along the northeast-southwest axis, shifting somewhat closer to an east-west direction in the southwestern tip of the commonwealth's territory. Such a pattern of narrow stripes (see page 18) has added to the variety of the topography as different degrees in hardness have presented varying degrees of resistance to erosion: hence the alignments of parallel ridges in the Allegheny

New River from the top of Castle Rock, near Pembroke
Norfolk and Western Magazine

Mountains, which repeats itself westward in West Virginia and northward in Pennsylvania; hence the somewhat steeply rolling landscape in
parts of the Piedmont. The upper crests of the ridges seem generally to
reach only one given height, as if the tops had all been shaved at about
the same altitude by an immense razor aiming at one upper level. This
level corresponds to the floor of an old peneplain, dissected again by erosion after having been uplifted. Erosion follows the general pattern of
the geological map on the former peneplain, digging out softer strata,
leaving the harder ones to tower.

The ribbonlike disposition of the strata on the peneplain level adds
variety to the local climatic conditions, as the ridges get more wind and
often more rain than the sheltered bottoms of the depressions; the opposition of the slopes is a well-known feature of the climate in mountain
ranges, those looking eastwards or southwards receiving more sunshine
than those facing west or north. The contrast is particularly sharp between exposures to the northwest and to the southeast, which are quite
numerous under the conditions created by the Appalachian folds. These
same original features in the geological map impress themselves, last but
not least, on the distribution of soils, which are extremely varied through-

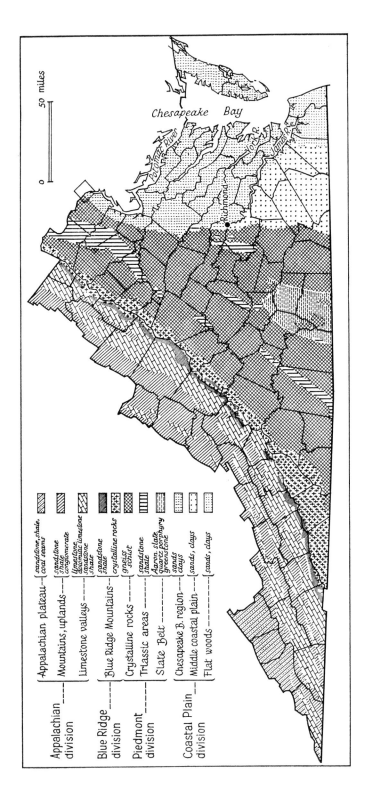

The Physiographic and Soil Divisions of Virginia
Simplified from V.P.I.'s *Virginia Soils*

out western Virginia and even on the Piedmont, where alternating strata of granite, gneiss, greenstone, sandstones, schists, etc., provide an equal variety of soils. The existence since an early period in geological history of the great depression along the western edge of the Blue Ridge, commonly called the Valley of Virginia or the Great Valley and filled with sedimentary calcareous deposits, has added a last touch of variety to the map of both climate and soils and therefore to land use. Thus, amidst narrow ribbons of crystalline rocks, covering on the whole a vast area, a somewhat wider ribbon of limestone floor supplies additional diversification.[1]

The coastal plain, the story of which is much more recent and simple, has had even so a number of periods marked by forward surges or retreats of the sea. Several different levels have been observed in different parts of the Virginian coastal plain: such levels, called terraces, are attributed to different stages in the process of accumulation in recent geological times; most of them can be traced apparently to the effect of the great glaciations and of interglacial periods. The most recent period, which followed the last glaciation, was marked by some progress of the sea into the continent, drowning the estuaries of rivers and widening the channels of streams as far as the tide could progress inland—that is, generally, to the fall line. The total area under tidal waters has thus been substantially increased in Virginia, as well as the length of the Tidewater shores. This recent geological history helps also to explain the scalloped contours of the Tidewater. The same development underscored the relative isolation of the various peninsulas and necks of land of which the Tidewater is formed. Geology is thus the first and major factor contributing to variety among the natural conditions of Virginia. It has largely determined the map of the soils. Its influence on the climate, though already stressed, is limited chiefly to local phenomena and to what is often called the *micro-climate*. Weather results from influences from outside the area.

Climatic factors

Virginia enjoys on the whole a mild and warm climate. The July average temperature stays between 70 and 80 degrees Fahrenheit over almost the whole of Virginia, with the exception of the mountainous areas where altitude moderates the heat. Thus in the higher valleys of the Allegheny ridges, Hot Springs (elevation: 2,195 feet) records a July average of 69.5

[1] The standard source of reference on the geological past is N. M. Fenneman, *Physiography of the Eastern United States*, New York, 1938.

Flame Azalea from the Blue Ridge Parkway. *Virginia Chamber of Commerce*

and Blacksburg (elev. 2,100 feet) 71.3, while stations in the Tidewater register several degrees more (78.3 in Norfolk, 78.0 in Richmond, 77 in Quantico). Piedmont stations show in-between figures, i.e., in the middle seventies: Lynchburg (elev. 681 feet) 77.2, Culpeper 75.3, Charlottesville 76.9; but it is rather hot in the southern half of the central Piedmont, as Farmville and Danville both register 79.5. The stations in the Great Valley show lower averages for July: Winchester 76.6, Staunton 74.8, Marion 72.3; such a decrease of the heat southwestward is due to a slight increase in altitude on one hand and to a definite increase in the continentality brought about by the mountainous environment, higher ridges screening the depressions from outside influences. Such continental influences make for greater ranges in the variation of temperature both within the year and within the day. Maritime influences, predominating in the east owing to both the Chesapeake Bay and the proximity of the ocean, have on the contrary a moderating effect on the ranges of temperature. Thus the maximum and minimum recorded (in the shade) until 1940 were in Norfolk 105 and 2, in Richmond 107 and −3, in Lynchburg 106 and −7, in Staunton 106 and −13, in Blacksburg 100 and −27; the annual amplitude ranged therefore from 103 degrees in Norfolk to 127 in Blacksburg. Altitude and continentality both increase the contrast in temperature between the seasons as well as between day and night. In the middle

Mountain Laurel from the Blue Ridge Parkway. *National Park Service Photo by Arthur Fawcett*

latitudes to which Virginia belongs, however, continentality has a trend to increase the summer maxima while the altitude chiefly depresses the winter minima.

The thermal regime has a direct and considerable impact on vegetation and agriculture. Average dates of killing frosts set the limits of the period of safe plant growth: they are a decisive factor in the choice of crops and in the sequence of farming activities within a given area. On the whole the growing season (i.e., the frost-free period) varies between 150 and 250 days. The records show averages of 244 at Langley Field (near Newport News) and 243 at Cape Henry (near Norfolk), 218 at Richmond, 204 at Lynchburg, 211 at Danville, 180 at Staunton, 168 at Blacksburg, 150 at Burkes Garden (in Tazewell County and in an intramontane basin at 3,200 feet of altitude). The Tidewater benefits therefore by a growing season two to three months longer than that of western Virginia, which is a considerable difference in terms of agricultural opportunity. The last killing frost in the spring is usually in late March or early April in the Tidewater, and in late April or early May in the western valleys, depending on the elevation. The first killing frost in the fall occurs sometime between mid-November, in the vicinity of the warm ocean waters, and mid-October in the upper valleys.

It must be remembered that considerable variation with respect to

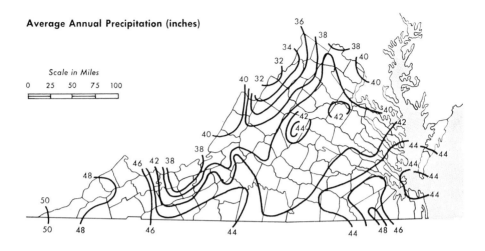

Average Annual Precipitation (inches)

Scale in Miles
0   25   50   75   100

these dates, as well as to extremes of temperature and their duration, can
be expected from year to year: while climate is a study in *averages,*
weather is described rather in terms of data on *extremes.* Some definite
trends have been observed in connection with changes in the climate, i.e.,
in average type of weather to be expected. The most important of these
trends to become obvious from records compiled in the United States, a
long-range trend covering approximately the last hundred years, is a
gradual warming up of the climate, chiefly through a greater frequency
of shorter and less cold winters. This trend does not preclude occasional
and impressive new offensives of cold in certain years. This trend is true
in Virginia as well as in the rest of the eastern United States and is
apparently worldwide. Most of the meteorological figures quoted above
were obtained on the basis of observations made in Virginia between 1890
and 1940; this may seem good as an average, but it may well happen, for
instance, that averages for as short a span as the 1950–1960 period will
show on the whole some warming up of the annual averages and a shortening of the cold season.

Precipitation is the other important component of climate: Virginia is
rather happily situated in this respect in the middle section of the humid
eastern United States. Average annual precipitation over most of its
territory is between 35 and 45 inches; such was the average for the period
1899–1938. There are usually close to 100 days annually in which precipitation amounts to more than 0.01 inch. The number of days in which
snow covers the ground varies in annual average from ten at the gates
of Chesapeake Bay to sixty on the ridges along the West Virginia border;
over most of the Piedmont the number is about twenty days per year.

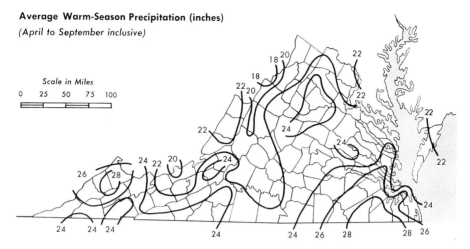

Average Warm-Season Precipitation (inches)

(April to September inclusive)

Scale in Miles

0   25   50   75   100

Snow, therefore, is seldom a problem, aside from some sudden and infrequent storms in the cold season. More frequent are the powerful storms with thunder and abundant rainfall which occur in the summer, and the Piedmont of Virginia is one of the few areas in the United States where the maximum precipitation within one hour reached over 4 inches. The average number of days with thunderstorms stands in the proximity of forty, which is close to the usual figure for the Middle-West but below the averages of most of the Southeast.

The distribution of precipitation over the commonwealth is naturally influenced by topography as well as proximity to the ocean. (See map, page 22.) The predominating air currents being from the west, the easterly influences of the sea do not penetrate far inland, although the inland expansion of the Bay and rivers helps this penetration somewhat. The moderating influence of the sea is felt of course all along the Tidewater and particularly on the Eastern Shore of Virginia, where the peninsula between the Chesapeake Bay and the open sea narrows down towards Cape Charles to a long and thin promontory. Influences from the west are not however entirely "continental." They may be defined so when cool and rather dry air masses of "polar" type flow from the northwest, i.e., from Canada. But during the warm part of the year, humid and often warm air masses flow into Virginia mainly from the west or southwest, originating in the vicinity of the Gulf of Mexico. Thus dampness comes to Virginia from two possible sources: the water spaces to its east, or the general system of circulation of air masses of "tropical" type that rise from the Gulf, move northwards over the continent and swing northeastwards towards the Atlantic coast. The major sources of precipitation seem to lie in the tropical air masses from the southwest.

Average January Temperature

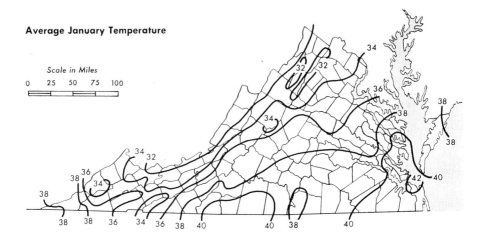

Average July Temperature

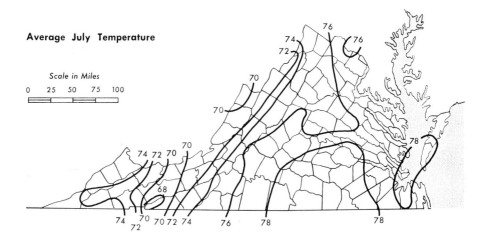

Average Number of Days without Killing Frost

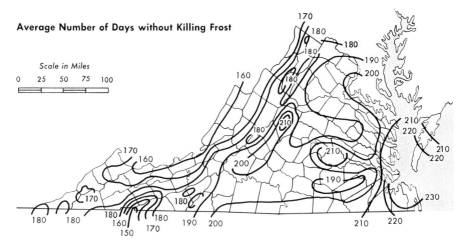

A farmhouse in Rappahannock County in winter
Library of Congress Photo by Arthur Rothstein

The general pattern of rainfall distribution over Virginia appears to depend upon exposure to or protection from certain humid winds. Within the same area the annual average varies considerably between weather stations exposed to humid winds and stations somewhat screened from such winds. Thus, sheltered valleys will have much less precipitation than neighboring slopes looking towards the west or southwest in the mountainous part of Virginia; and, in the Tidewater area, exposure to the sea winds is also important. Some of the highest recorded averages of precipitation are in the counties of Norfolk and Princess Anne, at the contact of ocean and continent; other maxima (i.e., averages around 50 inches per year) are found at the southwestern tip of the commonwealth, at such sites as Big Stone Gap in Wise County (50.34 inches), Elk Knob in Lee County (48.46), Dante in Russell County and Speers Ferry in Scott County (49.44 and 48.57 respectively). The distribution of rainfall has been summed up as follows by a Weather Bureau specialist: "The variation from north to south is from 36 to 44 inches, with an average of 50 in the extreme southeast and southwest corners of the State. The heavy amounts in the southeastern counties are due, of course, to the nearness of the ocean, while those in the southwest represent condensation from

Holiday Lake. Woods, waters, and mountains cooperate to create many beautiful landscapes in Virginia.
Virginia Forest Service

moist southerly winds rising over the higher ranges of the Alleghenies. Rain during the growing season is normally ample, averaging from 22 inches in the north to 26 or 28 in the south." [2] The distribution of precipitation over the year is fairly equal; there is, however, some slight concentration of rainfall in the warm season, i.e., April to September, which amounts almost everywhere to over one half of the annual total.

The months of heaviest precipitation are usually June to August, while the autumn months often show a trend towards drought. The actual distribution of rainfall in time varies greatly from year to year: thus in 1953 the Roanoke weather station reported the driest growing season on its records, which go back to 1912—only 6.47 inches in the July–November period, instead of a normal average of 19.04. In Danville, where the average annual precipitation reaches 42 inches, only 29.1 were recorded in 1930, but 51.9 in 1920 and 54.8 in 1891; in Williamsburg, 55.1 inches fell in 1923 and only 29 in both 1914 and 1930; in Hot Springs, in the Alleghenies, the annual amount ranged from 21.4 in 1930 to 55.5 in 1901. Continentality and altitude increase the amplitude of the range between recorded extremes for rainfall as well as for temperature, stressing one

[2] From "Supplementary Climatic Notes for Virginia," by Foy N. Hibbard, in *Climate and Man. Yearbook of Agriculture,* Washington, 1941, pp. 1168–69.

more contrast between the Tidewater and the western mountainous section. Thus while Diamond Springs, at an elevation of 25 feet in Princess Anne County, and Burkes Garden, at an elevation of 3150 feet in Tazewell County, show a similar annual average of 46.3 inches, the former recorded variations from 63.9 (in 1924) to 33.6 (in 1930) and the latter ranged from 63.7 in 1901 to 27.6 in 1930. In Richmond, relatively well screened from possible excesses of both oceanic and continental origins, between 1900 and 1930 the driest year showed 30.6 inches in 1921, and the rainiest year was 1908 with 52.8; however, Richmond records go much farther back in the past, and it appears that a maximum of 72 inches was reached in 1889 and an ebb of 27.6 in 1875.[3]

The more one looks into the records gathered by the Weather Bureau, the more evident the possibility of freak meteorological conditions becomes, since they have happened in the past. It remains obvious, however, that the differences in the precipitation distribution over Virginia lack in time as well as in space the spectacular variety so frequent in some other parts of America. The climate of the commonwealth is on the whole a moderate one, rather well supplied in both rain and warmth, with some variation of course from year to year and from one end of its area to the other, but not very much variation. As a factor in shaping the regional aspects of Virginia, climate works more for unity than for division. It underlines somewhat the effects of topography in terms of temperature, and the effects of latitude in terms of rainfall. Though moderate by American standards, the climate of Virginia is, and undoubtedly was in the seventeenth century, quite different from what the settlers of European origin were used to. As Carl Sauer put it, "This was indeed a lustier land to which the settlers had come, a land of hotter summers and colder winters, of brighter and hotter sun and more tempestuous rain, a land suited to and provided with a greater variety of vegetation than the homelands of Europe."[4] This fact was to have some influence on the process of settlement, and the relatively moderate climate throughout the whole area certainly favored a scattering of the settlers throughout.

Restrictive natural influences

With such an evenly distributed and rather favorable climate over a diversified topography, Virginia was bound to offer inducement and re-

[3] See *Climatic Summary of the United States,* Sections 93 (Central Virginia) and 94 (Southern Virginia), published by U. S. Weather Bureau, Washington, D. C., 1933.
[4] Carl O. Sauer, "The Settlement of the Humid East," in *Climate and Man. Yearbook of Agriculture,* Washington, 1941, p. 159.

Sand dunes on the low coast of Cape Henry around 1900. At present this area is occupied by a military installation. Virginia Chamber of Commerce

ward to the settlers, although the natural conditions would not be quite the same all over. It was endowed of course with a long and varied network of streams, so that conditions of navigation or transportation varied, chiefly with the topography from Tidewater to Piedmont, and then from valley to valley. Virginia was endowed also with a varied and complicated mosaic of soils; this was determined by the geology, and the shades of climate added to it. The map of the vegetation must reflect to some extent all the differences of topography, climate and soils, but in a fairly generalized way: Virginia is and seems to have been for many centuries predominantly an area of forests, as is most of the humid east of the United States. These forests were rarely pure stands of a single kind of trees: usually a mixture of species made it difficult to draw simplified maps; some species did however prevail in certain areas. Human action has greatly altered the picture of two or three centuries ago; although they may not be the same as around 1600, certain species prevail within the mixtures found in the different regions. The three main divisions of the commonwealth are again differentiated as to their predominant species: pines, chiefly the *loblolly pine,* predominate in the coastal plain, with an increasing frequency to the north of the "Virginia" or scrub pine;

hardwoods predominate in the western mountainous parts, although some white pines and hemlocks are locally found in the valleys followed by tracks sometimes called the "trail of the lonesome pine"; on the Piedmont a great variety of mixtures of hardwoods with pines constitute the prevailing picture. Most of the grasses presently found in Virginia are not native to the area but were imported since the seventeenth century, and their distribution is at present undergoing much change.

These being, in broad outline, the main features of the physical endowment of Virginia, the question still arises whether—besides the regional differences that required different responses from the men who settled these parts and put them to use—there existed some natural conditions which restricted locally in some special way either settlement or economic utilization.

How much nature restricted the development of the Indian civilizations in that area, if at all, before the advent of the Pale Faces, is a matter for speculation beyond the frame of this study and irrelevant to the problems of our time. The first settlers from Europe were already technically equipped to deal with forested areas; the old fear of the deep forest that permeated European history in ancient times had been largely overcome. Peasants in Western Europe knew how to do away with trees and how to utilize them: timber was then the prime raw material of western civilization, and deforestation had already gone so far in some countries, England especially, that the search for bigger and better timber supplies was in the seventeenth century one of the major driving motives for the development of North America.

Nor was altitude and the mountainous topography of the western parts much of a problem in the eighteenth century, when settlers came up to the Blue Ridge and the Alleghenies. These old mountains, several times planed in their long geological history, were not raised to forbidding heights; on an average, the lofty crests range in altitude from 3500 to 4500 feet; very few peaks tower to heights above 5,000 feet, such as Mount Rogers (5,719 feet) and Whitetop (5,520 feet) in the Blue Ridge, close to the North Carolina line. These are not excessive altitudes, as such slopes can be easily scaled by pedestrians or horses; these mountains were quite comparable to the ranges of England and Wales. The warmth of the spring would rapidly melt whatever snow winter might have thrown over the highlands. The forest cover was dense and deep on those ridges but should not have been much of a problem after 1700. The mountains must, on the contrary, have seemed attractive for the cooler summers they offered and the variety of lumbering and of pasturing opportunities they provided.

Steep slopes nevertheless are to some extent a deterrent to settlement, and these mountains were not occupied as densely and fully as the flatter areas or the bottoms of the valleys. The bottomlands were another problem area in some cases: they may be so flat that drainage becomes difficult and water impregnates the soil, making it marshy. Such marshy areas are found in many parts of the coastal plain in the south; Virginia claims a large section of the northernmost of these marshes, the famous Dismal Swamp, to the southwest of the Norfolk-Portsmouth metropolitan area. This Swamp has been and still is an area difficult of access and passage. On the map of Virginia and Maryland so carefully drawn by Augustine Herrman in 1670 (see page 56), the area near the Dismal Swamp is inscribed as follows: "The Land between James River and Roanoke River is for the most part Low Suncken Swampy Land not well passable but with great difficulty. And herein harbours Tiggers Bears and other Devouring Creatures." The Dismal Swamp was thus recognized rather early as a barrier to traffic and development and as a source of threats. A scheme for its drainage was drawn in the eighteenth century and George Washington directed some of the planning and operations towards its drainage. Today the Swamp still occupies a substantial area; although a few canals and trails make it less impenetrable, getting around within its area is not yet easy; lumbering activities started there by two large companies still proceed with difficulty, and plans are being drawn anew for a more complete drainage with a view to a fuller use of the forest resources. The Swamp is at present the largest block of territory in eastern Virginia completely free from permanent inhabitants. (See map, page 35.)

Marshland has therefore had a restrictive influence over settlement and development, though in some local cases it was eliminated through successful drainage. Small patches of marshy and empty land are still found inside the meanders of the York River; but, divided into small crescent-shaped sections by the course of the stream, they do not amount to much as a whole. Some tidal marshlands occupy more space along the coast of the Eastern Shore peninsula, especially on the ocean side, and they have contributed to the isolation of some of the many small islands scattered offshore along that coast.

A glance at the map of uninhabited areas within Virginia (see page 35) confirms the general impression that swamp and slope have been and still are the main restrictive influences of physical nature. The slopes, even where quite steep, were utilized in the past much more than they are today. Most of the lands remaining empty at present on the slopes of western Virginia mountains have been reconquered by woods owing to government action: they are under national forests or in the Shenandoah National Park. In some cases the unpopulated areas were artificially ex-

A gully being carved into the soils of the Coastal Plain
Virginia Forest Service

panded and the people scattered through them were resettled elsewhere. This was found necessary in order to protect slopes on which erosion was working havoc or threatening to cause trouble. The strength of run-off waters and therefore of erosion is greatly increased by the steepness of the slope. It is further increased when the slope is deprived of a dense cover of trees and grass. In other words, deforestation and wandering live-stock have much more dire consequences on sloping lands than on flats. The steeper the slope, the more easily the damage is done; even on rela-tively gentle hillsides, erosion works with greater force than on a plain that does not roll much. Thus erosion is not much of a threat on the coastal plain but becomes more and more active as the development of the land progresses inland, since slopes are often steep in the Piedmont and frequently quite steep in the Ridges and Valleys area.

Erosion carries away the topsoil on unprotected slopes and exposes the bedrock. This effect is quickly achieved in rugged areas; it takes more time where the land rolls gently. Land use by farmers is, however, more intensive and more permanent on lower, rolling lands; if the soil is im-properly managed for a generation or two, the results obtained in terms of erosive action can be compared to what happens more quickly in the mountains. Moreover, human action can greatly assist erosion, even on flat terrain, by causing chemical exhaustion of soils, which then resist much less the dissecting endeavors of even the weaker erosive forces. Land management must therefore be especially careful in hilly country; but even in more favored topography the possible erosion that can develop as a result of careless agricultural practices should not be disregarded.

As a consequence of slope, soil exposure, or soil exhaustion, erosion is a constant and quasi-universal threat, restricting the free use of the land. It manifests itself differently according to local conditions of topography and soil, the latter depending largely on the parent rock material, which is in Virginia much differentiated owing to the geology. Soil exhaustion and deterioration may occur in the deeper soils of the coastal plain; they develop much faster in the Piedmont. In the hillier parts of the western Piedmont, erosion has often caused severe damage, but the most spectacular trouble of course occurred on higher mountain slopes in the Blue Ridge and in the Alleghenies. Throughout the commonwealth, therefore, the general term *erosion* carries very different meanings in terms of threats and ways of restricting human activities. The kind of restriction actually imposed by erosion depends largely upon the characteristic human practices, past and present, with regard to the soil in the area concerned.

There again, nature provides a set of circumstances that make for variety in space but also for considerable variety in time, the development of these local conditions depending on the treatment given by people to whatever raw materials the natural conditions have supplied locally. The end result that offers itself to our sight and study in present-day Virginia, in its landscapes, on its maps, has been manufactured out of these "raw materials" which could have potentially served many purposes and taken different shapes.

The distribution of population

Virginia is a fairly well populated state by American standards. The 3,318,680 inhabitants reported by the census on April 1, 1950, gave it fifteenth rank in the Union and an average density of 83 persons per square mile. This density of population was above the national average of 51 and the average figure of 54 for the entire South. Only twelve states had a higher average density. Curiously enough, both West Virginia and North Carolina showed in the census the same density of 83, while Tennessee appeared more thinly populated with 79 people per square mile. A vast area in the northern part of the southeastern states offers thus

Shipyard workers at Newport News
Library of Congress Photo by Pat Terry

some uniformity in the density of population. The areas to their south are definitely less populated (South Carolina having an average density of 70, Georgia of 59, Alabama of 60), while the areas to the northeast showed much thicker densities (Maryland 237, Delaware 161, Pennsylvania 233, New Jersey 643). Thus Virginia appears a transitional state indeed in the general pattern of population distribution in the nation.

This fact, however, should not induce us to expect an equally dense distribution of population throughout the territory, nor a regular thinning of the density from northeast to southwest. Looking at the map of population density by minor civil divisions of 1950 (see page 36) destroys any impression of such a regular trend. One can make a broad generalization about some difference between the lower densities over most of the central parts of Virginia and the higher ones on the periphery; but such a statement would be too much of an oversimplification in view of the large patch of thicker population around Richmond, a patch surrounded almost completely by thinly settled areas; and a similar situation obtains for the cities of Roanoke and Lynchburg. Even between the Washington metropolitan area and the Richmond area there are rather empty patches. It is true that most of the thickly popu-

Planting corn in the fertile Shenandoah Valley
Library of Congress Photo by Marion Post Wolcott

lated sections seem to be on the periphery—around Washington, along
the banks of the Chesapeake, and in the southwestern triangular tip of
the commonwealth—though here again at least one major exception has
to be allowed for the Richmond area. The enumeration of the three main
areas with dense population suggests a remarkable variety of motives for
such concentrations of people: city growth has gathered people around
Washington and the Hampton Roads area, as well as around Richmond.
But other high densities along the banks of the Chesapeake and especially
on the Eastern Shore peninsula cannot be related to urban development:
here agricultural prosperity seems the major motive, mixed with maritime pursuits. And something else again must be responsible for the
southwestern area of higher densities, where the phenomenon seems to
cover sections with very different kinds of economic activity: valleys and
ridges, mining country and rich valley soils, backward rural areas, and
strings of flourishing industrial centers. In 1940, "southwest Virginia was
the area in which high densities were most prevalent," wrote Miss Gilliam, commenting on the population map.[5] In part, she observes, this

[5] Sara K. Gilliam, *Virginia's People* (Population Study Report No. 4), Virginia State
Planning Board, Richmond, 1944.

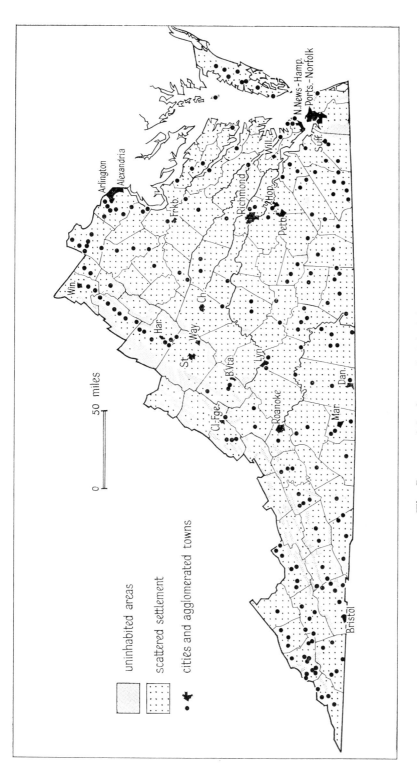

The Pattern of Settlement in Virginia, 1950

uninhabited areas

scattered settlement

cities and agglomerated towns

0   50 miles

N.News.-Hamp.
Ports.-Norfolk
Suff.
Will.
Richmond
Hop.
Petb.
Arlington
Alexandria
Frkb.
Win.
Har.
St. Way. Ch.
Lyn.
B.Vta.
Cl.Fge.
Roanoke
Dan.
Mar.
Bristol

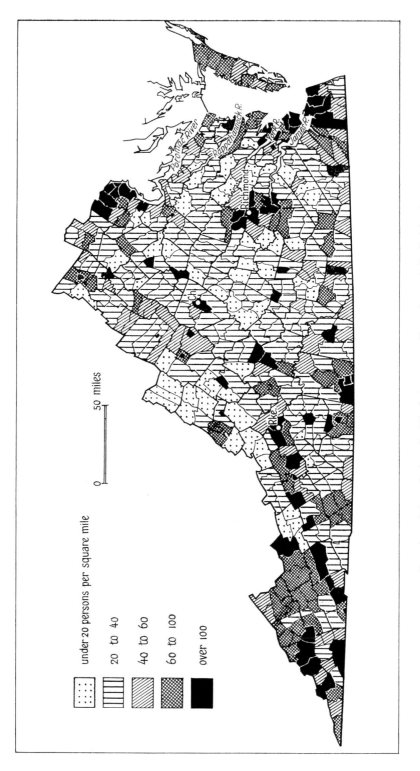

under 20 persons per square mile

20 to 40

40 to 60

60 to 100

over 100

Density of Population in Virginia, 1950. (By minor civil divisions)

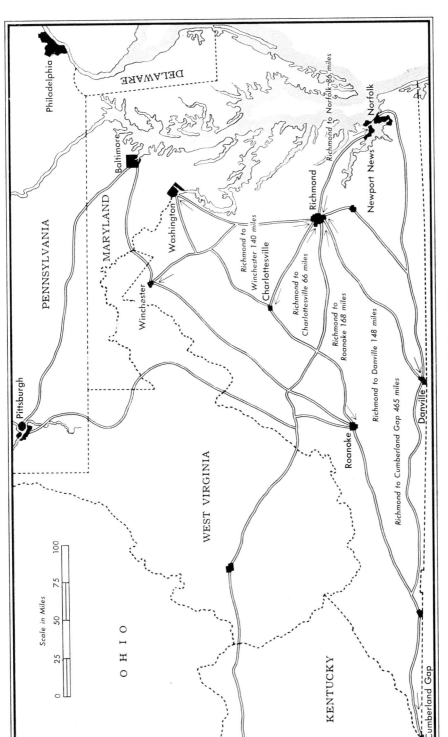

Distances along Virginia's Major Highways

Fishing boats in the harbor at Newport News
Library of Congress Photo by Paul Carter

was due to the rapid increase in total population in the area, and to the absence of any considerable amount of migration out of the area. This situation remains to a large extent true today. As a result of some psychological attitude, the local people remain within this area whether or not the economic conditions make it reasonable and attractive to do so.

Just by looking at the broad features of the map of population density, we have discovered the variety and complexity of the factors to which the existing pattern may be ascribed. Examining such a map in further detail can only confirm our sense of the complexity of these causes and discourage too-simple explanations of the mosaic of small regions with unequal densities. Another generalization may perhaps be added to that concerning the peripheral position of the main areas of greater density: greater masses of population are concentrated in the eastern parts of Virginia, i.e., the Tidewater plus the fall-line zone. The fall-line zone has been since early times a favored site for towns: today it is followed by the famous U. S. Route No. 1, a major artery of traffic along the Atlantic coast. Washington, Fredericksburg, Richmond, and Petersburg are the main links in this urban chain, the southern extension of an immense urban and suburban ribbon that stretches almost without interruption from Washington, D. C., to points in Massachusetts north of Boston. Such urban-suburban continuity has not quite been established across Virginia, but the metropolitan areas of Washington and Richmond are slowly growing one towards the other, helped by the presence of the city of Fredericksburg halfway between.

It is quite understandable under such conditions that eastern Virginia today contains the greatest concentration of population, although another string of towns develops, but on a much smaller scale, along another major highway, U. S. Route No. 11, from Winchester to Bristol via Roanoke. While U. S. Route No. 1 follows the axis of the fall line, U. S. 11 follows the axis of the Great Valley of the Appalachian system. The concentration of population it causes is emphasized on the map by the remarkable densities of the southwestern triangle of Virginia.

This brief look at the distribution of the population as a whole does not as yet provide any basis for a real division of Virginia into regions. It draws our attention, however, to the importance of the urban developments, and it demands some consideration of the distribution of the two main kinds of habitat, urban and rural, as different elements. This distinction brings into the picture the accompanying variety of economic pursuits, the description of which ought to help us differentiate economic subdivisions. Hence, finally, we shall explore the composition of the population according to origins, levels of income, etc., studying the pertinent maps and statistics. Then we may be able in conclusion to draw a first tableau of regional aspects within the Old Dominion.

Urban and rural habitat

The definition of urban population was revised by the Bureau of the Census for the 1950 count in order to include more decidedly non-rural elements of the population. According to the new definition, 47 per cent of the total population of Virginia is classified as urban; as this proportion has been steadily on the increase in this century, it seems reasonable to assume that at the time of publication of this study the population of the commonwealth is divided almost equally into one urban half and one rural half. According to the old definition of the term *urban,* this element accounted for 40.3 per cent in 1950 and 35.3 per cent in 1940 of all the residents. Thus the growth of the urban component within the total has been rapid and is continuing apace.

The urban population of Virginia amounted in 1950 to 1,560,000 people. It was distributed over 78 communities, of which 2 had more than 100,000 inhabitants each, 8 had from 25,000 to 100,000 inhabitants, 34 from 5,000 to 25,000, and 34 others from 2,500 to 5,000. Considered in terms of the proportion of the total population they aggregated, the places of more than 100,000 were responsible for 13.4 per cent, those of

Farmers outside a warehouse during a tobacco auction. *Library of Congress Photo by Marion Post Wolcott*

25,000 to 100,000 for 12.6 per cent, those of 5,000 to 25,000 for 9.2 per cent. One cannot miss being impressed therefore by the relative importance within the commonwealth of the cities of Richmond and Norfolk, which are the two places in the top category; both are, however, centers of metropolitan areas of much greater importance than the population of the cities themselves could suggest: Richmond had in 1950 230,000 inhabitants as a city, but its metropolitan area accounted for 328,000; Norfolk City had 213,500 people, but the Norfolk-Portsmouth metropolitan area had 446,000 inhabitants. The Hampton–Newport News area, which could be included with the Norfolk-Portsmouth area, since the two urban groups face one another across the Hampton Roads waters at the gates of James River, accounts for 143,000. Virginia has a fourth metropolitan area, centered on the city of Roanoke, with a total of 133,000; and, last but not least, the commonwealth participates in the much vaster metropolitan area of Washington, D. C. The national capital's area totaled 1,464,000 inhabitants in 1950, of whom some 303,000 lived in the Virginia section. Adding the populations residing in the five metropolitan areas in Virginia territory gives a total of 1,353,000 people thus concentrated in five small areas, i.e., about 40 per cent of the total population of Virginia. Compared to these agglomerations, the other scattered urban places are of meager importance as regards the total number of people,

General Store, Diascond, Virginia
Library of Congress

since they represent less than 15 per cent of the whole population. The largest city outside the five metropolitan areas in 1950 was Lynchburg, with 47,700.

Besides four large urban systems—Washington (most of which is outside Virginia), Hampton Roads, Richmond, and Roanoke (see map, page 36)—Virginia's population remains scattered through rural districts with a number of small urban centers rather evenly distributed over the territory. The large urban centers have naturally emptied the neighboring rural country to some extent, but the most recent trends recall what happened earlier and is still developing in the great *Megalopolis* area, as we call the Washington-Boston urban stretch: an *outer suburbia* spreads out around the large cities, many people preferring to commute over distances of twenty to fifty miles and live in the country. As such town workers who are country dwellers scatter along the winding rural roads, the distinction between urban and rural populations grows more vague and difficult to define. Cities today are indeed what *downtowns* used to be, while the notion of *uptown* has expanded spatially and adopted a variety of forms quite hard to delimit. A large part of northern and eastern Virginia is occupied today by an inextricable puzzle of farming and resi-

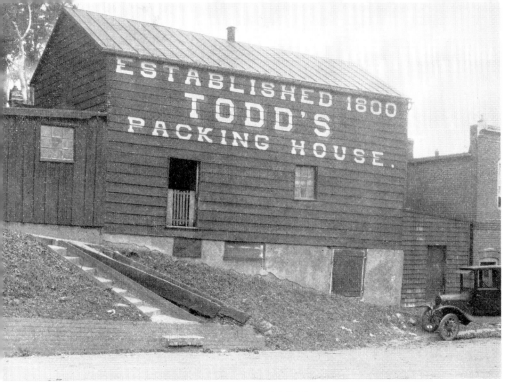

Original home of Todd's hams, Smithfield, around 1930
Virginia Chamber of Commerce

dential uses of the land. Similar trends develop in less spectacular fashion in western Virginia, as, instead of building mill towns, new industries prefer drawing manpower from a widely scattered habitat.

It may be worth while therefore to glance at the map showing the density of population by counties, cities excluded (see map, page 142). It is clearly demonstrated on this simplified map of densities distribution that the concentrated populations are found along the banks of the Bay, around Washington, Richmond, Roanoke, and Danville, and in the southwestern triangle. Most of the Piedmont and most of western Virginia north of Roanoke are rather thinly populated, with less than 60 inhabitants to the square mile. It is noteworthy, however, that few counties (exactly 5 out of 98) show average densities below 20 inhabitants per square mile, and that only two, Craig and Highland in the western mountains, show the minimum density for Virginia, i.e., 10 per square mile. The vast majority of the counties have a density of 20 to 60 per square mile, which means a thin but substantial settlement.

The population residing in rural territory is rather widely scattered through the land. Areas completely devoid of habitations are rather limited in number in Virginia. On the basis of the recently revised county maps published by the commonwealth's Department of Highways, we have tried to single out the sections that can be described as empty of buildings and people. The resulting picture (see map, page 35) shows some large unpopulated patches on the ranges of western Virginia, mainly to the north of the latitude of Roanoke. These areas belong to the national forests or to the Shenandoah National Park; they have been committed to federal care and in some cases inhabitants have been resettled in order to better protect the mountains against erosion and the basins of the rivers downstream from possible floods and other difficulties caused by the streams; at the same time these government measures have provided refuges for wildlife and protected natural landscapes for the enjoyment of the people. East of the Blue Ridge very few areas are actually void of resident population: the largest such patch and the only impressive one is the Dismal Swamp; elsewhere a few scattered patches indicate some military camps, wildlife refuges, sandy strips and tidal marshes along the ocean shore. There is almost no notable empty space, even in such highly wooded counties as Buckingham, Cumberland and Appomattox, in the central Piedmont. Some farm units or other habitations are scattered through the whole territory of the Piedmont and of the coastal plain; empty lands are very limited also in the southwestern triangle, although its topography is rugged.

Virginia appears covered rather completely by a scattered pattern of habitat, with a small number of large-scale urban clusters situated mainly in the Tidewater. Empty areas are relatively scarce and disposed mainly on the high-altitude ridges. Most of this uninhabited land was in the past occupied by a thin scattering of farms, a fact which shows how little resistance natural conditions actually offered to human occupation and exploitation. Trouble often resulted later and was sometimes felt at a distance—for instance, with the flooding of valleys downstream. These difficulties provoked government intervention to prevent the people from speeding the normal action of erosion. The exhaustion of soils in other areas, particularly in the Piedmont, did not drive the population away to the extent of causing a local exodus. True, Virginians stick to their land with perhaps greater stubbornness than farmers of the Middle West or West; but certainly, whatever mismanagement and impoverishment of the natural endowment may have occurred, the circumstances did not cause local catastrophes comparable to the Dust Bowl in the Great Plains or even to the depopulation of some parts of mountainous New England. Virginia's physical endowments do not permit of such extremes; and they do insure the subsistence, at a level acceptable to the local people, of rural populations over almost all the commonwealth, except for some steep mountainous slopes and the Dismal Swamp area.

As the larger cities developed, contacts between urban and rural ways

Singing hymns at the evening service of the Helping Hand Mission, Portsmouth
Library of Congress Photo by John Vachon

of life were increased and the two became entangled, a situation which develops even outside the standard metropolitan areas. Virginia is not yet highly urbanized, whatever may be the visual impressions of one who travels the roads from Washington to Virginia Beach. In 1950, a population percentage of 47 in urban territory was not in any respect an outstanding one on the nation's map: the national average of total urban (new definition) population stood at 64 per cent. Thirty-two states had a higher proportion of urban population than Virginia, and among them were states essentially agricultural and rural, such as Maine (51.7%), Oregon (53.9%), Kansas (52.1%), and Wisconsin (57.9%); even Iowa had a slightly higher proportion of urban people, with 47.7%. The population of Virginia is more scattered than the nature of its economy and its geographical position at the southern tip of the great urbanized Megalopolis might suggest. The twelve states with a higher proportion of rural population are situated chiefly to the south and southwest of Virginia, emphasizing again the state's transitional role.

Although rural settlements are scattered throughout the commonwealth, they take a variety of forms in the different parts of it. Here again topography plays an important role: centers of habitation often cling to the roads along the bottoms of valleys in areas of steep parallel ridges; they scatter more freely on flatter terrain. However, many variables influence this pattern: in some hilly areas people prefer to build their farms halfway up the slope; in others, such as the Cumberland Plateau, which is deeply dissected into many small hills separated by narrow winding valleys, houses are found either in lines along the valley bottom or widely scattered on the narrow hilltops. Over the rolling Piedmont many different patterns can be observed, and still others exist in the coastal plain. Why is it that so many different patterns of distribution occur within areas that are neither very different in their physical conditions nor so vast as to differ in age of settlement and type of economy? This same question may be asked in many other regions of the world; however, the types of settlement in the United States usually differ from area to area on a scale that requires, for variation to exist, bigger dimensions than Virginia's Piedmont or Tidewater can offer. It is always possible to explain such diversity by the determining influence of some subtle shade in the landforms, or the climate, or the system of crops; but the fact is that the causality of so "natural" a thing as the distribution of people's residences through the land is a much more complicated thing. Many historical factors play upon it: the former system of land use or of transportation may be responsible, or the former structure of society may have imposed one mode of grouping rather than another. In some cases the existing pattern may reflect the survival of an older type of settlement over which the new development, owing to a new highway or to the expansion of some neighboring town, has superimposed a novel network.

The distribution of settlement reflects many features of the local habitat: its past and present, the economic, social, and natural setting. Its variety gives an important characteristic to the landscape, particularly as one avoids the main highways to travel on secondary roads. Attention must be given to the patterns of distribution in the different sections we shall consider within Virginia, as well as to the past or present differences in this respect between the Old Dominion and other states in the East. Such patterns translate curiously on the map and in the scenery the variety of the people of Virginia, of their origins and of their modes of life.

Distribution according to origin and color

It is usually agreed that Virginians are a fairly homogeneous population, descended mainly from the early settlers of pre-Revolutionary times and predominantly of Anglo-Saxon blood. The settlers came to the Tidewater in the seventeenth century from various parts of England; during the

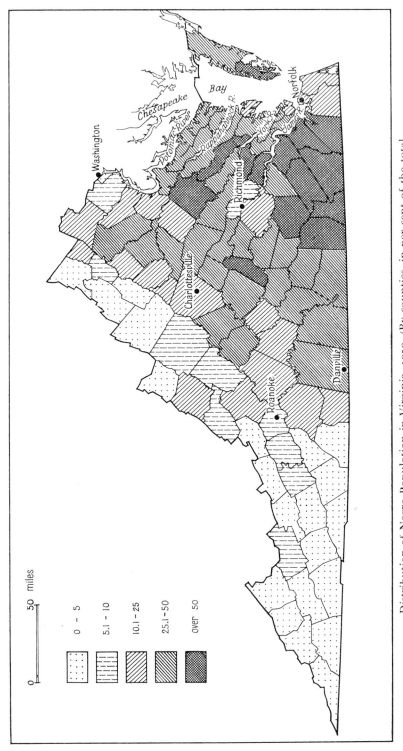

Distribution of Negro Population in Virginia, 1950. (By counties, in per cent of the total population of each county. Independent cities are not shown.)

Spectators at the horse races, Warrenton, Virginia
Library of Congress Photo by Marion Post Wolcott

eighteenth century a substantial immigration of Germans and Scotch-Irish flowed into western Virginia chiefly from Pennsylvania; a few French Huguenots came to the Tidewater; and the landowners began early in the seventeenth century to import Negro slaves for their plantations. These were the origins of the bulk of the population of the commonwealth, the most populous of the thirteen original states in the Union: the Whites were predominantly of British origin, although with a substantial German component, especially in the Great Valley; the Negroes formed the main non-Anglo-Saxon group, more than 40 per cent of the total around 1800. At that time there were still some Indians left in the state, but mainly in its western mountainous parts. Their numbers dwindled rapidly, and if some of them mixed with either Negroes or Whites, the adjunction of Indian blood seems on the whole negligible; about one thousand Indians were listed in Virginia by the 1950 census. Throughout the nineteenth century, Virginia was mainly an area of out-migration, sending some of its natives to populate other parts of the Union, chiefly the West. Nowadays the trend has changed and Virginia has become an area of in-migration from other states, at least for White people, as Negroes still leave it in greater numbers than they come to it.

A shipyard worker and his daughter, Newport News. *Library of Congress Photo by Pat Terry*

At no time since the Revolution has Virginia received any significant number of immigrants from abroad; it ceased to be a leading "pier of debarkation." The percentage of foreign-born in the total population of Virginia has been in the vicinity of two per cent; it remains close to one per cent at present, most of these living in the urban areas of the Tidewater. Since the vast majority of the population was of American stock, and the white people of British and German extraction, the basic differentiation in the population was therefore one of race and color. Regional variety appeared there again, as the proportion of Negroes to Whites differed greatly from one section of the commonwealth to the other.

The Negro population of Virginia, according to the Census of 1950, amounted to 734,211—that is, 22.1 per cent of the total; the White population accounted for 77.8 per cent and 0.1 per cent represented all non-White races other than Negro (some 1,056 Indians, 565 Chinese, etc.). The percentage of Negro population was more than twice as high as the national average, which was 10 per cent; it was lower than the same proportion in seven other southeastern states and the District of Columbia. About 45 per cent of the Negroes live in urban territory, which, compared with the urban 47 per cent of the total population, implies that the Negro group is slightly more rural but not much more so than the Whites in Virginia. Virginia's Negroes are definitely more urbanized than the Negro populations of the other southern states, where their proportion in

This shack and its ten residents, photographed in the early 1940's, were moved to make way for the army maneuver grounds in Caroline County. *Library of Congress Photo by Jack Delano*

the total is higher (the Carolinas, Georgia, etc.). In the cities the non-White population varies greatly in importance, from 1.8 per cent in Falls Church, a suburb of Washington, and 4.2 per cent in Buena Vista in the Valley, to 16 per cent in Roanoke, 18 per cent in Charlottesville, 22 per cent in Lynchburg, 30 in Danville and Martinsville, 31.7 in Richmond, 38.8 in Portsmouth, 42.2 in Petersburg and 43.2 in Newport News. The main concentrations appear to be situated in the cities of the Richmond and Hampton Roads metropolitan areas.

The general distribution of Negroes is best shown by the map of their proportion in the total population by counties (cities excluded): there are few Negroes to the west of the Blue Ridge; all the counties with more than 20 per cent of Negroes in the total population are east of the Blue Ridge. Most of the Piedmont counties record 20 to 60 per cent Negroes, the proportion increasing southwards: it is usually 20 to 40 per cent north of the James River and 40 to 60 per cent south of it. In the southern half of the Piedmont, the proportion of Negroes increases rather steadily eastwards, from 8.4 in Patrick County to 49.5 in Mecklenburg County and 65.3 in Nansemond. The highest concentration is achieved in Charles City County, with 81 per cent; this percentage does not, however, indicate a large number of people, as the total population of that rural and partly suburbanized county amounts altogether to 4,767 persons. Some curious patches of relatively low concentration of Negroes appear in the vicinity of the large urban centers (see map, page 46): thus the relatively low proportion in Henrico and Chesterfield Counties, to be explained by the heavy agglomeration of colored people within the city itself and their lack of opportunity to move out to the newer and more desirable suburban residential sections recently developed at a distance from town. Similar trends have developed around Norfolk and Portsmouth: while the concentration is great in the cities proper, the counties of Norfolk and Princess Anne show a much lower proportion of non-White people than the more rural counties immediately to the west, beyond the Dismal Swamp (thus the contrast of 65 per cent in Nansemond and 16 per cent in Norfolk).

The valleys and ridges of western Virginia are populated almost entirely by White people, except for the cities in the Great Valley and the richer central section of the Valley; industries and hotels attract some Negro manpower to the Roanoke area; and the highest proportion west of the Blue Ridge is found in Bath County (10.5 per cent) because of the personnel requirements of the large hotels in this mountain resort area. The lowest proportions on the whole are found west of the Great Valley on the ridges thickly settled by small farmers and backward mountaineers who would resent such strangers in their vicinity. Craig County shows just 0.5 per cent and Scott County 1.0 per cent; Buchanan County has no Negro inhabitants at all, as the local people long since decided against letting colored people settle among them. One Negro landowner was once found in Buchanan County, but his neighbors eased him out; a similar systematic policy of excluding Negroes is applied by the neighboring McDowell County across the line in West Virginia.

The percentage of non-Whites in the total varies throughout Virginia from 0 to 81. Thus the distribution of population offers anything but a homogeneous pattern for the whole commonwealth: the racial picture adds to the complexity of the actual pattern. Within the White population itself differences are to be found from one area to another, as the German and Scotch-Irish elements have been stronger in the western parts since the eighteenth century and as the elements that recently immigrated from other parts of the Union are more numerous along the Tidewater and fall line.

Changing regional patterns

This chapter has reviewed many factors pertaining either to the physical plant or to the human endowment of Virginia, each of which contributes to the variety; each factor breaks up the unity in some fashion, some of

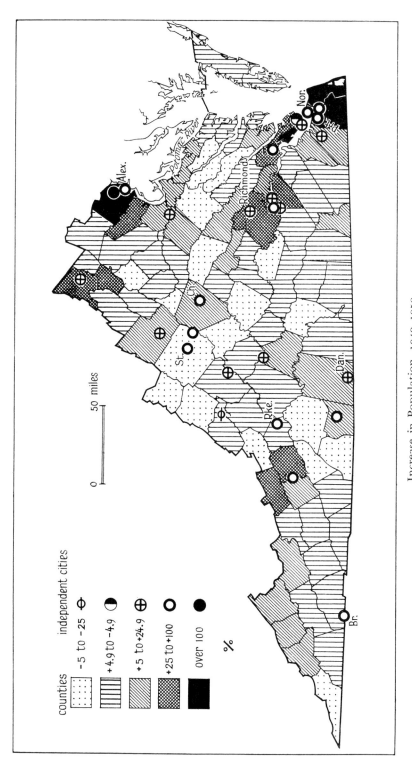

Increase in Population, 1940–1950
(By counties and cities, in per cent of 1940 totals)

them introducing striking differentiation, others working in a subtler way. In fact, other forces, not surveyed here as most of them belong outside the present territory of the commonwealth, have reshaped several times the limits of the Old Dominion. The separation of West Virginia during the Civil War was the latest and most painful of these changes in the territorial layout.

Within the present limits we have found many reasons for diversity in the distribution of both natural conditions and the people's characteristics. We spoke here of things that appear plainly on maps as they are plain facts in distribution. These facts do not mean much unless they are related one to another in space and these relationships understood in their evolution during the recorded past. Truly, the light in which one regards the agglomeration of chiefly White people in Arlington and Fairfax Counties depends upon whether he knows that this is a recent development or whether he believes it to be a permanent feature on the Virginia map as far back as the record goes. If the second proposition were true, one might expect some local physical characteristics or a combination of them to have fixed in a permanent way the existing arrangement; if the former proposition is recognized as correct, and in this case we know that it is, one must ask himself what determined this condition for this location beginning with a given date; the process of constant change of the earth's surface as a result of human activity modifies from one period to another the practical meaning and value of sites and areas for a given purpose.

Virginia is changing fast right now; its landscapes, populations, and resources have changed greatly within the last thirty years, even more in the last hundred years. The present situation, with its particular problems and trends, is the product therefore of three hundred and fifty years of change, beginning with the first lasting settlement at Jamestown. It is logical for historians and for local authorities to glorify the coming anniversary of the beginnings, made in 1607, of the greatest known development in the history of colonization. Such an approach, however, is of interest chiefly for measuring the progress accomplished between the early seventeenth century and the middle twentieth. Another approach is needed for the geographer who wants to understand how it came about that things and people are what they are and where they are. He cannot escape facing the exciting puzzle of the variety of Virginia. For while the factors are many, and we have not touched upon all of them by any means, they concur to create several compartments within the commonwealth that are substantially different one from another, though each retains some sort of internal unity.

To divide one area in whatever regions it includes is generally a tedious and dangerous venture, for the number of regions is a matter of interpretation; it depends on the aim the author has assigned to his analysis. Many times we came upon the basic distinction of the three principal geological and historical regions: the coastal plain, the Piedmont, and western Virginia with its valleys and ridges. But within each of these three we often had to introduce subdivisions: the various peninsulas of the coastal plain; north and south in the Piedmont, as well as its central section and the fall-line zone; then the Blue Ridge, the Great Valley (itself quite divisible in sections), the Allegheny ridges, and the southwestern triangle, all the four latter within western Virginia. It would not be difficult to subdivide still further each of these subdivisions: every county is in some respects a unit in itself, a compartment of territory, and every city is another. This alone would lead us into breaking Virginia up into over a hundred regions. Since many counties have different kinds of regional aspects within their own limits, we could arrive at a puzzle of several hundred pieces very easily simply by following the breakdown of statistics and topography and by observing reality more closely when investigating matters in the field. This would, however, confuse our understanding of Virginia, of what it is and what it is striving to become; it would not help us to shape our impressions of the area in its entirety. This has been the approach of scholarly research in too many cases: trying to overcome the obstacle by reducing it to an infinity of smaller and smaller pieces, forgetting that infinity is the greatest of all obstacles, the one leading to despair. Even without going so far, just by accumulating a greater number of cases than our memory can retain or our knowledge manipulate at a time, we would have created confusion where we were seeking enlightenment. Let us remain closer to a unified, interwoven system and unit limited in space, the commonwealth of Virginia, by avoiding dismantling it and separating its parts from the whole.

First of all, we have endeavored to see how varied and intricate this region is. We know approximately what it looks like as a still picture, which it is not. We must now attempt to understand the main trends of the process of which the present offers a cross-section: it must be done by a review of historical evolution; then we may be able to better understand how the present organization of this space came about and what its variety means on an enlarged scale. The past of the Old Dominion is a store of many transformations. It is useless to compare it to other States of the Union today unless we know what Virginia has been for some time in the past—and we may discover that supplying Presidents to the United States has not been its only problem.

2. Three and a Half Centuries of Change

THERE IS a wealth of historical lore about Virginia. Many authors wrote about the Old Dominion's past, particularly the era from its beginnings to the early nineteenth century. The first two centuries were indeed an epoch of greatness for Virginia. It was the largest British colony in America and produced in the eighteenth century an extraordinary array of great men who contributed significantly to shape the American nation and culture. Such an inheritance has made Virginians rightly proud of being natives of a land the sons of which achieved such glory. It appeared to many that the story of the past generations of Virginians merited being told and recorded in full detail. Much of the historical literature on the area or on parts of it is indeed devoted to biographical data and genealogy.

As families achieved local leadership and kept it for generations, they became interested in their own history; some of them felt their prestige might be enhanced by genealogical research that would show them related to some notable family of Europe. Genealogists and local historians rapidly discovered all the benefits they could derive from such popular interest. Entire libraries were written on the genealogy and biography of Virginians, and much of this material was printed. The famous names of Elizabethan and Stuart England were mentioned in such quantities in connection with the early settlement of Virginia that descent from English families of high rank was claimed by an increasing number of Virginia families. Few large nonspecialized libraries can boast as many volumes on genealogy on their reference shelves as are displayed at the State Library in Richmond.

Works aimed at establishing the aristocratic origin of the Virginians naturally elicited a response to the effect that most of the early settlers were sent from England because they were convicts or felons, or in any case belonged to the lowest strata of the English population! Out of this dispute many interesting volumes came, analyzing with great skill and competence the social history of early Virginia. Because of the work of such historians as John Fiske, Philip Alexander Bruce, Thomas Jefferson Wertenbaker, and Thomas Perkins Abernethy, we now know a great deal about colonial Virginia, perhaps more than we know about the Old Dominion's social and economic history since 1870. In the work of these historians, emphasis was of course placed on the social and political organization of Virginia in the early period when it prepared, at least in part, the national American tradition and more definitely that of the South.

The history of settlement and socio-economic organization may be related, for the purpose of this study, briefly in five periods: the seventeenth century and the situation around 1700; the eighteenth century and the situation around 1800; the nineteenth century prior to 1860; the War Between the States and its aftermath; and the first half of the twentieth century. These are broad divisions of a long period of evolution, rich in events and in personalities. We shall have to give to each of these categories of historical data less attention than is usually considered indispensable, for our goal is to understand the upbuilding of the habitat, the organization of the land and society and of the resources and relations with the outside. However, even limiting ourselves in this fashion, we could be easily overwhelmed by the abundance of documents and scholarly works available on the subject. We have been compelled to make a hard choice, considering the wealth of data, to restrict to a short chapter our sketch of Virginia's beautiful and stormy past.

The seventeenth century

The seventeenth century was in Virginia the era of the Tidewater. Several times after 1580 English squadrons tried to establish permanent settlements on the shores of North America near Chesapeake Bay. Sir Walter Raleigh, who was the main driving force in London behind these stubborn endeavors, obtained the permission of Queen Elizabeth I to give to the country being claimed in the New World the name of *Virginia,* in honor of herself, the Virgin Queen; [1] a generous grant of land was awarded Raleigh around the point of first settlement. After some

[1] William Strachey, *The History of Travaile into Virginia Britannia,* London, 1849 (in Hakluyt Society Publications No. 6), p. 140.

The Augustine Herman Map of 1670. *Bibliothèque Nationale, Photo S.P.B.N.*

"Three Ships to Jamestown"—Painting in the State Capitol at Richmond
Virginia State Chamber of Commerce

unfortunate experiences, the first lasting settlement was made during King James' reign at Jamestown on the James River in 1607. The small colony endured many hardships in the first years of its existence, due to an unknown physical environment and even more to the hostility of the Indians. The number of the settlers nevertheless grew rather quickly: there were 210 in 1610, 2400 in 1620, and probably 7,640 in 1640. By 1680 the population was estimated at close to 49,000. Jamestown itself never grew into an important town, and the settlers scattered rapidly on plantations along the James River banks, through the peninsula between the James and the York, and then towards the Rappahannock and Potomac Rivers as well as to the Eastern Shore peninsula. The rapidity of the expansion of settlement along the Tidewater and inland on the narrow peninsulas is rather startling as one considers the length of the coast involved and the number of brand new sites of habitation that resulted. One can follow this progress in occupation of the land on the old maps of the time (see reproductions, pages 56–57, 59, 61, and 63).

Transportation by water was easy for people who had crossed the At-

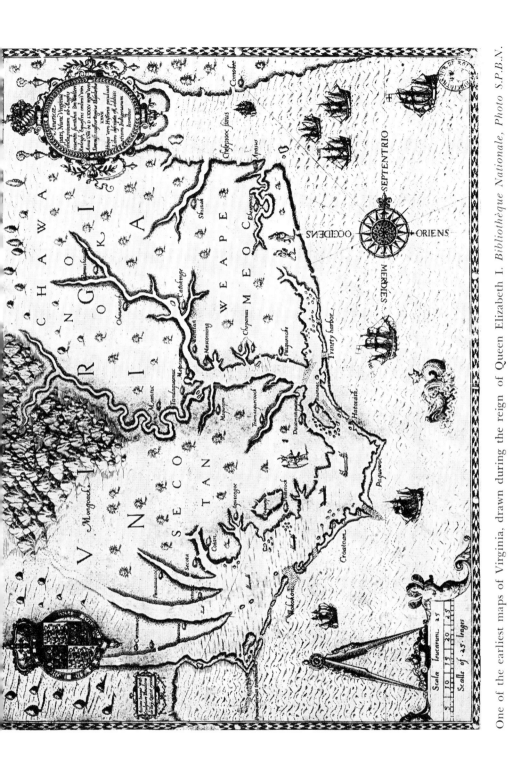

One of the earliest maps of Virginia, drawn during the reign of Queen Elizabeth I. *Bibliothèque Nationale, Photo S.P.B.N.*

lantic to come there; distances to be covered by land were never considerable within the peninsulas of the Tidewater or in the fall-line zone
around the rapids on the streams. The colony was divided into counties
for administrative purposes; the seats of the county courts rapidly became
centers of social life during the court sessions. This rapid expansion could
not have occurred without a steady stream of newcomers who claimed
and cleared new land and grew the crops necessary for the needs of the
local population as well as for trade with the outside. The kinds of men
who came first to populate Virginia have been quite fully described in
the works of T. J. Wertenbaker. The London Company, which directed
the colonization of Virginia until 1624, counted among its shareholders
many distinguished noblemen; it is possible that people belonging to the
best social circles of the time may have been induced to participate directly in the Virginian venture: some of the first settlers belonged to
influtial families.

"That the First Supply took with them a perfumer and six tailors shows
how utterly unsuited they were to the task of planting a new colony," remarks Wertenbaker. "Many, doubtless, were men of ruined fortune who
sought to find in the New World a rapid road to wealth. When it became
known in England that gold mines were not to be found in Virginia and
that wealth could be had only by the sweat of the brow, these spendthrift
gentlemen ceased coming to the colony." [2] The London Company itself
learned rapidly that a new commonwealth would be better developed by
less sophisticated settlers of more practical professions; hence laboring
men of humble origins filled most of the immigrant vessels, and the conditions of the transatlantic crossing aboard crowded ships were such as
to discourage those who could stay home in decent living surroundings.

As the colony developed, the opportunity for gaining substantial profits
attracted to it more varied categories of people: in addition to a few
dissipated but adventurous gentlemen, many gifted and courageous people came from either merchant or artisan families. Many of the leading
planters of the seventeenth century were of the mercantile class and be-
haved as such in the New World. Those, however, constituted only a
sort of gentry, while the mass of the settlers came as indentured servants
and originated with the lower layers of English society. During the civil
strife of the English Revolution a great variety of people were sent to
Virginia: with Cromwell's victories, many Cavaliers fled to Virginia,
where the governor showed stubborn fidelity to the King; when Virginia
recognized the authority of the Protector, prisoners taken by Oliverian

[2] Thomas J. Wertenbaker, *Patrician and Plebeian in Virginia*, Charlottesville, 1910,
p. 6.

A seventeenth-century map of Virginia and Maryland. *Bibliothèque Nationale. Photo S.P.B.N.*

forces on various battlefields were shipped to the colony; and a similar fate awaited Cromwell's veterans with the restoration of Charles II. The episode of opposition of the Virginia authorities to the Revolution in England and the fact that the colony offered asylum to Cavaliers, who belonged to a political party and held a certain faith, and did not necessarily represent a higher stratum of nobility, led many people to indulge in the belief, magnified by popular novels in the nineteenth century, that the whole colony had been populated by exiles from the Court of Saint James.

The flow of immigrants into Virginia must have been quite an impressive one for the time, as the mortality was very high both on board ship and in the colony. Some of the documents tell a frightful tale of hundreds of thousands of deaths in the colony. Actual statistics are inadequate for those days, and exaggeration is often necessary to description, especially when a writer wishes to strongly impress a distant correspondent. The fact that all such rumors and some actual setbacks, either epidemics or massacres by Indians, did not prevent the population from growing apace and the settled area from expanding testifies that the plantation of Virginia rapidly became a recognized success. This must have been admitted, in spite of the disappointed expectations of those who inspired the venture and encouraged it the more actively during its first stages.

What did England expect to find in the land Queen Elizabeth called Virginia? The usual answer is that England was looking for new sources of raw materials and particularly for more timber. Forest products played a predominant part in the European economy of the seventeenth century: England had at that time been largely cleared of forests. The progress of deforestation aroused fears for future supplies precisely at the time when an expanding economy needed more of such resources for building up a powerful navy and for many kinds of equipment. The first navigators reported that the Atlantic coast of North America was heavily forested with great old trees. It looked like a godsend to naval supplies. Moreover, the Spaniards and Portuguese had found great riches of gold and silver in their colonies in the New World. The rise of Spain and its claims to the whole of the Americas served as a challenge to other western European countries, particularly England, France, and Holland. It must have seemed obvious to the cultivated opinion of that epoch that no real national prosperity and power could be then achieved without an overseas empire which had to include a section of the New World. The arguments used by Richard Hakluyt in his pamphlets preaching English colonization of Virginia may have convinced a few influential people, but the

An illustrated map of Virginia, drawn in the seventeenth-century. *Bibliothèque Nationale, Photo S.P.B.N.*

stream of settlers that followed the first permanent establishments demonstrates a faith on the part of the people that Hakluyt, Raleigh, and others expressed and fanned rather than created. And the expansion of enclosure uprooted a great many peasant families who then looked for new land.

From the first trip to Jamestown, Newport brought back a gold nugget and some earth which his men thought to be gold-bearing; later the news spread of the jewels adorning some Indian chiefs; thus Virginia seemed to promise a new Eldorado. Disappointment followed rapidly, however. The mistakes made in an environment strange to the settlers and the resulting lack of food almost brought about the abandonment of the colony in 1610. Captain Peter Wynne, writing an enthusiastic letter about the area to his patron, Sir John Egerton, in 1608, admitted: "The Commodities as yet knowne in this Country whereof ther wilbe great store, is Pitch, Tarr, Sope ashes, and some dyes, whereof we have sent examples. As for things more precious I omit till tyme (which I hope wilbe shortly) shall make manifest proof of it. As concerning your request of Bloudhoundes, I cannot learne that ther is any such in this Country . . ."[3] In 1616 Chamberlain, in England, summed up the information about the disappointing resources of Virginia in a letter to Carleton as follows: "I heare not of any riches or matter of worth, but only some quantitie of Sassafras, tobacco, pitch and clapboord, things of no great value unless there were more plentie and neerer hand."[4]

Thus, less than ten years after the first plantation, London had heard about Virginia tobacco but did not expect much from it. Tobacco had first been brought to Europe early in the sixteenth century from the Spanish West Indies. It was well known in England after 1570, at least at court. Queen Elizabeth spoke of it as "a vegetable of singular strength and power." King James delivered against it in 1604 *A Counterblaste to Tobacco,* declaring it to be "loathsome to the eye, hateful to the nose, harmful to the brain, . . . dangerous to the lungs."[5] The weed that Indians called *uppowoc* or *opoak* was not in Virginia of a quality comparable to that of the West Indies. Beginning with 1612, however, John Rolfe, secretary of the Colony and husband of Pocahontas, experimented in the cultivation of tobacco with some seeds of unknown origin and obtained a product which was soon declared of excellent quality and marketable in Europe. Profits from the first shipments made tobacco the most

[3] *Newes from the New World,* ed. by Louis B. Wright, San Marino, The Huntington Library, 1946, pp. 10–11.

[4] Lewis Cecil Gray, *History of Agriculture in the Southern United States to 1860,* New York, 1941 (Carnegie Institution of Washington Publication No. 430), Vol. I, p. 21.

[5] Quoted in Matthew Page Andrews, *Virginia, the Old Dominion,* New York, 1937, p. 10.

popular crop around Jamestown, and for more than a century the production and trade of tobacco dominated the history of Virginia.

In 1619, the method of curing tobacco by hanging it on lines instead of letting it sweat in piles was introduced by a Mr. Lambert, and in that year 20,000 pounds were shipped to England. The crop shipped in 1622 amounted to 60,000 pounds and in 1627 to 500,000 pounds. The English market began soon to sink under such affluence, and the planters of Virginia soon received the visits of Dutch ships that took cargoes to the continent and others taking tobacco to the Portuguese colonies in South America.[6] This trade in tobacco and in the supplies sent in exchange for it to Virginia was important enough to cause, from 1651 on, the celebrated Navigation Acts, restricting to English ships and ports all the external trade of the American colonies. Thus began, some fifty years after the establishing of the first plantation in Jamestown, the conflict between American settlers and English merchants that would follow the road to the Boston Tea Party and to Yorktown. It is probable that the rapid development of seafaring activities among the New Englanders was largely responsible for the Navigation Acts; but the tobacco trade was not less important in the early stages, as the ships that moored at the many wharves of the scalloped Virginia coastline did a most profitable trade. It seemed right in Westminster to reserve to English metropolitan interests this source of profits, just as it appeared wrong to the Virginians to be denied the freedom of trading to the best of their ability and in their own best interests. In fact, according to James A. Williamson in *The Ocean in English History,* King James and, later, Charles I helped to create a market for the tobacco grown in their American colonies by prohibiting the cultivation of tobacco in southern England, where it had been successfully introduced. Good agricultural soil was said to be too scarce in England for the production of luxuries; moreover, the King favored the development of a merchant marine, which would never develop if England remained self-sufficient; and, last but not least, tobacco could be taxed in the ports of debarkation, while no machinery was then provided for the taxation of domestic agricultural produce. These considerations on the part of the English government opened to Virginia tobacco a vast market which it retained for centuries.

The Virginia plantations were scattered all along the edge of the Tidewater, or had easy access to it. Every planter liked to deal directly with the captain of the ship that came to his wharf. These ships brought a variety of supplies to the planters and exchanged them against the hogs-

[6] L. C. Gray, *op. cit.,* Vol. I; Philip A. Bruce, *Economic History of Virginia in the Seventeenth Century,* New York, 1895, Vol. I, Chapters VI–VII, and Vol. II, Chapters XV–XVI.

heads of tobacco and some other goods, chiefly forest products, which the planters might be selling. Each of these gentleman-planters was in effect trying to build up a small economic and social unit of his own on the plantation; he dealt directly with the world at large and naturally felt independent of authority, local or remote. The settlers came from many different parts of England, as is illustrated by the dispersal over the map of the mother country of the place names gathered even now along the James and in the Tidewater. While Sussex, Surrey, Southampton and Portsmouth, Isle of Wight and Kent belong to southern England, they are neighbors in Virginia to Norfolk, Suffolk, Warwick, York, Northampton, Gloucester, and other names reminiscent of eastern and central England. Moreover, immigration to Virginia was not inspired chiefly by motives of political refuge, as with the Puritans of Massachusetts. Englishmen of various creeds came to Chesapeake Bay; although the Church of England was the official state church, no discipline was enforced by local authorities, and an Act of Tolerance was passed in 1689. The political opinions of the settlers probably varied, too; some of them may have been devoted to the Stuarts and others opposed. The Civil War in England sent a number of Cavaliers to Virginia and the Restoration some Roundheads. Political prisoners were sent there from battlefields where the Irish or the Scots had been defeated. The variety of the origins, beliefs and opinions made for a desire for autonomy among the settlers; the scattering of settlement helped achieve it. This variety made also for an attempt by the colonial government to enforce conformity and for repeated demonstrations of dissent. P. A. Bruce and T. J. Wertenbaker have both emphasized and beautifully illustrated this double trend, which created in Virginia a population of freedom-lovers and of gentlemen insisting on a great deal of practical autonomy in daily life—conservative in the majority, but determined in the defense of local rights.

The rural aristocracy was certainly a ruling element, though they were not numerous. The bulk of the population was made up of indentured servants, with an increasing number of freemen, many of whom had started as servants; and there were many African slaves. The first Negroes were brought to the James River plantations by a Dutch privateer in 1619, and a steady flow of slaves into Virginia continued throughout the seventeenth century. The cultivation and curing of tobacco needed many hands. Moreover, though land was cheap and plentiful, it was wooded land with tall trees, the clearing of which was necessary as the soils under crops got tired. "The planter sowed the same crop year after year in the same spot until the diminishing yield warned him that the time had come to clear new fields. A plantation of five hundred or six hundred acres usually consisted of a goodly expanse of virgin forest, a restricted area of cultivated land, and perhaps one or two abandoned fields." [7] Clearing the land and removing the stumps consumed a great deal of time and labor. One man alone could not clear much space in a lifetime; hence the economy of the plantation grew thirsty for manpower, which caused the acquisition of Negro slaves in great numbers and the building up of the population of Virginia in general.

Tobacco was not, of course, the only crop grown on the plantations, although it was certainly the preferred one. America was too far from other parts of the world, in an international economy still largely based on regional self-sufficiency, to import its food supplies. Grain crops and various pulse were grown from the early years of settlement. Hogs prospered in the woods, feeding on acorns, and it was quickly found that in the prevailing climate cattle did not need shelter even in winter. Livestock was abundant, though lean and on the average of lower quality than in England. Indian corn was more popular than wheat. Many other crops were tried in the beginning: flax and hemp, pineapples and other fruits, and vineyards; even silk production was attempted several times, as mulberry trees were quite common. Most of these attempts failed. Tobacco for export and the staple foods for local consumption remained the main aims of production. There were few craftsmen in Virginia; blacksmiths, millers, coopers, and others usually enjoyed remarkable prosperity and great respect. They were in such demand that the development of certain products was held up by the lack of opportunity for processing; thus the cultivation of wheat remained limited for want of mills and millers. Almost all manufactured supplies were imported in exchange for tobacco, a situation which favored the interests of the merchants and craftsmen of England and was calculated to maintain Virginia in her status as an agricultural community.

This economic system made every plantation very nearly self-supporting, since each could trade directly with ships coming to its wharf. The personnel living on the plantation was entirely dependent on the master for food and upkeep; hence the social stratification was strictly upheld by the economic system. As was rightly observed, "While class consciousness is strong, class conflicts do not readily develop. One reason for this was well established custom. The Englishmen who came to America had never known anything but a stratified society and they accepted subordination as a matter of course. The fact that in Virginia class distinction was implicit in the organization of both church and state tended to prevent any change in the social structure. Furthermore, in a rural com-

[7] T. J. Wertenbaker, *The First Americans (1607–1690)*, New York, 1929, p. 37.

munity where each family had its own system of subordination and where there were few towns to offer a rendezvous for the more restless spirits, there was scant opportunity for the dissemination of equalitarian ideas." [8] The political traditions of self-government inherited from the English tradition gave to the gentry, as well as to the yeomanry of smaller planters, the possibility of expressing themselves on matters of mutual concern and the chance to vote for the House of Burgesses. The laws endeavored to protect servants against inhuman treatment by their masters; until 1692 slaves were tried by juries. It was only in the very end of the century that government turned less liberal on all such matters and authority began to be felt with greater weight.

The colony around 1700

Several descriptions of Virginia were published in London in the 1720's and 1730's which enable us to visualize with some precision life in the colony around the turn of the century. By 1700 the Tidewater had been quite completely occupied, though by scattered establishments. The total population at that date must have reached 72,000 and was growing fast, owing to the importation of Whites as well as Negroes. Opinion as to the resources and conditions of life in Virginia seems at that time to have been somewhat divided, as a group of distinguished gentlemen reported:

It is astonishing to hear what contrary Characters are given of the Country of Virginia even by those who have often seen it, and know it very well; some of them representing it as the best, others as the worst Country in the World. Perhaps they are both in the Right. For the most general true Character of Virginia is this, that as to all the Natural advantages of a Country, it is one of the best, but as to the Improved Ones, one of the worst of all the English Plantations in America. . . . If we enquire for well built Towns, for convenient Ports and Markets, for Plenty of Ships and Seamen, for well improved Trades and Manufactures, for well educated children, for an industrious and thriving People, or for an happy Government in Church and State and, in short, for all the other Advantages of human Improvements, it is certainly, for all these Things, one of the poorest, miserablest and worst countries in all America, that is inhabited by Christians. [9]

Even an enthusiastic Virginian like Beverley had to concur in many points with a somber view of the use to which the natural endowments of Virginia were put:

[8] Thomas Perkins Abernethy, *Three Virginia Frontiers*, Louisiana State University Press, 1940, p. 16.
[9] Hartwell, Blair, and Chilton, *The Present State of Virginia and the College*, London, 1727, pp. 1-2.

These and a thousand other advantages that country affords, which its inhabitants make no manner use of. They can see their Naval Stores daily benefit other people, who send thither to build Ships; while they, instead of promoting such undertakings among themselves, and easing such as are willing to go upon them, allow them no manner of encouragement, but rather the contrary. They receive no benefit nor refreshment from the sweet, and precious Things they have growing amongst them, but make use of the Industry of England for all such Things . . . What Advantages do they see the neighboring Plantations make of their Grain and Provisions while they, who can produce them infinitely better, not only neglect the making a Trade thereof, but even a necessary Provision against an accidental Scarcity, contenting themselves with a Supply of Food from Hand to Mouth, so that if it should please God to send them an unseasonable Year, there would not be found in the Country Provision sufficient to support the People for three Months extraordinary. . . . By reason of the unfortunate Method of Settlement, and want of Cohabitation, they cannot make a beneficial use of their Flax, Hemp, Cotton, Silk, Silk-grass and Wool, which might otherwise supply their Necessities, and leave the Produce of Tobacco to enrich them, when a gainful Market can be found for it. . . . Thus they depend altogether upon the Liberality of Nature without endeavoring to improve its Gifts by Art or Industry. They spunge upon the Blessings of a warm Sun and a fruitful Soil, and almost grutch the Pains of gathering in the Bounties of the Earth. I should be ashamed to publish this slothful indolence of my Countrymen, but that I hope it will some Time or other rouse them out of their Lethargy, and excite them to make the most of all those happy Advantages which Nature has given them; and if it does this, I am sure, they will have the Goodness to forgive me.[10]

Robert Beverley may have exaggerated the "lethargy" of his countrymen. A son-in-law of William Byrd I, he belonged to the most active and enlightened circle of Virginia's large landowners, men who were ambitious for their country and who would have liked it to develop at a pace and on a scale far beyond the actual trend. Beverley has been suspected of being the author of an essay published in London in 1701 setting forth the political claims for self-government of the American plantations.[11] Such daring spirits can be found at any period in almost any land, complaining about the slowness of progress and the unsatisfactory use of all the riches of the land; such men are necessary everywhere. It is noteworthy that such an élite had already arisen at this time in Virginia, out of local people, independent of London. Another suggestion appearing in Beverley's volume, as well as in the report by Hartwell, Blair, and Chilton, is to be remembered: the economy of Virginia seemed to them less diversified and less well developed than that of other English colonies in America. Comparison would normally be made with New England,

[10] *The History of Virginia, in Four Parts, by a Native and Inhabitant of the Place* (R. Beverley, Gent.), 2nd edition, London, 1722, pp. 283–284.
[11] *An Essay upon the Government of the English Plantations on the Continent of America, By an American* (1701), edited by Louis B. Wright, San Marino, The Huntington Library, 1945.

Main Building of the College of William and Mary, Williamsburg, designed by
Sir Christopher Wren
Virginia State Chamber of Commerce

New York, and perhaps the Carolinas; a little after 1700, Pennsylvania
also enters the arena. The other colonies had a greater variety of products,
more industries and seafaring activities, more towns, and better education.

This matter of towns was of great concern to many authors who wrote
about Virginia throughout the eighteenth century. Hartwell, Blair, and
Chilton emphasize this point strongly. "This fundamental Error of letting the King's Land lye Waste, together with another of not seating in
Townships, as they did in some other Colonies, is the Cause that Virginia
at this day is so badly peopled . . . Seating by their Law is building one
House (no matter how small) and keeping Stock one whole year." In
New England men were obliged to settle in groups which developed into
towns; no single man was permitted to settle and take up land alone.
Though orders from London and laws voted by the Assembly in Virginia
required towns to be set up with central warehouses for the control of
the quality of exported tobacco, the settlers proved more and more
"averse to cohabitation." An ingenious Virginian argued "that they might
observe already, wherever they were thick seated, they could hardly raise

any Stocks, or live by one another: much more," he concluded "would it be impossible for us to live, when a matter of an hundred Families are coop'd up within the Compass of half a mile of Ground." [12] Virginians obviously disliked the idea of gregarious town life; they were strongly individualistic, and the patriarchal family system of the plantation had quickly become their ideal. True, by 1700 it was decided to move the colony's capital to Williamsburg, where a capitol and a college were to be erected; moreover, for several years the town of Norfolk had been developing on the Elizabeth River at the entrance of Chesapeake Bay. Norfolk was, however, of benefit chiefly to North Carolina because of the centralization in its harbor of the coastwise trade from Albemarle Sound. Neither of the two towns started around 1700 in Virginia developed at a pace comparable to cities like Boston or Salem, New York or Philadelphia. By 1710, Boston counted 9,000 inhabitants and New York over 5,000.

An interesting attempt to establish a town west of the fall line was made in 1700–1701 by French Huguenots. As Protestants were again being persecuted in France, many French Huguenot refugees who had gathered in London were offered the chance to emigrate to the American colonies; they were granted some land and the possibility of settling together at Manikin Town. These were immigrants of high quality, and several colonies competed to attract them. Colonel William Byrd, then Auditor of the colony, led the Virginia authorities who sponsored this experiment. Several hundred Huguenots came then, the largest group to settle at one time in Virginia. It was hoped that they might establish a thriving township, as many of them were experienced craftsmen and tradesmen, and develop in Virginia the silk and wine industries in which France was already the leader. The experiment did not last very long; Manikin did not develop according to expectations, and the same Virginia leaders who had eagerly invited the refugees to come soon asked their friends in London to stop shipping them. The people of Manikin soon broke away from the community and scattered about, following the usual pattern of Virginia planters.

The wide scattering of settlement in Virginia had many important consequences for the future of the colony. By 1700 it had created conditions of living and economic development of a special kind, well described by Beverley, Hartwell, and other eighteenth-century writers. It established the plantation as the economic and social cell on which all the systems had to be based: each plantation having access to the shore could trade directly with the ships coming from England, Holland, or the

[12] Hartwell, Blair, and Chilton, *op. cit.*, Sections II and III.

West Indies. The planter was at the mercy of the prices and conditions of bargaining imposed by the ship's captain, although he could make the captains of several ships compete among themselves. However, the ships were not too numerous, while the plantations were many. The economic advantage that the planter could obtain was to escape official control of the quality of his tobacco; a great deal of spoiled tobacco was often mixed in the hogsheads put on the ships. This practice ruined the reputation of the merchandise sent from Virginia to London and other ports. At that time, it is apparent, Virginia authorities had already begun their fight against trash in tobacco, a struggle which was to last for centuries. The average planter sought, nevertheless, the greatest possible freedom in dealing as he pleased with his products and avoided unnecessary intermediaries between himself and the European consumer.

Life on the plantation was limited by the narrow horizons of the locality and varied only by dealings with the captains and crews of the visiting vessels. In such a system it was easy to maintain tobacco as the main means of exchange and trade. Very little money circulated in Virginia. When a planter was short of tobacco he could ask for credit until his next harvest came. Those who dealt through warehouses used the receipts of these tobacco stores as money; most of the prices were quoted in hogsheads of tobacco, as were also estimated taxes and fines. It is obvious that more money would have been needed and a wider system of credit would have been organized had there been towns with active centers of trading.

"For want of Towns, Markets and Money, there is but little encouragement for Tradesmen and Artificers, and therefore little Choice of them, and their Labour very dear in the Country." They had to travel from one to another of the scattered plantations to get work and orders, and they were paid in tobacco, "the Collection whereof costs about 10 per cent and the best of this Pay coming but once a Year, so that he cannot turn his hand frequently with a small Stock, as Tradesmen do in England and elsewhere, all this occasions Dearth of all Tradesmen's Labour, and likewise the Discouragement, Scarcity and Insufficiency of Tradesmen . . . It is an usual thing with Ships to lye three to four Months in the Country which might be dispatched in a fortnight's time if the Tobacco were ready at certain Ports; and this enhances the freight to almost double the Price of what it needed to be, if the Ship had a quick Dispatch. . . . The Want of Money which is another great Obstruction to their Improvement is chiefly occasioned by the Governor who finds in his interest to encourage the Tobacco and discourage the Money Deal-

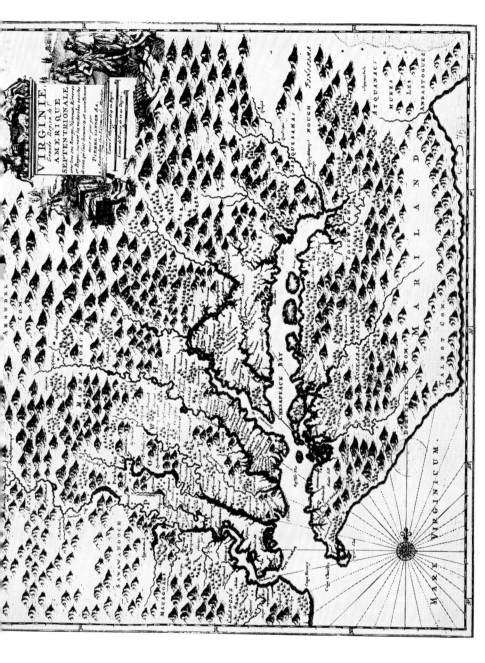

Virginia around 1700. *Bibliothèque Nationale, Photo S.P.B.N.*

ings . . ." [13] The report of Hartwell, Blair, and Chilton painted a somber picture of the Governor's administration and probably exaggerated the consequences of some of the Governor's measures. The influence of the scattering of the plantations and the planter's wish to live in a rather isolated fashion were, in fact, at least as great as they reported them to be; many other sources concur in this view, and many Governors tried in vain to remedy the situation.

The consequences of the scattering were not only economic. The plantation was too small as a social unit to have its own school and its own church with adequate people in charge of these institutions. There was a notable shortage of ministers in Virginia: "They are only in the nature of Chaplains and hold their Livings by annual Agreement with the Vestries," [14] being dismissed or retained at the pleasure of the vestries. Ministers had to travel from one church or chapel to another, and many plantations had little regular contacts with the church at all. The lack of educational facilities was even worse. The planter's budget could certainly not afford the maintenance on the plantation of good teachers, who were scarce in those times all over the world. Some of the "First Gentlemen of Virginia" had impressive libraries at home and could take care of the education of their children to some extent, but such fortunate families were few. A good education could be had only outside the colony; wealthy people went to England. In 1691 the General Assembly decided to establish the College of William and Mary at Williamsburg and endowed it generously, the Governor and many notables contributing to the endowment. Although most of the pledges were not fulfilled, the college soon began operating, and its grammar school thrived. It was out of reach, nevertheless, to the majority of young men in Virginia; good education was still available only to the élite.

This does not mean that there was no concern for education in early Virginia.

. . . There was a persistent struggle to provide opportunities for education. Virginia planters prosperous enough to look forward to the advancement of their families in the New World were just as concerned over the proper training of their sons and daughters as were their Puritan brethren of Massachusetts Bay. But the scattered nature of the plantations made the establishment of schools less easy than in the more densely settled townships of New England; as a result, education in the Chesapeake region tended to become an individual rather than a civic enterprise. The rising landed gentry . . . provided tutors and plantation schools according to their means, or in rare cases sent their children back to England. Nor were they completely unmindful of their social responsibility to

[13] Hartwell, Blair, and Chilton, *op. cit.*, Sections II–III. (Written 1697, though published only after 1720.)
[14] *Ibid.*

the less prosperous, as is indicated by repeated, though often unsuccessful, efforts to provide facilities for the education of poor children scattered on farms throughout the length and breadth of the colony. Virginia's lack of towns, rather than any callous neglect or evil policy on the part of the ruling class, was responsible for the breakdown of schemes designed to improve the educational opportunities of the children of the poorer planters . . . it was impossible to support enough schools to be accessible to all the country population. While wealthy planters could afford to hire teachers for their own and immediate neighbors' children, many poor families were out of range of any school.[15]

The scattering of settlement therefore shaped many aspects of life in Virginia. It provided the foundation of the differentiation that developed, from the seventeenth century on, between the Southern colonies and New England. We may begin to ask ourselves why Virginians were so different in respect of their pattern of settlement from the people in the Northern colonies. Was their pattern the result of factors inherent in the nature, in the physical conditions of the country, or of some social and cultural trait? The physical pattern of Virginia is not so different from the physical pattern of New York and Massachusetts as some have endeavored to demonstrate. It is true that the Tidewater along the Chesapeake and the wide rivers of Virginia provided the means of wide scattering, but so did the scalloped coast of New England and of the Delaware, and the long tidal channel of the Hudson. Whether tobacco, grain, or timber was produced for export would not affect greatly the problem of the distribution of settlement. This distribution obeyed the laws and the emotional needs of the settlers. If laws forbade individual scattering in Massachusetts, but did not forbid it in Virginia, nature had no responsibility in the matter. The Puritans needed a well-knit, closely settled community for the observance of their religion; they counted among themselves many craftsmen who were eager to engage in industry and trade; they did not want to use much slave manpower. For all these reasons scattering would have hampered them in many ways, and they settled in towns. Virginians did not have the same urge either in religion or in trading. They settled at some distance from each other because they preferred it, because they seemed from the very beginning to put considerable emphasis on individual freedom of action and the way of living of free men. They were less concerned with civic life and, according to some witnesses, with religion as well. Dissenters appeared among them quite early. "Drastic legislation was passed in 1699, and re-enacted in 1705, against those avowing 'Atheisticall Principles'—which were defined as denying 'the being of a God or the Holy Trinity,' or asserting or maintaining 'there are more Gods than one,' or denying the truth of the

[15] Louis B. Wright, *The First Gentlemen of Virginia*, San Marino, 1940, pp. 95–96.

The old capitol at Williamsburg, restored
Virginia State Chamber of Commerce

Christian religion . . ." [16] Thus the differences between the two major
English colonies developed at the outset because they apparently attracted different kinds of people. Seventeenth-century England was a
varied nation, with lively oppositions within itself, and it could supply
settlers of different beliefs, opinions, and characters to the colonies.
Some people came to each colony who were not definitely of one kind or
the other, but these were prepared to follow the local leadership and
conform to the already existing way of life. Leadership has been different
from the beginning in Virginia and in the colonies to its north, and the
tradition took its own original pattern in each place.[17]

Of this pattern the scattering of settlement was a product rather than
a source. It translated into a mode of organization of the land certain
features inherent to the newly formed Virginia society; but, once established, the pattern of scattering perpetuated itself and imposed upon the
way of life, the economic and social structure of the country, a number of
characteristics and consequences which themselves had to be incorporated

[16] Sadie Bell, *The Church, the State, and Education in Virginia*, Philadelphia, 1930,
p. 73.
[17] Fairfax Harrison, *Landmarks of Old Prince William*, Richmond, 1924, Vol. 2.
Chapter 23, "The Paper Towns," presents clearly the influence of scattering.

in the tradition of Virginia. What was called in the language of that time "a lack of improvements" through "aversion to cohabitation" developed into a basic factor operating to shape the future of the colony.

This complex set of circumstances was quite apparent to many wise visitors, but it did not necessarily announce a decline in Virginia's prosperity or in the part it could play in the British Empire. Most of the criticism to be heard in Europe against Virginia around 1700 was related to its climate or insalubrity. Beverley pointed out the actual facts in defense of his country:

That which makes this Country most unfortunate, is, that it must submit to receive its Character from the Mouths not only of unfit, but very unequal Judges; for all its Reproaches happen after this Manner. Many of the Merchants and others that go thither from England, make no Distinction between a cold and a hot Country; but wisely go sweltering about in their thick Cloaths all the Summer, because forsooth they used to do so in their *Northern* Climate; and then unfairly complain of the Heat of the Country. They greedily surfeit with their delicious Fruits and are guilty of great Intemperance therein, through the exceeding Plenty thereof, and Liberty given by the Inhabitants; by which means they fall sick, and then unjustly complain of the Unhealthiness of the Country. In the next place, the Sailors for want of Towns there, were put to the Hardship of rowling most of the Tobacco, a Mile or more, to the Water-side; this splinters their Hands sometimes, and provokes them to curse the Country. Such Exercise and a bright Sun made them hot, and then they imprudently fell to drinking cold Water, or perhaps new Cyder, which, in its Season they found in every Planter's House; or else they greedily devour'd the green Fruit, and unripe Trash they met with, and so fell into Fluxes, Fevers and the Belly-Ache; and then, to spare their own Indiscretion, they in their Tarpawlin Language, cry, God D . . . m the Country. This is the true State of the Case, as to the Complaints of it being sickly . . . If people will be persuaded to be temperate and take due Care of themselves . . .[18]

All the criticism aimed at Virginia did not cause the Virginians to doubt of the great destiny coming for their country. At the May Day, 1699, exercises at the new College of William and Mary, one of the student speakers put their hopes as follows: "Methinks we see already that happy time when we shall surpass the Asiaticians in civility, the Jews in religion, the Greeks in philosophy, the Egyptians in geometry, the Phoenicians in arithmetic, and the Chaldeans in astrology. O happy Virginia!" [19]

While the future seemed so great, the present was more modest, though the new college was started under most favorable auspices. Having care-

[18] R. Beverley, *op. cit.*, pp. 257–258.
[19] Quoted by Louis B. Wright, *The First Gentlemen of Virginia*, San Marino, 1940, p. 109.

fully studied Virginia's literature in the seventeenth century, Howard Mumford Jones concluded:

Theirs is a pragmatic literature, a literature content with worldly values and worldly content, a literature which, as the period draws to its close, sets up the Horatian ideal of a just serenity as its aim. The writers are therefore perturbed by social disturbances in proportion as this peaceful aim is threatened. They take human nature easily, they are curious about personality, but they do not search character, for this would entail more effort than they care to expend. The world as it goes—this is enough for them. It is therefore, despite modern historical interpretations of Bacon's rebellion, a literature fundamentally anti-democratic in value. From Percy and Smith to the Burwell papers and the Berry-Moryson *Narrative* the Virginians believe in government by the wise and the good, by those appointed or born to govern . . . For the sweaty multitude the writers have an almost Shakespearian disdain. The development of a more democratical literary spirit must await the eighteenth century.[20]

The eighteenth century

The eighteenth was Virginia's great century, when she became the "Mother of Presidents" and the most important state in the Union. The population grew from the estimated 72,000 in 1700 to 880,000 in 1800. The territory expanded greatly inland. This century of greatness for Virginia was also a century of pioneering and quickly advancing settlement. When William Byrd I died in 1704, the falls of the James were still known as "world's end"; no settlements existed further west, although a few trappers had ventured into the Piedmont, then Indian territory. A few settlements of French Huguenots or of German iron miners were attempted to the west of the fall line in the very beginning of the century, but the actual onslaught of settlement in the Piedmont was started with the much celebrated expedition to the Blue Ridge of the "Knights of the Golden Horseshoe" led by Governor Spotswood in 1716. A treaty was negotiated with the Indians by the terms of which, in 1722, the Iroquois sachems agreed to keep their people to the west of the Blue Ridge, officially opening the Piedmont to settlement by White people from the Virginia Tidewater. Two new counties were then established by the Assembly: Spotsylvania and Brunswick, covering the approaches to the two gaps then known in the Blue Ridge.

Large land grants were then inaugurated, mainly in favor of the leading families of the Tidewater. Spotswood himself pre-empted 68,000 acres on the Rapidan River, an estate on which he established himself after being removed in 1723 from the governorship. At this same time a large

[20] Howard Mumford Jones, *The Literature of Virginia in the Seventeenth Century* (Memoirs of the American Academy of Arts and Sciences), Boston, 1946, p. 47.

St. John's, Richmond, where Patrick Henry made his "liberty or death" speech
Virginia State Chamber of Commerce

stream of immigrants was flowing into the American colonies. Many new settlers, finding most of the Tidewater occupied, proceeded inland to claim land on which to seat themselves. The example of such notables as Spotswood encouraged the newcomers, who were no more only Englishmen; to the French Huguenots were added, after 1714, Swiss and Palatine Germans. They were first brought in at Spotswood's suggestion and settled beyond the falls of the James and Rappahannock Rivers to carry on the mining of iron ore deposits recently discovered there. Many of these settlers soon left the mines to settle on lands they claimed and cleared farther upland. Most of the German and Swiss immigrants at that time went to Pennsylvania rather than Virginia, but from the state of Penn they soon began scattering inland.

The Blue Ridge did not long remain the western boundary of White settlement. Following some well-known Indian trails, the first settlers, coming from Pennsylvania, settled in the northern part of the Shenandoah Valley beginning with 1732. While the majority of the first group of settlers was British, German settlers followed very soon. The British element itself was becoming more diversified: many settlers came from Northern Ireland; others were Scots who were granted access to the English colonies by the Act of Union in 1707. While the Tidewater had been populated chiefly by Englishmen, the settlers of the Piedmont were of more diversified origins; in the Valley a mixture of Scotch-Irish and Germans predominated. People arriving in the Tidewater as indentured servants endeavored, as soon as their terms were over, to proceed westward, into the wilderness, where they could at least establish themselves as squatters, live by subsistence farming and perhaps in time develop into wealthy landowners. The land was abundant and cheap; more and more hands were needed. The Tidewater planters imported Negro slaves in increasing numbers, and the large landowners who developed estates on the Piedmont brought slaves to that area. Without them, Spotswood, William Byrd, and the Randolphs could not have developed the vast tracts of land that they obtained for their families.

To this same period belongs the foundation of towns that lasted and developed, as few Virginia towns founded earlier had done. Norfolk in the 1730's probably had a population of 2,000 to 3,000 people and was beginning to look like an important center of trade.

The Norfolk merchants were alert, enterprising, close-bargaining business men. 'The two cardinal virtues that make a place thrive, industry and frugality, are seen here in perfection,' wrote William Byrd in 1728. No doubt the spirit of thrift was a part of Norfolk's Scotch inheritance, for many of her leading merchants came from Glasgow. . . . The inventories of the Norfolk merchants, even in the first part of the eighteenth century, show how extensive were their operations. When John Tucker died in 1736 his warehouses contained European goods to the value of £469.4.0½ including woolens, sheeting, silks, ticking; thread, tape, ribbons, laces; razors, lancets, combs, buckles; Bibles, primers, hornbooks, writing paper; rugs and blankets; dishes, basins and plates of pewter; hatchets, chisels, hammers, locks, saws; hour-glasses, kettles, and compasses of brass. His three sloops and one shallop were appraised at £445. His stock of Madeira wine totalled £690, his rum £851.14.1, his sugar £223.15.4. He had European goods yet unpacked worth £239.19.10; wares at 'Mr. Mason's store' worth £2014.18.11; he owned six slaves worth £147.10; 88 ounces and 13 pennyweight of gold wedges worth £310.5.6; and cash to the amount of £2443.12.1.[21]

Like most of the other Atlantic seaports, Norfolk traded chiefly with Britain, the West Indies (from which came rum and sugar), and the coast of Africa (which supplied slaves). The population of the town was estimated at 6,000 in 1775. Two other ports of some importance, though slowly yielding to Norfolk, were situated on the peninsula of Williamsburg: Yorktown, on the York River, and Hampton, facing Norfolk at the gate of the James, which was said to have 3,000 people by 1750.

New towns were founded in the Tidewater: William Byrd II realized

[21] T. J. Wertenbaker, *Norfolk: Historic Southern Port,* Durham, N. C., 1931, pp. 49–50.

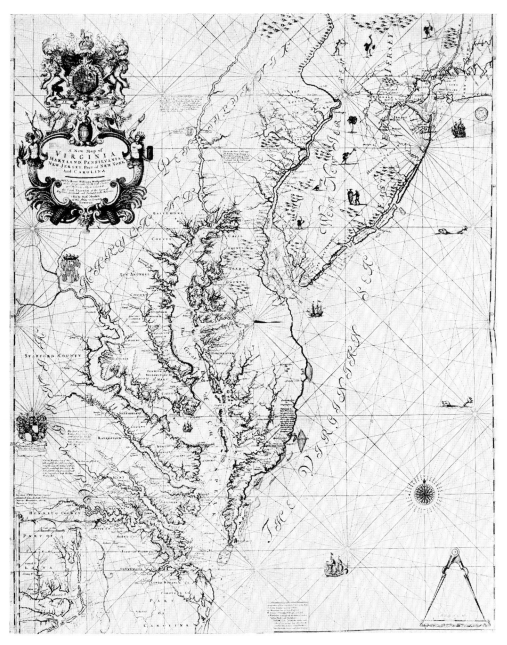

Virginia in the eighteenth century
Bibliothèque Nationale, Photo S.P.B.N.

the advantages offered by the falls of the large rivers as sites for towns. He had a town laid out on the falls of the James beginning in 1737: Richmond was incorporated by the General Assembly in 1742. Colonel Byrd also suggested building a town called Petersburg on the falls of the Appomattox, where the town was laid out in 1748. Fredericksburg, on the falls of the Rappahannock, was started in 1727 and developed rapidly in the 1730's. Alexandria was started in 1748 at "Hunting Creek warehouse" on the Potomac, and became the county seat of Fairfax County in 1752. Thus towns began to rise in the Tidewater, usually in the proximity of the fall line. Most of them started as sites of public warehouses where tobacco was inspected before shipping—a control which had become easier to maintain than previously, as the cultivation of tobacco had moved into the Piedmont with advancing settlement, and inspection and storage could be performed more easily where the planters did not have direct access to the seashore. Storage was more than ever necessary, as the harvest was frequently overabundant and reasonable prices could not be obtained.

Much Virginia tobacco now went to Glasgow rather than London; and Scottish merchants established a town that flourished for a few years at Dumfries, on the Quantico. Started in 1741, Dumfries lasted until the 1780's, when the silting up of the creek and a shift in agricultural production from tobacco to wheat in northern Virginia killed the town. The inspection and storage of tobacco was attempted by legislation in Virginia as early as 1633; but the actual control began after the passage of the law by Governor Spotswood in 1713, and at that time the Scots were already coming to America. Much later, in 1827, President Madison was reported to have remarked: "Scotch merchants in Virginia used to have a meeting twice a year to decide the rate of exchange, the price of tobacco and the advances on the prices of their goods. This was the substantial legislation of the colony." [22]

As the settlement of the Piedmont proceeded, smaller towns arose there and in the Great Valley, usually as county seats: where the courthouse was built, an inn and some stores would open to serve the people coming to the sessions of the court. These sessions had been since the seventeenth century the main occasions for social gatherings and discussion of local problems. Thus Charlottesville started in 1762 around the county courthouse, and many of the smaller towns of the Piedmont had a similar origin. The courthouse played the same part in the Great Valley, where the first town was Winchester: a small village was established on

[22] Quoted by Fairfax Harrison in *Landmarks of Old Prince William,* Richmond, 1924, Vol. II, p. 371.

that site in 1732; it became the county seat in 1744, and the town was laid out and christened Winchester in 1752. Urban life was, however, very modest and provincial in Virginia at this time. Whether they began as tobacco warehouses or county courts or both, these towns had only a local function of a very limited radius. Even Williamsburg, the animated capital, contained only an estimated 2,000 inhabitants in 1779, and thereafter it declined. In 1775 Richmond was "still a petty trading post," and it began its real growth only after becoming the capital of Virginia in 1779. Norfolk, with its 6,000 people, probably appeared to be the economic metropolis of Virginia until the Revolution, when it was burned. Even before its destruction, it was but a minor city in comparison with the leading seaports at the end of the colonial period: in 1770, the population of Philadelphia reached 28,000, that of New York 21,000, and that of Boston 15,500; among the Southern cities, Charleston, S. C., led with 10,860. Thus Virginia remained throughout the eighteenth century a region with a scattered rural population, with small boroughs performing the indispensable functions of local marketing and administrative centers, most of which could be described as villages by British visitors.[23]

A census of the population in the American colonies was attempted in the middle of the century as a result of inquiries made by the Board of Trade in 1755–56 surveying colonial resources and defense problems at the time of the French and Indian Wars. Governor Dinwiddie forwarded to the Board of Trade in London a population estimate prepared by James Abercromby, agent for Virginia. The colonial authorities based their estimate on the number of tithables, that is, White men of sixteen to sixty years of age, and Negroes, men and women over sixteen years of age. The number of tithables in 1755 amounted to 43,329 Whites and 60,078 Negroes. From this data it was estimated that the total population could be computed as comprising twice as many Negroes and four times as many Whites as there were tithables (since White women were not counted for the tax). A total of 300,000 was thus reached, which was certainly not accurate, but probably was not too far from the truth. Actually, many White settlers in the western forests escaped the tithe and were not accounted for; on the other hand, the Governor's assumption that there were as many White women as White men in the colony conflicts with the well-known fact that in the frontier areas there were fewer women than men. If the number of White men was underestimated and the number of White women overestimated, the two mistakes could well balance one another. It seems even more probable that the number of

[23] See *Richmond, Capital of Virginia*, Richmond, 1938; and U. S. Bureau of the Census, *A Century of Population Growth*, Washington, 1909.

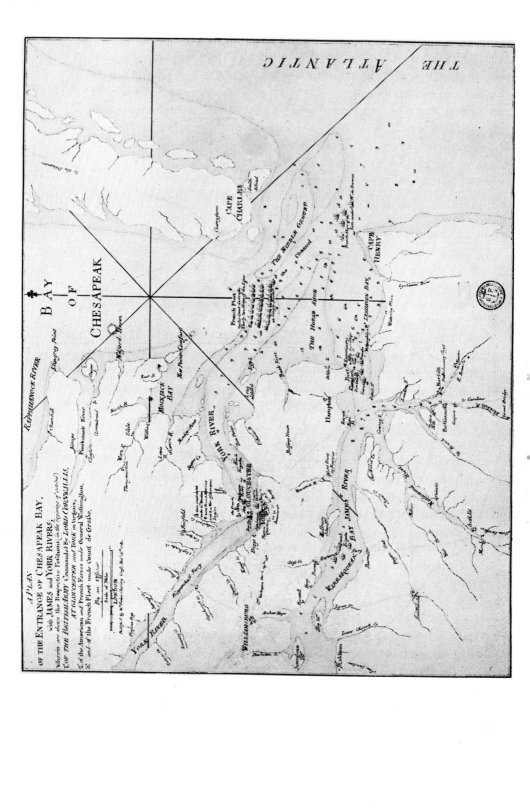

A PLAN
of THE ENTRANCE of CHESAPEAK BAY,
with JAMES and YORK RIVERS;
Wherein are shewn the Respective Positions (in the beginning of October)
I. OF THE BRITISH ARMY Commanded By LORD CORNWALLIS,
AT GLOUCESTER and YORK in Virginia,
2. of the American and French Forces under General Washington,
3. and of the French Fleet under Count de Grasse,
By an Officer

Scale of Miles

LONDON

THE ATLANTIC

CAPE CHARLES

CAPE HENRY

THE MIDDLE GROUND

the Channel

THE HORSE SHOE

BAY OF CHESAPEAK

RAPPAHANOCK RIVER

YORK RIVER

MOBJACK BAY

GLOUCESTER
YORK

JAMES RIVER

WILLIAMSBURG

HAMPTON

Negroes was underestimated, as employers and slave owners had long since learned the principle of tax evasion. Thus, while the report computed the total number of Whites at 173,000 and that of Negroes at 120,000, these two figures may well have been closer to each other.

In the annex of the Board of Trade's report to King George II, a breakdown of the number of tithables is given by county and race.[24] The best-populated counties appear to have been those on the Tidewater, and they account also for the larger numbers of Negroes: Gloucester had 4,421 tithables (of whom 3,284 were Negroes), Norfolk—2,540 (1,408 Negroes), Accomack—2,641 (1,135 Negroes), Northampton—1,511 (902 Negroes), York—2,069 (1,507 Negroes), Charles City—1,595 (1,058 Negroes), James City—1,648 (1,254 Negroes), etc. The Northern Neck, between the Potomac and Rappahannock Rivers, was already fairly densely settled: Lancaster—1,610 (1,124 Negroes), Northumberland—2,414 (1,434), Richmond—1,996 (1,235), Prince William—2,800 (1,414), Fairfax—2,233 (921). Several of the better-populated counties were entirely in the Piedmont; these counties being on the average larger in area than those of the Tidewater, the density of population must have been thinner: Hanover—3,790 (with 2,621 Negroes), Amelia—2,903 (1,652), Lunenburg—2,192 (983), Caroline—3,882 (2,674), Culpeper—2,438 (1,217), Albemarle—3,091 (1,747). It seems that as the distance from the Tidewater increased, the proportion of Negroes in the total population tended to decrease; it decreased also northwards along the Potomac. But the greatest contrast in this respect is to be found in the Great Valley: in Frederick County, out of a total of 2,513 tithables, only 340 were Negroes, and in Augusta, out of a total of 2,313, only 40 were Negroes! Thus the contrast between Tidewater and western Virginia was being clearly shaped 200 years ago.

For many reasons, settlement had advanced much further to the northwest than to the southwest. The wide channel of the Potomac was navigable rather far upstream, so that plantations were soon established as far up as the falls, the present site of Washington. Again, travelling was easier inland here, the Blue Ridge crests being lower and less massive than to the south. Finally, relations with the Indians were better here, and the settlers were closer to the westward-advancing frontier of Pennsylvania and Maryland immediately north of the Virginia territory. A last significant factor was the granting of a massive area of land in the Northern Neck by Charles II to some of his favorite companions. The proprie-

[24] Data from manuscript, "Board of Trade Report on His Majesty's Colonies and Plantations in America," 1756, a contemporary copy in the Loudoun Papers, in the collection of the Huntington Library, San Marino; and from a manuscript by James Abercromby on the number of inhabitants in Virginia, January 1, 1756, in the same collection, quoted with the Library's permission.

Gateway to the Governor's Palace, Williamsburg. *Library of Congress Photo by Howard R. Hollen*

torship of the Northern Neck had a picturesque and troublesome history from 1669, but particularly after 1702, when some aggressive agents were entrusted with the development of the area, which extended over most of northern Virginia. "One verb told the story of the proprietorship for almost a century: it was grab, grab, grab," wrote Douglas Southall Freeman. "The rest was detail, always interesting, and sometimes amusing, but detail only." [25] The main development came in the eighteenth century at the periods when Robert Carter was agent and, after 1719, also lessee of the proprietary.

His very name had the clatter of outriders and the rumble of a coach and six. 'King' Carter he was styled, and during his last years he was as regal in his manner of living as the resources of the Colony permitted . . . he was free to share to the utmost in the new trend toward farther-spreading estates of rich, virgin soil. Nor was it his opportunity alone. . . . No poor man could do what was required. In an earlier generation William Fitzhugh had said that the opening of a new plantation cost almost 30,000 lbs. of tobacco. The best start usually was made by sending skilled indentured servants to build the necessary structures on the chosen site. For the opening of the forest and the cultivation of the land, the Negro slave was satisfactory under competent overseers.[26]

[25] Douglas Southall Freeman, *George Washington, A Biography*, Vol. 1, New York, 1948, p. 6.
[26] *Ibid.*, pp. 10–12.

The house in Fredericksburg in which George Washington's mother spent the last years of her life (1772–1789)
Virginia Dept. of Conservation and Development

When Spotswood's negotiations with the Indians and his land grants opened the way for the planting of the Piedmont, "there was to be a new manorial, almost a new feudal age in Virginia. To them who had, more was to be given. From the expenditure of little, much was to be gained." [27]

As land was cheap and plentiful, it was used carelessly. Tobacco and other crops were grown in successive years on the same ground until the soil showed signs of exhaustion; then other land was cultivated. New tobacco centers developed, advancing inland. In 1750, a great deal of tobacco was grown around Petersburg and farther to its south and west. In some areas where soils had been depleted, the lower yields of tobacco brought a decline in the standard of living; this increased the migration westward. Nevertheless more and more tobacco was being produced, and fluctuations in its price regulated the prosperity or depression periods of the Virginia economy.[28]

The colony as it appeared around 1750 has been described in great

[27] *Ibid.*, p. 14.
[28] Avery Odelle Craven, *Soil Exhaustion as a Factor in the Agricultural History of Virginia and Maryland, 1606–1860*, Urbana, 1926.

detail and with a magnificent abundance of data by Douglas Southall Freeman. Some of the large landowners led a quasi-feudal life which gave its society "a certain glamour, but these men were, had been and remained numerically a minority. . . ."

The agrarian economy of Virginia was decaying in 1750 and in hard reality, though not by public admission, had little prospect of recovery. Agricultural producers who could not control the price of their tobacco were forced to pay normally £7 and occasionally as much as £16 a ton freight, plus 2s per hogshead export duty. Then, with inferior currency, they had to purchase in England, from the proceeds of their tobacco, almost everything they could not grow, weave or fabricate on their own acres. Nothing of quality was manufactured in Virginia for general sale. Conditions had not greatly changed after that time of economic mockery, about 1691, when the first William Byrd, a large exporter of leaf, repeatedly directed his London agent to send him a box of smoking tobacco. Virginians of 1750 accepted their economic disadvantage as a matter of course. They were born to it; they blindly believed they would overcome it as the Colony developed; they regarded compliance as part of their duty to a King, among whose 'most zealous' subjects they counted themselves.[29]

Some twenty-five years later, Virginia was to lead the Revolution. It was in the Virginia Convention in 1775 that Patrick Henry, a delegate from Virginia, was to utter his famous battle cry, "Liberty or Death." It was under the leadership of another Virginian, George Washington, that the King's armies would be defeated and forced to surrender at Yorktown. It was under the leadership of a half-dozen other Virginians that the Republic would receive her Constitution and the national life of the new states be organized—Thomas Jefferson, James Madison, James Monroe, John Marshall, to mention only the greatest. Seldom have entire nations offered within one generation such an array of great men and minds. The question arises: why did eighteenth-century Virginia play such a part within the United States from 1770 through 1820? Such a geographical concentration of political influence and intellectual brilliance requires some attempt at explanation. In many respects New England was more determined in the fighting of the Revolution than most of the population of Virginia seems to have been; and the colonies to the north were richer and economically more developed and versatile than the Old Dominion.

Thomas Jefferson himself wrote on his native state the *Notes on Virginia,* which describe in great detail the physical features and the legal and political system of about 1780.[30] But none of the many well-estab-

[29] Freeman, *op. cit.,* in Vol. I, *Young Washington,* the long Chapter IV, "Virginia During the Youth of Washington (1740–1752)," pp. 73–189.

[30] *Notes on Virginia,* reproduced fully in all the good editions of Thomas Jefferson's works, was written in 1781–1782 to answer queries submitted by the Marquis de Barbe-Marbois, then Secretary of the French Legation in Philadelphia.

Wolfe Street in Alexandria, supposed to have been built by Hessian prisoners during the Revolution, as photographed in 1916
Bureau of Public Roads, U. S. Department of Commerce

lished works provides an answer to the question concerning the relative importance of Virginia in American political and cultural life for half a century. We may, however, risk the statement of some reflections inspired by the historical works already quoted in this chapter. The extraordinary role of Virginia in that period was due to a small number of Virginians rather than to the collective attitude or endeavor of the whole population. This population was large by American standards of the time, but in 1790, when the first census was taken, it represented only 19 per cent of the total population of the United States. Virginia was then apportioned 19 out of 106 Representatives in the House, but Maryland, North Carolina, and South Carolina together held 24 seats, and the three of them were far from wielding an influence comparable to that of Virginia in national affairs.

Virginia can rightly claim great historical memories because she produced such men. What could have been the reasons why at least some Virginians were so superior to most of their contemporaries? Virginia had early among her natives an élite of brilliant men. This we noted as early as 1700. Some of these men were impatient with the lack of improvements in their country, or, as Beverley put it, with the "lethargy" of their countrymen, and they were obviously looking for leadership. There are perhaps several reasons why the conditions of life in Virginia favored the rise of an élite composed of a small number of men well trained for leadership: the plantation system is not simply one designed for graceful living and leisurely enjoyment of life; it is also a system in which occupants of limited compartments of land, relatively isolated one from another, endeavor to be small, self-sufficient worlds. Each of these units needs a great deal of administration. Those planters who took their duties to heart were faced with more responsibilities and problems, had more decisions to make and more daily management to accomplish with limited means than had a merchant in his office or a New England town-dweller who could seek the solution to his problems in the town meeting. While New England and Pennsylvania may have offered the common man more opportunity for the cultivation of individualism within the framework of a strict social contract, the planter of Virginia enjoyed more freedom, but at the same time had more daily responsibilities to his family, personnel, slaves, and land.

So long as Virginia was restricted to the Tidewater, there were perhaps only a few planters who felt some social responsibility and urge to solve problems beyond the boundaries of their own land. There was constant commerce with the visiting ships, and the many ties with England and the West Indies were thus often brought to play. The seventeenth-century people of the Tidewater still felt essentially English rather than American, but as time passed, the proportion of those who knew only their American environment grew greater; and with the progress of settlement inland, ties with the system of overseas relations were loosened. The continental frontier moved to the Piedmont and the Valley. There, problems had to be solved locally, with the help of neighbors, perhaps, but rather distant neighbors to whom there was no easy access by navigation over a broad waterway. The Indians were more threatening as they could surround a settlement and cut off all land or river approaches. Local conditions were more decisive. And there were more and more planters who, without enjoying all the prosperity and advantages of the Carters, Byrds, Lees, or Spotswoods, were faced with similar daily responsibilities and difficulties, though on a smaller scale.

Responsibility and pride are the two great virtues that make up the common concept of "aristocracy." For these two virtues the Virginia system of plantations was a good school in the eighteenth century. The scattering of settlement and the social structure resulting from it militated toward the early emergence of an élite among whom leadership qualities and aristocratic appearance were rather common. Such a prod-

Mount Vernon
Bureau of Public Roads, U. S. Department of Commerce

uct did not come so much from wealth and easy education as from the hardships inherent in the plantation system.

Economic conditions helped, too, in putting to work these qualities produced by Virginia life. Although land and tobacco were plentiful, the material conditions of living were difficult for almost all, with the exception of a not-too-numerous minority of large landowners. This was a purely rural economy, with few towns or traders of its own. It produced one staple, one raw material, the sale of which depended entirely on markets which were far away, which it could neither control nor influence, and which it could reach only through channels that were also out of the control of rural Virginia. In such a situation, Virginians were bound to grow dissatisfied. Many witnesses in the middle of the eighteenth century reported growing opposition and bitterness between planters and merchants.[31] The plantation people could purchase less and less overseas and, on the whole, were evolving towards a local autarchy which, given their small means, was a miserable one for all except a few families. A conflict with the whole system directed from London was bound to arise, especially if the King's taxes grew heavier and if the privileges of the merchants were reinforced. The Virginia élite, trained

[31] See A. O. Craven, *op. cit.*, p. 68: "The merchant and the planter had become bitter toward each other; the merchant was 'cursing the planters continually' while every honest planter felt that he had been 'got by a merchant.' "—It is thus easy to understand that the people of Norfolk and Richmond were closer to the Tory cause and that, as Wertenbaker has shown, Norfolk was burned chiefly by order of the Virginia Convention (in which the rural element predominated).

for leadership, could supply just the kind of opposition to the British controls which such measures demanded. It is noteworthy that most of the leaders of the Revolution came from the Piedmont (as did Patrick Henry, Jefferson, and Madison) or from people who familiarized themselves early with the inland frontier (as Washington did).

Thus the part Virginia played in American history in the last third of the eighteenth century seems to have resulted from interwoven factors, some arising from the economic circumstances of the period. These economic conditions had driven many planters into debt; the debtors' jail was a dreaded but important institution in local life. Several counties have preserved to this day as monuments the buildings that housed these small prisons where debtors suffered so bitterly in the past. Charles A. Beard demonstrated in his early works [32] the considerable importance the debt problem had during the period when the Constitution of the United States was hammered out and adopted.

> More than a decade after the conflict over the Constitution . . . Chief Justice Marshall described it in effect, though not in exact terms, as a war between mercantile, financial, and capitalistic interests generally, on one hand, and the agrarian and debtor interests, on the other. Half a century later, Hildreth . . . declared that 'in most of the towns and cities, and seats of trade and mechanical industry, the friends of the Constitution formed a very decided majority.' . . . In Virginia, the opponents of the Constitution included many of the great planters and 'the backwoods population almost universally,' and the opposition of the planters was to be, in part, ascribed to the fear of having to pay their debts due to British merchants in case the Constitution went into effect.[33]

The fact that from the beginning of the history of the United States as an independent and united nation the political debate took a turn unfavorable to the rural South makes it even more interesting that several Virginians assumed leadership in national affairs and attempted to conciliate the opposition of regional interests. Thus Virginia naturally took over the leadership of the Southern rural areas: she could do so because of historical seniority, because of the size of her population and of the quality of her élite. The leaders of Virginia were certainly worried at that time over the present state and future prospects of their commonwealth. Jefferson showed this concern on many pages of his *Notes on Virginia* and in some of his letters; however, he believed in the possibility of improvement and fought any pessimism founded on pseudo-

---

[32] Charles A. Beard, *Economic Interpretation of the Constitution,* New York, 1913, and *Economic Origins of Jeffersonian Democracy,* New York, 1915.

[33] Quotation from the latter of Beard's works, pp. 7–8.

scientific data that made nature responsible for the existing situation.[34] Those Virginians who rose to high positions in Washington may have taken some comfort from their knowledge of the rapid pace at which the whole nation advanced; Virginia was part of it and could not avoid benefiting by her integration in this much bigger and richer system.

Virginia around 1800

On the threshold of the nineteenth century, Virginia was the largest state in the union. Kentucky had been separated from it and had become the fifteenth state; earlier claims of Virginia to extend as far as the Mississippi could no longer be advanced, but the commonwealth's territory included a long stretch of the Great Valley and beyond it a vast mountainous area reaching the Ohio Valley. It was no longer a Tidewater country only and no longer a producer of tobacco alone. Of the total population in 1800, amounting to 880,000, about 42 per cent were Negro slaves and 2.5 per cent more were free Negro people. The Negroes were a majority in the population of the Tidewater, but there were relatively few in the Valley and beyond it.

Readjustment to the newly created economic system came slowly after the Revolutionary War. After 1783, the British merchants re-established with amazing rapidity their former commercial predominance. In fact, Virginians almost asked for it; they did not have other channels to market their tobacco abroad. The tobacco cultivation shifted westwards, expanding in the central and southern Piedmont and appearing in the south of the Valley. At the same time, Virginia was running into the competition of new producing areas: not only North Carolina but also South Carolina and Georgia were exporting tobacco in growing quantities. Charleston exported 643 hogsheads in 1783, but 9,646 in 1799. After 1800 these southern areas shifted to cotton, but without neglecting tobacco entirely. The important shift in Virginia itself was the trend in the Tidewater toward giving up tobacco cultivation in favor of grains: both the eastern states and Britain were good buyers of wheat, corn, and flour. This gradual evolution had begun on the more progressive plantations, such as George Washington's, in the 1760's. The wars of the

[34] A large part of the *Notes* is devoted to a systematic refutation of the ideas then prevalent among European naturalists that climate and soil in North America were not fitted for much development and that all the difficulties encountered there resulted from natural obstacles that could not be overcome. As the *Notes* were written to answer queries of the French Legation, and later first printed in Paris in 1784 by the author, it seems probable that he mainly aimed his manuscript at convincing groups of French scholars.

Rotunda of the Library of the University of Virginia at Charlottesville
Library of Congress Photo by John Collier

French Revolution and Empire in Europe made the market good, though irregular, for grains. Lands exhausted by the repetitious planting of tobacco could better produce wheat or corn; fresh lands inland were reserved for tobacco.

Northern Virginia and the lower Valley specialized in the production of wheat for export, chiefly through the port of Alexandria. In 1795, the merchants of that town exported 150,000 barrels of flour and 1,500 hogsheads of tobacco. In 1801, Alexandria was temporarily included in the District of Columbia and may have expected from this new federal position a considerable development. Actually, the trade that formerly went to it was being steadily attracted either to Baltimore or to Richmond.

Sea trade, flour milling, and some other industries began to develop more actively than they heretofore had in the towns of Virginia. Richmond was the largest city in 1800 with 5,737 inhabitants, but Norfolk was growing up again and trading with the West Indies as well as Europe. Other towns, either on the fall line or near the Blue Ridge (like Charlottesville and Winchester), were gaining in importance. From 1790 to 1810, while the rural population of Virginia increased by 24.5 per cent, the urban population rose by 158.8 per cent. Considering the fact that

Statue of Jefferson at Charlottesville. *Library of Congress Photo by
John Collier*

there were almost no towns to speak of in 1790, even this rate of increase
does not mean much, but it shows some progress as against the complete
absence of urban centers (except for Norfolk) in colonial times.

Several travellers who visited Virginia at a date close to 1800 have left
lively and detailed descriptions: a French aristocrat, the Duke de La
Rochefoucauld-Liancourt; a distinguished British diplomat, Sir Augustus
John Foster; and an English clergyman, the Reverend Harry Toulmin.[35]
Moreover, data abounds on the state of Virginia in that period in the
papers of Jefferson, Madison, and some of their less famous contemporaries. It appears to have been still a rural land, largely forested, with
some pastures scattered among the wooded areas, and fields that covered
only a small portion of a farmer's land. The foreigners were astonished
at the rather primitive modes of cultivation and livestock raising, particularly in the Tidewater. Toulmin reports:

The country round Norfolk has a very discouraging appearance. Till you get
to the woods, you see nothing but some large neglected fields which are covered
with scarce anything but a course looking grass which they call the 'bustard
crab-grass' . . . you see horses, cows, and bulls (about the size of one-year old

[35] See Duke de La Rochefoucauld-Liancourt, *Travels through the United States of
North America*, Vol. II, London, 1799; *Jeffersonian America. Notes on the United States
. . .* by Sir Augustus John Foster, edited by Richard B. Davis, San Marino, 1954; *The
Western Country in 1793: Reports on Kentucky and Virginia*, by Harry Toulmin, ed.
by M. Tinling and G. Davies, San Marino, 1948.

calves) belonging to fifty owners, mixing together . . . they are in general neat-made cattle but remarkably small. I don't find that any attention is paid to their calving and though it may be twelve months since the cow had a calf, the owner does not know whether he may expect another. You will not wonder therefore, that they give but little milk.[36]

On his arrival in Norfolk, the Reverend Toulmin was shocked at seeing people playing billiards on Sunday, and he attributed it to the nefarious influence of the French planters from Haiti who had gathered in this port after fleeing from the Negro Revolution on that island. A little later, while travelling further north in Virginia, he was forced to accept the idea that Virginians paid little attention to religion, a fact also noted by other travellers, and he observed while in Urbanna: "This little paltry place seems to abound with indolent young men, who have no religion and no business, and who kill their time on more than perhaps six days in the week at a public billiard table." [37]

There is general agreement among these travellers that agriculture in the Shenandoah Valley, where Germans from Pennsylvania were the leading farmers, was better conducted than east of the Blue Ridge. La Rochefoucauld-Liancourt definitely testifies to it. He also remarks that in this area the Whites work in the fields beside the Negroes and do not leave all the hard work to slaves. In central and northern Virginia, a group of gentlemen-farmers of high standing, led by Washington and Jefferson, were trying to instruct the rural population in better methods of land use. They imported new machinery, or manufactured it them-selves, encouraged the development of handicrafts on their estates, and tried to make of the plantations well-equipped, self-sufficient units. Jefferson's Monticello, carefully restored in recent times, offers the twentieth-century visitor a good picture of what was probably the most advanced estate in Virginia in the 1810's.

It was shortly after 1800 that the iron plow began to replace the old wooden or light shovel plow in Virginia. Deep plowing became more fre-quent on the lands of progressive farmers who were trying to reclaim gullied and "butchered" fields. The use of manure, essentially animal manure, began to be adopted only at that time. "The adding of artificial fertilizers seems to have been almost as widely practiced as was the use of animal manure," wrote A. O. Craven. "The substances tried included marl, lime, plaster or gypsum, marsh mud, ashes, sea ore, fish, common salt, and almost every kind of vegetable matter from oak leaves to pine cones." [38] A few progressive landowners, like Col. John Taylor of Fort

[36] Toulmin, op. cit., p. 26.
[37] Ibid., p. 30.
[38] A. O. Craven, op. cit., p. 93.

Monticello, Jefferson's home near Charlottesville

Royal on the Rappahannock, and John Alexander Binns of Loudoun County, began in 1803 to publish articles or pamphlets explaining why and how agricultural improvements should be brought about. The road towards progress was thus being slowly laid out. These endeavors reached, however, in the first years of the nineteenth century, only a few farmers. The majority of the landowners still had too much land at their disposal to bother much about the maintenance of fertility. Virginia was already feeding a current of out-migration westward where more land and more resources were to be had. Out of the 100,000 inhabitants of Kentucky in 1792, probably close to one-half had come from Virginia. From 1790 to 1800, some 23 out of 40 counties in Virginia lost some White population owing to the migration westwards and southwestwards. True, the birth rate was high and large numbers of slaves were being imported and distributed not only through the Tidewater but also all over the Piedmont.

Thus Virginia agriculture had become more diversified at the beginning of the nineteenth century. Although tobacco continued to be a predominant crop in the Piedmont, especially in the central and southern parts of it, wheat and corn had taken on increased importance, particularly in the Tidewater, northern Piedmont, and the Valley. Cotton appeared, as the invention of ginning was rapidly expanding the export market for the fiber. The main center of commercial cotton cultivation in Virginia was in the southern section of the coastal plain, between the Dismal Swamp and the fall line. The state produced about 10,000 bales in 1801, which was considerably less than South Carolina and Georgia produced. Cotton was here a plantation crop, not a frontier one.

The Piedmont was ceasing to be an actual frontier, although it still counted many "backwoods people" among its inhabitants. The real frontier had moved further west; it was in the Great Valley, and even more in the narrower valleys between parallel ridges in the Blue Ridge and Allegheny Mountains. Even there, civilization was coming rapidly, as the Rev. Dr. Doddridge remarked in his *Notes:*

> The horse paths, along which our forefathers made their laborious journeys over the mountains for salt and iron, were soon succeeded by wagon roads, and those again by substantial turnpikes, which as if by magic enchantment, have brought the distant region not many years ago denominated 'the backwoods,' into a close and lucrative connection with our great Atlantic cities. . . . The rude sports of former times have been discontinued. Athletic trials of muscular strength and activity, in which there certainly is not much merit, have given way to the more noble ambition for mental endowments and skill in useful arts. To the rude and often indecent songs, but roughly and unskillfully sung, have succeeded the psalm, the hymn, and swelling anthem." [39]

The good Reverend is here certainly himself composing a hymn to the rapid change that occurred in the valleys. These were still rough parts, except for the immediate vicinity of a few major highways, leading mainly to Philadelphia. But it was a rapidly changing world, becoming settled now that the Indian menace had been largely eliminated, and as livestock raising on grassy pastures, timber logging, and the cultivation of cereals developed. This was a country of White men chiefly; the descendants of Englishmen were here less numerous than those of the Scots, Irish, and Germans; here the Episcopal Church was not in the lead, but was replaced by a variety of denominations: the Methodists, Presbyterians, Lutherans, Moravian brethren, Quakers, and even some Catholics.

Thus the division was developing between eastern and western Virginia. There were, however, many links between the two areas: the main route passed along the James River, which had been made regularly navigable beyond the falls as far as the present site of Lynchburg, then followed the valley across the mountains, where the highway, a crude

[39] *Notes on the Settlement and Indian Wars of the Western Parts of Virginia and Pennsylvania,* by the Rev. Dr. Joseph Doddridge, publ. in Samuel Kercheval, *A History of the Valley of Virginia,* Fourth Edition, Strasburg, Va., 1925, p. 292.

The statue of George Washington by Houdon, in the State Capitol in Richmond. *Virginia Chamber of Commerce*

road, descended into the Kanawha Valley. Here a large salt mining industry developed, especially after 1808. Large herds of cattle passed over the mountains along the Kanawha Turnpike. Some Piedmont people planned to link the Kanawha and the James by a canal and thus establish an easy waterway from Richmond to the Ohio; this was far too ambitious a scheme, of course, but it was discussed for many years.

By 1800, over 200,000 people lived beyond the Blue Ridge in Virginia; though the figure testifies to the rapidity of settlement in an area of rough topography, one should not overestimate the relative importance of this section at this time. The vast majority of the population was still east of the Blue Ridge, and the aristocracy of the Tidewater, partly transplanted to the Piedmont, carried on the leadership of the commonwealth through most of the century.

The nineteenth century, prior to 1860

Although it opened under seemingly favorable auspices, the nineteenth century was one of tragedy for the Old Dominion, as for the whole South: the War Between the States came at a time when the rural economy of Virginia was enjoying a new prosperity.

The first two decades of the century saw a slow consolidation of the existing trends: more settlement in the western parts, more diversification of the agricultural production, steady growth of the main towns (chiefly on the Tidewater). But before 1820 two events of great local moment occurred: the first came in 1816, when a convention meeting in Staunton claimed that the commonwealth's constitution should be revised, for there were already more *White* people west of the Blue Ridge than east of it in Virginia, while the representation system in the Assembly still gave a large majority to the eastern area; the second was the passing of legislation that gradually forbade the importation of slaves from abroad. The first event shows the deepening of the political rift between eastern and western Virginia, a situation which worsened and took on traditional aspects as the easterners were able to delay the reforms asked for by the westerners. The end of the foreign slave trade had important consequences: already, in 1778, in the midst of Revolutionary fervor, Virginia had adopted a measure prohibiting the introduction of slaves with a few exceptions. In 1806, the importation of slaves was entirely forbidden. Other acts, passed in 1811, 1812, and 1819, introduced a few exceptions to the general prohibition. During this time importation from abroad had become almost impossible for the whole country, as Congress had prohibited it (1808), and in London Parliament had forbidden slave trading (1811) under the British flag. None of the leading maritime nations permitted the transportation of slaves in their ships. Thus domestic trade of slaves developed when, after 1815, the cotton plantations expanded to the southwest and the settlement of the continent proceeded apace. The old plantation states were naturally led to engage in the exportation of slaves to the newly settled areas, and commercial slave breeding was organized on a large scale.

Virginia led the other states in the sale of slaves.

In 1832 the number from Virginia alone was estimated at 6,000 per annum. About 1836 the movement was enormous. An estimate published in October, 1836, probably exaggerated, placed the total number in the past twelve months at 120,000, of whom 80,000 were carried out by their emigrating masters . . . Thomas Jefferson Randolph declared in the Virginia Legislature, in 1832, that the State was 'one grand menagerie, where men were reared for the market like oxen for the shambles.' Thomas Roderick Dew asserted: 'The slaves in Virginia multiply more rapidly than in most of the Southern States; the Virginians can raise cheaper than they can buy; in fact, it is one of their greatest sources of profit!' [40]

The total population of Virginia rose from 880,000 in 1800 to 1,211,000 in 1830 and 1,421,000 in 1850, but the only decade in the area's history

[40] L. C. Gray, *op. cit.*, Vol. II, p. 661.

in which its population declined (about 1.8 per cent) was 1830–1840. The number of Negro slaves stood at 340,000 in 1800 and 453,000 in 1830, declined to 432,000 in 1840, and climbed only as high as 452,000 in 1850. While the percentage of the slave population to the total declined in Virginia from 40.3 in 1810 to 33.2 in 1850, it rose from 47.3 to 57.6 per cent in South Carolina and from 36 to 51 per cent in Mississippi. In Maryland and Delaware it declined, as these old plantation states were exporting their slaves just as Virginia was, but on a smaller scale, since they were smaller states.

The slave trade thus provided a new and profitable commercial pursuit to the planters of the Tidewater and Piedmont. At the same time, after 1820, an actual agricultural revival started and developed until the terrible years of the War. The great name in Virginia's agricultural research at that time was that of Edmund Ruffin. He had noticed that the worn and exhausted soils of the Tidewater and Piedmont were usually acid, while the soils derived from limestone parent rock were more resistant to exhaustion. The limestone provided its soils with calcareous materials in which the soils derived from crystalline rocks were deficient. Pennsylvania settlers, who had discovered a limestone basin there, emigrated towards the limestone area of the Valley of Virginia, then towards other limestone basins in Tennessee and Kentucky: they were convinced by experience of the superiority and longevity of calcareous soils, especially for an economy based on grains and livestock. Ruffin found that marl, a marine deposit rich in calcareous material, was a good cure for worn-out acid soils. To promote this system of improvement, he began an actual crusade, which developed from a few articles in the *American Farmer* into his *Essay on Calcareous Manures,* a volume of 493 pages in its 1852 edition. In 1833, Ruffin began publishing his own agricultural magazine, entitled the *Farmer's Register.* His ideas spread slowly, encountering, like any new technique, a great deal of skepticism at the start. It was not until the 1850's that the real results of his teaching were widely felt in the improvement of cultivation practices in Virginia and in neighboring areas.

Ruffin included as an essential accompaniment to the use of marl the application of manure and insisted that without organic materials other applications were of little value. . . . He urged the growing of the southern cow pea and the adoption of improved crop rotations as a necessary part of improvement. . . . A good rotation as he saw it was one which gave largest profit, added most to the fertility of the soil and in which each crop prepared the ground for the crop that was to follow. . . . A declining fertility of soil had produced a declining population and its attendant ills. The way out was to remove the cause. To that end Ruffin labored.[41]

[41] A. O. Craven, *op. cit.,* pp. 140–141.

A rural church in northern Virginia. *Virginia Chamber of Commerce*

The Tidewater lands were the main beneficiaries of Ruffin's method of soil improving. The yields of grain and fodder crops increased considerably during the 1840–1860 period, and the price of land went up appreciably. Ruffin was not the only reformer who worked towards a new and more efficient agriculture in Virginia. In 1831, Cyrus H. McCormick built the "Virginia reaper," the first machine that made possible the harvesting of grain more easily and quickly than the sickle or the scythe. This Virginian, from Rockbridge County, was definitely a Westerner from the Valley section, where Negroes were few and the labor of the slave had never been accepted as the final solution to easy agricultural production. McCormick patented his reaper in 1834, but had to move to Chicago, the new metropolis of the vast open spaces in the West, to find the real market in which this herald of the American system of mechanized agriculture could be fully developed.

As agriculture in Virginia became modernized, new practices were constantly put to work. After 1843, Peruvian guano became a much-used fertilizer and helped to restore the fertility of many fields. Marl, gypsum, lime, bone, and animal manure continued to be used and on an increasing scale. Local erosion on the gently rolling slopes began to be checked through the use of grasses and adequate crop rotations. Many scars caused by gullying were healed. In the 1850's it appeared that the time was gone when even such prominent farmers as Jefferson and Madison could complain constantly of the small revenues provided by their estates and of the "butchering" of the lands around their own by neighboring farmers, and during the absences of the masters by overseers.

The term "worn-out land" was going out of use and prosperity was general . . . The traveler could still see plenty of lands lying idle and grown with "briars, bushes, and a long, coarse grass of no value," and the local reformer could still find much to complain of in the practices of many of his neighbors. Yet thousands of acres of land once in an exhausted condition had now been restored to productiveness. It was now known that lands could be improved and the methods of so doing were well understood. The new agriculture did not greatly exhaust [the land]. . . . It is thus apparent that by 1860 soil exhaustion had ceased to be a problem in Virginia. . . .[42]

Many new kinds of farming had developed in Virginia during this middle part of the nineteenth century. In the Valley and along the Piedmont foothills of the Blue Ridge, many orchards had been established, producing fruits of diverse kinds. On the Tidewater also some garden-farming developed, but here the horticultural production of various vegetables for the cities further north, particularly Washington and Baltimore, had become quite important. Dairy farming was a specialty of the Valley. Throughout the Piedmont, but also in other parts of the state, the small farmer had become a diversified producer who could count on several cash crops instead of a single one, thus escaping the threat of price fluctuations on one single market.

Tobacco had not been forgotten by Virginia farmers. It was still the one most important cash crop of all; it was still the predominant element in the Piedmont's agriculture, and burley tobacco expanded to the southwest in the Valley. The market became more stable in the nineteenth century as domestic consumption increased much more rapidly than foreign purchases. Virginia developed the manufacturing of tobacco in Lynchburg, Richmond, and Petersburg. Lynchburg specialized in chewing tobacco of the sun-cured quality grown in the central Piedmont. Around 1850, at least 50,000 hogsheads of tobacco were manufactured in Virginia, and a large part of the North Carolina production was absorbed by the Virginia market.

The cultivation of tobacco had expanded greatly to the west and somewhat to the south beyond the old plantation states. In 1839 Virginia supplied about 34 per cent of the total production in the United States, and in 1859 some 29 per cent; this relative decrease in percentage must be viewed against the considerable increase in quantity within the state.

[42] A. O. Craven, *op. cit.*, pp. 157–161.

Pittsylvania and the adjacent counties formed the region of greatest concentration of tobacco production. In 1859, Virginia's harvest of tobacco reached 123,968,312 pounds. This figure was more than double that of 1849, and the development of the production and manufacturing of tobacco must have been one more factor in the prosperity of the commonwealth on the eve of the War. Prices at the Virginia warehouses remained somewhat unstable, but were on the average higher in the 1850–1860 period than they had been during most of 1800–1850. Virginia maintained her rank as the leading state in the Union as regards tobacco, and this function grew in practical significance and in size of profits with the growth of the national market and of the consumption of tobacco in Europe.

Grains were the other great source of agricultural income. Corn was prevalent in the Tidewater, while the northern Piedmont and the Valley specialized in wheat. Wheat and flour were shipped out of Virginia in large quantities, much of it via Baltimore, which was conveniently linked to northern Virginia, but also through the port of Richmond, where large milling facilities had been built. Reports of the average yield per acre of wheat witness to the rapid improvement of tilling practices: in 1800 the average yield in the Tidewater was estimated at 5 to 6 bushels; by 1830 it was estimated at 7 in the Piedmont and 12 for the Valley; in the 1850's the general average for northern Virginia was close to 15 bushels, though crops of 30 to 40 bushels were frequently reported by the good farmers. These were much higher figures than could be found further south.

This agricultural prosperity could not have been achieved without a substantial improvement in transportation facilities throughout the commonwealth. For a long time Virginia concentrated all her endeavors in this field on waterways. The Virginia tradition was born on the Tidewater and had gone inland along the valleys of substantial streams, particularly the James. Although portages were needed at certain places, many small rivers of the Piedmont were navigable by small rafts, and a substantial amount of traffic used the waterways. These could carry, however, only small loads at a time west of the fall line. Transportation by land was at first limited to short distances; so long as hogsheads of tobacco were the major cargoes to be transported throughout the territory, the rolling could be effected over rough trails. Livestock had the great advantage of being able to transport itself, again along little improved tracks. With the newly adopted economy and a variety of cargoes to be moved, better roads were needed.

In the beginning, highways followed the Indian paths. Early pioneers seldom risked themselves outside these well-established and long-trodden itineraries. The Indians had known well the topography of their lands; they did not have the wheel and hence either walked or rode horseback over enormous distances. Their paths followed the easiest and safest possible itinerary within the area. Pioneers, followed by waves of settlers, continued to use these same itineraries with only a few short deviations. Thus the newly occupied spaces were organized according to a pattern inherited from the Indians' routes. In 1796, La Rochefoucauld-Liancourt found that the roads throughout Virginia were "in general good"; he spoke, of course, for his time, when few countries maintained good systems of highways. At about this time stagecoaches began to circulate in Virginia; until the very end of the eighteenth century only privately-owned individual carriages or wheeled "chaises" were used.

Virginia had a number of roads in the early eighteenth century, some linking the Tidewater with the Valley, some linking north and south. The most important was probably the "Potomac Path," which led from Washington to Alexandria and Fredericksburg and then to Richmond, approximately along the fall line. Another road went southwards across the Piedmont and was usually called the Carolina road; it followed the foothills of the Blue Ridge. Another important road followed the main axis of the Valley to the south and southwest. The Valley, however, seems to have been better linked with Baltimore to the north than with Richmond; hence the Maryland metropolis drained a great deal of the traffic from western Virginia. Washington and Jefferson felt that the Potomac River offered a great opportunity to Virginia and that a canal linking the Potomac below its falls to the Ohio River would bring to the Old Dominion's Tidewater most of the traffic of the newly opened trans-Appalachian area. They believed this plan to be even better than the projected James-Kanawha waterway favored by Richmond. Discussion of a Chesapeake and Ohio canal started in the General Assembly in the 1770's, and in 1784 a Patowmack Company was established to build it. The work proceeded slowly: navigation was made possible up to 30 miles above Cumberland and 60 miles up the Shenandoah by 1820. But a "low water survey, carried out in 1822, revealed that the river was really navigable even by the shallowest draught flat boats, only during the high water periods, which were normally limited to ten days in the autumn and thirty-five days in the spring of each year. For this consideration the commission recommended that adequate navigation could be secured only by building a continuous slack water canal." [43]

By that time the existing facilities had helped the development of an active local traffic towards the Potomac in grain, flour, and whiskey, but

[43] Fairfax Harrison, *op. cit.*, Vol. II, p. 547.

it was certainly not worth the expenditure. The Erie Canal had given to the Hudson and to New York a priority over the draining of the western traffic. The merchants of Baltimore, who, fearing a southward diversion of their trade with the west, had opposed the plans of the Virginians since 1775, were still reluctant to cooperate and prepared to invest in a railroad towards the Ohio Valley. Virginia still stuck to the idea of a waterway. The Chesapeake and Ohio Canal was then pushed. As Fairfax Harrison has shown, this enterprise, started after 1824, contained "the elements of tragedy." [44] The Erie Canal was opened in 1825, while the Chesapeake and Ohio Canal was opened to navigation as far as Cumberland in 1850, and the Baltimore and Ohio Railroad reached Wheeling in 1852. "The fate of the canal is pathetic enough, but the tragedy it illustrates lies in the fact that while canal and railroad were fighting on the Potomac, and Virginia was wasting on her James River and Kanawha Canal the millions which might have accomplished the dream of Washington and Jefferson, had they been concentrated on the Potomac, the 'Yorkers' on the one hand and the Baltimore merchants on the other had established themselves in possession of the trade of the Ohio country . . . As it was, Virginia lost, beside much treasure, her greatest commercial opportunity." [45]

The 1850's saw the beginning of the end of boating transportation on the rivers above the fall line. The wide tidal channels and the vast Chesapeake Bay continued, of course, to carry a substantial maritime traffic, but inland the waterways had given way to the railroads and the turnpikes. Since 1796, several companies had been chartered to build and operate turnpikes. In 1816, a fund was established for internal improvements under the authority of a Board of Public Works, ancestor of the modern Department of Highways. High standards of construction were set up for turnpikes which were to be financed partially with public funds. The turnpikes were not popular in the nineteenth century, and they could hardly, at the time of horse-driven carriages and wagons, withstand the competition of the railroads.

From the early 1830's, there was some interest in investing in railroads in Virginia, particularly in Loudoun County in the northern Piedmont, which stood between Washington and Alexandria on the Potomac on one hand and easy passes across the Blue Ridge on the other. But the two Southern cities which acted first and most efficiently in the matter were outside Virginia and were at the same time the two larger cities and sea-

[44] *Ibid.*, Vol. II, see Chapter XXIX, "The Failure of the Waterways."
[45] *Ibid.*, Vol. II, p. 549.

ports in this section: Baltimore in Maryland and Charleston in South Carolina. The Baltimore and Ohio Railroad Company was chartered in 1827 and succeeded in reaching the Ohio twenty-five years later. Baltimore immediately attracted some of the traffic of the Valley, as from Winchester the railway connected with the B. & O. at Harpers Ferry by 1836. Alexandria was then threatened with losing the flour trade from the Valley, and, in fact, the B. & O. did succeed in destroying the function of Alexandria. But it was not alone in the work. Of all the towns of Virginia, Richmond was the most active in pushing the railroad near its site to attract trade from various directions. In 1844, nine independent railroad companies operated in Virginia with only 200 miles of line altogether. Three of these first radiated from Richmond: the Richmond, Fredericksburg and Potomac (R. F. & P.), the Richmond and Danville (R. & D.), and the Richmond and Petersburg (R. & P.). The latter connected in Petersburg with the Norfolk and Petersburg (N. & P.) and also reached the Portsmouth and Roanoke (P. & R.), which served the southeastern section of the state. Thus the Atlantic Coastline system was beginning to take shape in the Tidewater. The B. & O. operated in the northwest and took over the control of the line to Winchester. In 1848, Alexandria, still attempting to keep some place in the system that Baltimore and Richmond seemed to have divided between themselves, established the Orange and Alexandria Railroad Company. The plan was to extend the road towards the counties of Orange and Culpeper, serving at least a part of the northern Piedmont. The line reached Culpeper in 1852, Warrenton in 1853, and Gordonsville in 1854.

From 1850 on, the Manassa's Gap Railroad Company worked toward linking the main line of the O. & A. with Strasburg in the Valley, crossing the Blue Ridge at the gap of that name. It reached the Plains in 1852 and finally Strasburg in 1854. This was achieved largely because of a group of energetic farmers of Fauquier County who financed the enterprise and broke Baltimore's quasi-monopoly on running iron horses into the Valley of Virginia. This success revived Alexandria enough to make it start a new company, endeavoring to reach the Hampshire coal fields beyond the Blue Ridge. But by 1860 the Alexandria, Loudoun and Hampshire Railroad had been actually built only as far as Leesburg. Thus Virginians established links between the northern section of the Tidewater, centered in Alexandria, and the Shenandoah Valley. They created an east-west axis of traffic across the northern Piedmont, breaking the spell of Baltimore and Pennsylvania, which had exercised such influence earlier on the development and daily life of the northern Valley.

"Wheeling in Virginia," from *The United States Illustrated* by Charles A. Dana, New York, 1855
Bureau of Public Roads, U. S. Department of Commerce

But this trend also limited the northwestern expansion of Richmond and the James River area. It contributed to create a clear differentiation between the two parts of the Piedmont north and south of the James, but it may also have helped to integrate the northern part of the Valley more firmly into the commonwealth's system.[46]

Beyond the Valley, most of the western mountains of Virginia were conquered by the rails from Baltimore in the 1850's. At the same time, the steamboat trade on the Ohio was booming, and it linked Wheeling and the Monongahela Valley actively with the lands further downstream, which had been settled from the New England or Middle Atlantic states, and with the new world of the Great Lakes and Middle West that was being quickly organized and expanded. The transportation system attracted this area towards a set of interests extending to the north of Virginia, a factor which must have been important later on in shaping the final boundaries of Virginia's territory. It should be mentioned also in this connection that active interests centered in Richmond and Lynch-

[46] See Fairfax Harrison, *op. cit.*, Vol. II, pp. 583–596; and Charles W. Turner, "Virginia Railroad Development, 1845–1860," in *The Historian*, Autumn 1947, pp. 43–62.

burg succeeded in linking the Tidewater capital not only with Danville in the southwestern Piedmont, but also with the Virginia and Tennessee Railroad, which, starting from Lynchburg, entered the Valley near Salem, then proceeded to the southwest, crossing the New River, and reached the Tennessee line in 1856, aiming at the Kentucky trade through Cumberland Gap. Thus a close link with the old Tidewater and southern Piedmont tobacco section was established for the valleys of southwestern Virginia.

The railroad expansion era seems to have created powerful regional links and reoriented the diverse parts of the commonwealth's territory during the 1850's. This was a period of prosperity, largely as a result of the expansion of trade made possible by the railroads. Thus we see that southwestern Virginia was part of the orbit of Richmond, while the northwestern section felt more solidarity with Baltimore, Pennsylvania, and Ohio. Here again, in creating this situation the system of transportation was only one among several powerful factors. Another decisive factor was the difference between the economies of eastern and western Virginia: the absence of the plantation system of agriculture and the small number of the slaves in the west. The number of White people was much higher in the 1840's west of the Blue Ridge than to its east. Counting the Negroes, the eastern section was still more heavily populated and had refused, therefore, to yield its predominance in the General Assembly. A compromise was ironed out at the Constitutional Convention of 1850, by the strength of which the eastern section still retained a majority in the upper house of the Assembly. The unequal distribution of the slaves still made the westerners feel unjustly treated, since for taxation purposes property was assessed at actual value with the exception of slaves. The reasons for opposition were thus manifold, and the conflict was growing sharper.

Increasing prosperity and the sharpening sectionalism of Virginia must also be considered in the light of another factor: the growth of cities at mid-century. Virginia was no longer a commonwealth without townships, as she was on the morrow of the Revolution. The census of 1850 shows in the commonwealth six cities of more than 5,000 inhabitants each: Richmond led with 27,570, followed by Norfolk with 14,326, Petersburg (13,950), Wheeling (11,435), Alexandria (8,734), and Lynchburg (8,071). Of these six cities, four, including the three principal ones, were in the Tidewater; one was at the other extremity of the state, on the Ohio; and one was in the central Piedmont. There were almost no towns to speak of between the fall line and the Ohio besides Wheeling and Lynchburg; in the Valley, Winchester counted 3,857 inhabitants and Staunton 2,500. All the other towns, such as Charlottesville and Danville, Lexington,

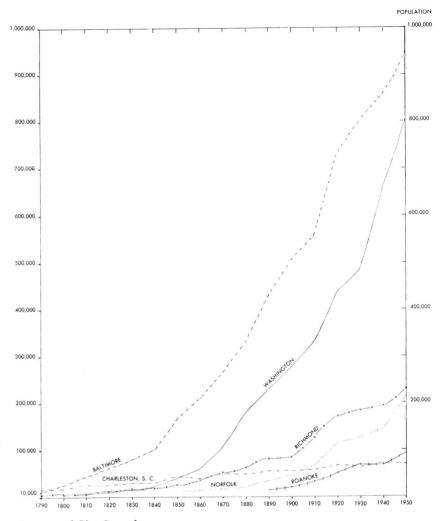

POPULATION

Patterns of City Growth
This graph shows the growth of population from 1790 to 1950 in the major cities of Virginia (Richmond, Norfolk, and Roanoke) as compared with other eastern cities (Baltimore, Washington, and Charleston).

Parkersburg, and Charleston-on-the-Kanawha, had less than 2,000 people each.[47]

By the middle of the nineteenth century the world had gone through the first stages of the industrial revolution and the liberalization of trade. Great fortunes were being accumulated by great centers of trade and manufacturing in rapidly expanding cities. The United States was ac-

[47] See *Statistical View of the United States, Being a Compendium of the Seventh Census*, by J. D. B. DeBow, Washington, 1854.

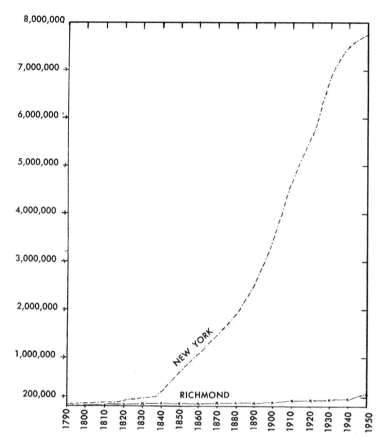

Patterns of City Growth, continued—The population of New York compared
with that of Richmond

tively participating in that expansion of urban activities and gathering
of wealth. In 1850, New York City had a population of 515,000, Greater
Philadelphia counted 340,000 inhabitants, Boston—136,000, Baltimore—
169,000, New Orleans—116,000. There was no city of over 50,000 in the
South besides the metropolis of the Mississippi delta; even Charleston,
S. C., counted only 43,000, still much more than Richmond. Thus, whatever actual urban life and wealth existed in Virginia was in the Tidewater and was of a modest size for the period. The notable progress made
in 1850–1860 was still slow compared to that of the great northeastern
cities.

Richmond was becoming an impressive regional capital. It was, in the
1850's, linked by rail or waterway with most of the commonwealth. It was
a substantial industrial center; in 1845 a survey recorded thirty-one tobacco factories, eight iron and foundry establishments, and four flour and

corn mills; other plants produced carriages, soap and candles, cotton goods, woolens, paper, nails and cutlery. By 1859, sawmills, brick works, and lime kilns had been added, and the tobacco factories numbered forty-three. The Virginia Woolen Company manufactured blankets, flannels, tweeds, broadcloths, etc. The plant of the James River Manufacturing Company worked 4,000 spindles. Thus textiles and iron works (including even the manufacture of locomotives) developed side by side with the processing of tobacco and the milling of flour. The port traded actively with other American and many foreign harbors; in the 1850's, France, Belgium, Austria, and Brazil maintained consulates in Richmond to take care of the substantial trade these countries carried on with Virginia. The census of 1860 ranked the city thirteenth in the United States in importance of manufactures, its factories employing then 7,474 workers and representing a total capital investment of $4,534,000. A large part of the working population still consisted of slaves: "Wageless, subsisting upon the cheapest food and supplied with the most primitive clothing, these patient black workers competed with white labor. As a result, many of the more enterprising of the whites took the first opportunity to emigrate to the West. There was a strong sentiment against the institution even at the period of the South's greatest agricultural prosperity." [48] The industrialization of Richmond had been furthered by the mining of coal not far away, on Falling Creek in Chesterfield County. A horse-driven railroad brought the coal into town and harbor from 1831 on; it was replaced by the steam-driven Richmond and Danville Railroad after 1851. Considerable wealth by Southern standards existed then in the Virginia capital. The Bank of the United States had a branch there, and at least two local banking organizations had flourished since the beginning of the century: the Bank of Virginia and the Farmers Bank of Virginia; five other banks were chartered between 1853 and 1860. This credit system was substantial, but essentially local. Owing to this wealth and the variety of activities and contacts in the city, Richmond displayed in its best sections an elegant mode of life led by the Tidewater aristocracy. The State Capitol, designed by Jefferson, was a much admired building. There was a great deal of artistic and political activity. Indeed, in Richmond was concentrated the essence of urban civilization in Virginia. To its south, Petersburg seemed a smaller Richmond with similar industries, but without the political and cultural functions.

Norfolk was about half the size of Richmond in terms of population and was a much more specialized city. It was the seaport at the entrance

[48] See *Richmond, Capital of Virginia: Approaches to Its History,* Chapter II by Roy C. Flannagan, Richmond, 1938, p. 17.

of Chesapeake Bay. Large vessels were constantly leaving from here for Europe, the West Indies, Charleston, or New York. Like any place with wide-open horizons overseas, Norfolk was usually bristling with activity, a gay, cosmopolitan place. The Dismal Swamp canal had since 1814 linked it to the Roanoke River and Albemarle Sound by an inland waterway. T. J. Wertenbaker has described admirably the life of the town and its people during the nineteenth century. He showed the constant disappointment of Norfolk's people at realizing between 1812 and 1860 that most of the imports of Virginia and most of the immigrants from Europe were now entering through the greater seaports up north. "For a place possessed of one of the best harbors in the world, within an hour or two of the ocean, and flanked by a network of inland waterways, the situation was disappointing indeed. Completely outdistanced by New York, Boston, Philadelphia, and Baltimore, the people of the 'old borough' ruminated sadly over her unfortunate history and enquired among themselves for the proper measures to secure the prosperity and commercial greatness which by right was theirs." [49]

The northern cities were, perhaps, not the greatest competitors of Norfolk. The city at the ocean's gate was being cut off from most of the trade that could have come to it from the interior by the cities of the fall line, mainly Richmond and Petersburg. As the railroad era came, these two towns became the main knots of rail traffic, and they, particularly Petersburg, opposed granting good communications to Norfolk, though the physical layout of the land around Norfolk might have "destined" the other cities to be hinterland. But coastline design and topography are seldom decisive in matters of distribution of wealth and power. The fall-line interests in practice blockaded Norfolk from the land, and the port did not have enough maritime interests of its own to take up the fight with any expectation of success.

Wertenbaker puts the matter in plain words:

The period for internal improvements was for many states and cities marked by glorious success, by expanding trade, growing wealth, increasing population. For Virginia, and especially for Norfolk, it was a time of wasted opportunities and bitter disappointment. The proud Old Dominion, once the undisputed leader in the Union, saw one state after another pass her in all that makes for influence and power. . . . Norfolk, of course, laid the blame upon Richmond. Richmond, because of the suffrage law, controlled the elections of at least twelve counties and so exercised an overwhelming influence in the legislature. Looked up to as the metropolis, the great social and commercial center of the state, her men of wealth connected by relationship or interest with the leaders of other

[49] Thomas J. Wertenbaker, *Norfolk, Historic Southern Port,* Durham, N. C., 1931, p. 181.

sections, she partitioned out the honors of the government to those who would aid in her aggrandizement. . . . In the Civil War, Virginia needed warships to break the blockade and protect her commerce, but the discrimination against her one natural port made the creation of a navy most difficult; she needed the support of all sections of the state, but the isolation of the western counties left them no alternative save separation; she needed a network of modern railways to move and supply her troops, but her mileage was comparatively low, her lines improperly located; she needed all her sons to fight her battles, but tens of thousands of young Virginians had gone to seek new opportunities and build new homes.[50]

It may well be that Wertenbaker's picture of Virginia's failure to fully profit by her natural endowment is somewhat embittered by the patriotism of a Southerner disappointed by the outcome of the War. The entrance to a vast bay penetrating deep inside a continent is not necessarily a predestined site for a great center of maritime activities. More often the port is situated at the end of the bay, as far inside the continent as seafaring vessels can navigate. Hence the early and general good fortune of the fall-line position: Philadelphia is not at the entrance of the Delaware Bay, where no port of any importance developed; Boston is not at the tip of Cape Cod, nor is Montreal at the entrance of the Gulf of St. Lawrence. The development of Richmond at a time when the usual sea-going ship could easily reach its harbor was quite in line with the customary exploitation of natural conditions.

Few people would, however, take issue with the general wisdom of Wertenbaker's sad remarks. There is little doubt that Virginia was governed from Richmond by circles who delighted in the maintenance of graceful living and who were often themselves people of great charm and culture, but who were generally unaware of the major driving forces shaping the world of that century. Many mistakes of the first two centuries of Virginia's development were somewhat remedied by the reforms and improvements of the period 1820–1860: some cities were growing, some industries were operating and expanding, better cultivation practices had been introduced, and the economy had been made more versatile. But there remained other problems to be dealt with: one section of the commonwealth kept control of the whole; slavery was still upheld as a substantial source of profit for a part of the state and a cause of division and bitterness; the economy was still mostly rural and dependent on outside markets; and, last but not least, good education was still the privilege of a few.

The period of prosperity preceding the War was also a period of concern over educational matters. It was not the first time that an outcry

[50] Wertenbaker, *op. cit.*, pp. 204–205.

about the condition of the schools had been heard in Virginia. The Jeffersonian period was one of great endeavors in this field, usually inspired by the great man's personal ideas and drive. Writing a general description of the United States in the beginning of the nineteenth century, an American diplomat remarked: "Less attention has been paid to common schools in this than in other states, owing partly to the great inequality of fortune, and the employment of private tutors, but the legislature, in their session of 1815–16, appropriated nearly 1,000,000 dollars for the support of schools." [51] While Benjamin Franklin and, after him, Thomas Jefferson were American Ministers to France, they organized a group of famous French scholars to discuss the matter of the establishment in America, preferably in Richmond, of a new advanced school or academy. This led to the plan drawn up by Quesnay de Beaurepaire, son of the well-known economist, for an Academy of Arts and Sciences (1788–1789), in the preparation of which the chemist Lavoisier probably participated. The Quesnay Academy was presently erected in Richmond, but it was not successful, and its impressive building soon became a theatre.[52] Jefferson at the end of his life obtained some substantial appropriations for schools and established in Charlottesville the University of Virginia, which he considered to be one of the greatest achievements of his life (1819).

In the middle of the nineteenth century Virginia had, besides the University and the old College of William and Mary at Williamsburg, Washington and Lee University at Lexington (founded in 1749, when settlement was still brand new in the Valley); a military school, the Virginia Military Institute, also at Lexington, established by the commonwealth in 1839; and several colleges created chiefly by churches as seminaries at the start: Hampden-Sydney College, established by the Presbyterians as early as 1776; Richmond College, founded in 1832 by the Baptists in Richmond; Randolph-Macon College, founded the same year in Ashland by the Methodists; and Roanoke College, established by the Lutherans in Salem. A Virginia Mechanics Institute was founded in Richmond in 1854. President F. W. Boatwright of the University of Richmond wrote in 1937:

For most of the first century of her two hundred years of history, Richmond was primarily a frontier trading post, and then a town chiefly concerned with

[51] David B. Warden, *A Statistical, Political and Historical Account of the United States of North America,* Edinburgh, 1819, Vol. II, Chapter: Virginia.
[52] See F. W. Boatwright, "Education," in *Richmond, Capital of Virginia,* Richmond, 1938, pp. 207–208; also Denis Ian Duveen, in a lecture on Lavoisier, 1954, privately circulated by French Engineers in the U. S., Inc.

trade. Her homes were built of wood, with no architectural beauty; her streets were unpaved, and the main business of her citizens was to earn a living. Moreover, for those persons who were interested in higher education there was the ancient College of William and Mary, less than sixty miles away, and there were always graduates from Yale or Princeton willing to act as tutors, and a number of genteel spinsters to give private instruction to young ladies.[53]

Such was apparently the situation in 1845 when the matter of the lack of education in the people was impressed upon a "respectable meeting of citizens held in Richmond under the chairmanship of his Exc. James McDowell." The meeting appointed a Standing Committee which reported in August, 1845, in an "Education Address to the People of Virginia," that the situation called for improvement: the census of 1840 recorded that in a White population of 740,698 there were 58,787 illiterates; the ratio of the illiterates in the total White population stood thus in 1840 at 1 to 12.5, while it was 1 to 164 in Massachusetts, 1 to 300 in New Hampshire, 1 to 92 in Ohio, 1 to 49 in Pennsylvania, 1 to 53 in New York. The population of Massachusetts was then slightly lower than that of Virginia, and the number of pupils attending primary schools was there 160,000, of whom 158,000 were studying at public charge, while Virginia counted only 35,321 pupils attending primary schools and just 9,791 of them at public charge. The Standing Committee's conclusion aroused good will and urged action: "We are deeply impressed, fellow citizens, with the difficulties with which we are surrounded. We know that our territory is extensive,—that much of it is mountainous and rugged; our population, in many parts of the State, is widely scattered; that our estates are large, our streams unbridged, our roads bad—and perhaps, what is worse than all, the funds at the disposal of the State are inadequate. The greater the difficulties, the greater the triumph if we overcome them." [54] But the remedies were not immediately applied. The 1850 census reports that the percentage of illiterates in the total White population stood at 8.6; out of the 31 states then in the Union, only five had a higher proportion, and those were all Southern states: Arkansas, Georgia, Kentucky, North Carolina, Tennessee. The ratio in Massachusetts was 2.8 per cent, in Connecticut 1.3, in Pennsylvania 2.5, in Michigan and Wisconsin 2, even in South Carolina 5.7 per cent! The percentage of illiterates among free Negroes stood at 21.19, a much higher ratio than in South Carolina (9.82) and Georgia (15.93). The percentage of native Whites in school in 1850 in Virginia stood at 12.26, which was

[53] F. W. Boatwright, *op. cit.,* p. 206.
[54] "Education Address to the People of Virginia," *Southern Literary Messenger,* XI, October 1845, p. 605.

the lowest among the states except for Florida and California, then frontier states where there were few children.[55]

More measures were advocated and some adopted during the 1840's and 1850's.[56] On the whole, education remained a luxury in the Old Dominion until the Civil War, and there probably there the Virginians lost their greatest opportunity. Their failure to maintain their eighteenth-century leadership in the nation was to a large extent due to the feeble numbers of their educated élite. The 1850 census mentions the fact that about 388,000 people born in Virginia were living outside the commonwealth, the total population of which then stood at 1,120,000. It is possible that among those who left were the more energetic and efficient individuals, who went either west or north to look for greater opportunity. But the prosperity of the 1850's attracted also some immigrants from northern states, in much smaller numbers, of course. The picture of Virginia at the eve of the War is not altogether somber, but to the historian it is full of the seeds of decline.

The War and its aftermath

The War Between the States still remains the most striking episode of Virginia's past. The history of the war itself, what the conflict meant to the military forces as well as to the civilian population, has been the object of detailed study and masterly description in many works. In a brief review of the background of the present situation, it is necessary to outline the momentous changes brought about by the conflict. Three main points must be stressed: a large section of Virginia broke away from the commonwealth as the new state of West Virginia was set up; the physical destruction over most of the commonwealth's territory was great and devastating, as Virginia remained a major battle area without interruption from 1861 to 1865; the disorganization of the whole economic

[55] *Compendium of the Seventh Census, op. cit.*

[56] "In February, 1846, the Assembly enacted legislation establishing district free school systems in *about 20 counties,* for the most part circling along the periphery of the state from the southeastern to the northwestern borders. [Acts of Assembly, Feb. 25, 1846, 37] The inauguration of these systems *was left to the voters of the various counties* and was responsible for the creation and continued activity of the education associations inspired by a January meeting in Richmond, as well as publicity in the press on the subject of education. The act provided that all *white* children from 5 to 21 years of age were to receive tuition free of charge; no class distinction was made . . . The curriculum, which went beyond the three R's to include English grammar and geography, and, when practicable, history, especially of Virginia and the United States, and the elements of physical science, made no reference to the inculcation of morality or religious training. School commissioners, however, were forbidden to appoint teachers without examining either by themselves or by special deputy into the qualifications of teachers for teaching and their moral character." (Sadie Bell, *op. cit.,* p. 354.)

system was immense, as slavery was one of its essential foundations, and as most of the population depended on cash crops marketed outside the area.

The secession of West Virginia in 1863 took away from the Old Dominion about 35 per cent of her land area and one-fourth of her population. It increased the proportion of Negroes in the state's population; and it left to a reduced Virginia the whole and enormous public debt accumulated before and during the war. The one hundred counties left to Virginia still comprised an important stretch of land beyond the Blue Ridge: the whole of the section of the Great Valley and several alignments of ridges and valleys to the west of it. Thus the commonwealth was not deprived of much of its diversity within the narrowed limits. It was apportioned only nine representatives in the House in 1870, while West Virginia occupied three seats in a total of 293 representatives.

The destruction of the territory of Virginia was frightful, chiefly because of its geographical position. Virginia was the advanced front of the Confederacy facing the North, and its proximity to Washington and to such important areas as Maryland and Pennsylvania made it imperative for the South to hold Virginia and for Federal strategy to endeavor to control the area. The capital of the Confederacy was set up in Richmond for both symbolic and practical reasons rooted in the history and the geography of the Old Dominion. In no other part of the South were the campaigns so long, so frequent, so decisive. Towns and hills changed hands many times, in some cases dozens of times within four years. Probably nowhere was Southern resistance to a growing Federal predominance in forces and supplies as stubborn, bitter, and efficient. The maps of the Virginia campaigns are the most complicated of the Civil War; they show the belligerent armies on the march again and again through the same areas, chiefly in the Shenandoah Valley and the Piedmont.

The growing naval power of the North blockaded the Tidewater and gradually occupied sections of it; Northern land forces were pushing from the northwest towards the fall-line cities, particularly towards the Richmond-Petersburg area, the heart of Virginia, without which it seemed obvious that the Confederacy could not survive.

Sherman's march through Georgia may remain in American history a symbol of great destruction, but most of Virginia was swept by marching armies again and again for four years. As the wheat- and meat-producing areas of the commonwealth were controlled by the South only at times during the conflict, and as the maritime blockade was increasing in efficiency, one wonders how Virginia, little prepared economically for war, was able to hold out so long. The remarkable spirit of the individuals composing the Confederate Armies and the extraordinary genius of Robert E. Lee are probably the main answers to that question.

Of the hundred counties remaining to the Old Dominion after the dismemberment that resulted in forming the State of West Virginia, there were few that had escaped the ravages of war, in one way or another. Although many towns had suffered severely, they had been spared total destruction; but, on the other hand, the devastation that swept over the surrounding countryside defies description. . . . Stretch upon stretch of the great battle area in eastern Virginia appeared to be entirely deserted by human beings. . . . Returning soldiers found fences burned, cattle and domestic animals gone, with outbuildings and even farm implements destroyed. The counties not directly in the path of contending armies had suffered from the raids of cavalry detachments bent on errant destruction.[57]

The whole economy of Virginia had been for four years geared to war, to supplying the army and the immediate necessities of the civilian population of Confederate areas. From a system oriented towards the production of raw materials for export, with a minor section devoted to manufacturing, it was to remain for a long while after the war a small regional economy striving to maintain even the lowest level of self-sufficiency. It seemed that reconstruction had to remake the whole country. The social structure itself seemed to have been blown up by the emancipation of the slaves, by the inevitable coming, in the wake of defeat, of the waves of carpet-baggers, by the ruin of the wealthy of day of yore whose fortune had been based chiefly on the ownership of lands that were not worth much for the moment, of slaves who had gone, or of urban enterprises that had been integrated in the ruined system of the Confederate economy.

To anyone who returned at the end of World War II to a European country like France, devastated by military campaigns sweeping repeatedly across its territory and by several years of occupation and administration by enemy forces, the picture of Virginia on the morrow of the surrender would probably have seemed familiar. Such periods necessarily cause deep demoralization of the population, which was rendered much worse by complete political and social defeat in a war started because of a difference in political and social opinions. Poets, novelists, and historians have given beautiful expression to the feeling of the end of a world, of the death of a civilization, that apparently pervaded the South, and especially eastern Virginia, in the first years after 1865. That reconstruction was afterwards long and difficult must be attributed, at least in part, to the bitterness of these feelings.

For five years following the surrender, Virginia waited to be readmitted

[57] M. P. Andrews, *Virginia, The Old Dominion,* New York, 1937, p. 527.

Old stone bridge at Bull Run Battlefield, Manassas
Library of Congress Photo by Paul Carter

to the union and was administered as "Military District Number One" by a general (at first General Schofield, succeeded by General Stoneman) who supervised the local government. For a time the commonwealth was run by the "Underwood Convention," so named for Judge Underwood, who presided over it, with a majority of Radicals, among whom Negroes and carpet-baggers were many. Of this majority General Schofield wrote: "The same baneful influence that secured the election of a majority of ignorant blacks and equally ignorant or unprincipled whites, to the Convention, has proved sufficient to hold them firmly to their original purpose. They could only hope to obtain office by disqualifying everybody in the State who is capable of discharging official duties, and all else to them was of comparatively slight importance."[58] Such periods of narrowly partisan and brutal government always leave deep wounds in the memories of the people. For the brilliant but conservative élite of Virginia, this period prolonged and deepened the feeling of a "Götterdammerung" as a consequence of the North's victory.

[58] From a letter of Schofield to General Grant, April 18, 1868, printed in John M. Schofield, *Forty-six Years in the Army*, New York, 1897, pp. 400–401; quoted in M. P. Andrews, *op. cit.*, p. 542.

The elections of 1869 brought the Conservatives to power, as Gilbert C. Walker, a native of New York, who had resided in Norfolk since 1864, was elected Governor. On January 26, 1870, Congress readmitted Virginia to her place in the Union. It was a much impoverished Virginia, whose State Treasury was in debt for a number of reasons, among them the debt accumulated by the bonds issued in the 1850's for railroad building and other improvements in a period of prosperity. Wartime interest had accumulated on these bonds and West Virginia refused to assume any share of this burden. The financial measures attempted in the early 1870's to handle the situation, while the commonwealth's budget increased its deficit, were not successful. This treasury problem dominated the local government's worries for at least one generation; it created in Virginia's politics a nightmare about bond issues and state indebtedness. If, at the time when the Constitution of the United States was adopted, political issues were greatly influenced by the opposition between merchants' and debtors' interests, on the private level, the Civil War deeply impressed Virginia politics for the better part of a century with the fear of public debt. The financial weakness resulting from this debt paralyzed to a large extent the commonwealth's endeavors at reconstruction and made it more immediately dependent on credit from the outside, that is, from the North.

The economic system was so deeply shattered that there could be no talk of restoring it along prewar lines. The whole transportation network needed rebuilding; markets had to be won again. In some cases, as with wheat, Virginia came up against the competition of the Great Plains, now opened up to settlement beyond the Mississippi and well connected by rail with the East. The old plantation economy had lost its slave manpower; the emancipation of the Negroes, who had not been prepared or educated for such an eventuality, created the worst problem of all and the most far-reaching. The freedmen often mistook the liberty that had been granted them for a right to full equality and a life of leisure and contentment at public expense. Some propagandists may have induced the more naive elements of the Negro population in the South to take this view, and the local authorities were either unwilling, if Radicals, or unfitted, if Conservatives, to make this mass of ignorant people understand the problem. Virginia might have had less difficulty weathering the long crisis had the Negroes been more enlightened; but even for the mass of the White population in 1860, the opportunity for education was quite limited.

The Whites felt the necessity of creating new legislation and machinery to apply it in order to cope with the multiplying problems that resulted from the emancipation of the slaves. The cities were worried and frightened by the influx of unequipped Negroes from the open country, who had left the plantations thinking they would find a better and more pleasant life in the towns. Rural areas were paralyzed by the mass exodus of Negro workers and terrorized by the pilfering of nomad unemployed freedmen. Federal authorities could not very well solve from above a problem which was slightly different from county to county and required daily attendance. The vast majority of the White population in Virginia favored the establishment of a system that would destroy the political power of the Negroes and create a police force to keep the former slaves "in their place." What kind of place this was to be was defined in varying terms by a great diversity of opinions. In practice it resulted in the reinstitution of a poll tax (sometimes officially called the "capitation tax"), which drastically limited the voting body, and in many measures enforcing segregation, as in most of the other southeastern states. It resulted also, before legislation was brought to bear efficiently for the same purpose in daily life, in the rise of organizations of White people who took in their own hands the policing of certain areas; such were the Knights of the White Camelia, the White League, the secret orders usually designated by the generic name of "Invisible Empire" or Ku Klux Klan. Tension between the races was great in Virginia for some time after the war, but it was not so bitter and lasting as in other states of the cotton belt further south, beginning with South Carolina and Georgia.

Social and economic reconstruction proceeded at a pace considerably slowed down by these problems, which weighed heavily on the future, but nevertheless it continued by the very necessity of survival after so complete a catastrophe. The population within the reduced area of postwar Virginia numbered 1,219,000 inhabitants in 1860; the census of 1870 gave the figure of 1,225,000, which, after subsequent revisions, seems rather to have been 1,338,000.[59] Wherever the actual increase in the decade of the war, it appears that the population grew more quickly during the period 1870–1900 than it did in 1830–1860. The census for 1880 reported 1,512,000 inhabitants and the 1900 census 1,854,000 inhabitants. The net annual increase seems to have averaged 1.1 per cent, about one-half of the national rate of increase, in that period. Virginia was too poor a land, with too many problems and not enough opportunities, to attract many of the new immigrants landing in rapidly increasing numbers on American soil; on the other hand, as many other

[59] The Bureau of the Census revised the 1870 total figures in 1920; the Virginia figure was adjusted by Sara K. Gilliam in *Virginia's People* (Population Study Report No. 4. Virginia State Planning Board), Richmond, 1944.

parts of America offered better opportunities, enterprising Virginians went to look for a better living westward or northward. The census of 1880 reports that the number of people born in Virginia and living in other parts of the United States was higher by 407,608 than the number of people born in other states and living in Virginia; however, this difference, showing how much the internal domestic migrations impoverished Virginia in terms of inhabitants, was reduced to 333,152 in 1890 and 237,077 in 1900. Thus it would seem that the end of the nineteenth century saw the numerical weakening of the trend of out-migration from Virginia; this may well be the cause of a slightly higher rate of population growth than in prewar years, although the latter could have resulted also from a gradual improvement in the ratio of natural increase. In these years the foreign immigrants who trickled in were from the United Kingdom, Germany, Russia, Canada and Austria-Hungary.

In 1870, Virginia was still producing much less tobacco, wheat, and corn and had less livestock than in 1860. By 1880, there were more farms, and their average size was smaller. Many of them were operated and have since been operated by *sharecropping,* by which the land owned by a White landlord is leased to Negro tenants. The landlord or even a loan-agent could thus control a group of many tenant-farms. Vast areas, however, seem to have returned in the 1860's to woods after having been cultivated in prewar times. Such was particularly the case in the northern Tidewater between the Potomac and the James.

In the 1870's, a strong feeling arose in Virginia that the commonwealth, to regain prosperity and wealth, needed to attract the attention of the richer parts of the country and procure wider markets for her agricultural products and larger capital investments to build up equipment and industries. In 1876, the commonwealth published a volume entitled *Virginia: A Geographical and Political Summary,* prepared and published under the supervision of the Board of Immigration, which pleads eloquently all the advantages the state offered to all kinds of economic activities. True, most of the economic statistics relate to 1860 and little mention is to be found in the 320 pages of the wartime destruction and the need of reconstruction, but the prospects for development are constantly emphasized. It is somewhat paradoxical, but significant, to see in the preface a rather conservative state government quote a resolution adopted in March, 1867, by the General Assembly, under the pressure of carpet-baggers, inviting "all classes of men, from all countries, to Virginia, to settle the surplus lands and engage in all the great industrial pursuits." Eminent Virginians, and among them the famous oceanographer, Commodore Maury, were then active in bringing to the attention of the outside world all the potential resources of the Old Dominion calling for development. Later the Commissioner of Agriculture was directed to issue handbooks presenting all the major data concerning Virginia, particularly her advantages. In 1888, the issue entitled *Virginia as She Is* was prepared, followed by another handbook in 1893.

The end of the nineteenth century was, however, for Virginia a period of slow recovery and reorganization; the commonwealth's economy remained chiefly an agricultural one and this was a period of low prices for agricultural products. In the southeasternmost section of the state, around Norfolk, truck farming brought substantial profits and it developed also on a large scale in the two counties of the Eastern Shore. These oceanic areas enjoyed a warmer and damper climate which put them in a better situation than the lands up north for the production, in the spring and early fall, of a variety of vegetables consumed in increasing quantities by the growing cities of the northeast. Ships loaded with such vegetables left on a regular schedule from Norfolk and the smaller harbors of the Eastern Shore for Washington and Baltimore, Philadelphia and New York. The Commissioner of Agriculture in the Handbook of 1893 quoted a document drawn up by "Farmers and Truckers" of Norfolk, in 1889, describing the magnitude of the agricultural interests within a ten-mile radius of the city:

Within this circle more than forty thousand acres are entirely devoted to truck crops such as kale, cabbage, spinach, peas, beans, radish, lettuce, turnips, beets, onions, melons, potatoes, tomatoes, eggplants, celery, asparagus, strawberries, and numerous similar crops, while many thousands of acres within this circle are devoted to the growing of crops of corn, rye, oats, hay, peanuts and sweet potatoes, and other staple annual crops. The aggregate sales of the truck crops grown in this circle amount to from $3,000,000 to $4,000,000 annually . . . and are constantly increasing. The value of these trucking lands exceeds the sum of eight million dollars. The value of fertilizers used annually is placed at one million dollars . . . In the prosecution of this great work fully ten thousand laborers are given steady employment throughout the year, while during the very busy season of April, May and June the number of laborers runs up to thirty thousand.[60]

The counties of Norfolk, Princess Anne, Nansemond, and Northampton were most active in truck farming. Norfolk had daily connections by sea with New York, and trains or barges leaving from the Northampton harbors supplied the Chesapeake Bay cities. In 1892, the Chesapeake and Ohio Railroad started from its Hampton Roads terminal a fast truck and fruit train to the northwest, carrying Virginia products as far as Chicago.

[60] *Virginia: A Handbook,* prepared by Thomas Whitehead, Commissioner of Agriculture, Richmond, 1893, p. 85.

In southern Virginia, proceeding inland from Norfolk, a series of agricultural belts was taking shape, each specializing in one predominant cash crop, although many other crops were encountered on the sharecroppers' farms. To the west of the truck farming area, in the counties of Isle of Wight, Surry, and Sussex, was the largest peanut-producing area in America. In Southampton County and further west, cotton became important (although Virginia ranked only twelfth among the cotton-growing states in 1880 with a produce of about 20,000 bales); further west, on Piedmont lands the "Virginia leaf" was taking over and was the leading product of Halifax, Pittsylvania, Patrick, Henry, Franklin, and Bedford Counties. Tobacco was also grown further north in the central Piedmont, especially in the counties of Amherst, Nelson, Albemarle, Orange, and Greene. Beyond the Blue Ridge, in the narrower valleys of southwestern Virginia, large quantities of burley tobacco were grown. But the main specialty of the Great Valley was livestock husbandry. Cattle and sheep were to be seen in impressive herds; southwestern Virginia exported beef cattle, and other parts of the Valley had a thriving dairy-farming industry. The United States Department of Agriculture was beginning to advocate the expansion of the cattle economy on the rich perennial pastures of Virginia west of the fall line: it seemed to be one of the best-endowed areas in the United States for rearing and fattening cattle, within easy reach of the largest consuming markets.

Some central parts of the Piedmont and the Tidewater north of the James were among the poorer and less specialized areas of the rural economy of the state. These areas had largely gone into woodlands after the Civil War. Some parts, such as Caroline County, which produced a special quality of sun-cured tobacco renowned for its use in chewing tobacco, had many small farms. The northern Piedmont raised pure-bred horses and had many farms of diversified economy. Loudoun County claimed to have the best farming and highest yields in the state in 1880–1890. In the central Piedmont and in the Tidewater peninsulas between the Potomac and James Rivers, lumbering was rapidly becoming an essential industry. Fisheries and the shipping of oysters northwards secured additional benefits.

A new agricultural map was thus taking shape in Virginia which the first half of the twentieth century was going to alter in many respects, but preserve in the main lines. However, the great agricultural expansion of the nineteenth century within the United States and on other continents made agricultural products cheap. The size of the production units became important, and the small farms of Virginia, on rolling ground, could hardly compete with the wide open spaces being put to work in the West and abroad in the British Dominions and Russia. The end of the nineteenth century saw, nevertheless, in Virginia the start of two new trends of industrialization and urbanization that prepared the larger developments of the next period.

Industrialization came to the South soon after 1865. Northern capital found it profitable and wise to install new plants in an area where labor was abundant and cheap, certain raw materials (such as cotton, timber, and coal) were produced nearby, and taxation was less heavy. Most of the textile industries went further south than Virginia, closer to the heart of the cotton belt, into North Carolina, South Carolina, and Georgia. Nevertheless, Virginia was not entirely by-passed. In 1882, a group of local businessmen started the Riverside Cotton Mill in Danville, which developed into a huge textile plant in the following fifty years. Lumbering was expanding steadily: in 1899, Virginia's lumber production was estimated at 959 million board feet; the Old Dominion ranked fifteenth among the states as a lumber producer. Many diversified industries manufactured a variety of products from this lumber, which came mainly from yellow pines, oaks, and poplars.[61]

Mineral resources were put to work: iron furnaces were scattered through the Piedmont and along the foot of the Blue Ridge. In 1884, 153,000 tons of iron ore were smelted in the state. Coal was mined around Richmond in Henrico and Chesterfield Counties, where four active mines produced 60,000 tons in 1870. Small quantities of coal were also mined near Farmville and in the southwestern Valley in Montgomery and Pulaski Counties. In 1873, coal was discovered in Tazewell County, and the town of Pocahontas was established in 1882. Then production was begun in the southwestern coal fields: Tazewell County supplied in 1883 about 119,000 tons of low volatile bituminous coal, and the Norfolk and Western Railway began carrying it to the Tidewater cities. In 1900, the county produced 970,000 tons of coal. From Tazewell, coal mining spread to Wise County a few years later. This rapidly developing mining industry led the N. & W. Railroad to develop its network in the area and to start the new town of Roanoke, where large yards and the headquarters of the company were established.

The manufacturing of machinery seems to have been the leading industry of Virginia in the 1890's; then came the aggregate industries working wood. In Richmond and Roanoke large machine shops built a variety of engines, boilers, saw mills, railroad equipment, and rolling stock, including locomotives. Lynchburg and Richmond continued, of course,

---

[61] According to Henry B. Steer, *Lumber Production in the United States, 1799–1946* (USDA, Miscellaneous Publ. No. 669), Washington, 1948, pp. 28–29.

their older specialization in the manufacturing of tobacco, and Lynch-burg specialized also in leather goods. These industries provided employ-ment and developed wealth in the fast-growing main cities of Virginia. Richmond, Lynchburg, and Norfolk were at last providing Virginia with a few substantial urban centers. Roanoke and Danville were beginning to develop on a smaller scale as the century drew to an end.

The development of the railroad network from the Hampton Roads and Richmond areas toward the west and south gave Virginia the en-viable and promising function of a funnel channeling most of the trade of the southeast toward the northeast. Lines fanned out southwards from the Washington-Baltimore area across the Piedmont and fall-line zone of Virginia. True, the railroad development was controlled from New York and Boston; true, the tariff wars of the 1870's and 1880's were going to concentrate the export trade and the control of transportation for the whole country even more in the great northeastern cities, but Virginia was too close to that group of metropolises not to benefit somewhat by it. The famous debate about tariff differentials, of which the South so often complained, affected Virginia insofar as a small part of her territory was within "Southern territory"; but most of Virginia was included in eastern or "official" territory and therefore did not suffer much from rate differ-entials. What really prevented the North-South rail traffic through Vir-ginia from becoming more important was the relatively slow pace of development in the whole Southeast. Lines linking the northeastern cities with the Great Lakes, the Ohio Valley, and the region to the north of the Great Plains were already more active than the lines towards the Missis-sippi delta (from which a great deal of the transportation could be done by coastwise shipping), Florida, the Georgia Piedmont, or the Tennessee Valley.

Industrialization and the rural exodus of the postwar period made cities grow fast. Richmond reached 81,000 inhabitants in 1890 and 85,000 in 1900, while Roanoke passed from 16,000 to 21,500 in the same years and Norfolk from 34,800 to 46,600. In this last decade of the century, the growth of Norfolk was probably the most spectacular. The port was booming with the development of the network of the N. & W. and the coal exports; the coastwise trade in vegetables, fruits, and peanuts was still developing, and some cotton and tobacco were being exported. The city's suburbs were rapidly expanding, and the local authorities predicted that Norfolk would become, like Washington, "a city of apartment houses." On the ocean shore to the east the development of Virginia Beach was begun in 1883 by Norfolk residents.[62]

[62] See T. J. Wertenbaker, *op. cit.*, on Norfolk.

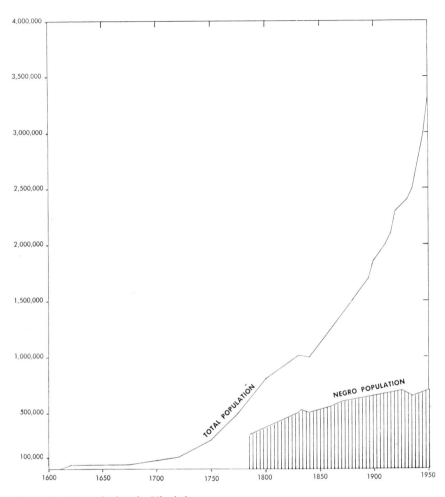

Growth of Population in Virginia
The graph shows the total population from the founding of Jamestown to 1950,
the Negro population from 1790 to 1950

Smaller towns were growing and creating a framework of urban centers
throughout Virginia. The end of the century marked one important
change in the prospects of the various regions of Virginia: chewing tobacco became less fashionable, and the recently introduced cigarette began to sweep the market. This change dealt a hard blow to the central
tobacco belt from Caroline County to Bedford, and to the town of Lynchburg, the prosperity of which was largely founded on plugs of chewing
tobacco. Richmond took over the manufacturing of cigarettes and kept
its control in Virginia, making substantial benefits as the market expanded. In 1870, Americans consumed 13.9 million cigarettes; in 1890,

they were already smoking 2,200 million cigarettes. Thus the Old Belt bright-leaf tobacco of the southern Piedmont acquired a new and immense market, while the sun- or fire-cured tobacco of the central Piedmont and Tidewater had to face shrinking outlets. Nevertheless, a number of people in Virginia remained attached to the older forms of tobacco consumption: chewing and snuff.

Much more important than the gradual changes caused by the evolution of the geography of land use and of industrialization was the reform of education in Virginia. In the postwar period the necessity for a public school system appeared imperative. Something had to be done about the education of Negro children, as well as the many Whites impoverished by the social revolution that the war had effected in practice. In 1879, W. H. Ruffner, then Superintendent of Public Instruction, prepared for the first report of the Commissioner of Agriculture a note on what his task had been in the organization of the first large-scale network of public schools in the commonwealth.

There was no real public free-school system in the State prior to the war, although there was in existence some provision for the education of the children of the poor; that is to say for the whites. In 1850 there were, in all the schools of the State, private and public, 52,000 children; in 1860 there were 67,000 (all white), of whom 31,000 were pauper children. The constitution framed for the State in 1868, under the reconstruction acts, provided for a system of public free schools to be supported by taxation, State and local, and by the interest received from the literary fund (derived from fines, forfeitures and escheats). The system was to be administered impartially as between the races, and to be in full operation by 1876. . . . In the year 1870 the number (of children attending public schools) was only 59,000, of whom some 10,000 were colored pupils (attending schools established by Northern societies and the Freedmen's Bureau). A great change occurred immediately on the introduction of the State school system. In 1870–71, the total number of children at school rose to 158,000 . . . In 1875 the whole number of pupils (white and colored) enrolled in the public schools was 184,000; . . . in 1877 the number was 205,000. To these are to be added about 25,000 attending private schools, which would give as the whole number of children now enrolled in all the schools of the State, 230,000. Of the 205,000 in public schools in 1876–77, 140,000 were white and 65,000 colored.[63]

In 1891 there were 342,720 pupils distributed over 7,689 schools and being taught by 7,718 teachers, which shows on the average one teacher per school and per 44 pupils. The same teacher had thus to teach children of quite varying ages and could not devote much time to each of them. Nevertheless, this was a beginning, a successful and very important one. After the period of the Civil War and its immediate aftermath,

[63] Quoted in *Virginia: A Handbook, op. cit.*, Richmond, 1893, p. 122.

during which education had been worse neglected than ever, the younger Virginia generation badly needed an improved school system. The older institutions of higher education carried on with somewhat expanded means as Reconstruction progressed. The land grant donated to the several states by Congress in 1862 for the endowment of colleges was accepted by Virginia in 1872; the Virginia Agricultural and Mechanical College was opened that same year, and in 1887 and 1890 it benefited by additional grants from Congress. It was located in Blacksburg, in one of the southwestern valleys, not far from the growing towns of Roanoke and Radford.

For the technical and higher education of the Negro youth in the state, two new schools were founded: the Hampton Normal and Agricultural Institute, opened at Hampton, near Fort Monroe, in 1868, the first permanent school for freedmen in the South; and the Virginia Normal and Collegiate Institute opened in 1883 at Petersburg. From Virginia came the celebrated Negro educator Booker T. Washington, who called on his people to turn away from political ambition and bureaucratic careers and to prefer going into more technical professions or trades. Though this was in many ways a wise doctrine, it could scarcely be expected to meet with the unanimous approval of many Negro people, who felt that holding office and playing a role in politics was for them as indispensable a way as for any other group to make sure of full respect for their rights. Booker T. Washington certainly never meant that no Negro should endeavor to hold office, but he knew that if too many attempted those careers, many would end in bitter disappointment. The first need was to educate the Negro people in a way that would enable them to make a decent living and to occupy a better place in an expanding society. To this end the two institutions established in Virginia worked to the best of their ability.

As the twentieth century opened, Virginia had achieved physical and economic reconstruction, the restoration of conservatism in government, and a *modus vivendi* acceptable to the various sections of the population following the bitter social revolution of the tragic postwar years. It may be said that, though some problems continued to weigh heavily upon the commonwealth's functioning and its destiny, Virginia was well on the way to prosperity by 1900. She had accomplished more toward recovery than several other Southern states in which the destructions of the Civil War had been less thorough. The traditional want of towns had been succeeded by the growth of three important urban centers and the scattering of at least a dozen smaller towns, removing the ancient shortcomings of scattered settlement. Owing to the development of her railroads, she maintained a strategic position integrated in the mighty transportation system of the United States. Owing to the creation and development of a public school system and to the greater attention given to matters of education, Virginia was better preparing her people for the sweeping changes and the coming prosperity of the twentieth century.

The saga of the twentieth century

This century has brought to the Old Dominion such transformation as most Virginians would have been reluctant to forecast and boast about even in the 1910's. From a rural state with a few middle-sized urban nuclei and an altogether modest rank among the states, with the sole exception of historical seniority, Virginia has become in the 1950's one of the most rapidly developing states in the Union, attracting in-migration, highly urbanized, and powerfully industrialized. Never since the middle of the eighteenth century could Virginia assume that her progress and development would be so rapid and fruitful in almost all fields.

Much of this saga was due to the gradual recovery of the South as a whole, much more still to the extraordinary rise in the past fifty years of American wealth and standard of living; however, Virginia might have been by-passed by these developments if Virginians had not helped themselves to a considerable extent. This time they were able to see their geographical position making good the hopes long pinned on it. True, this geographical position did not have the same meaning when the state was only the closest Southern neighbor in the Atlantic seaboard area to the North, through which the inner portions of the vast continent were being developed. This had been the case in the previous century; but now Virginia found herself in the very midst of the Atlantic East, being fitted to face new responsibilities in a changing world, and being prepared for a fuller integration into the greater prosperity of the American nation.

From 1900 to 1950 the population of Virginia almost doubled, increasing from 1,854,000 to 3,318,000. In 1900 the state ranked seventeenth among the states in population, and in 1950, fifteenth. Having sunk to the twentieth rank from 1910 to 1930, Virginia gained her new advantage after 1930. This statistical detail brings to our attention the fact that these fifty years have not been for Virginia equal ones in the rhythm of growth and improvement. It may be important to outline briefly the major trends and events of the period.

The predominating trends of the evolution of the whole Southeast in recent decades have been aptly summed up in the following dictum:

Pohick Church, looking north along the Post Road, April, 1914
Bureau of Public Roads, U. S. Department of Commerce

"Cotton goes west and cattle comes east, the Negro goes north and the Yankee comes south." This way of encompassing a complex and manifold evolution into four major symbolic migrations is particularly applicable to Virginia. In the Old Dominion, the cultivation of cotton, which had never been an essential crop, covered about 25,000 acres in the 1890's and went up to 100,000 acres in the mid-1920's, to sink rapidly after 1929 to a negligible figure: 19,000 acres in 1951. Production of cotton decreased from 51,000 bales in 1929 to 14,000 in 1951 and 23,000 in 1952, out of a national total of over 15 million bales in the latter year. In the national total, therefore, Virginia's cotton contribution is very small indeed. Cattle, meanwhile, has been steadily on the increase since the 1870's. Virginia counted less than 800,000 head until 1910, but 896,000 in 1940, 1,129,000 in 1950 and 1,410,000 in January, 1954.

The Negro population, although enjoying a substantial rate of natural increase, did not see its numbers grow much from census to census. In the 1920–1930 decade there was even a decrease of about 6 per cent. After 1930, when the figure stood at 650,000 people, it rose slowly again to 661,-000 in 1940 and 734,000 in 1950. The last decade showed thus an increase of 11 per cent for the Negro population; but the White population in the same interval increased by 28.3 per cent. The number of Negroes would have grown much faster had there not been a constant migration out of Virginia. The statistics for the Whites show, on the other hand, an increase faster than the natural addition. Although demographic data may often be differently interpreted, it appears safe after a thorough examination to state that the out-migration was still higher than the in-migration until about 1930, but that the in-migration surpassed the out-migration from 1930 to 1950 and represented chiefly the influx of White people from the north and the west—Yankees by Virginia standards. The 1950 census estimates that there still were more people born in Virginia residing in other states than people born in other states residing in Virginia, but that difference was reduced to 103,000 persons, much less than earlier in the century. The percentage of Negroes in the total population stood at 22.1 per cent in 1950, reduced from 35.7 per cent in 1900 and 27 per cent in 1930.

Whether population or agricultural data are studied, the same trends show up. Virginia has been turning away from her traditional economic patterns and social structure towards something new, not necessarily contrasted with the past, but definitely less Southern and more Northern. The plantation has been succeeded by a kind of ranch and the predominantly agricultural manpower by industrial workers (as agriculture employed only 23.9 per cent of the total labor force in 1940, and 14.6 per cent in 1950); the number and proportion of Negroes in the population is receding, and the growth of large urbanized metropolitan areas has definitely removed the old want of towns. Whichever major kind of statistics is used as an index, these trends seem slow and somewhat hesitant until the 1920's, but take a positive, accelerated pace from the 1930's on. Two periods have to be considered, therefore, within the recent half-century.

The first quarter of the century was marked by two major events for Virginia, the first of global import, the second local: World War I was the first; and the undertaking by the state government of a policy of financial recovery and road building in the middle 1920's was the second. World War I brought to the whole United States a rapid expansion of industries and a better standard of living. Federal authorities designated the Hampton Roads area to become a principal naval base, a large center of shipbuilding, and a leading port for shipping coal and grain overseas in massive quantities. Thus Norfolk, Newport News, and the area around them received a sudden and tremendous impulse which has been maintained, with varying intensity, as the international responsibilities of the United States grew in a troubled world. At about the same period, new large industries came to the South, and some of them chose plant sites in Virginia: thus in 1917 the American Viscose Corporation started operations in a factory at Roanoke which claimed for a while to be the largest rayon manufacturing plant in the world. In Richmond the number of wage earners jumped from 17,282 in 1914 to 21,759 in 1919, a figure not to be reached again for almost twenty years afterwards. In order to better handle the inflated exports of the Hampton Roads ports, the railroads serving them improved their facilities and equipment and developed traffic across Virginia. It was worth it: in 1917, as the United States entered the war, the exports of Norfolk and Portsmouth alone amounted to 10.9 million tons, most of which was coal.

Thus, while the first fifteen years of this century brought to the economy of Virginia a gradual development of the more encouraging trends that appeared at the end of the nineteenth century, World War I precipitated this evolution and benefited both the large cities and the rural areas on a vast scale. Agricultural prices soared during the war and remained rather high for several years after the armistice in Europe. From 1900 to 1925, the largest waves of immigrants arrived in the United States, creating a boom in the rate of population growth. This fact greatly expanded the domestic market in several respects, particularly with respect to smoking, which could not but be significant to the Piedmont tobacco growers and the Danville processing interests, as well as the Richmond cigarette manufacturers. Average per-capita consumption of tobacco in the United States rose from 5.4 lbs. in 1900 to 7.3 lbs. in 1917 and oscillated between 6 and 7 pounds through the 1920's. Cigarettes accounted for only 2 per cent of the total consumption of tobacco in 1900, but for 19 per cent in 1920; and cigarettes were made essentially of flue-cured and burley tobaccos, specialties of southern Virginia.

The great prosperity period created by the world's war needs continued, although at a somewhat slower pace for Virginia, through the 1920's. It is true that just after 1920 employment receded notably in Richmond and Norfolk and the demand for tobacco went down slightly; but a more reliable upward trend set in afterwards. In the early 1920's, the chemical industries continued coming to Virginia, now on a larger scale; a rayon plant was started in 1919 at Hopewell, then another "silk mill" at Covington; in 1929 the Du Pont de Nemours Company built a rayon plant in a suburb of Richmond and another at Waynesboro. Virginia seemed to be specializing in rayon and became the leading state in the union in the manufacturing of artificial silk yarn. Many endeavors to develop the silk industry in the Old Dominion, based on the abundance of mulberry trees, had failed one after the other for three centuries; but

Southwest Virginia, near Norton
Virginia Chamber of Commerce

"artificial silk" was developing on a grand scale. Textile and timber industries grew steadily.

The generally scattered pattern of settlement in Virginia may have seemed a drawback in the possible utilization by large plants of the abundant and gifted potential manpower. Should new mill towns be established as they were in earlier days in New England? Or should the population be left scattered on farms within a radius of a dozen miles or more around the site of the plant? To be within reach of the plants, the workers needed a network of roads passable the whole year round. The coming of the motorcar in the 1920's and the new importance thus acquired by the highways was not lost for the leaders of Virginia. The scattering of the population made it necessary to establish a long and rather dense network of highways. The commonwealth did this in some twenty years.

Until the beginning of the twentieth century, the task of building and maintaining roads had been left to the counties, the quality of whose achievement was very unequal. To procure funds for road building and improvement, the counties issued bonds, which often overburdened their treasuries. The public was dissatisfied with the state of the roads in the 1890's, and a series of conventions was held to discuss the matter in Richmond and Roanoke. In 1906 the General Assembly responded and passed three laws bringing the state government into the field with a State Highway Commission to coordinate the counties' efforts. A State Convict Force was created to provide less expensive labor for road making. In 1918 the Assembly took the next step and established a state highway system: it consisted of 28 routes, was about 4,000 miles long, and linked the major communities in the commonwealth. Thus the System of Primary Highways was born. To put it into shape a great deal of work was necessary, and money was lacking. License and registration fees of cars were not gathering enough money. Since the number of motor vehicles was increasing rapidly and the traffic of common carriers across the state expanded, more road building became indispensable. In 1923 a popular referendum decided the question of the way to provide the necessary funds: the choice was between issuing state bonds and taxation. The public chose the "pay-as-you-go" system, which was from that time applied to as much of Virginia's finances as possible and to which the name of Senator Harry F. Byrd will remain attached.

To the license and registration fees for passenger cars were added in 1923 an annual fee to be paid by common carriers and a tax on fuel which was set in the beginning at two cents to a gallon of gasoline, but rose to five cents per gallon by 1928 (when it was the highest tax on gasoline paid in any of the states) and was extended to other motor fuels. Now the state had the means to maintain and improve the roads. When the primary highways were in good enough shape and the depression made the financial burden of the county governments especially heavy, the State Highway Commission took over the secondary highways by the "Byrd Road Law" of 1932. This act gave to the State Department of Highways jurisdiction over all of the public roads, causeways, landings, and wharves that had been under county supervision, and in effect removed (with only a few exceptions) from the counties the burden of constructing and maintaining their parts of the highway system. This secondary system was a network of about 36,000 miles, improved to make all parts of it passable in any kind of weather. In 1945, Virginia's state highway system totalled 47,000 miles of public roads. Federal aid to highway construction helped the state treasuries, as the Union's budget matched dollar for dollar the state's expenditure. After World War II, it was obvious that expansion of motor traffic called for more road building and improvement. A twenty-year plan was then drawn up by the State Highway Commission. It was revised in 1954 when the Department of Highways presented a new report on highway needs and when it was decided to build a turnpike bypassing the Richmond-Petersburg urban area to let the traffic of U. S. Route No. 1 cross the state without being held up by bottlenecks in these cities.[64]

The establishment of a good road network in the era of motorcar transportation was by its consequences even more important for Virginia than the railroad development on the morrow of the Civil War. Not only did it speed industrialization and the scattering of manufacturing plants throughout the country, providing more wealth and employment to heretofore purely rural areas with surplus manpower, but also it made possible a fuller utilization of the geographical and historical endowment of the commonwealth. Virginia's geographical position between the rest of the Southeast on the one hand and the great urban and industrial complex of the Atlantic Northeast on the other made necessary, besides the rail connections, major highways, adequately built and maintained, linking Florida, Alabama, Tennessee, and Texas with Pennsylvania, New York, and Washington. Routes No. 1, following the fall line, and No. 11, following the Great Valley, were bound to attract a tremendous amount of traffic, both commercial and private. Linking the farms to markets by an easy network was the best inducement the commonwealth could give to her farmers to make the soils more fruitful. Finally, as tourism developed, Virginia needed good roads to give the crowds from all over the nation and the world full access to the many historical shrines that dotted her map: Mount Vernon and Monticello; Arlington, Jamestown, Williamsburg, and Yorktown; the battlefields of the Civil War, the Surrender Grounds and the White House of the Confederacy, to mention only the most famous among so many landmarks. The long and picturesque Tidewater coastline with parks and sea resorts on the one hand, and the beautiful vistas, cooler summers, vast forests, and well-known spas of the western ridges on the other hand, added to the attraction Virginia could not avoid exercising for tourists from afar as well as from the crowded cities to the north.

All these advantages, whether natural or man-made, were put to account once a good highway system gave access to all the points concerned. An intensive travel trade, which became after 1935 a substantial source of wealth, was one of the consequences of highway development. It must be added that the penetration of the entire territory by motorcars caused many changes that went much deeper than economic uplift. Owing to the better roads, children could be transported more quickly to schools, particularly in rural areas of scattered settlement; and the influence of the

[64] See State Highway Commission, *A Twenty-Year Plan for the Development of Virginia Highways*, Richmond, 1945; and Virginia Department of Highways, *Virginia's Highway Needs*, Richmond, 1954 (both mimeographed).

outside world came to remote and previously isolated corners of Virginia. A study of the hollows of the Blue Ridge conducted by a group of specialists in 1929–1930 brought back the description of incredibly backward communities situated within a radius of one to two hundred miles from the national capital. The same was true in an even greater degree of the creases of the mountainous land further west and south. The degree of backwardness could always be related to the degree of isolation, and was usually signalled by the condition of the road linking the community concerned with the outside world.[65] As good roads came, and along with them the invitation to get out, become better acquainted with more modern conditions of living, learn more and gain more, the antiquated ways of life of these valleys began to change. A visit to the hollows after 1950 shows only rare, exceptional cases of the closed little worlds that were so common for the "hollow folk" in 1930.

As the roads improved, events of world magnitude helped to awaken the more isolated parts of the country to a new life, greater prosperity, and greater responsibilities. A series of carefully compiled and presented works began to draw the public's attention to the problems of the South, the poorest and least well-equipped section of the country. Books by Howard W. Odum and Rupert H. Vance of the University of North Carolina stirred up considerable interest in the 1930's. The depression of the early 1930's brought about larger spendings by the federal authorities to bolster the dwindling national economy. Price supports of agricultural products considerably helped rural areas that on the whole had not been well-to-do for a long time. The two periods characterized by an economy of relative scarcity, during World War II and the Korean War, made prices of foodstuffs and raw materials soar again, and the agricultural sector profited. Peanuts became a major crop in southeastern Virginia; truck farming, amounting only to a few farms in the vicinity of Norfolk, developed on a large scale on the Eastern Shore; fruit orchards expanded along the foot of the Blue Ridge; animal husbandry brought better revenues as meat, poultry, and dairy products saw their markets rapidly growing. Large-scale industries, becoming crowded in New England and the Middle West, came more and more to the Southeast, and Virginia received a good share of this migration of factories. The trends begun during World War I were blown up to unsuspected new dimensions after 1930.

As a result of the depression, the New Deal, and the foreign wars, federal activities and expenditures increased to previously unknown dimensions in terms of budget, employment, and variety. The national capital

[65] Mandel Sherman and Thomas R. Henry, *Hollow Folk*, New York, 1933.

In earlier times, bridges in Virginia were often covered.
Virginia Forest Service

grew more quickly than ever, broke the line limiting the District of
Columbia, and spilled over it into the two neighboring states of Virginia
and Maryland. The metropolitan area of Washington, according to the
1950 census, comprised in Virginia the counties of Arlington and Fairfax,
and the cities of Alexandria and Falls Church. In fact, suburban areas
linked to Washington extend much farther into Virginia: most of Loudoun and Prince William Counties and part of Fauquier County were
within the outer suburbia of the capital by 1954. Military establishments
abound, their situations determined by the proximity of the federal capital, in many parts of the Tidewater, linking Washington to the Hampton Roads area, where Norfolk has become the major American Naval
Base and the headquarters of the Atlantic Fleet, while Newport News is
one of the principal shipbuilding centers of America. Every week end,
crowds of relatively well-paid government employees, of officers quartered
in the area, and of Washington diplomats have no better direction to
take for an outing in their family cars than the many tourist spots of the
Old Dominion.

Federal funds come into Virginia thus in many direct and indirect
ways. Federal aid helps the state maintain not only the highways, but

also the schools and welfare institutions. In 1950, about ten per cent of the total revenue of the commonwealth came from federal aid funds. But the proximity of Washington and the size of military and civilian federal activities located in Virginia makes federal aid the greatest single source or category of revenue. The whole nation profits, of course, by federal expenditures, but it may be safely stated that Virginia benefits from these expenditures to an extent generally above the national average. In 1952, wage and salary payments by the federal government in Virginia reached the amount of 922 million dollars, representing 29 per cent of the total gross wages and salaries paid to individuals in the state that year, while for the whole country the percentage is 14 per cent.[66] This demonstrates perhaps better than anything else how Virginia benefits by her geographical position in the nation.

Independently of government revenues, the income derived by the population from increased industrialization and urbanization continues to grow. Nonagricultural employment rose in the Old Dominion from 533,000 workers in 1939 to 878,600 in 1952, an increase of 64.7 per cent, which was above the national average of 58.2 for the same period. Among the forty-eight states, Virginia rose from seventeenth in 1939 in terms of size of nonagricultural employment, to fourteenth in 1952. However, she ranks lower in terms of manufacturing employment and owes the above-mentioned fourteenth rank more to the development of services and the number of office workers than to industrialization proper.[67]

Though it may be that federal services have reached within the region one of their peaks in recent years, and that Virginia should not expect these graphs to mount in the future as steeply as they did in the last twenty years, the slower upward trend of the curves describing the process of industrialization and travel development can definitely be expected to continue. A new Virginia is indeed arising from the changes that have precipitously occurred since the beginning of this century within the framework of which the Old Dominion was a part. This time the resulting state of things is so different from what Virginia used to be that it would be misleading to speak of it as the result of reconstruction and recovery after the Civil War. That process was completed by 1915. Since World War I, Virginia has been caught in the turmoil of an expanding economy and of horizons opening towards wider expanses within America and abroad.

[66] According to Department of Commerce statistical data.
[67] See U. S. Bureau of Labor Statistics, *Employment and Payrolls* (Annual Supplement Issue), April, 1953; and a study by Seymour L. Wolfbein of that Bureau, *The Changing Geography of American Industry.*

Three and a half centuries of change have shaped the region; the last half-century of that period has given Virginia a new momentum. How a local tradition, peculiar to this commonwealth, has slowly been wrought, is easier to understand after even as brief a review of the past as that above. How this past has shaped, within the physical mold provided by nature, the present main regional differences existing in Virginia, is also becoming clearer.

Before we come to study the use made of the many resources of the commonwealth, and before we attempt to assess, in the light of the recent changes, the present problems and trends, let us draw a general sketch of the regions and modes of life in Virginia in the middle of this century. What the actual economic and social evolution of Virginia has been and is in this period will be more fully described in the chapters that follow.

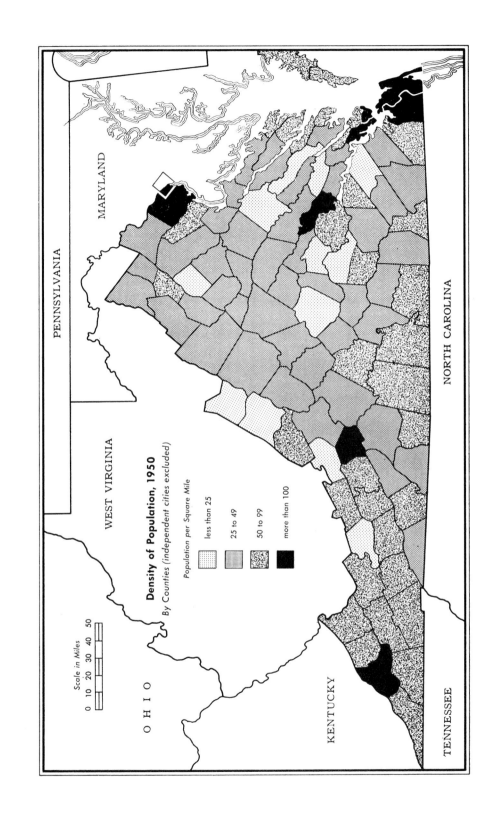

PENNSYLVANIA

MARYLAND

WEST VIRGINIA

O H I O

KENTUCKY

NORTH CAROLINA

TENNESSEE

Scale in Miles

0 10 20 30 40 50

Density of Population, 1950

By Counties (independent cities excluded)

Population per Square Mile

less than 25

25 to 49

50 to 99

more than 100

3. Regional Divisions and
Modes of Life

MANY NATURAL FACTORS lending physical variety and many historical and cultural reasons for regional differentiation have been reviewed in the preceding chapters. From whatever point of view one looks at Virginia, the essential differences between east and west appear. The Tidewater and the mountains provide the two main contrasts in natural history as well as in the history of settlement. Topography thus appears as the principal divider: there is a line to the east of which the degree of slope is of little consequence, but to the west of which it is of great moment. This line passes slightly east of the main alignment of mountains of the Blue Ridge, including with western Virginia the hilly knobs rising on the upper parts of the Piedmont. These Piedmont knobs, although clearly aligned in the landscape with a predominant axis parallel to the Blue Ridge, interspersed with isolated pyramidal mounts of the "Monadnock type," are not important in the landscape north of Charlottesville. But they begin to give a more mountainous character to the terrain from Charlottesville to Lynchburg and then again south of the Roanoke River, in Franklin and Patrick Counties.

The approximate boundary thus established between eastern and western Virginia corresponds also to certain agricultural and social regions. Practically all the flue-cured and fire-cured tobacco is grown to the east of it. Such crops as cotton, peanuts, and soybeans are, of course, much further east. All the important areas of burley tobacco cultivation, of apple and peach orchards, and of poultry raising are to the west of the line. In lumber production, softwoods predominate to the east and hardwoods to the west. The agricultural differences may all be related to the

143

fact that a climatic boundary passes in the vicinity of this major line: to its west there are, on the average, no more than 190 days per year without killing frost; to its east the number of such days remains everywhere above 180 and in most parts above 190 per year (see maps pages 18, 23, 24, 240). Finally, in terms of population, this line leaves to its east all the counties where the Negro people amount to more than 30 per cent in the total population (1950) and, with the exception of two, Amherst and Nelson, all the counties where this proportion exceeds 20 per cent. This fact leads us to suggest that the proposed boundary between eastern and western Virginia marks also the limit of the westward extension of the plantation system in this area. (See maps, pages 46 and 326.)

The opposition between the two halves of the commonwealth thus divided can be found in many other fields. We have mentioned here only a few basic differences, easily documented by the mapping of available statistics. There are also well-known but more subtle differences in speech and in political attitudes. What remains essential for our present purpose is the legitimate division of Virginia into two major provinces; the essential axis of the eastern province is the fall line, at the contact of the Piedmont and the Tidewater; the main axis of the western province is the Great Valley.

EASTERN VIRGINIA

The eastern is the more "Southern" part of Virginia, as the outsider usually visualizes the South, with great old mansions standing amidst ancient plantations, with fields of tobacco, peanuts, and occasionally cotton, with a high proportion of Negro people in the population and careful segregation of the races. Today, however, eastern Virginia is largely organized around the axis of the fall line, as it has been since the middle of the eighteenth century; the fall-line zone is no longer the inland terminus of maritime navigation, as too many of its harbors are no longer accessible to the large sea-going ships of today, and as concentration of traffic has occurred towards Norfolk on the one hand and Baltimore on the other. But the fall line is the path of Route No. 1, the major north-south artery of traffic of the Atlantic seaboard for both motor and rail traffic. The two main centers of attraction of eastern Virginia are in the fall-line zone: the cities of Washington and Richmond, the capitals of the nation and the state. A third center develops nevertheless in the Hampton Roads area. Eastern Virginia is far from being homogeneous.

Hog killing on Milton Puryeur's place in the vicinity of Dennison, Halifax County. Old shoes and pieces of leather are burning near the heads of the hogs to keep the flies away.
Library of Congress Photo by Marion Post Wolcott

The Tidewater and the Piedmont are the two main geological and historical divisions of eastern Virginia. Describing them as two regions does not, however, give an adequate picture of the diversity of the area. The Tidewater must be considered as subdivided by the Chesapeake Bay and the large tidal streams flowing into it. In its northern section, from Stafford County to Arlington, the Tidewater is reduced to a narrow strip of land between the Potomac and the fall line; this section is entirely under the spell of Route No. 1 and of its proximity to Washington. It should properly be considered with the northern Piedmont, also much influenced by the vicinity of the great capital. The Piedmont itself must be divided into three sections: the northern section looks towards Washington chiefly; the central and the southern are separated approximately by the course of the James River. Thus eastern Virginia is broken up into at least seven regions: three in the Piedmont and four in the Tidewater. The two major urban regions of Richmond and Norfolk are so extensive in area and agglomerate such a large population that they ought to be considered separately.

The Tidewater regions

The Tidewater, for the purposes of this regional sketch, is essentially the coastal plain area of Virginia. It has a certain amount of unity in its being cut up by arms of the Chesapeake into peninsulas, in its close access to navigable tidal water, in its low altitude, flat topography, and predominantly sandy soils. The section south from the James River to the North Carolina line is at once the largest unit of uninterrupted land, the most interesting section of the Tidewater, and the liveliest. Aside from this section, the coastal plain is broken up into four peninsulas: the Eastern Shore, well isolated from the rest of Virginia and attached in the north to the territory of Maryland's eastern shore; the peninsula between the Potomac and Rappahannock Rivers, which was in the seventeenth and eighteenth centuries singled out as the "Northern Neck"; the peninsula between the Rappahannock and the York Rivers; and finally the peninsula between the York and the James, which juts out from the mainland in the vicinity of Richmond towards Hampton Roads, and on the southern shore of which Jamestown once stood.

The Eastern Shore, the south side (south of the James), and the historic peninsula of Jamestown and Williamsburg must be examined separately, as they are in fact three different regions. The two northern peninsulas can be rapidly described together as one region that stretches from the lower Potomac to the York River.

The "Northern Necks"

Between the York and the lower Potomac the two peninsulas of the coastal plain are the sleepiest and most rural part of the Tidewater. These peninsulas, considered as one area and for the sake of simplification called the Northern Necks, are curiously enough the least well serviced in the state by the various means of transportation. No rail line comes within the area, and most of it is outside the ten-mile radius of open freight stations, the largest chunk of land devoid of rail service in the commonwealth. There are, of course, highways linking all the communities of the Northern Necks with the outside, but they are not heavily traveled. In fact, for density of highway traffic the counties between the Potomac and the Rappahannock rank again among the lowest in the state; there is more movement between the York and the Rappahannock, but this whole area remains below the average density of motorcar traffic for Virginia counties.

The isolation of the section is somewhat tempered by the deep pene-

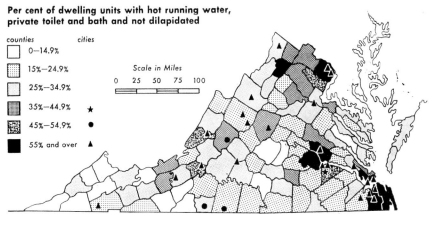

Per cent of dwelling units with hot running water, private toilet and bath and not dilapidated

counties cities

- 0—14.9%
- 15%—24.9%
- 25%—34.9%
- 35%—44.9% ★
- 45%—54.9% ●
- 55% and over ▲

Scale in Miles
0 25 50 75 100

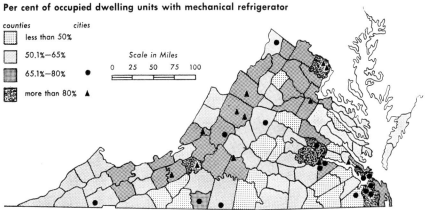

Per cent of occupied dwelling units with mechanical refrigerator

counties cities

- less than 50%
- 50.1%—65%
- 65.1%—80% ●
- more than 80% ▲

Scale in Miles
0 25 50 75 100

tration of navigable waters. But the time when "Tidewater" conveyed the meaning of easy transportation is long since gone. Besides a few ferries, there are no common carriers in these waters any more, only some barges carrying pulpwood to the paper mill at West Point, on the edge of this area. Fishing and oystering are actively engaged in, particularly in Matthews County, the only one in Virginia where the main source of income in 1951 was fisheries. For most of this section the main source of income is agriculture; the main source in Northumberland, Lancaster, and King William Counties appears to be manufacturing; and the payroll of the federal government constitutes the principal income of the counties at the two extremities of this section—King George County, near Washington, and Gloucester County, linked by the excellent Yorktown Bridge with the Hampton Roads area. Both the latter counties have some military installations, the payrolls of which were, in 1951, more important than the other principal sources of income.

Of the different subdivisions we shall consider within eastern Virginia, this is indeed the most isolated. It is, nevertheless, served by a good highway system, and it is close, in its western parts, to the great arteries of the fall-line zone. It has chosen to remain deeply rural. There are no "cities" within this area, only scattered little towns, usually of less than 2,000 people each, and many dispersed farmsteads. The density of population is higher on the eastern periphery, along the shores of the Bay. It is, on the whole, a stable population, showing a slight trend to decrease in the last 25 years, with the exception of some growth in the north along the Potomac shore, which may be interpreted as a southern extension of the Washington "outer suburbia."

The soils in this section are predominantly sandy with some sandy loams and, in the subsoil, clayish levels. Further down, the parent material is made up of marine deposits of sand, silt, and clay. Westward, in the proximity of the Piedmont, some of the soils have developed impervious hardpans at a depth. Agriculture in this section has been in rapid evolution for the past dozen years. Tobacco disappeared almost entirely quite some time ago, but grains, chiefly corn and wheat, with some soybeans and tomatoes, were its heirs. On the larger estates these cash crops are being rapidly replaced by permanent pastures and careful development of hay. Cattle is increasing on these expanding meadows, mainly in the last five years. Some farms, well situated with respect to city connections, are going into dairying. Others specialize in beef cattle. One of the large farms near the Rappahannock prides itself on an outstanding herd of Angus cattle; in addition to spectacular barns, this farm has its own sales shed and a full-time veterinarian on the staff.

Such estates are not very common, however. Many farms are small units dedicated to a few cash crops. By far the largest number of workers are part-time fishermen, oystermen, or employees of nearby military establishments. Near the York, many small farmers work in some capacity for the large paper mill at West Point. Close to the Piedmont other part-time occupations have developed in the vicinity of major highways, such as U. S. 301, the "Motel Route" of the northerners going to Florida for a vacation. A few miles further west U. S. 1 passes. The small industries scattered through the Northern Necks process local foodstuffs—flour mills, fish and tomato canneries, and others. There are also a few small mechanical plants and many sawmills.

The proportion of Negroes, usually between 25 and 55 per cent, increases towards the west. There are communities of Negro farmers, usually descendants of slaves who once worked the same land. Although many of these farms are among the poorest of the area and are not always well managed, their owners are much attached to their land. Some of these farms are used generation after generation as places of retirement for people who have spent most of their active years in New York, Detroit, or Pittsburgh.

In the recent half-century this region has also grown as a producer of long-range crop timber for pulpwood, growing especially the loblolly pine. Some paper and lumber companies own a great deal of acreage, usually scattered in small patches, where they endeavor to grow the kind of wood they prefer. In all the counties here, with the sole exception of King George, more than one half of the total land area is forested (according to statistics of the survey made in 1946). Adding to the somewhat "underdeveloped" aspect of this area, small groups of Indians still live on the swampy flats of the meandering Pamunkey and Mattaponi Rivers. These Pamunkey Indians claim to be descended from the people of Powhatan and Pocahontas. They are the only living remnant of Virginia's Indian past.

History does not play an actually important part in the economy of this region, although some national monuments are situated here, such as George Washington's birthplace. The historical value of Virginia's Tidewater has been fully developed in the third peninsula between the York and James Rivers.

The historic peninsula on the James

The neck of land stretching from Richmond to Point Comfort, between the James to the south and the York and Pamunkey to the north, is a small but very special region. In many parts of it, along the smaller roads, the landscape may appear similar to that of the Northern Necks. Farming, where it predominates, is indeed of a similar nature to that just described in the area north of the York. But the major sources of income are different here: it is manufacturing in the counties of New Kent and Charles City, close to Richmond, then the government payroll approaching the Hampton Roads area with its tremendous naval installations. Vast forests through this peninsula have been fenced off and serve as proving or storing grounds for the Navy.

In its middle part, where the peninsula is narrower, three great sites neighbor on one another, summing up the three major acts of colonial Virginia: on the southern shore is the monument erected on the site of Jamestown, from which the country started; in the interior is the eighteenth-century colonial capital of Williamsburg, which has been restored in large part to its pre-Revolutionary appearance, providing a liv-

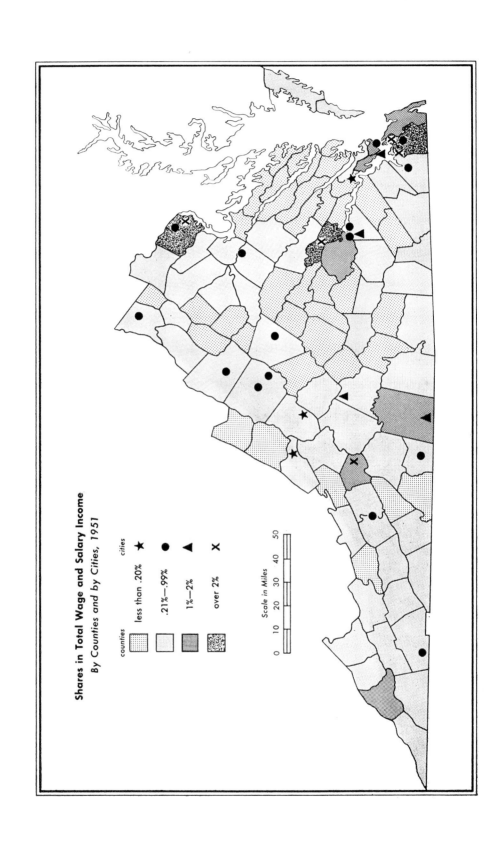

Shares in Total Wage and Salary Income
By Counties and by Cities, 1951

counties   cities

less than .20%   ★

.21%—.99%   ●

1%—2%   ▲

over 2%   ✕

Scale in Miles

0   10   20   30   40   50

ing and lively museum of American history, owing to a generous endowment of Rockefeller funds; on the north shore, Yorktown, where the British forces surrendered to the American and French forces under George Washington's command, is surrounded by a national park commemorating the siege and final battles of the Revolutionary War. Within a small perimeter, American history developed from the first permanent settlement, to the capital where the Virginia Assembly entered upon its conflict with royal authority, and to the battlefield where the military decision insuring independence was won. The reconstruction of colonial Williamsburg has crystallized the historical significance of the place better than ordinary monuments could have. Everything has been done to attract the visitor and facilitate things for those desirous of making a pilgrimage to these historical sites. Sophisticates and intellectuals may sometimes reflect with melancholy on the mixture of two different worlds: the milling, motorized twentieth-century crowds on the one hand and the gracious architecture and elegant decorum of life of the 1760's. But the restored Williamsburg remains a source of inspiration and an unparalleled historical museum piece.

A great variety of travel services fill the needs of tourists in this area. If one leaves the major highways for small winding roads, however, he will find in the western half of the peninsula many truly rural districts. As one drives along the beautifully landscaped Colonial Parkway linking Williamsburg to Yorktown, he may think himself in a forested region where only historical sites and principal roads have remained cleared. But the fact is that on that peninsula small farms and large estates, of a type similar to those of the Northern Necks, are abundant. The quantity of tourists attracted by the historical sites has caused the owners of some of the older plantations to restore them to a status resembling their past glory, at least insofar as the structure of the buildings is concerned, and open them to visitors. Fees from these visits during the tourist season may well surpass, on these estates, the revenue from agricultural products.

Some of these old plantation-estates have been carefully modernized and provide good examples of the agricultural evolution of the Tidewater. After a detailed examination of Berkeley Plantation, E. C. Higbee reported in 1953:

The land-use history of Berkeley Plantation on the James River in Charles City County illustrates the fluctuations of fortune in this region. Berkeley was first settled in 1619, abandoned and later reoccupied in 1636. It was the home of Benjamin Harrison, signer of the Declaration of Independence, and the birthplace of President William Henry Harrison. It is across James River from the

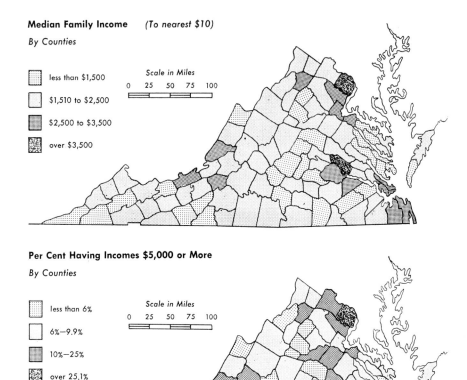

Median Family Income *(To nearest $10)*

By Counties

▦	less than $1,500
▢	$1,510 to $2,500
▦	$2,500 to $3,500
▩	over $3,500

Scale in Miles
0 25 50 75 100

Per Cent Having Incomes $5,000 or More

By Counties

▦	less than 6%
▢	6%—9.9%
▦	10%—25%
▩	over 25.1%

Scale in Miles
0 25 50 75 100

Coggins Point farm once owned by Edmund Ruffin. All the vicissitudes associated with tobacco plantations were experienced by the succession of proprietors at Berkeley. It was from Berkeley's docks, now vanished but still known as Harrison's Landing, that hogsheads of tobacco were rolled aboard ships bound for England and the continent. There were built ships of Virginian timbers later sold to traders in the British Isles. By strange coincidence, as family records have revealed, a Scottish progenitor of Berkeley's present proprietor once bought a ship made at Harrison's Landing and delivered to Scotland. When the soils of Berkeley would no longer produce tobacco profitably, its slaves grew corn and wheat for which there was a market in New England, the West Indies and in Virginia's own Piedmont whence tobacco culture had migrated. The principal cash crop sustaining this estate during the half century preceding the Civil War was its Negro slaves bred and raised for the cotton planters of Alabama and Mississippi.

In 1799 the last inventory taken at Berkeley before the death of Benjamin Harrison revealed: 23 work oxen, 28 milch cows, 19 heifers, 17 calves (3 dead), 8 work horses, 2 mules, 2 mares, 8 colts, 4 chair and riding horses, 137 sheep and 56 hogs. Today there is one team of horses, 4 tractors, 400 fine Herefords and 200 sheep . . . To do the work on his estate, the elder Benjamin Harrison had 107 Negro slaves. Today there are but three hired men working for its proprietor and only one of them lives at the plantation. That is the contrast in capacities of human labor and machine power to make a land productive. Part of this reduction in human dedication is also owing to the change in purpose to which the land is now applied. On this 1,200-acre farm, of which 468 are in open land in a high state of productivity, only 40 acres are planted to annual crops of corn and wheat. The remainder are converted to superb hay and grazing meadows. The corn is grown for silage to supplement winter pasturage of orchard grass. During the past winter the cattle grazed continuously on pastures, which even by April still had such luxuriant growth upon them they seemed scarcely challenged by the long season of heavy usage so recently past.

As late as 1929 Berkeley had ten Negro tenant families and all its tillable land was divided among them for the purpose of raising corn as a cash crop. All these families are now gone just as they have vanished from large sections of the southern landscape where grass and cattle have replaced corn, cotton and tobacco in recent decades. Growth of the cattle enterprise at Berkeley over the past 20 years has been one of steady progress from a modest beginning in 1933 when 30 head of grade animals were purchased at $28 each. Two years ago at the peak of the cattle prices, the herd had grown in numbers to nearly 400 with a conservative value of $78,000. Twenty years of breeding to fine Hereford sires has so improved the quality of the Berkeley cattle that little if any trace of their grade ancestry is now apparent.[1]

Thus the modern trend towards a cattle economy, taking advantage of the remarkable aptitudes of this area for permanent pastures, has helped restore the prosperity of some of the large estates. Other large farms, closer to the urban centers, have engaged in dairying primarily. But the western counties of this peninsula remain populated predominantly by a poor, semirural, Negro population. Charles City County had, in 1950, the highest percentage of non-White population among all the counties in the state: 81 per cent; New Kent had a lower proportion, 54 per cent. New Kent lost some population during the 1940–1950 decade, while Charles City gained 9.4 per cent. Both counties send many of their residents to work in Richmond, and Hopewell, with its large industries, is just across the river from Charles City. Both counties are also heavily forested (76 per cent of the land area in New Kent, 74 in Charles City) and supply substantial quantities of lumber to sawmills in Richmond and to paper mills in West Point and Hopewell. Suburban residences are beginning to grow up along the better roads. This area provides a curious mixture of suburbia and diversified agriculture.

There is little space left for purely rural landscapes besides the forests

[1] Edward C. Higbee, "The Present Condition of Agriculture in Virginia," an unpublished report prepared for this survey in 1953.

in the southeastern part of the peninsula. Here, as the impact of the historical section ends, the suburban influences of the Hampton–Newport News area begin. In fact, this area belongs to the vast complex of towns established on both sides of Hampton Roads and based on maritime activities and on the Navy. The Chesapeake and Ohio Railroad has its terminal at Newport News, the great shipbuilding center where many warships and liners have been launched, including the *United States.*

Ups and downs in employment in the naval services and in the shipyard's activities have made for notable fluctuations in the labor force of this group of towns. Many people from the densely populated valleys of western Virginia came during the war to work in the shipyards. Few of them remained long in the area. As employment shrinks, these workers prefer to return to their mountainous home country. Now that a bridge-and-tunnel road is being built across Hampton Roads from the tip of the peninsula to Norfolk, the direct route from Washington to this great port and naval base will follow the historic peninsula. It is bound to add to the traffic and speed the industrialization and urbanization of the area.

The southside coastal plain

South of the James the landscape changes. The three peninsulas, though all made of low sedimentary deposits, offer some gentle rolling to the traveller as their central parts belong to a formation or "terrace" levelled off at about 200 feet of altitude. In its southside section the plain rarely reaches such elevation. Most of it remains at an altitude of 60 to 100 feet, sloping down slightly towards the east, where the lower terraces of the Dismal Swamp and Princess Anne do not rise more than 25 feet above sea level. The sandy soils are often poorly drained and require some artificial drainage to keep them from turning to marshes. To the very southeast of this section the ground is so flat and so poorly drained that Virginia's Dismal Swamp area has remained to this day the largest piece of uninhabited and little utilized land in the state. Peat is being formed in the Dismal Swamp, and from many standpoints this vast marsh is a natural reservation where types of flora and fauna that have disappeared from other parts of the commonwealth have been preserved because of the absence of man. Between the Dismal Swamp and the ocean, an area called the Flatwoods needs attentive drainage.

Tobacco has left this section of the Tidewater, too, and has gone west to the Piedmont. Southwards, in North Carolina, tobacco is still successfully grown on soils similar to what is called the *Norfolk series* in Vir-

Harvesting peanuts near Suffolk
Virginia Chamber of Commerce Photo by Flournoy

ginia. Cotton used to be important here, but it has shrunk to a few fields in the southwestern section of this region. The two principal cash crops today are peanuts and corn, which complement one another very well, since, as the adage goes, "a wet year is good for corn and bad for peanuts; a dry year is good for peanuts and bad for corn." Similarly, drier soils suit peanuts, and damper, heavier ones can be devoted to corn. Both peanuts and corn are good food for hogs, and the area has specialized in hog raising and the production of Virginia hams, particularly of the Smithfield quality.

Hogs used to be fed on peanuts around Smithfield in earlier times. The policy of strong price support for peanuts and the high value reached by this cash crop during World War II has made it far too expensive to fully maintain the tradition. Part of the year hogs are fed with corn (which they can gather in season directly from non-harvested fields), and after the peanuts are harvested they are turned into the fields. The harvesting of the nuts always leaves a substantial amount in the ground; it has been estimated that from 100 to 500 lbs. of peanuts are left in every acre after the vines have been lifted by the harvesters in the fall. These the hogs root out of the ground and thus convert what might otherwise

A feeder ditch in the Dismal Swamp
Virginia Chamber of Commerce

be a waste into a marketable product. At least three quarters of the peanut growers keep hogs in order to reap this dividend.

To the peanut-corn-hog system must be added a fourth element encountered on most of the farms in this section: the woodlot of loblolly
pines, also a cash crop, which the farmers prefer to leave today to grow
until the trees become big and valuable timber. Sawmills and pulp mills
pay good prices for pine wood, and the larger the diameter of the trees,
the better by far the price. Farmers here have made good money on
peanuts and hogs; they can wait until their trees put on enough annual
rings to achieve respectable size. In most cases, of course, the land would
return a larger income to the owner under cultivation or pasture than it
will in timber. But in this fashion the farmer achieves a more versatile,
better-balanced economy, and he needs much less manpower to run his
acreage. This is an important consideration, as hired labor is scarce with
two large industrial areas in the vicinity attracting workers—the Hampton Roads cities and the Richmond-Petersburg-Hopewell area. Thus the
southern coastal plain bears some of the most beautiful stands of loblolly
in Virginia.

Cattle has been slow to come to this area, where the prospects of per-

A typical old middle-class home in Smithfield

manent hay on damp soils should be excellent. Hogs and timber, and the high price of peanuts, have combined to give soundness and stability to the existing system of land use. The customary crop rotation over three years leaves a field two years under corn, often with soybeans sown between the rows of corn, and the third year under peanuts; every winter some cover is provided by crimson or ladino clover, rye grass, or small grain. The importance of soybeans increases eastward, and between the Swamp and the sea this crop almost replaces peanuts. The sandy and marshy Flatwoods are less well forested, and the suburban development of Norfolk daily encroaches more and more upon them.

This whole southside Tidewater is forested in proportions varying in each county from 60 to 76 per cent. There is a high percentage of Negroes in the population: 52 to 66 per cent in the rural counties, but much less in the suburbanized areas. Thus in Norfolk and Princess Anne Counties to the east and Prince George and Chesterfield to the west the percentage is less than 30, and these four counties also showed a rapid increase in population during 1940–1950, while the rural counties showed a very slow increase. There are still many farm units managed by Negro tenants in this section. Successful peanut raisers bid high prices for additional farm units of 10 to 15 acres, each of which will be allotted to a tenant family receiving two-thirds of the peanut income and one-half the returns from the corn-soybean-hog enterprise.

The section is well serviced by a good network of both highways and railroads; it is no dead end, like the Northern Necks, for it leads to the port of Norfolk or southward to the coastal plain of North Carolina. Traffic is active on all the means of communication. Many varied industries are scattered through the smaller towns. Suffolk is the capital of the Virginia peanut industry, and shelling and processing plants are important here, where the lobby of the main hotel proudly exhibits in a special window samples of peanuts graded according to size. This city of 12,300 in 1950 had increased by only 8.8 per cent since 1940; Negroes amounted to 36.7 per cent of the population. Situated at some distance from the Norfolk-Portsmouth urban agglomeration, though rather close to the gates of that metropolitan area, Suffolk has a very active trading section, supplying the farmers of the peanut belt with a variety of implements. Further west, Franklin provides a much smaller local market, with a large wood-processing industry. To the northwest, Petersburg, Colonial Heights, and Hopewell form an impressive urban triad which in fact belongs to the greater Richmond metropolitan area. By far the larger and more rapidly growing urban area of the southside is the one centered in Norfolk. Its suburbs have invaded most of Norfolk County and consolidated the seaside development of Virginia Beach with the whole urban complex.

Metropolitan areas, with their own intricate urban problems, their large industries and maritime activities, are better described together in a study of urbanization in Virginia. We shall therefore leave discussion of the two areas centered around Hampton Roads and Richmond for Chapter 9 and restrict ourselves here to pointing out, as we have done, the powerful impact of their proximity over the section as a whole.

The Eastern Shore

The fourth section of the Tidewater is set well apart from the rest by the wide expanse of Chesapeake Bay. The vast peninsula between the Bay and the ocean is divided up between the states of Delaware, Maryland, and Virginia. The commonwealth owns only the southern tip, the area south of a line crossing the peninsula at a point south of the Pocomoke River where it suddenly narrows. Near Cape Charles, a ferry line links the southern tip to Little Creek, near Norfolk. Other ferries have been discontinued, and the road from Virginia's Eastern Shore to the northern part of the state would lead one in a half-circle through Mary-

Aerial view of fields and forests in Princess Ann County: the Flatwoods
U. S. Department of Agriculture

land and across the Chesapeake on the recently built Bay Bridge.

The economy of the Eastern Shore is in fact more closely linked with the great cities to the north along the Atlantic seaboard than with northern Virginia. In the two counties of Northampton and Accomack, one of the major truck-farming centers in North America has developed. A railroad line (of the Pennsylvania Railroad) and an efficient system of highways (of which U. S. 13 is the main artery) lead toward the cities of Delaware Bay and beyond. A century and a half ago Norfolk was the center of a large-scale truck-farming area, supplying northern city markets. Today, there are very few large farms around Norfolk producing vegetables for remote markets; what is produced there is easily consumed within the Hampton Roads area. The Eastern Shore has inherited the tradition and some of the markets. It has also by now developed the production of truck crops on a scale never achieved in the area in earlier times. Its produce encounters on the great northeastern markets the competition of Maryland and the Carolinas, Long Island, Florida, and even California. The prices obtained by the Virginia truck farmer depend upon weather and many other unforeseeable factors.

The advantages of this area are mainly its warm climate and its abundant and relatively regular rainfall. Precipitations average 40 to 44 inches annually. The frost-free season averages 220 days. The liabilities are the flat topography, generally less than 20 feet above sea level, making drainage difficult, especially after drenching rain and during high tides. Even in the Flatwoods, south of Norfolk, it is difficult to remove underground waters toward inner reservoirs such as Drummond Lake in the Dismal Swamp. Still, such internal systems could be controlled by an adequate integrated system of drainage. The Eastern Shore is a long and narrow peninsula, deeply penetrated along both shores by tidal swamps or narrow creeks. Most of the farms that are not on the higher, well-drained sassafras soils have had to provide a system of drainage by excavating costly ditches and laying tile drains underground at depths of one to three feet. Many a farm has cultivated land below high tide level with drainage ditches fitted with tide gate outlets. To insure regular watering, especially in periods of drought, irrigation is highly desirable. The growth of the crop can thus be better controlled. There were only 20 irrigated farms on the Eastern Shore of Virginia in 1947, but 91 in the spring of 1953. These are the trickiest soils of Virginia, and they are expensive: drainage alone usually doubles their cost.

The good warm climate and the proximity to the large markets makes the effort and expense worth while, though competition may be severe at times. Higbee has described the attitude of the Eastern Shore producers:

There is always the chance that someday, some week, some year and just somehow all these competitors will be temporarily short of what is "moving." Then "The Shore" will plug the gap and make a "killing." It has been done. Nearly everyone knows someone who made his that way and all have had a taste of fortune as well as rain. The tempo of the truck market is such that all men cannot take it. It divides them as they themselves say into two classes: the "plungers" and the "stayers." The plungers are gamblers who stake everything on their crops. They buy land or rent it at high prices. Some will pay more to rent for a year 200 acres in Northampton than it would cost to buy that much with scrub timber on it in Buckingham ($20 to $45 an acre). Good vegetable land in Northampton with scarcely a building of any account will bring now as much as $500 an acre. In northern Accomack the price is closer to $250, for the season is one or two weeks later, but the soils may be the same. Getting to market "ahead" is worth all that! The stayers are the conservatives; the ones with long memories and some with land titles in their families dating back to the King's grants. They are the ones who rent the lands to the plungers or play it safe and contract their crops to jobbers at low guaranteed prices. They never have bonanza years, but they never lose their farms as long as they remain this cautious. It takes a strong will and a deep respect for tradition to remain a stayer when the plungers "hit it" and are able to flip coins for $100 a toss and offer to bet

Wachapreague, on the Eastern Shore
Virginia Chamber of Commerce Photo by Flournoy

dealers double or nothing for a new car on a throw of dice. At least that is what some will testify they have witnessed and expect to see again "some year, maybe this one"! [2]

In the beginning of November, 1953, when a powerful snowstorm had blanketed in deep snow most of Maryland's Eastern Shore, as well as the area further north, we witnessed in the south of Northampton fields of green peppers and spinach being gaily harvested under a warm sun. Some "plungers" must have been happy that week.

The season opens in late April and ends in early November. In its midst, mainly in August, there is a lull, as many other areas are in full production at the same time, but something is still harvested throughout the Shore for six months in a year. Almost all possible kinds of vegetables, 65 kinds of them, are grown here, as well as strawberries and other rapidly maturing fruits. The length of the season and the labor needed for gathering such a variety of different crops created the need for an influx of migratory workers, chiefly in the spring and fall. From 12,000 to 18,000 Negro laborers from Florida are recruited every year for that migration by a special state representative sent down from Richmond. During the

[2] Edward C. Higbee, *op. cit.*

Pony penning at Chincoteague
Virginia Chamber of Commerce Photo by Flournoy

ebbing season of mid-summer most of these workers go further north to
help with the harvest in areas with a shorter growing season. Many
proceed thus to Long Island and to the Connecticut Valley. In August,
1954, a crew that had temporarily left the job in Northampton County
was working in Maine. Of this large number of temporary workers, most
of whom bring their families with them, some find housing with the
farmers who employ them, and others use the facilities of special camps
for migratory workers established and maintained by county services. As
the season draws to an end, this crowd flows back to Florida, and many
of them return the following year.

Needless to say, the major source of income throughout the Eastern
Shore is agriculture. Truck farming does not absorb, however, all the
gainful activities of this population of 51,000. Poultry raising has developed on a large scale; Accomack County was the second in the state in
1950 for the number of chickens raised and sold, and it produced a fair
number of turkeys as well. Feed is important, of course, and it comes
from the Middle West. A great number of food industries are scattered
through the small towns of the Shore, primarily to process and can the
part of the harvest that does not go to market fresh. Some of them also

Harvesting potatoes on the Eastern Shore
Virginia Chamber of Commerce Photo by Flournoy

process the fish and oyster catch, both quite important on both coasts of the Shore. The creeks and the islands off the ocean coast, deeply indented by tidal swamps, offer salty meadows where oysters and clams grow well and in abundance. The Chincoteague variety of oyster, produced around the island situated just off the mainland of the Shore to its northeast, has acquired a special reputation. Shell fishing does not consist simply of harvesting: oysters and clams must be cultivated. Small or "seed" oysters are dredged down the bay from public oyster rocks and brought by the bargeload to chosen grounds where they are planted and left to grow under some protection from their natural enemies. Clam cultivation is simpler, as the small-sized clams of each harvest are kept for planting. Clamming can go on all year without the summer interruption of the oyster season, and the returns to the growers are usually larger from clams than from oysters. Nevertheless, the latter is the more popular and talked-about aspect of shell fishing. A small town on the sea here even bears the name of Oyster!

Forestry is less important on the Eastern Shore than over most of the Tidewater. Only 29 per cent of the land area is forested in Accomack and 37 per cent in Northampton. But there are still substantial stands of

Main Street, Tangier Island, a small isolated community on an island in the Chesapeake Bay off the Eastern Shore
Virginia Chamber of Commerce Photo by Flournoy

pines and occasionally some hardwoods, too, throughout the Shore. A number of lumbering firms operate here, the largest of which employed 230 persons in January, 1953, and manufactures 14,000,000 board feet per year. The Chesapeake Corporation regularly buys pulpwood on the peninsula and ships it from Harborton by barges across the bay and up the York River to the mill at West Point. Manufacturing industries, besides canning, are few: recently some shirt factories opened, providing employment for women.

Tourism is not yet as much developed on the Eastern Shore as in some other parts of the Tidewater. This is nonetheless historic country, one of the oldest areas of early English plantations in America. Many well-preserved and beautiful buildings still testify to it. U. S. Route 13, sometimes advertised as "the shortest route from pines to palms," takes traffic from northern cities to the ferry linking the southern tip of the peninsula with the Norfolk area. On the shore itself, seaside resorts could be put to greater use. Fishing, boating, and hunting attract crowds of outsiders at certain seasons. The two main sea resorts are Cape Charles on the southwestern coast and Chincoteague on the island to the northeast.

Chincoteague is famous not only for its oysters but also for ponies, and as a wildlife refuge. The Eastern Shore is an important section of the great Atlantic flyway, a route that migratory birds follow up and down in their seasonal travels. The low sand dunes, covered with succulent plants and beach grasses, are here interrupted often by wide ribbons of tidal salt marshes, filled with tough-rooted salt-marsh hay or "cord grass." This is waterfowl country, most attractive to geese and ducks flying along the coast. Geese feed on the roots of cord grass or Spartina; a variety of small goose known as the American Brant was decimated about 1930 when a blight struck the eelgrass which was its favorite food.

To make it possible for birds to live and migrate along a long coastline which is becoming much too civilized to fit the purposes of waterfowl, areas of wilderness must be preserved and set aside for their use. To this end the United States Department of the Interior has established wildlife refuges as relays along the major flyways. There are two along the Virginia ocean coastline, one on the dunes of Back Bay between that bay and the sea, just above the North Carolina line; the other is next to Chincoteague, on Assateague Island, just south of the Maryland line. A variety of birds as well as deer, foxes, and racoons find good living conditions in the scattered patches of woodland on the refuge. Some cattle pasture on the clearings, and there also lives a herd of semi-wild ponies. These horses, whose ancestors allegedly swam ashore from a shipwrecked galleon, are rounded up and driven to Chincoteague once a year in July, where they are sold at a carnival ceremony to the benefit of the town firemen. The Chincoteague pony-penning carnival attracts numerous visitors.[3]

Along the long sand-beach line of the Eastern Shore, towards the ocean, rows of beach dwellings are being built in new developments which may alter the somewhat wild and truly rural character of this section. Chincoteague and the whole north of Accomack County have already benefited by the building of a large naval air base. They would like, however, to see the seaside activities of the resorts further north, such as Ocean City in Maryland, expand in their direction. In August, 1954, it was decided to build a road bridge from Chincoteague Island to Assateague and a highway on this sand spit northwards to join with a road coming down the dunes from Ocean City.

To the Eastern Shore belongs also a small island in the Chesapeake Bay called Tangier Island, a community of about 1,100 people living on five square miles of sand and swamp. A decadent little world because of its

[3] See Rachel L. Carson, *Chincoteague, A National Wildlife Refuge* (Conservation in Action, No. 1), U. S. Department of the Interior, Washington, D. C., 1947.

isolation, Tangier has only one car, the minister's Crosley, no sewage system, and little activity.

Such is the remarkable variety of this small peninsula which, when first settled, was an important part of Virginia, lived through sharp decline, and is regaining nowadays a remarkable prosperity and drive.

The Piedmont's subdivisions

In many respects Virginia's Piedmont has been historically an extension of the Tidewater. Settlement came here from the beginning of the eighteenth century chiefly from the Tidewater. In the wake of the first settlers came tobacco and large land grants. The plantation economy is perhaps more alive in its older forms in parts of the Piedmont than elsewhere in the state. The speech of this area is more like that of the Tidewater than that in the Great Valley. Nevertheless, it is today an area fairly well differentiated from those to the east and west of it.

The fall-line zone that separates and also unites the Piedmont and the Tidewater is closely linked to the Piedmont in the north of Virginia, but to the coastal plain further south. Geological differences, which determined the original differentiation of the three main regions of Virginia, have little to do at present with modern subtleties of regional division. In the north, as a narrow coastal plain belt follows U. S. 1 along the Potomac, the whole life of the area is linked either to the District of Columbia or, if we choose to remain within Virginia, to the state's northern parts, belonging to the suburbs, immediate or remote, of the national capital. Further south, one is out of Washington's radius of influence, soon to enter that of Richmond. Here the urban and suburban expansion of the large cities has transgressed the line of contact of sedimentary and crystalline strata with general indifference. Only south of Petersburg does the fall line begin to appear in the pattern of land use, and even there the transition is gradual and provides no clear-cut contrast.

The topographical signs marking the beginning of Piedmont territory are the deeper and more regular undulations of the surface. Instead of the predominantly greyish shades encountered in most soils of the coastal plain, here the reddish shades are predominant, although yellow and grey soils are found in many places, too. When the topsoil is well preserved, its thin cover is grey in most cases; the yellow to red shades are those of a thick subsoil. Over most of the Piedmont the soils result from the weathering of basic rocks which are crystalline: gneiss, granite, schists. The latter are often fine-grained schist rocks that give rise to soils of poor fertility, today largely under forest. The dark-colored basic rocks have

A rural road in Fairfax County
Library of Congress Photo by Marion Post Wolcott

often provided much richer soils. On the uplands of the area some caps of triassic sandstones or shales have been preserved in places. They have developed a somewhat different type of soil. Finally, in the south, the out-croppings of the "Caroline slate belt" offer another series of soils, of finer texture and less well suited to the cultivation of bright tobacco, but responding well to the culture of small grains and forage crops.[4]

Almost all these soils are acid and poor in calcium, which results from leaching by the heavy rainfall, chiefly during the warm season. The length of this warm season increases southward, as does the annual aver-age precipitation. Soils are generally poorer in the southern part of the Piedmont than in the northern part, for both geological and climatic reasons, but the middle section suffers from a wide expanse of rather unproductive soil derived from schist. To avoid rapid exhaustion, Pied-mont soils require substantial amounts of chemical and organic fertiliza-tion.

Travel has always been easy over most of the Piedmont. The hilly re-lief causes difficulty only on the approaches to the Blue Ridge and in areas excluded for our present purposes from our definition of eastern

[4] *Soils of Virginia*, Virginia Polytechnic Institute and U. S. Dept. of Agriculture Ex-tension Service, Blacksburg, March, 1953 (Bulletin 203).

Virginia. The Piedmont is a broad, undulating, plain-like surface dissected by many streams, most of which are quite small, but have caused valleys to develop. Most of these valleys are winding, either because of the gentle slope, or, more frequently, because the general direction of the drainage is from the Blue Ridge towards the Tidewater along a north-west-southeast axis perpendicular to the main axis of the Blue Ridge and Appalachian folding. The valleys thus have to cut through ribbons of various geological textures, opposing unequal resistance to erosion. Sometimes they are deflected from their general orientation, and sometimes they obey it.

The route followed by the James River across Virginia and particularly through the Piedmont illustrates on a grand scale the successive impact, in an alternated fashion, of the two main axes of folding and erosion. In fact, both are deeply inscribed in the geological structure of the Piedmont and contribute to a checkering of it. On the one hand, many crests east of the Blue Ridge and its foothills rise above the general level of the surrounding Piedmont, but along an axis strictly parallel to that of the Blue Ridge and Alleghenies. As one proceeds inland from Tidewater, the first line of such ridges, although irregular and frequently interrupted, can be easily followed from northeast to southwest, as it is staked out by the "mountains" bearing the following names: Catoctin, Bull Run, Pond, Mount Pony, Southwestern, Long, Smith Mountains, Carter Mountains, etc. The main interruptions in this irregular fence usually occur along lines which, if continued westward along perpendiculars to the folds' orientation, lead to the major gaps through the Blue Ridge. There is thus a frame of main lines that determined the principal aspects of the area's layout. The James Valley from Lynchburg to Scottsville follows the general axis of folding, but in the sections above and below, the valley follows the perpendicular orientation, that of normal drainage from the mountains to the sea. Such checkering resulting from two perpendicular axes is frequently found in other regions with old, planed mountains.

Settlement remains extremely scattered through the Piedmont. The main towns were established at the contact of the eastern Piedmont and the western foothills, on the roads to the principal Blue Ridge gaps, as were, for example, Charlottesville, Lynchburg, and Martinsville. Danville alone is more centrally situated. Lynchburg probably owes its relative predominance to its situation on the James, which made it for a while the terminal of the westward canal which, from Richmond, was being pushed to the Kanawha. It is a frequent occurrence throughout the world that cities of importance arise as markets and crossroads at the contact of contiguous areas with different characteristics. Such was the origin of the cities of Virginia, both along the fall line and along the western limit of the gently rolling Piedmont. As the city grows and organizes the surrounding country into an economic system, of which it becomes the center, the original impulse provided by the contact of different economies may be lost from sight. Some topographical or agricultural features may survive, however, to remind us of the origins.

For our present purposes Virginia's Piedmont will be subdivided into three main regions: the northern is limited by the present influence of Washington's urban area; the middle region is a transitional one, still influenced by the four cities framing it; and the southern section, south of the James, will appear as the most rural and traditional one, where a puzzle made of woodlots, corn fields and tobacco fields may be used to define the landscape.

The northern Piedmont

The northern Piedmont gravitates towards Washington, D. C. The standard metropolitan area of the capital comprised, in the definition of the Census of 1950, the Virginia cities of Alexandria and Falls Church and the counties of Arlington and Fairfax. In fact, the outer suburbia of this urban system encompasses as well the counties of Loudoun, Fauquier, Prince William, and Stafford. It reaches along the fall line as far as Fredericksburg. This may not appear plainly on the map of population density (see p. 36), for some densities of less than 20 inhabitants per square mile are found in parts of this outer suburbia. But some vast sections of land are kept open either because they belong to military establishments requiring substantial open space, or because the landlords are speculating on the forthcoming increase in the price of these grounds, as better roads and more residential projects come into being. On the outside ring of this area a number of large estates have been recently developed, perhaps bringing the local population figures down, but creating a new and better system of land use, which owes its origin partly at least to the proximity of Washington.

The properly urban aspects of the landscape are limited to a relatively small area in the northeastern corner of this section, in the immediate proximity of the District of Columbia. This includes the cities of Alexandria (61,800 inhabitants in 1950) and Falls Church (7,500), the eastern half of Fairfax County and the whole of Arlington County. In fact, Arlington, with its 135,450 people residing on 24 square miles had a city-like density of 5,644 per square mile, much higher than that of Falls

Aerial view of fields and forests in Culpeper County
U. S. Department of Agriculture

Church. As its urban development is consolidated in space with Alexandria's suburbs, Arlington fears being swallowed up in a future increase of the territory of this neighboring city and has asked, as yet in vain, to become a city in itself. Population numbers and densities have increased since 1950, when the Census was made, as residential projects blossomed all around, as shopping centers, new roads, and more public institutions were built.

As the distance to Washington increases, and even as the distance from the major speed highways increases, the landscape takes on a more rural appearance. One should not mistake, however: even where growing grain or cattle pasturing on grassy meadows shows that the land is not left idle, agriculture is not the major occupation of the residents. Many of those who own these farms and live on them are city workers. Government employees, doctors and engineers, professors and businessmen often prefer living outside the city, though within easy commuting distance from their offices in town. Most of them work on their own farms and like to milk the cows, plow up their fields at dawn, occasionally kill a sheep. The farm is for them a hobby, an investment, and a means to a pleasanter way of life than a dwelling within the urban area could offer; and it seems sounder, healthier, even more economical, if one can afford the original investment and the cost of maintenance for the first years. This semi-rural suburban life is not within the reach of the majority of the city people, but it has been obtained by a continually increasing number. As people retire from government employ, either in the civil or military services, many of them prefer to remain in the vicinity of the capital where they have friends and where they may still occasionally find some way of utilizing their energies fruitfully. Thus many retired high officials, generals, and admirals buy acreage not far from Washington, often in the northern Piedmont.

Loudoun and Fauquier Counties have recently received many newcomers who established large estates and helped improve the land and the standard of living of the local people. The western part of the northern Piedmont is becoming a sort of beautiful country club, the members of which still work or have some interest in Washington, and among whom one could find an impressive repertory of names famous in American industry, finance, or politics. This migration to northern Virginia has taken place mainly since World War I and was encouraged by the development of motor transportation on better highways, so that the trip to or from Washington would not take on the average more than an hour or, in some cases, two; its results do not necessarily show on the regional statistics of income, as many of the landowners here have their main residence elsewhere and as some of these estates can be run at a loss without damage to the family budget. The reasons for selecting this region for such a development are several and easy to understand: this is a warm, temperate climate, where the gradual rise in altitude of the Piedmont and the proximity of the western hills help to moderate the summer heat; winter is short and seldom severe; the rolling landscape is quite beautiful and is embellished by the rise of the ridges to the west; soil and climate favor animal husbandry, which does not require too much labor at any time of the year; there are in this area long-standing traditions of careful raising and selective breeding of horses and cattle; there is also a very lively tradition of horseback riding and fox hunting as pastimes; there are the mildness and temperance of character prevalent in eastern Virginia, and many elegant mansions left from the heyday of the plantation. Last, but not least, the proximity to Washington makes this impressive and restful setting appropriate for entertaining prominent people who live and work in the capital.

A variety of factors concur to make the northern Piedmont a farming area attractive to medium and very high income brackets and a choice location for the part-time residences of important or wealthy people.

Aerial view of fields and forests in Rappahannock County
U. S. Department of Agriculture

Since the proximity of Washington plays so decisive a part, we feel justified in including the whole section within the outer suburbia of the capital. Estate riding and fox hunts have today, in and around Leesburg, Middleburg, and Warrenton, as much importance as the natural assets of the place, and perhaps more. City dwellers, as well as actual small farmers in the more truly rural areas of the neighborhood, sometimes refer to this region as one of "station-wagon farming"; they probably ought to add "fox farming" to this expression as the red fox is here a highly valued and carefully protected animal, to make for better hounding. But such "station-wagon and fox farming" makes for better land management; probably no other area in Virginia has as high an average acreage of carefully tilled land.

Of all the open ground in Loudoun and Fauquier Counties, less than one-fifth goes under the plow in an average year. The perennial meadow is the most common type of land utilization. A variety of grasses are used, and a special state-owned experimental farm near Middleburg helps the farmers to make their choice and manage their property. It is not unusual to find on the larger estates of this area cattle of different breeds that make those of the experimental farm look like merely average and not very remarkable animals. Cattle and horses here not uncommonly receive almost luxurious care and attention. Even in the nineteenth century Loudoun County claimed some of the best farming in Virginia. It has maintained its high standards, which in part were established by Quakers who settled here early and handled the area as an advance position of the Pennsylvania economy and society in Virginia. The higher quality of agriculture came to Fauquier more recently with the spreading of large "suburban" estates in this county.

The majority of the local farmers in these two counties, however, have for some time lived by agriculture only, as have many of Fairfax County. The land is attractive not only for its aesthetic value and its strategic location, but for its productivity as well, which is the result of careful management, heavy expenditure in improving and fertilizing it, and an open and inquisitive attitude toward farming. In many respects, this has been and undoubtedly remains one of the most advanced sections of Virginia, leading the way toward a better use of the soil and a better society. The advantages of location and of the presence of great wealth are not of course available to every area; but the northern Piedmont may provide good suggestions to people further south in Virginia.

Leesburg, Middleburg, and Warrenton are still small towns that look like the quiet centers of a rural area, with very little industry, but more and more marked with the stamp of the travel trade as a result of the traffic going through, to visitors to the horse shows, and the active social life of the vicinity. As one comes closer to Washington, motels and shopping centers multiply along the main roads, with housing projects between them. Arlington, Fairfax, and the adjoining cities have the common problems of the suburban parts of the metropolitan area. This area has little industry, but contains many military establishments that probably serve the same purpose. Even a town like Alexandria has barely a few blocks that could be called a "downtown," its downtown being, in fact, just across the bridges over the Potomac. Traffic problems are serious and various solutions are at present being debated. To solve the problems arising from the expansion southward and westward of Washington's suburbs, the Northern Virginia Regional Planning Commission has been established with the participation of the local governments of Alexandria, Falls Church, and the counties of Arlington, Fairfax, and Loudoun; Prince William County has also at times participated in the Commission.

In Loudoun and Fauquier the main source of income was still agriculture in 1951. It may remain so if the area maintains, as it should, its vogue among people moneyed enough to put its land to good use. In the rest of the northern Piedmont, the major source of income was government salaries in 1951 and should by all logic continue to be. This region is at present the southern extremity of a long ribbon of urban and sub-urban areas that stretches without interruption from Fredericksburg, Virginia, to Manchester, New Hampshire. According to the Bureau of the Census and data gathered in the spring of 1950, the "standard metropolitan areas" stretch uninterruptedly from Hillsborough County in New Hampshire and Essex County in Massachusetts to and including Fairfax County, Virginia. In fact, owing to the "station-wagon farming" to the west and southwest of Fairfax and to the many military establishments along the Potomac to the south of Fairfax, this vast urbanized area, unique in the entire world and deserving in our opinion the name of *Megalopolis,* extends over most of the northern Piedmont in Virginia; here it takes on a very special and very Virginian character, with an élite of gentleman-farmers enjoying a special combination of personal cultivation, of distinguished local tradition, and of social and political advantages of location.

The middle Piedmont

It is customary to extend the limits of the northern Piedmont much farther south than has been done here. Most such regional delimitations are based on climatic and agricultural data rather than on economic and social characteristics. It is true, of course, that nowadays lines delimiting counties are in no way actual boundaries. The elegant life represented by the gentleman-farmers' estates of the northern Piedmont is found in smaller areas in parts of Orange and Madison Counties, as well as around Charlottesville, in places embellished by the undulating lines of the Blue Ridge on the horizon. True, also, one finds in Fauquier and even in Fairfax poor White farmers who show little regard for their soil, live in wretched houses, and make some additional money every two or three years by selling the "sod," the topsoil, of their fields to merchants whose business it is to supply the cities with raw material to keep the parks and the lawns beautifully green.

The middle Piedmont is usually interpreted as extending beyond the James River. It seems to us that this valley is a rather important dividing line between north and south in the Piedmont, as it is in the Tidewater; for this reason we shall limit our definition of the middle Piedmont to the area between the northern section described above and the valley of the James to the south. The influence of the Washington metropolitan area is little felt here except as the proximity of a large market to absorb a great deal of dairy and meat products. Pastures and the cultiva-

Cattle on a farm near Charlottesville
Soil Conservation Service

tion of alfalfa and some grain for feeding cattle are the major agricultural activities here. Agriculture is again the main source of income on the periphery of this section: in the counties of Culpeper, Madison, Fluvanna, and Goochland and in the parts of Albemarle and Hanover that belong by our definition to the Piedmont. But in the center of the section, Orange, Spotsylvania, and Louisa claimed, in 1951, manufacturing as the major source of income. Important manufacturing centers seem to have chosen to stay on the outskirts of the area, where Richmond, Fredericksburg, and Charlottesville are located. Textiles and lumber industries are scattered through this central part of the middle Piedmont. Forested areas in 1946 covered 43 per cent of the land area of Culpeper County, but 57 per cent in Orange, 70 to 73 per cent in Louisa, Fluvanna, and Goochland, and 77 per cent in Spotsylvania (see map, page 240).

Through most of the central part of the middle Piedmont (the western part of Spotsylvania, most of Orange, the western half of Louisa and Fluvanna, the eastern section of Albemarle) extends the belt of acid schists that give rise to the poor soils of the Nason-Tatum series and which are better used under woods than for pastures or cultivation. These woods often shelter a scattering of poor, small, marginal farmsteads occupied by White people. The 1930 Census of Agriculture showed this area to be the largest continuous stretch in Virginia of very low net income per capita among agricultural workers. While the state average was $589, the counties of Spotsylvania, Louisa, Fluvanna, and Goochland all showed averages varying from $306 to $391. Even though lower figures were recorded in a few counties of southwestern Virginia, the latter at least had the resources of part-time coal mining or moonshining. Neither of these two complements to farm income was available to any extent in the poorer section of the middle Piedmont. Many farms were abandoned in that area and most of this section shows a substantial decrease in population between 1930 and 1950. Only the eastern half of Goochland County seems to have benefited by the expansion in this direction of Richmond's outer suburbia.

Immediately to the west, closing in on the first ridges of the Charlottesville area, the poor soils derived from schists are replaced by a long ribbon of quite rich soils of the Davidson-Mecklenburg-Iredell series, usually with a deep, dark-red subsoil. These are derived from igneous basic rocks and produce, when properly managed, good yields of grain, grass or hay. Peter Jefferson chose well the land he cleared and on which he settled his family. When one reads, however, of the difficulties Thomas Jefferson had in making his Monticello estate bring a decent income during his long absences, one wonders what kind of living the much poorer schist soils of the area to the east may have offered to small farmers and tenants. The cultivation of dark, fire-cured tobacco, the shrinking market for which made the remnants of its cultivation retreat southwards, is perhaps partly responsible for the exhaustion of the soil. The insufficient care given it by most of the farmers until very recent times is another reason for agricultural debility. Finally, this area of Virginia was one of the most constantly disputed throughout the Civil War and had great difficulty recovering from the disaster. It is indeed in a middle position, too far from the main urban centers, and not far enough south for cash crops like bright tobacco or cotton. Its agricultural prosperity depends on the expansion of livestock raising, with the appropriate pastures and crops of legumes and corn.

The transitional character of this area is also apparent in the steady increase, as one comes from the north and proceeds southwards, of the proportion of Negroes in the population. It varies from 23 to 50 per cent, the latter figure being that of Goochland. The general tendency of the Negro people here is to migrate towards the towns and out of the area; but a good number of small farmers and tenants still remain on the land.

Two cities may be included in this study of the middle Piedmont, as they are rather well integrated with the area: Fredericksburg on the fall line and Charlottesville at the gates of the foothills of the Blue Ridge. The former lives chiefly by its geographical position about halfway between Washington and Richmond, the through-traffic being quite important, as well as the local market function. The latter is chiefly the town of the University of Virginia, and the permanent station of many state technical services, which found it useful to be located in the immediate vicinity of the main center of learning and research in the commonwealth; the town is also the central commercial point for Albemarle County. Neither, however, is a place of great importance: Fredericksburg is limited in its growth by the two spreading metropolitan areas between which it is located; Charlottesville cannot derive much more than travel trade from the vicinity of the Blue Ridge, occupied by national parks and forests to a large extent. To the southeast and southwest the much larger urban centers of Richmond and Lynchburg exert far more attraction than the university town of Charlottesville for the middle Piedmont itself. Moreover, the section as a whole is neither large nor prosperous enough to supply the foundations of very active urban life.

The southern Piedmont

The southern section in our subdivision of the Piedmont is by far the most extensive and offers the characteristics that would seem the more consistent with Virginia's traditional reputation. This is a land of woods, tobacco, and corn, of many Negro and White sharecroppers, of widely scattered farmsteads. The Piedmont widens here and the land rolls more as one crosses the ribbonlike structure of the underlying rocks. There is something more stable in this deeply rural landscape than in the rest of eastern Virginia.

Since 1930, the density of population has not changed much in this area, though on the whole, more areas within the southern Piedmont have lost population than have gained it. Loss of population and general decline of the scattered rural farms was more prevalent in the northern parts, close to the middle Piedmont; this subdivision was closer to the cities of Richmond, Lynchburg, and Roanoke, and felt their attraction. It was also within the area of cultivation, now only partly maintained, of dark fire-cured tobacco. It had on the whole poorer soils, with a great deal of schists in the underlying parent strata. Further south, the belt of the bright flue-cured tobacco has held its own in a greater degree. Here even the small farms resisted the inroads of recent times. In Halifax

Harvesting tobacco in Pittsylvania County
Virginia Chamber of Commerce

County, for instance, there were 5,981 farms in 1930 and 5,619 in 1950. The number of non-White operated farms remained almost unchanged in this period; it was the White tenants who were chiefly reduced in numbers, as the percentage of tenant-operated farms in the total shrank from 58.3 per cent in 1930 to 51.8 in 1950. This trend was not exactly prevalent throughout; in the vicinity of the expanding industrial centers of Danville and Martinsville to the southwest of this Piedmont section the evolution was more rapid; but Halifax County is rather typical of vast rural parts of the southern Piedmont. In Appomattox County, further north, the shrinking of the number of farms was greater and the per cent of tenant-operated farms in the total went down from 36.6 to 18.2; but Halifax is tobacco country to a greater extent than Appomattox.

A great deal of this stabilization of the southern Piedmont was due to the relative stability of bright Virginia tobacco, a stability which resulted from both an expanding consumer market and federal policy. Since 1933, the production of tobacco in the United States has been stabilized in large part by the government tobacco program, aimed at regulating production and at maintaining prices at a certain level. The government program for flue-cured tobacco establishes marketing quotas

Aerial view of fields and woods in Charlotte County
U. S. Department of Agriculture

and acreage allotments, with penalties for excess marketing and price support for complying farmers. Farmers who do not exceed their acreage allotments are entitled to price support at 90 per cent of parity; the grower who exceeds his allotment loses the right to direct price support and pays a tax on the excess tobacco of 40 per cent of the previous year's average price for that type.[5]

In other words, the federal government guarantee of a minimum base price for each market grade of tobacco assures the grower an attractive return on his investment and labor. The allotments were made to the exactness of one-tenth of an acre and were based on the tobacco acreage history of the farm. From then on the value of a farm in the southern Piedmont is usually in proportion to the number of acres of "base." Until 1953, each "acre of base" was generally worth between $500 and $1,000 in addition to the normal value of the farm. Thus one was paying for the license to grow tobacco with the price-support privileges attached to a piece of land rather than for the land itself. Each period of uneasiness as to future trends of federal policy in tobacco prices causes some

[5] Federal Reserve Bank of Richmond, Research Department, *Flue-Cured Tobacco: An Economic Survey*, Richmond, 1953.

A tobacco auction in Petersburg
Virginia Chamber of Commerce

fluctuation on the real-estate market of this section. However, from 1933 to 1953, tobacco brought handsome profits on the average, and the prosperity of the region advanced rapidly. The proportion of farms in Halifax County having power-line electricity was 2.5 per cent in 1930 and 53 per cent in 1950; in the same period and county the number of farms with one or more tractors increased from 187 to 928, while in Appomattox County the number of farms with tractors went up from 46 to 330 in 1930–1950.

Tobacco is not the only cash crop of the southern Piedmont, of course, and does not explain everything there. Corn and wheat are still important by acreage and by the revenues they bring. The acreage under grain crops shrank considerably in recent years, but the yields were improved to a point of maintaining almost the same volume of output. Hay showed the greatest increase in acreage. As in the rest of the Piedmont and most of the Tidewater, the new trend in agriculture, besides the stabilization of flue-cured tobacco, is toward increasing the role of cattle raising, more for meat than for milk, though dairy farms are also encountered and some of them demonstrate an impressive degree of prosperity.

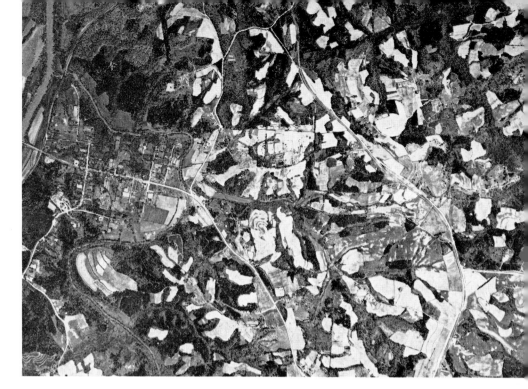

Aerial view in Halifax County
U. S. Department of Agriculture

Grass grows even better here, in the more southerly section, than it does north of the James, because the warm season is longer. However, to start a cattle or dairy farm which could quickly bring a good revenue, a substantial investment is needed in order to buy high quality animals, an investment prohibitive for the many small farmers of the tobacco belt. Instead, many small farmers look for a complementary income from work in an industrial plant or from some service in town. Growing attention is paid to forestry, as the demand for pulpwood is high and rather stable, and as the prices for hardwood timber have remained fairly high in recent years. In some of the southern Piedmont counties, a very high proportion of the total area is under woods: in 1946, this percentage was 77 in Buckingham and Lunenburg and 81 in Powhatan. Generally speaking, the proportion of wooded lands remains above 60 per cent in the northern and east-central parts of the southern Piedmont, between 50 and 61 per cent in the southside.

The great majority of the counties in this section get their major income from agriculture. The county of Nottoway listed government as its major source of income in 1951 (mainly owing to the expenditure of military installations). Pittsylvania, Henry, Campbell, and Bedford indi-

Frank Petty, owner of the wagon, has just had his mule shod and his corn ground and has bought some kerosene in the combination filling station, garage, blacksmith shop, and grocery store in the background. Danville, Pittsylvania County. *Library of Congress Photo by Marion Post Wolcott*

cated manufacturing as their major source. This western part of the southern Piedmont sends a great many workers from rural areas to the industrial centers of Lynchburg, Danville, Petersburg, Martinsville, and to smaller centers scattered through the area. This is the beginning of a system, encountered on an even larger scale in western Virginia, of factories the personnel of which commutes from rural homes. The good system of secondary highways found here and the generalization of automobile ownership has made it possible to associate industrial and agricultural work in a more intimate fashion here than has been achieved in other parts of the United States north of the Potomac or west of the Appalachians. The Dan River Mills, a very large textile manufacturing firm in Danville, gives its personnel, among other privileges, two days a year free for "hog killing."

The Bureau of Population and Economic Research at the University of Virginia prepared some extremely interesting reports on the changes occurring in Charlotte County as a result of the construction of a new industrial plant in a heretofore purely rural area. This plant, Drakes Mill, located at Drakes Branch, employed 293 persons in November,

Aerial view in Pittsylvania County
U. S. Department of Agriculture

1949, of whom 62.1 per cent resided outside a five-mile radius of the mill; in February, 1951, Drakes Mill employed 455 persons, among whom 66.6 per cent resided beyond the five-mile radius, and 22.2 lived more than 10 miles from the mill. The survey showed that such new industrial employment provided in a rural agricultural area increases the rural non-farm population. A number of families discontinue farming operations and use their holdings for purely residential purposes. In many other cases only one member of an agricultural family is employed in manufacturing, and the rest of the family still works on the farm. The necessity of commuting causes some shifts in the location of residences towards better roads, but there is little endeavor to get closer to the plant. Commuting distances of 10 to 12 miles are common and are regarded as quite easy.[6]

Textile, lumber, and chemical plants are the main industries found at

[6] Bureau of Population and Economic Research, University of Virginia, in cooperation with the Virginia Department of Highways and the U. S. Bureau of Public Roads, *The Impact of a New Manufacturing Plant upon the Socio-economic Characteristics and Travel Habits of the People in Charlotte County, Virginia*, Charlottesville, 1951, and, in the same series, *An Analysis of Changes in the Seasonal Patterns of Road Use from 1949–1951 in Charlotte County, Virginia*, Charlottesville, 1952.

This farmland in Mecklenburg County was planted in kudzu to stop the gullying.
U. S. Department of Agriculture

present scattered through this area. But tobacco still appears to be the focus of the area, and the processing and trade of it permeates the whole landscape, particularly from August to November. The curing sheds are everywhere in sight, along the roads and amidst the fields. The familiar silhouette (see page ooo) of these large, high, dumpy log cabins, windowless but with a towering metallic smokestack, means tobacco all over the southern Piedmont; in some areas the sight of such curing sheds falling into ruins reminds the passerby of the abandonment of formerly more extensive tobacco fields. A number of small towns have built their economies around warehouses for tobacco auctioning. This necessary function should have been the primary focus for urbanization in Virginia's Tidewater in colonial times, and it was repeatedly demanded from London, but in vain. Nowadays tobacco warehouses are a major activity in only one important city, Danville, which is the largest tobacco market in Virginia and used to be the largest in the United States. It is well situated in the middle of the Old Belt of bright-tobacco cultivation on the Piedmont and draws a great deal of tobacco from the northern part of North Carolina's old belt. Smaller towns deal each year in lesser quantities of

Aerial view in Pittsylvania County
U. S. Department of Agriculture

tobacco than Danville, and they do not have many other industries besides this; such is the case in South Boston, South Hill, and Emporia. There are also active tobacco warehouses in Richmond and Petersburg.

Besides the period of tobacco auctioning in the fall, the small towns of the Piedmont, though they may have a few small industries, serve mainly as marketplaces and centers of regional gatherings and social life. Many of these towns came into existence because of a county courthouse, according to the old Virginia tradition. The trend of the population has been in some degree to concentrate in or around the small towns. The purely rural areas, although they preserve to a large extent their scattered pattern of settlement, are the areas showing loss of population from census to census. With the decrease in the number of farms and the development of the trend towards an economy of cattle, pastures, and woodlands, which requires less permanent manpower, part of the population will naturally leave the rural areas unless employment is provided locally by new industrial plants. Even the curing of tobacco nowadays requires less labor and less constant attention. Along State Route 40, across the central Piedmont, one can still see the hickory wood heaped up by the curing sheds and the bunks set up near the furnaces for the man who keeps the fire going night and day. In other places, however, oil stoves supply the heat and smoke for the curing and do not need constant attendance.

Many changes are coming now to the southern Piedmont, but it still remains a somewhat archaic area. The central part of it, as one gets away from the larger cities at the periphery, looks more backward than the rest. In other places, where industry has flourished recently, such as the area of Altavista, a textile center, or of South Hill, animated by the traffic of U. S. 1, more prosperity and activity have brought some modernization. Most of the area remains today very rural. Financial security has been assured to thrifty farmers of modest means by federal support of the prices of tobacco and other agricultural products, as well as by the heavy demand for lumber. The possibility of migrating out of the area and finding jobs easily in cities has greatly decreased population pressure and the threat of poverty. The proportion of Negroes has decreased in this area. In 1950, it varied between 56 per cent in Cumberland County, 50 in Amelia and Mecklenburg, to 24 per cent in Henry, Campbell, and Appomattox. But the number and the proportion of marginal farms remain here quite impressive. In the whole section, the number of farms with telephones was in 1950 below 10 per cent of the total. The median family income in 1950 varied with the counties from $2340 in Henry County, due to the industries around Martinsville, to $970 in Cumberland. The latter was the lowest among all the counties. The state average in that year stood at $2602. However, in the total value of farm products sold in 1949, these counties did not show up so poorly; this total increased rapidly south of the poor middle area of the Piedmont, and the southside counties showed enviable figures, much above the average among the counties of Virginia. Pittsylvania, in fact, came second, surpassed only by the rich poultry-raising county of Rockingham. Thus tobacco was not an unrewarding crop. But in the tobacco area, wealth is unequally divided, and many sharecroppers' families have little cash income (see maps, pages 150, 152 and 321).

The problem of the distribution of income is in some respects confusing. One must admit that in terms of agriculture this is a rather prosperous section. In terms of density of population its does not seem overpopulated, although densities are higher even in rural areas south of a line from Petersburg to Lynchburg than they are to the north and in the middle Piedmont. But in terms of per-capita or per-family income, this is poor country. One wonders what might become of these people if the price of tobacco were to sink much below the averages of recent years. The crisis hinted at since the fall of 1953 by the large cigarette manufacturers threatens the bright tobacco belt. If any such threat should materialize, the southern Piedmont would undergo hard times and probably substantial out-migration. The cattle economy which is slowly coming here, too, needs few hands and would meet competition from many other regions of the country. The apparent stability of the southern Piedmont is not entirely a sign of a sound economy.

WESTERN VIRGINIA

West of the demarcation line we drew between the two main parts of Virginia, the land is much more sharply partitioned than to the east. Mountain ridges and valleys in close alternation outline a puzzle of compartments. Each of these compartments, whether small valley or narrow ridge, has characteristics of its own. But its generally mountainous topography lends the whole of western Virginia many elements of unity. The first of these elements is the frequence of oppositions in alternating altitudes, in kinds of rocks and soils, and in the psychology of the local people. The second element of unity is the constant importance of the slope, as the steepness or gentleness of it determines the difficulty of access and the conditions of transportation as well as the potential of erosion. A third unifying trait is the small proportion of non-White people in the population.

Variety is certainly the dominating note on the map of western Virginia. Whether altitudes or soils, major occupations or standards of living are being measured, every ridge and every valley is somewhat different from the rest. That crests of mountains always serve as boundaries in some sense is a well-known fact throughout the world, as two slopes are never identical. It will be interesting to implement this generalization in many cases in western Virginia. The constant importance of the slope, its degree, its orientation, and its position with respect to other slopes or depressions always has to be accounted for when one wishes to understand the reasons for the land-use or for the existing relationships among the various parts of this country of hills and vales. While always important, the slope is only one factor among many, and it is decisive at times only, and then for localized phenomena rather than for general features. Nevertheless, where it is quite steep it makes erosion stronger and road building more difficult, and excludes the kind of large-scale field tilling that prospers on flatter grounds.

The elevation throughout western Virginia varies from about 1,000 feet in the lower part of the Great Valley to about 5,000 feet on the highest crests. Two summits located in the southwestern part of the Blue Ridge close to the North Carolina line reach higher than 5,500 feet:

View of Galax, in the Blue Ridge-Intermountain area
Virginia Chamber of Commerce Photo by Flournoy

Mount Rogers (5,720) and Mount Whitetop (5,519). However, heights of more than 4,500 are exceptional, while altitudes of about 4,000 are rather common. This contrast in altitudinal range with eastern Virginia has immediate climatic consequences. The higher altitudes are cooler throughout the year. Nevertheless, during the summer months the lower parts of the valleys can be just as hot as areas situated at a lesser elevation. In winter, however, it is colder through the whole of western Virginia, as the warming influence of the maritime spaces to the east is not felt much west of the Blue Ridge. This increasing continentality also limits for the lower valleys the cooling influence of the sea in the hot season. Western Virginia has thus greater extremes of temperature. The rainfall also varies from slope to slope, but generally speaking it increases to the southwest. Snow is much more common in winter in western Virginia, especially over the ridges; the greater length of the period of possible killing frosts shortens the safe average growing season, and this could be expected to put the western lands at a disadvantage as compared with the eastern areas regarding agricultural development; but such was not the case. The Great Valley and some of the smaller valleys further west have long had the reputation of being among the better-used lands in the eastern United States. The Shenandoah Valley farmers are still famous for their economy, which is largely oriented towards animal husbandry.

Topography and climate combined in this hilly area to suggest a kind of farming quite different from that of eastern Virginia. Moreover, the people themselves were different here from those in the east: they came to some extent from the east, but at least as much from the north, principally from Pennsylvania. These settlers did not benefit by the large land grants of the eastern section; most of them did not have the means to develop such tracts of lands. They were of Pennsylvania German or Scotch-Irish stock rather than English; and some of them represented old American stock migrating towards the southwest from the northeastern states. Let us not forget that the settlement of the Great Valley actually developed only after 1750, and the narrower valleys in the Blue Ridge and the Allegheny were settled chiefly after the Revolution, most of them during the nineteenth century.

Curiously enough, it is in these mountains that students of dialects and linguistics have found the largest group of people in America still speaking English in an archaic way which was decided to be Elizabethan. Many authorities can be quoted as having shown that the Virginia mountains harbor in their folds to this day an Elizabethan pronunciation of English because Virginia was first settled in Elizabethan and Shakespearean times. It is true that many witnesses testified through the seventeenth and eighteenth centuries that in Tidewater centers, such as Norfolk and Williamsburg, the same English was spoken as in London. Documents of the end of the eighteenth century do not indicate that the English of the Tidewater was then different from that of the London of Pitt's time, which was no longer exactly Elizabethan. It was only at that period that the settlement of the smaller western valleys started, and it was made more by Scotch-Irish and Germans than by English people. One wonders how it came about that the archaisms found today in the language of the mountaineers are so close to the forms reputed to be Elizabethan in English. There is no doubt, however, that the spoken language of western Virginia tends towards archaism and that the trend was much more pronounced a quarter of a century ago, particularly in the "hollows" of the Blue Ridge.[7]

It was not only in their speech that western mountaineers showed a tendency to be archaic; it appears in many aspects of the whole way of life outside the Great Valley. The main axial depression of western Vir-

[7] See Hans Kurath, *A Word Geography of the Eastern United States,* Ann Arbor, 1949; and many other sources, including E. F. Shewmake, *English Pronunciation in Virginia,* Charlottesville, 1927, a dissertation submitted to the University of Virginia.

Mabry Mill, on the Blue Ridge Parkway
National Park Service Photo by Arthur Fawcett

ginia was from early times characterized by advanced techniques and progressive land use and industrial development. There was, therefore, between the Great Valley and the mountains framing it a contrast not only in modes of life but in the general rhythm of evolution. Since the 1920's, however, the small valleys squeezed between the ridges have been given a quick push forward: this came with the great progress of communications in the second quarter of this century, with the motorcar and better roads, with electricity and telephones, with radio and the drive-in theatre; television and better schools are bound to accelerate the change.

Although this recent trend brings all parts of western Virginia closer together, the hills have not yet caught up with the Great Valley; even if and when they do, differences in geology, topography, and past history will keep these divisions somewhat different one from another. The hilly areas are not all alike, either, and there is a substantial difference between the Blue Ridge knobs and foothills on the one hand and the more regularly parallel and deeper alternation of valleys and crests of the Alleghenies. Thus three main regions take shape within western Virginia: the Blue Ridge, the Great Valley, and the Allegheny; a fourth one must, however, be added: Virginia territory extends to the southwest a triangular wedge reaching the Cumberland Gap at a junction of Kentucky and Tennessee. This southwestern triangle is a peculiar area where a large valley is oriented east-west, where the topography of narrow, sharp ridges is intermingled with a puzzle of rounded hills, and where the coal-mining economy becomes the arbiter of regional activities. Western Virginia will, therefore, be divided into four sections, within each of which a certain amount of variety is a rule and a characteristic.

The Blue Ridge

A modest line of low hills along the western fringe of Loudoun County in its northernmost section of Virginia, the Blue Ridge boldly rises higher and expands in width as one follows it southwards. In the southernmost section, near the North Carolina line, it can boast the highest summits of Virginia, and it encompasses entire counties within its range, such as Floyd, Carroll, and Grayson, while in the north its main crest, lined, of course, along most of its length by strings of knobs on both sides, serves rather as a boundary between counties. The main change occurs in the vicinity of the Roanoke Gap, to the south of which the Blue Ridge is a much more complicated chain of mountains than to its north.

To the north of Roanoke, the Blue Ridge appears as one main axial crest followed by less continuous lines of hilly knobs and foothills. The general northeast-southwest axis is quite close to a meridian orientation in northern Virginia, but in the south it turns gradually towards a direction closer to that of the parallels. This is a general trend of the Appalachian system, and the shift westward becomes more evident from the vicinity of Roanoke southward. In this way, relatively wide valleys provide easy passage through southwestern Virginia as far west as the Cumberland Gap. The Blue Ridge announces in many respects the Appalachian folds of which it is the first important one.

A relatively narrow system of highlands, the breadth of which rarely reaches ten miles north of Roanoke, the northern Blue Ridge has been, of course, deeply eroded by streams on both its main versants. The central crest often reaches 2,000 feet north of Front Royal, over 3,000 feet between Front Royal and Waynesboro, and up to 4,000 and more between Waynesboro and the James River gap across the whole ridge. South of the James, the Ridge gradually declines in average altitude and in breadth down to the wide, low gap in which Roanoke nestles. From these crests the slope is steep to the bottom of the Great Valley, which is approximately 1,000 feet in elevation, and the Piedmont, where such altitude is seldom reached. Erosion has attacked both slopes with great

Dogwood and the Blue Ridge Parkway in the Smart View area, April, 1938
U. S. Department of the Interior

ardor; the westward-looking slope was originally steeper as tectonics made it, but the low sea level was closer to the eastward looking slope, which was rapidly dissected into a more complicated pattern of foothills and small knobs.

Broad, rounded ridges include spurs and sharp knobs that protrude from the top of steep, often precipitous slopes, and fast-flowing small streams follow the deeply cut valleys. These valleys are at times narrow and gorgelike, but more generally they are rather wide, especially for the size of the streams, which drain relatively wide and damp bottoms. This topography is common in crystalline ridges made of granite, gneiss, schist, micaschist, and greenstone. Volcanic rocks are found locally—small intrusions testifying to the volcanism that was associated in remote ages with the strains of mountain erection. In a few cases rivers have managed to cut across the whole ridge in areas of lesser altitude and resistance; such are the water gaps of the Potomac, of the James, and of the Roanoke. If the gap of the Potomac is impressive at Harpers Ferry and for about two miles downstream, the gorges of the James between Glasgow and Lynchburg are much more spectacular. In most cases, however, roads cannot cross the whole ridge just by following river valleys, and they have to rise to high gaps by winding routes.

Many of the slopes and even the valley bottoms of the Blue Ridge are rock land or rock outcrops. The soils are shallow and very stony; in many areas there is scarcely any soil left after erosion has worked on the slopes left barren by deforestation, forest fires, and overgrazing for several generations. The northwestern slopes, made of highly metamorphosed sandstones, quartzite, and shale, are steep, and their soils, when they have soils, are quite poor. On the southeastern slopes, more deeply penetrated by ramifications of many valleys, soils are more often present and they are richer, being derived from basic rocks. Here, on the relatively gentle slopes of smooth mountain tops or flattened ridges, as well as in the wider valleys, the soils respond well to good management. Altitude reduces the length of the growing season, and above 2,000 feet the soils are frozen for prolonged periods in winter. Where the rocks are acid (schists, etc.) the soils are usually as poor as on the northwestern slope. Most of the higher grounds were being eroded so rapidly in the beginning of this century that the conservation of the whole area and the prevention of floods for the lower land situated on both sides of the ridges necessitated strict measures. Public ownership extends today over vast areas of the Blue Ridge, especially over the higher mountains and the steeper slopes. Between Front Royal and Waynesboro, the main crests and the hollows between them are now transformed into the Shenandoah National Park. Further south, as far as Roanoke, most of the mountains are under public ownership and managed by federal authorities as national forests. The George Washington National Forest extends over the Blue Ridge from the vicinity of Waynesboro to the valley of the James; beyond it the high grounds of the range are part of the Jefferson National Forest. Woods under private ownership cover a great deal of the foothills towards the Piedmont. For such eroded slopes and poor, shallow soils, trees provide the best use and offer the best chance for protection and recovery of whatever stability and fertility the local conditions may permit.

The National Park is well equipped for recreation and tourism. It is the park which is the closest to Washington and the southern part of *Megalopolis,* and it attracts over a million visitors annually. Some fishing is allowed in season in its streams, but no hunting. The trees are allowed to grow freely, as the park's administrators do not follow a set economic policy. A beautiful parkway follows the main crest of the ridge, providing the visitor with a smooth ride in the midst of rugged terrain and often opening superb panoramic vistas. Smaller roads, specially equipped

Highland pastures at Rocky Knob
National Park Service

and marked trails are offered to those who want to see this natural reserve closer and enjoy the wild aspects of it. When the park was established, some of the mountaineers had to sell their lands to the government and were resettled elsewhere. The national ownership of lands does not include in a strict way everything above a certain level; some farms have remained in a few hollows. But many more of the "hollow folk" are still found in the Blue Ridge south of the park area, in the territory of the national forests.

The Blue Ridge north of Roanoke cannot be called an agricultural region within Virginia. There is not enough agriculture left, properly speaking, for that. Most of the mountaineers' small farms that have stuck to the hollows are very small marginal establishments without actual economic significance other than restricting the consuming capacity of the local population. This area is of significance chiefly as an important region in the forest geography of Virginia. The forest has been left to develop freely on publicly owned lands, but parts of it have been devastated by huge fires. Such destruction is especially unfortunate because most of the trees at the higher altitudes are hardwoods and grow slowly. The national forests were constituted after the Weeks Act of 1911, and many parts of their present territory were purchased less than thirty years ago; thirty years is not a considerable period for hardwood growth. In many parts of the Shenandoah National Park, which was dedicated in 1936, the present forest cover is about twenty years old. Some thinning and cutting of trees is done under the supervision of the U. S. Forest Service. The forest will, if undisturbed for a long period, create on these mountains a great store of wealth in lumber, essentially oak.

In the valleys and on the lower slopes of the foothills of the Ridge, a gradual transition on the eastern side brings the hollows to the Piedmont. The foothills, of some altitude and steepness, occupy a particularly wide area in Nelson and Amherst Counties, as well as in the north of Bedford. Below the wooded tops, meadows are dispersed along the valleys, and grain fields are often seen. This is transitional agriculture chiefly, bearing the imprint of what is known through the southern Appalachians as "hill billy farming." The deeper the hollow inside the mountain mass and the more isolated it is, the more backward are the people and their mode of life. The remarkable inquiry summed up in the volume by Mandel Sherman and Thomas R. Henry under the title *Hollow Folk* [8] brilliantly describes the mode of life of the Blue Ridge valleys around 1930. A great deal of change has occurred since, owing to better roads, more frequent visitors, and the opening of new employment opportunities nearby; the hollow folk are being integrated into the progress of the regional life.

Since 1930, with the progress of communications and individual transportation, topography has become less an isolating factor than it used to be. It is not the topography alone that has changed its meaning in recent years; it is the psychology of the people as well. The hollows were settled chiefly since the end of the eighteenth century; while many of their contemporaries and cousins chose to go west and develop the wide open spaces, where very progressive communities arose, the ancestors of the present hollow folk preferred staying near the Valley of Virginia and went up into the mountains. Many degrees of isolation and backwardness developed. In some of the more isolated places the children were found to be uneducated in 1928–1929, never having seen the American flag or heard the Lord's Prayer, many of them completely unaware of the vast world around the hollow; tests given to the children and youths showed their complete lack of contact with ways of thinking outside the hollows, though they proved to be capable of learning fast. The mode of life of the poorer hollows seemed to be worse than what La Rochefoucauld-Liancourt observed in the Great Valley at the end of the eighteenth cen-

[8] This previously quoted volume, published in New York in 1933, presents the results of a careful survey in which the names of the communities and inhabitants are fictitious.

A view toward Massanutten Mountain from Skyland, showing Luray and the valley. See map on page 204.
National Park Service

tury. It seems that the more isolated hollow folk did not preserve the old way of life so much as let themselves sink much below the standards of their forebears who lived in the Valley or further north.

All this has changed, but some families, whose lands were not bought by public authorities, continue to live in the mountains in the fashion quite accurately described in *Hollow Folk*. Some of them can be seen along roads followed by tourist traffic. Opportunities for contact with and learning about the ways of the neighboring world have not been lacking; it is simply that these people prefer their way of life because it is theirs and because they hate and despise change, however detestable their way may seem to others. The economic motive, the desire for gain, is not absent from their minds and motivations, but it is entirely subordinated to the dominating aim of preserving their way of life. This conservative state of mind applies, first of all, to the place of residence, then to the kind of housing and the type of occupation. It does not necessarily follow that a similar attitude applies to the introduction of new technical devices if such are made available.

Western Virginia has in its mountains people of a strange psychology—

at any rate, of a psychological type that seems strange to anyone who knows the rhythms of America. In these mountains it may appear that the pursuit of happiness consists for the hollow folk in keeping the rest of the world away. But in many hollows nowadays only old people are left; the younger generation has simply moved out. In many hollows, middle-aged people still live in dwellings of distressing aspect, but own cars and have much more mechanical equipment than would be expected from the outside appearance of their houses. They may work in some plant in a larger town in the Great Valley or on the fringe of the Piedmont. The next generation will probably progress further. The same problems and the same kind of hollow people can be found in many valleys of the southern Appalachians in Virginia and in other states as well; the northern Blue Ridge has been perhaps better studied in this respect than other parts of Virginia because it is closer to Washington and to Charlottesville.

South of Roanoke, the Blue Ridge changes considerably in character. The range of mountains widens out in the form of a triangle, the summit pointed towards Roanoke, the base along the North Carolina line. Three counties are included in this triangle and constitute the southern Blue Ridge, properly speaking: Floyd, Carroll, and Grayson. The foothills to the east cover most of Franklin and Patrick Counties, widening the triangle in this direction. The Blue Ridge here has been reduced in places to a wide, rugged plateau into which powerful erosive forces have carved depressions and ridges, leaving the domes of more resistant material standing out as rounded knobs such as the higher summits to the south, Mount Rogers, Whitetop, and others. This is hilly country indeed, with the higher ridges framing the three central counties. This area is often spoken of as "intermountainous," since it extends, in fact, between the Piedmont and the Great Valley. Soils are deeper here and their stratification is better defined than in the Blue Ridge north of Roanoke, mainly as a result of gentler slopes over most of the section. Most of the soils are less erosive here than on the Piedmont or in the foothills. Floyd County and Carroll County show greater agricultural activity and better loamy soils than Franklin or Patrick. The "intermountain" soils are rather crumbly throughout their profiles; their coloration ranges from dark gray to brown, sometimes with red subsoils. This is deeply rural country with few towns of any importance. Floyd Courthouse is a village rather than a town, surrounding the central square around the courthouse itself. Further south Galax is the only town of any consequence.

More than half the three Ridge counties have been cleared of forests and turned to pasture or tilled land. Nearly three-quarters of the open

The Blue Ridge Parkway near Rocky Knob, with an old rail fence
U. S. Department of the Interior

land is under pasture in which blue grass predominates. A great deal of the cultivated land is gullied and shows the weakness of overworked soils. Yields are poor on the average, and there are too many people on the land. In the three counties of Floyd, Carroll, and Grayson, 81.3 per cent of the land area is in farms, which is less than in 1930, when this percentage stood at 89.7 per cent. But the number of farms has increased in this same period, and their average size has shrunk consequently from 89 acres in 1930 to 77 in 1950. The total acreage of harvested cropland and of unwooded pasture has also shrunk, but the area of pastured woodland is on the increase, which means that cattle are being put on too steep slopes where they will ruin the woods and the soil and accelerate the ravages of erosion. The main crop on the increase appears to be hay, which is indeed needed, as the number of cattle has almost doubled since 1930, reaching 80,200 head in 1950. The raising of hogs, sheep, and even poultry appears to be on the decline.

The southern Blue Ridge thus decidedly turns towards livestock in agriculture. One wonders how so many small farms, of decreasing size, can still provide a decent living for their occupants. The fact is that in 1951 only Floyd County in this part of Virginia still claimed agriculture as its main source of income. To the officially declared agricultural pursuits should probably be added moonshining. Many people in western Virginia contend that no county in the United States makes as much moonshine as Franklin, with its vast areas of steep, wooded hills. Whether the rather new and quite impressive houses one often finds in the wilds of Franklin and of some neighboring counties are to be explained only by the revenue from moonshine is a point unresolved and difficult to clarify. It may well be that the residents of such houses have an income other than from agriculture: and there are industrial and commercial centers nearby, such as Rocky Mount and Galax, and commuting to Martinsville, Roanoke, or the industrial centers of the Valley to the northwest is quite easy from many parts of the intermountainous area. All the counties in this section, with the exception of Floyd, announced manufacturing to be their major source of income in 1951. Here, even more than in the southern Piedmont, rural-looking areas supply the manpower for scattered industries.

There are not many industrial plants within the Blue Ridge proper. Floyd County has none at all. Some small textile or garment plants are disseminated through the hills in such places as Independence and Fries in Grayson County, Hillsville in Carroll County, Stuart in Patrick County, and Rocky Mount in Franklin County. The only town with a really important grouping of plants is Galax, which has large furniture factories, a weaving division plant of Burlington Mills, a smelting plant for metallic ores, some knitting, hosiery, and dairy factories. Galax is the largest urban center and the most important manufacturing center in the southern Blue Ridge. In the northern part of the range, practically all the industries are on the fringe and chiefly on the Valley side. In Rockbridge County, Buena Vista with its paper mill and lumber industries seems almost a mountain town, and Glasgow nestles in a valley at the entrance of the James River gorge through the Blue Ridge. Glasgow is not a mill town but draws thousands of workers from the surrounding area, mountain and valley, to work in its wool carpet mill of the James Lees and Sons Company. In fact, with the exception of Galax, all the substantial industrial centers along the Ridge must be considered as belonging to either the upper Piedmont or the Valley, though the Ridge supplies many of these industries with a good part of their personnel.

The Blue Ridge is no longer the great barrier it used to be, but between eastern Virginia and the bustling and progressive Great Valley it rises as an area partly backward, partly wilderness, generally a museum piece, but more and more penetrated by the motor traffic not only of the tourist but also of the salesmen. Change is taking place in the Blue Ridge both for the people and for the vegetation. The area is gradually turning toward an economy of woods and meadows, with a long-term policy of forest management and with increasing employment in manufacturing of the scattered rural population. The standard of living is slowly going up, and the area is still to be developed as a consumers' market.

The Valley of Virginia

There is in many respects a sharp contrast between the Blue Ridge and the Great Valley. The Virginia section of this great furrow inside the Appalachian system is an impressive and varied one. Though definitely a valley between mountain ranges, it is neither quite flat nor clearly continuous. This structural depression developed in this shape because of the geological architecture of the area. It is not a valley drained by one main stream, or even a depression drained by a group of streams running in the same direction. The Valley of Virginia is drained toward the Potomac by the rivers that flow northwards in its northeastern part; then a section in its middle is drained by the James, flowing, like the Potomac, toward the Chesapeake Bay. Further to the southwest the drainage is attracted by the Roanoke River, which empties into Albemarle Sound. To the west of Roanoke an irregular system of not-very-high crests serves as a divide between the area drained toward the Atlantic Ocean, to which all the rivers enumerated belong, and the basin of the New River, which flows westwards to the Ohio and belongs, with the whole Mississippi drainage basin, to the part of the continent drained toward the Gulf of Mexico. Still further to the southwest, the Valley of Virginia is drained straight to the south by a number of streams, chief among which are the Holston and the Clinch Rivers, both tributaries of the Tennessee and, beyond that, of the Mississippi. In the southwestern corner of Virginia lies part of the territory under the Tennessee Valley Authority.

Such a variety in the drainage signifies that the Valley of Virginia is no simple valley. In general outline it may appear to be relatively simple and unified, a broad longitudinal depression between the Appalachian ridges in its northern half, from Lexington to Winchester; south of Lexington and Buena Vista, the Valley narrows down to barely a corridor between the Blue Ridge and the Short Hills range (the altitude of which reaches over 2,500 feet). The James River almost fills up this corridor with its meanders, entering it through a narrow gate, almost a gorge, at Buchanan, where river, highway, and railroad tracks are squeezed between the foothills of the Blue Ridge and of the Allegheny ranges advancing to meet each other. South of that point the Valley widens again

View eastward from the Parkway, Shenandoah National Park
Virginia Chamber of Commerce

into a sort of quadrangular basin, the heart of Botetourt County. Then another narrow gate leads from that basin to the depression in which the city of Roanoke is rapidly expanding. Then a succession of low ridges interrupts the continuity of the depression and breaks up the Valley further south into a string of basins. This partitioning by geology and topography contributed to the multiplicity of drainage directions and made the Valley less uniform. Nevertheless, as an area of lesser altitudes than the surrounding areas, and different landforms, geology, and soils from theirs, the Great Valley remains indeed a unit on the map of Virginia's regions, clearly contrasted with the mountains and their narrow little depressions on both sides.

The Valley has probably been better surveyed geologically and agriculturally than any other part of Virginia. It has a great variety of natural resources, and the local people have shown a lively interest in all the possibilities of utilizing the riches of their land, to the point that the Valley acquired a reputation as the richest part of the commonwealth in terms of natural endowment, as well as in terms of management of resources. The natural endowment at least is well known. The basic difference between the Valley and the surrounding regions is that the floor

Aerial view in Rockingham County. Woods cover the ridges, and fields indicate valleys. *U. S. Department of Agriculture*

of the Valley, which is relatively flat, is made chiefly of limestone deposits, which means that the earlier plateau was composed of strata that were more easily excavated by erosion than the much harder crystalline material of both the Blue Ridge and the Allegheny range. The soils here have developed from parent material rich in lime; the soils from limestone are inherently fertile in general and are the best in western Virginia.

The Valley floor is not, however, uniform either in topography or geological foundations. It is a gently rolling floor, with steep slopes in some places. The frequency of steep slopes increases to the southwest, but even in the northern half, usually called the Shenandoah Valley, where the floor of the Valley is continuously wide and reaches twenty miles in width between Harrisonburg and Staunton, even here ridges rise above the Valley floor. The most impressive of these ridges in the Shenandoah Valley is that provided by Massanutten Mountain. It stands in the midst of the Valley, dividing it into two parallel branches, as if to remind everybody that the general axis of the Appalachian folds is present here. Made of interstratified hard sandstone and shale, the Massanutten is just a narrow wooded crest in its southern part, but in its northern half it

Aerial view in Shenandoah County showing the bends in the Shenandoah River
U. S. Department of Agriculture

widens out and separates into two main ridges framing an oblong narrow
depression inside the mountain. This northern part of the Massanutten
takes on the topographic map the outline of a "canoe" mountain, a frequent occurrence in the Appalachian area. Erosion has carved out this
elongated ridge just as Indians and early settlers used to carve canoes out
of the trunks of big trees. With a little play of the imagination one can
visualize the north of the Massanutten floating on the Great Valley floor
like a barge on a stream and proceeding to the northeast with two much
smaller barks tied one to the bow and the other to the stern of the main
ship; let us add that the ship has some long and narrow object in tow
to explain the southern crest of the Massanutten. This "canoe" image
appears clearly on certain maps (see page 204); indeed, the whole Shenandoah Valley is shaped like the stern of a gigantic canoe of which the
bow would be found far away in Pennsylvania.[9]

Ridges and knobs multiply on the Valley floor, disturbing the general
layout south of the corridor of Buchanan where the floor is at the most

[9] See particularly the plastic relief maps of this area printed and distributed by the
U. S. Army Map Service at the scale of 1:200,000. The Valley is mapped on such models
only north of Roanoke, on the sheets Roanoke (NJ 17–9), Charlottesville (NJ 17–6),
Cumberland (NJ 17–3), and Baltimore (NJ 18–1).

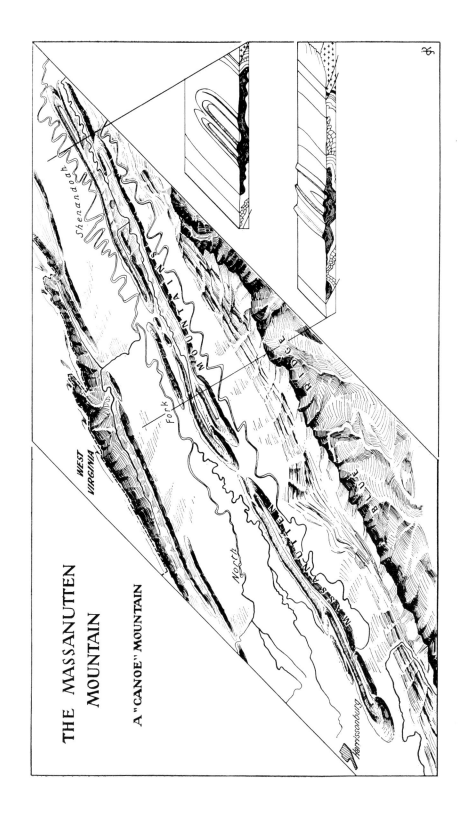

THE MASSANUTTEN
MOUNTAIN

A "CANOE" MOUNTAIN

A street in Marion
Virginia Chamber of Commerce

two miles wide. Some of the crests in the southwestern part of the Valley rise to 1,200 to 1,800 feet above the floor. The complexity of the topography results from both a very complicated geology and a diversified and long history of erosion. The variety of the drainage basins encountered testifies to the latter. Many of the major streams established their courses at a time when the region was a low, flat peneplain, so that rivers could meander in various directions. When the region was uplifted high above sea level and the slope towards the ocean was steepened, "the streams flowed faster, carried more sediment, and their eroding power was increased. Those that crossed truncated belts of the hard steeply inclined rocks were forced to cut into these rocks as the region rose higher. Thus they maintained the courses assumed before the elevation of the country began, and finally carved the water gaps seen." [10]

The known history of settlement is much shorter and simpler than the geological past. The main migration came from the northeast, from Pennsylvania, following the wide Valley floor and the rich calcareous soils

[10] Charles Butts, *Geology of the Appalachian Valley in Virginia* (Virginia Geological Survey, Bulletin 52), Charlottesville, 1940, Part I, p. 19. In technical terms such valleys are called "epigenic."

Picking apples in Byrd Orchard
Virginia Chamber of Commerce Photo by Flournoy

which had already demonstrated their qualities up north. As this stream of settlement progressed other currents trickled in through the gaps of the Blue Ridge from Tidewater and Piedmont Virginia. The population of the Valley is, therefore, of mixed origin. As the numbers of the people grew, especially during the nineteenth century, out-migrations took place in two directions: the major stream went further westward along the Great Valley and across the mountains; another stream settled the smaller valleys and hollows of the mountain ranges on both sides of the Valley; many of the Blue Ridge hollow folk came from the Valley.

On the maps of distribution of population and of various economic characteristics, the Valley stands out as a special area and a rather well-knit unit. From Winchester to Bristol and from Frederick County to Washington County, the Valley of Virginia is agriculturally rich, with carefully managed farms, better-equipped homes on the average, higher revenues, and a remarkable concentration of manufacturing industries. For instance, on the map of the percentage of dwelling units equipped with mechanical refrigerators, which seems to be curiously representative of the standard of living (see page 147), the Valley shows a clear stretch of high percentage across the state; similar proportions are found only in

Turkeys on a farm in the vicinity of Harrisonburg
Virginia Chamber of Commerce

the metropolitan areas and in the northern Piedmont. In fact, there is a sharp contrast between the modes of life on the flat central floor of the Valley and those of the ridges or of the fringes at the foot of the mountains. It would seem that the more hilly the terrain, the less advanced the ways of living. A distinction still exists in many places between the reputedly progressive farmer of the Valley bottom and the more backward mountaineer. Such variations are, of course, inevitable, emphasizing the higher level achieved by the Valley people as opposed to the people of the slopes and hollows; both are counted together in statistics given by counties.

Properly speaking, what the Valley is to most Virginians is its northern, wider, and more impressive part, the Shenandoah Valley, the first settled. The "Pennsylvania Dutch" early brought to it their superior agricultural techniques and their ability at handling livestock, chiefly cattle and hogs. As Kercheval pointed out over a century ago:

At the first settling the Valley was one vast prairie, and like the rich prairies of the west, afforded the finest possible pasturage for wild animals. The country abounded in the larger kinds of game. . . . These prairies had an artificial cause. At the close of each hunting season the Indians fired the open ground, and thus kept it from reverting to woodland. This was done to attract the buffalo, an animal that shuns the forest. The progressive deforesting of the lowlands of the Valley made the settlement by the whites very easy and rapid.[11]

The livestock economy has thus been, under many different kinds of land use, the tradition and destiny of this region.

In this part of the Valley the farms are usually of medium size and highly mechanized. The average size, according to the 1950 Census of Agriculture, was about 126 acres. The nonwooded pasture, too often in bluegrass, was the most popular kind of land appointment. Farm woodland was often pastured, although the notion that such a practice was deplorable had begun to spread. The harvested cropland was gradually shrinking and the number of cattle rapidly increasing. Hay was, here again, the only crop rapidly expanding in acreage, largely at the expense of grain. Sheep and hogs were still numerous, and their numbers appeared to be about stabilized for the past twenty years, especially the number of the hogs. A new branch of animal husbandry was added in the twentieth century and has been growing fast since 1930—poultry raising, both chickens and turkeys. The country around Harrisonburg in Rockingham County, where the Valley floor is especially wide and flat, appears to have become the center of the Valley's agriculture. Rockingham County in 1950 led all other Virginia counties by far in the value of its agricultural output; it claims an almost national supremacy in turkey raising. In 1950, the Shenandoah Valley, from Frederick County to Rockbridge County, raised 14.5 million chickens and 1.2 million turkeys. Feed dealers' warehouses today take an important place in the downtown sections of the Valley cities, particularly Harrisonburg. Thousands of farms obtain their principal cash income from poultry.

Poultry husbandry seems to have come here in order to occupy more fully the family of a farmer who owns 80 to 120 acres with tractors and mechanized implements. Such a farm would nowadays give a great deal of leisure to a diligent family; hence farmers develop dairying or poultry raising, preferably the latter. Few farmers make any effort to produce the feed their poultry consumes. The poultry farmer has become the keeper and feeder of stock on a commercial basis; he provides the housing facilities for the birds, but the feed dealer supplies him with poults, chicks, and feed, carrying the weight of most of the investment. The dealers take the risk of the transaction: the farmer receives the profits from the sale of the birds above the cost of stock and feed, estimated at their selling price; but the farmer does not make up the deficit if poultry prices

[11] Samuel Kercheval, *A History of the Valley of Virginia,* 4th edition, Strasburg, Va., 1925, p. 52 and footnote.

Beltsville white turkeys in the Shenandoah Valley
Virginia Chamber of Commerce

should fall so that the receipts are below the estimated cost of raising. In fact, the farmer risks only his labor and the small amount of space devoted to the raising of the birds. The Shenandoah farmers and dealers have in this way undertaken a somewhat risky enterprise in competition with several other areas of the country; just as the Eastern Shore truck farmers depend on the great city markets, so do the poultry raisers of the Valley, although their economy depends also in a major degree on the prices of feed.

To the north of the poultry and livestock area, the Shenandoah Valley specializes in fruit orchards and particularly in apples. Winchester is the capital of apple cultivation and trade in Virginia; peaches are produced on a large scale in impressive orchards further south in the Valley. Thus a diversified economy has developed here dependent on the vast markets of the nation and particularly of the crowded and highly urbanized northeast, and requiring also a great deal of machinery, feeds for animals, and fertilizers. It absorbs all the lands of the Valley floor, since traditionally almost all farmers favor limestone soils. Even where the up-tilted limestone strata have not weathered into gentle rolling country and where the white rocks outcrop with sharp little crests that make it difficult to move about, the farmer endeavors to plow and till. These rocky gardens are often quite extensive, even in the more central section of the Valley, though these grounds are in fact inferior to the shale soils, which, under adequate management, can provide good pastures and hay crops.

South of the wide and continuously flat-bottomed Shenandoah Valley, agriculture takes more traditional, less specialized aspects. Here the rounded knobs and the elongated crests rising above the rolling Valley floor are more generally capped by woods. The traditional land use is based on bluegrass for pasture, corn, small grains, and a little burley tobacco. Here the influence from Pennsylvania of the German, Amish, and Quaker farmers has been felt less. The English, Irish, and Scotch of southwestern Virginia have shown themselves more conservative farmers on the whole. There are more tenant farmers here, and the average size of the farm is somewhat smaller: around 100 acres. Away from the vicinity of the main towns situated amidst the best basins of alluvial and deep sedimentary soils, tilling methods are less mechanized and more traditional, and even horses and some implements dating back to the nineteenth century are used. A small farm is seldom sufficient to satisfy the needs of both an owner and a tenant; the tenant system works well only on units possessing a substantial tobacco acreage which is under restrictive controls. On the best soils some large farms have been set up with vast pasturing lands, and most of them have gone into dairying. The growing population of the nearby industrial centers encourages this trend. Livestock raising here, as well as in the Blue Ridge and in the northern Valley, is taking an increasing lead. Rural economists are concerned about this area and even more about the southwestern triangle because of the growing division of land among heirs: natality is high, and out-migration does not prevent a rapid increase in the pressure of population in rural areas.

, The Valley of Virginia is no longer, however, an essentially agricultural region. It has developed large industries and many small urban centers with the manifold functions of serving as trading centers for active rural districts, as manufacturing centers, and as relays on a great artery of travel trade. Apparently the Valley was in the seventeenth century the great Indian highroad between Canada and the far southern territories east of the Mississippi; it is today a central section of the route from Texas and Louisiana to Washington and New York via U. S. Route 11. Whoever drives from the Gulf Coast to the Atlantic *Megalopolis* usually follows this route the full length of the Valley of Virginia. And the highway is equipped for the entertainment of tourists, with all the hotels, motels, souvenir shops, snake farms, and other such attractions that one

Aerial view of a farmed clearing amidst woods in Rockbridge County
U. S. Department of Agriculture

could wish for. The automobile-servicing trades are quite important in all the small towns the highway passes through. The remarkable number of mink and chinchilla farms along this section of U. S. 11 may well have something to do with the frequent passage of travellers from or to Texas. In the 1920's, the traffic along U. S. 11 was more important than that along any other highway in Virginia; it is only recently that U. S. 1 surpassed it and established its primacy.

Railroads, coming before the motor car, had a very great influence in the Valley, especially in developing it as an industrial area. The Baltimore and Ohio first provided a good channel for shipping local products from the northern part of the Shenandoah to the northeast. Today, the Norfolk and Western Railroad is by far the most important in the Valley, as it is the only one that follows the whole length of the Valley across Virginia. Besides this longitudinal line, the N. & W. has three others branching out of Roanoke and linking this central city of the Valley with Richmond and Norfolk on the one hand, with Martinsville and the Old Belt in North Carolina on the other, and finally with West Virginia through the New River Valley. The Virginian Railroad comes across the Valley, too, which it follows from the vicinity of Radford to Roanoke on

Farm and woodlot south of Harrisonburg along U. S. Route 11, George Washington National Forest
U. S. Forest Service

its way from the West Virginia coal fields to Norfolk. North of Roanoke, the Chesapeake and Ohio drains a great deal of traffic along two itineraries across the Valley: one from Lynchburg to Clifton Forge along the James water gaps, the other from Charlottesville to Clifton Forge via Waynesboro and Staunton. The C. & O. also has branches radiating in different directions. The Southern Railway, more important in the Piedmont, also has tracks coming from Alexandria to Front Royal and Harrisonburg, and another line makes inroads in the southwestern extremity of the Valley at Bristol. Thus five major railway systems serve the Valley in its various parts. The network is on the whole quite adequate even for such an active region.

The city of Roanoke, largest urban and industrial center in the Valley and, in fact, a regional capital for western Virginia, is a railroad town. It was a creation of the Norfolk and Western at the end of the nineteenth century. The busy downtown section of Roanoke grew around the N. & W. station on one side of the track, while on the other side the vast office buildings housing the railroad's headquarters and the hotel built by the company towered proudly on a hillock. The N. & W. attracted vari-

Rolling farmland near Marion, with shocked corn, haystacks, and several types of fences
Library of Congress Photo by Marion Post Wolcott

ous industries by the great activity of its yard and because it offered transportation in all directions. The freight station of the Virginian Railroad added to the role of Roanoke as a rail hub. At present Roanoke stands in the middle of a metropolitan area the population of which reached 133,000 in 1950, having increased by 19 per cent since 1940. More industries were coming to it, adding to the variety of the manufacturing already concentrated there.

Roanoke is the only city of such importance in the Valley and in western Virginia as a whole. Given its age, not yet 70 years, it is a very young and rapidly developing city. It is more important as an industrial center than its population figure would indicate. The plants in and around the city employ a number of workers commuting from outside Roanoke County. The same is true to an even greater extent for the smaller towns that lie in a string in the Valley, most of them on U. S. 11 but some of them away from the major thoroughfare and closer to the hills at the edge of the Valley floor. From north to south these towns are Winchester, Front Royal, Strasburg, Harrisonburg, Staunton, Waynesboro, Lexington, Buena Vista, Blacksburg, Christiansburg, Radford, Pulaski, Marion, and Bristol. Other industries are situated in very small towns and draw their manpower from a vast radius around them: thus Chilhowie, Glasgow, Buchanan, Mount Jackson, and others. A few towns on U. S. 11 look like important agglomerations, but have little industry and serve mainly as central market places for rural areas: Wytheville and Dublin, for example. Lexington owes most of its activity to academic institutions. Both the Virginia Military Institute and Washington and Lee University are located there.

A great variety of industries is found in the Valley, since the good transportation network, an abundant labor supply and an easy power supply have attracted manufacturing. Food industries and plants working lumber and wood are scattered through the whole area, as its agriculture produces goods that need some processing and as the forested heights all around call for lumbering. Larger industries here are associated with the manufacture or the weaving of artificial fibers: the Valley is a great producer of rayon yarn, with two huge plants belonging to the American Viscose Corporation in Roanoke and Front Royal and one belonging to the Du Pont de Nemours Company in Waynesboro; then Burlington Mills, specializing in textiles made of artificial fibers, has plants in the southwestern part of the Valley in Dublin, Roanoke, Salem, Radford, Marion, and Chilhowie; and the Celanese Corporation of America has a plant at Staunton. There are also many other textile plants in the Valley at Waynesboro, Roanoke, Pulaski, and other places. Machinery and metal work are not absent; Roanoke has the largest of these plants, but Pulaski, Bristol, and Waynesboro work metals, too. Some mining of ores has been going on in the Valley since the eighteenth century. Iron furnaces are still scattered through the area, although they now have a purely historical function, since iron-ore extraction has practically ceased since 1940. But manganese is mined in several places, chiefly at a large mine north of Waynesboro. Small deposits of good quality coal were producing, until recently, in the southwestern section of the Valley (Montgomery, Pulaski, and Wythe Counties). All this could not be the main foundation for an important industrial activity. Construction and building are the most important industries based on local raw materials, as a variety of stones and woods can be found in the area.

Recently a new specialization appeared in the Valley as a result of the coming of electronics industries. A few small plants in this category are already working, as is one at Blacksburg, but much larger plants are being built by leading concerns like Westinghouse and General Electric at Waynesboro, Staunton, and Roanoke. To add to the variety, the Koppers Company has announced its intention to build a plant making railroad ties at Roanoke and the Hercules Powder Company has a large plant near Radford. Obviously the southern part of the Valley is the more industrialized, while the northern half is agriculturally richer and better developed.

The Valley of Virginia has not lost, with the recent industrialization, its reputation for gracious living. Although its style is different from that of the northern Piedmont or the Tidewater of the plantations, a section famous for lordly estates, it still has a tradition, more generally Virginian, of paying great attention to the material framework of life. In contrast to the mountaineers, the Valley people like good housing and well-equipped homes. There are many residential farms in this area, and sites providing beautiful vistas toward the mountains are frequent. As a major thoroughfare, the Valley has developed its attractions for tourists, and the limestone strata have supplied these attractions abundantly, owing to the special underground erosion of streams with curious natural beds. Thus the Natural Bridge has become a nationally known and advertised feature that travellers come to view from afar. The Valley is dotted with vast caverns which have been adequately fitted to interest and impress the visitor. Every group of dolomitic rocks that rises in ruiniform shape, as dolomite almost always does, has been elevated to the rank of a natural wonder of the world. The traveller has little opportunity to rest among the marvels offered to his curiosity. The landscape, nevertheless, is often worth attention and admiration, and many historical sites remind one of the part this great thoroughfare played in the building up of the country.

The Allegheny: valleys and ridges

West of the Great Valley rise the ridges that continue in parallel alignment as far as the valley of the Ohio. The commonwealth includes only the façade, often very shallow, of this vast mountain world. The West Virginia line usually follows the crest of a ridge, to cross suddenly over a valley and jump a few crests; then it again follows other ridges towards the southwest. In the very northeast, the design of the boundary of West Virginia left the Old Dominion barely one ridge, with a few wooded foothills; further south, in Shenandoah County, a few low ridges, the Little North Mountains, precede the Great North Mountains, which serve as the boundary; in Rockingham County the boundary shifts further westward to the higher and more impressive ridge called the Shenandoah Mountains, which extend eastward irregularly with deeply dissected foothills, giving some depth to the Allegheny region in this area. However, it

This former resident of Corbin Hollow, in the Shenandoah National Park area, now resettled, is the mother of twenty-two children.
Library of Congress Photo by Arthur Rothstein

is only further southwest that this region ceases to be just a narrow ribbon of hills and expands far enough westward to include entire counties and up to seven parallel ridges with the narrow valleys between them.

All of the following counties are included in this mountainous region: Highland, Bath, Allegheny, Craig, Giles, and Bland, as well as parts of Augusta, Botetourt, and Rockbridge. At times this region achieves considerable complexity; at other times it is reduced to essentially one valley with the ridges enclosing it. The complexity is emphasized in the Bath-Highland area, where the mountains achieve greater width; their parallelism, however, is a simplifying factor, and it does not prevent the valleys from communicating with each other by gaps, passes of different shapes and altitudes, and at times some slight inner depressions of basinlike shape, as for example near Clifton Forge and around McClung and Green Valley in Bath County. Most of the crests atop the ridges are around 3,000 feet in elevation, but some of them reach 4,000 and above. The heights are almost all forested, the valleys devoted to pastureland for cattle.

On the whole this region has little agricultural importance. The ridges are of massive sandstone, and their steep slopes have very shallow and stony soils; lower areas are made of shale and limestone, deeply eroded and dissected by many small streams. The area looks more mountainous than the southern Blue Ridge, for example, in Carroll and Floyd Counties. Except on a few well-drained terrace soils in which corn can be grown without hazard of erosion, hay and pasture are the best use to which the agriculturally useful soils can be put here. In the three mountain counties of Highland, Bath, and Allegheny, 77 per cent of the open farmland is in pasture, chiefly bluegrass, and 16 per cent in perennial hay. Forest covers about 80 per cent of this section: it is largely hardwood, with hemlock and white pine occurring not too frequently.

These mountains have been savagely deforested by several generations. They were long used as summer pastures for the livestock crowded in the Great Valley. As one follows the road from Staunton to Monterey in Highland County, one crosses three parallel valleys, each with a fast-running stony stream; the names of these streams are Calf Pasture River, Cow Pasture River, and Bull Pasture River. Then a meandering and picturesque gap through Jack Mountain leads to Monterey, in the wider valley of the Potomac's South Branch. Cattle in great numbers helped ruin the soils of these vales and crests. Then as settlers came to parts of the valleys, they put to the plow such steep and stony slopes that erosion seriously damaged many of them. With the destructive forces of nature thus unleashed, the mountain people had little chance of making a decent living in these hollows. Today one can still find in some of the valleys near Harrisonburg, in the midst of the national forest, small plots of land devoted to God-forsaken farms that represent some of the worst housing and living standards in the country. Other such farmsteads of "hollow folk" can be seen in Allegheny County to the southwest of Covington and within a short distance of this thriving town.

Where the valley farmers, on steep and stony slopes, continue to cut down trees and till according to primitive methods instead of restricting the damage of erosion with careful contour plowing, where flocks of sheep graze on the slopes or herds of lean cows pasture, the soil gets thinner every year, and stones and pebbles roll down into the beds of the rapid, singing streams. When a period of heavy rainfall comes and increases the usual strength of the flowing water, the mass of stone and gravel is pushed downstream with unexpected force and pours across roads and fields like flowing lava, causing even greater havoc as it enters wider and flatter sections of the valley. Such avalanches of stones suddenly brought down by the streams could be observed in 1952–1953 in southwest Rockingham County along such small rivers as Hone

Quarry Run and Briery Branch. Deforestation and too many pastures caused such destruction, and more of it is in the making. As one travels through the vast areas of national forest where vegetation is beginning safely to reconquer the ground and rebuild a secure cover for the steep slopes, one wonders whether resettling the few valley folk who continue to prepare local ruin would not be the best possible thing for the land as well as for the people. Precedents have shown that, once brought to civilization and given education, these people become useful citizens willing to alter a wretched way of living which constitutes a potential menace to those around them. But, failing resettlement, these families of hillbillies remain attached to their mode of life, as were those in the Blue Ridge. Enlightenment comes slowly in the hollows of the Appalachian inner ridges.

This same section of the Alleghenies offers many contrasts to this way of life. In Craig County the valley is wider and richer, the farms are customarily situated at half-slope, and they produce some food and feed. But the county remains one of the poorest in the commonwealth, and the people have what might be termed a "semi-hollow" psychology. Most of them farm with old implements and use horse-driven carriages and instruments. On the outside the houses look dilapidated and antiquated. They have been well maintained, however, and many fine specimens of nineteenth-century farm architecture can be found here. Though little gasoline is used in Craig County, the people are beginning to use increasing quantities of oil, especially for heating their homes. Of the dwelling units, 60 per cent are equipped with mechanical refrigerators, and 64 per cent of the farms have telephones. Thus the county is being slowly modernized, beginning inside the homes. The town of Newcastle, where the county courthouse is located, looks quaint and sleepy, though it is in the center of an important lumbering area and a C. & O. branch serves it. A sawmill adjoins the railroad station. At the other end of town a new low building houses a pajama factory owned by a New York firm and employing about a hundred workers. Thus the local people are no longer justified in pretending that the town has not changed much since the early 1900's. They would prefer, however, that such be the case. One feels the resistance to change, the desire to conserve things and people as they were. The only eating place in town—and practically the only one in the whole county—still exhibits on its walls and shelves calendars, photographs, and advertisements dating back to the years 1925 to 1932. The people are friendly, hospitable, and a little suspicious of and very curious about any newcomer: there is very little through-traffic here, and almost all the inhabitants of the valley are related to one another or at least

A resident of Corbin Hollow before resettlement to establish the Shenandoah National Park
Library of Congress Photo by Arthur Rothstein

believe they are. Craig County provides a good transitional example of the mountaineer's characteristic attitudes somewhat moderated.

Conditions are much better in neighboring Giles County. Here the valleys are wider, the limestone soils somewhat better, the people much more influenced by the active traffic of the railroads and highway along the New River Valley, in which a dam and a powerhouse have been built at the Narrows, near the West Virginia border. A few miles back in Virginia the vast rayon plant of the Celanese Corporation of America towers over the stream. This factory employs up to 4,000 workers at times of peak production and has awakened the whole area around it. Only about 53 per cent of Giles County is under forest.

Other industries have been established in larger towns. Covington and Clifton Forge are not so much mill towns as regional trade centers and important freight stations on the Chesapeake and Ohio Railroad. The yards of the C. & O. are largely responsible for the rise of Clifton Forge, where services and transportation made up the major source of income in 1951. It was the only independent city in Virginia to lose population in 1940–1950. Covington, in the midst of such heavily forested counties, has a large pulp and paper mill belonging to the West Virginia Pulp and

Paper Company; this mill specializes in sanitary wrapping paper, including a great deal of the paper in which cigarette packages are wrapped, a significant product in this tobacco producing country. Covington also has a small "silk mill" which produces rayon and is owned by the Industrial Rayon Corporation.

A wide, rich, limestone valley stretches to the north-northwest of Covington and crosses Bath and Highland Counties; it is drained by the Jackson River, a tributary of the James, almost as far as Monterey, beyond which it is part of the basin of the Potomac and thereafter West Virginia territory. But in its middle part, in Bath County, this valley becomes the main artery of a sophisticated resort area apparently organized around the main hotel which stands in Hot Springs. Besides being a spa with mineral springs, the Homestead at Hot Springs is a well-known mountain resort which owns tens of thousands of acres around its site and offers its customers a vast domain to roam and enjoy. Golf courses, carefully improved grassy pastures, and wild areas give the landscape in this valley of Hot Springs a superb but artificially manicured appearance. Bath is the only county in Virginia where services provided the main source of income in 1951. Several smaller hotels thrive at Warm Springs and other points nearby in the same picturesque, well-organized valley. Bath is the only county in the mountain area where the percentage of Negroes in the population rises slightly above 10 per cent, a result of the employment offered by the hotel business. In comparison, Craig County has almost no Negro population (0.5 per cent in 1950).

As one follows the same valley northwards to Monterey (another summer residential resort), the landscape takes on a more truly rural appearance, with relatively large farms standing amidst endless pastures dotted with multicolored cattle: the black are Angus beef cattle, herds of which alternate with the black and white Holstein and the brown and white Herefords. In the midst of the pastures, conical heaps of green or yellow hay are carefully protected from the cows by circular enclosures of chestnut splinters. As winter goes on, more and more of the hay heaps disappear, and the circular barriers, ready to enclose the next harvest, stand empty in the middle of the meadow.

Such is the variety of the Allegheny ridges-and-valleys country. At many points superb panoramas or charming valley corners delight the traveller. With the exception of the Hot Springs valley, this area has done little to attract tourism, although it is one of the better endowed by nature. To the beauty of nature it adds a wide gamut of modes of life, from the luxury of Hot Springs to the picturesque misery of the hollow folk.

The southwestern triangle

The southwestern tip of the commonwealth extends as far west as the Cumberland Gap and there encloses a triangle of great originality. Its topography is complicated, as some ridges of the Allegheny system mix here with offshoots of the Great Valley and with a system of confused hills and vales called the Cumberland Plateau. In fact, the "triangle" as it appears on the map consists of two regions: the coal-mining Cumberland Plateau to the north, and the valleys of the Clinch Basin and of Cumberland to the south. There are few towns, and only small ones, in this section. Mining is the main activity in the north of the triangle; it was, in 1951, the major source of income in five counties: Tazewell, Buchanan, Dickinson, Wise, and Lee; agriculture was the leading source of income in the southern counties of the triangle: Russell, Scott, and Washington.

In recent years practically all the coal production of Virginia (17,667,-000 tons in 1950) has come from the southwestern triangle. Coal fields lie in northern Tazewell County, all of Buchanan and Dickenson Counties, most of Wise, and parts of Russell, Scott, and Lee Counties. The coal-bearing strip extends some 110 miles from east to west and some 30 miles from north to south; it tapers down to less than one mile in width at its narrowest point in Lee County. The rocks bearing these medium and high-volatile bituminous coals are classified by geologists as belonging to the Pennsylvanian series of the Carboniferous age. Alternating layers of sandstone, shale, coal, and a few conglomeratic and calcareous strata originally formed a level plateau in the Cumberland region of the Appalachian system. Then the plateau, when uplifted, was dissected deeply by streams and wide gullies into a maze of high, narrow ridges of irregular shapes, the crests rising to altitudes around 3,000 feet. The term *plateau* usually applies to a relatively level area as differentiated from mountain ranges proper; one would look a long while for actual level ground in this part of the southwest. From the top of the crests it is apparent that most of these crests reach about the same altitude and testify to the existence, long ago, of a planed level out of which the present topography was carved. But according to an apt description, the Cumberland Plateau is all in slopes between the narrow floors of the innumerable valleys and the narrow crests of the hilltops.

The sharp-crested knobs often reveal, by the presence of mine entrances and tipples jutting out at mid-slope, a complicated underground life. Coal layers are carefully mapped by specialized geologists, and mining engineers then develop a way to extract the black gold and take it out

Curing barn for burley tobacco in southwestern Virginia
Virginia Chamber of Commerce Photo by Flournoy

to the market. A very special mode of life has thus evolved, mainly since 1904, when the development of the Virginia coal fields began on a large scale. The miners live in small communities, each usually entirely made up of the families of people working in the same mine or for the same company. A few small company-built and company-run villages have been created, such as the picturesque town of Jewell Ridge, occupying the top of a crest, like an eagle's nest, and barely visible from below. Such towns have their own schools and general stores and dense rows of neat little houses. But much more often the miners' homes are scattered about. In the Cumberland Plateau, almost nobody lives at mid-slope: the habitat is either the top of the crest or the narrow valley floor. The slopes of the hills are forested, and lumbering is carried on in order to supply the mines with the pitprops and other pieces of timber necessary to their operation.

The mining country is notorious for grim-looking housing and the small proportion of dwellings equipped with modern sanitary facilities. Nevertheless, the roads and driveways are crowded with large, expensive cars; almost every home has a television set, and over 55 per cent of them have mechanical refrigerators. It is densely populated country, and the small communities in the valleys look rather crowded, with a great number of children and young girls in the streets and on the porches. More than any other area of Virginia, the coal-mining district appears to suffer from population pressure. It is not, however, a low-wage area. The miners are largely unionized and are rather well paid, but, when estimated on a per capita basis, the income of these large families turns out to be rather low (see maps, pages 146, 150, 152). Many miners also have small farms that occupy their spare time and on which the women and old men of the family work; but the soils are poor, on sandstone and shale, and the slopes are very steep.

Even when the coal mines were working full blast, as has not been the case since the end of 1953, this area did not appear as prosperous as the many advantages won by the labor union for the miners might suggest. Housing looks terrible in most cases, though in part it is so largely by the will of the inhabitants, who share the characteristics of the larger family of mountaineers. Average income is rather low, too, as the birth rate is high and the density of population heavy. Moreover, the whole section offers little opportunity for gainful employment besides the extraction and transportation of coal and the servicing of the relatively limited needs of the local market. No large-scale trading center could develop here, since, with good highways and powerful cars, the miners' families can readily get out of the hills into the larger towns in the valleys—the Bluefields on the West Virginia line for some regions, and Bristol for others. But what is needed is additional industry which, using the cheap local supply of coal, could employ those elements of the population not working in the mines, particularly the women. This area would seem better endowed geologically than any other in the commonwealth, but even so it is decidedly a problem area.

Some small towns have grown up as local crossroads and administrative centers around a few railroad stations. The N. & W. is the main railroad through the area and drains the coal towards Roanoke and Norfolk. A town like Norton is largely a railroad town and is, in fact, a new one. Some others have small factories, as have Appalachia, Tazewell, and Richlands.

To the south and west, the "triangle" takes on a more rural character and the customary appearance of a valleys-and-ridges section, with many limestone valleys that usually provide soils rich in lime and more fertile than the average soils of Virginia. The large valleys around Big Stone Gap and towards the Cumberland Gap could maintain a prosperous agriculture if managed by large farms with modern means. This should be good cattle country. But the fact is that the land is split into too many

Road and farm near Big Stone Gap, March, 1911
Bureau of Public Roads, U. S. Department of Commerce

units, and the farmers still employ tilling methods and implements that were common in the Valley of Virginia at the time when Mr. Jefferson was modernizing Monticello. This is "back country" where sickles, scythes, and hayforks are used as in the eighteenth century. In the fields of the main valleys one still sees today farmers bending over horse-drawn plows as their ancestors did two centuries ago; and men on horseback are often met on the highways that remind one of the modern "cowboys" now so seldom found in the real West.

Appalachian lands such as Lee and Scott Counties, as well as Craig County further to the northeast, seem to have been left behind by the transcontinental march of the American people from Virginia westward, to have been by-passed by progress. Throughout the "triangle" population pressure is great and income is low, often in the same category on the maps of the commonwealth as the tobacco belt in the Piedmont or the southside Tidewater. But lower averages in the latter sections reflect the lower standard of living of the Negroes. The southwestern triangle is essentially White, some counties having practically no Negro population, Buchanan particularly. The mass of the White people live here in material conditions differing little from those of the Negroes in the tobacco and peanut country. Such a situation necessarily causes concern.

As more opportunities develop in other parts of the United States, many of the triangle's inhabitants move out and look for jobs in industrial centers. This out-migration supplied a number of the temporary workers in the Hampton Roads area and in Baltimore when the shipyards expanded to meet wartime needs. Large numbers went also to Detroit to the motorcar building industry. When employment in these industries shrinks, some of the migrants from southwest Virginia drift back to their home country. Indeed, it is beautiful country in some parts, and the mountaineers love their mountains; they feel like exiles in the low, flat Tidewater or the Middle West. But these traits, though most interesting psychologically and sociologically, do not help solve the problems of this curious area.

As industries develop in the south of the Great Valley, they may tap this source of manpower. Many people from rural areas in the south of the triangle commute to Bristol or Kingsport, Tennessee, to work in the large factories of these cities. However, this tendency has as yet developed on too small a scale to build up actual prosperity in the area. Since the market for coal seems to be dwindling and the mechanical industries in Detroit and Newport News are reducing their personnel, there is even greater cause for concern about the southwestern triangle.

THE UNITY AND DUALITY
OF VIRGINIA

The diversity of Virginia is great; the commonwealth is a world in itself. Perhaps now it is possible to better understand the variety of its problems and resources, having seen the state at closer range, reviewed its sectional aspects, and classified them in broad divisions. No classification of the regions within a country can possibly be all-embracing or satisfy all people and purposes. Our purpose has been to become better acquainted with the actual patterns of life and with the economic and social structure as it emerges from the study of many facts and many maps.

The puzzle which we have described has, nevertheless, a distinct unity. It does not stem from any physical feature imprinted on the earth's crust, but rather from the past and from a number of ancient connections and links established with some regard at first for the natural endowment and layout of the land. The main binding force of the whole comes from the fact that all these people are Virginians, that most of them have been so for several generations, and that all are proud of it. They have acquired as a result of this appurtenance many features which, put together, would probably represent as well as anything could the tradition of Virginia. It is an individualistic tradition, a proud one, and an aristocratic one, too—probably more so than that of any other part of the United States. With these attitudes goes a conservatism which is as clear among the hollow folk as among the Tidewater gentleman farmers.

This tradition, however, is not and could not possibly be quite the same in the east, with its Tidewater plantations, cotton, peanuts, tobacco, and large-scale truck or cattle farms, as it is in the west, with its valleys and ridges, forests and meadows, small farms and scattered industries, poor Whites and population pressure on the better lands. The two main parts of Virginia are different, although the differences are not easy to phrase in a few paragraphs. The differences stem largely, here again, from the historical background, from the fact that western Virginia has long felt technically more advanced and more enterprising, but deprived of the means of action that belonged to the large estates and leading families of the east. Devoted as they are to the Virginia system and ideal, the people in the western valleys are always ready to rally for a protest against what is being done or decided in Richmond. They feel that since the time they were refused proper representation in the General Assembly, around 1800, they have not played the part they were entitled to play in the conduct of the commonwealth's affairs. Western Virginia has a tendency to offer opposition; many of its counties have frequently voted Republican.

The duality of Virginia, like her unity, results from her variety of modes of life, of beliefs and traditions that have taken their present shape little by little in the course of three and a half centuries of evolution through the interplay of many physical and economic factors. While certain broad divisions persist on the map generation after generation, constant change is going on. Now, in the twentieth century, a brand new set of resources is being developed for Virginia which will necessarily make her different from what she was.

PART TWO

The Use of Resources

In an area the size of Virginia, there are always many resources; traditionally, they are analyzed one by one according to a long-established classification system. In actuality, all these resources are intricately interwoven in a pattern which constitutes the regional economy and which determines a great deal of the region's internal character as well as its relations with the outside.

The integration of resources into a regional unit is a natural phenomenon only to a very small extent. It is basically the work of the people. Every area is endowed by nature with a certain order—with certain materials in the vegetation, soil, bedrock, and underground; with a certain amount and a certain periodicity of rainfall and sunshine; and with certain cycles in the mineral and biological evolution. Man's activities have the primary effect of disrupting the existing order; even hunting and fishing on a large scale can disturb to some extent the "natural order" of the environment. Cutting down the existing vegetation, whether trees or grass, also interferes with an established rhythm; vegetation comes back, but almost never in a form identical to the earlier one. Cultivation exhausts the soil rapidly unless accompanied by the application of techniques that modify considerably the content and structure of the soil while aiming at maintaining its capacity to produce certain crops. Mining is even more destructive. In fact, nature does not produce for men. Men have assigned to certain natural phenomena the task of supplying them with certain materials they know how to use. As man's know-how expands, the quantity and variety of his demands upon the natural endowment of his habitat increase; and the order that existed originally is more and more interfered with, to the point that the environment is no longer "natural," properly speaking, anywhere on the earth, unless it be in the abysmal depths of the oceans and perhaps over parts of the Antarctic icecap. Even these exceptions could be disputed nowadays.

Virginia is no exception to the axiom that humans everywhere constantly endeavor to mold the natural endowment of their habitats to uses yielding resources. In the foregoing chapters we saw how often the aims of economic activities have changed within the last 350 years. We saw them changing somewhat because of local factors (such as soil exhaustion or railroad building), but much more because of factors developing outside the area proper and beyond the control of the Virginians (thus the fluctuations of tobacco prices on foreign markets, the legislation against the slave trade and the prohibition of slavery, the growth of federal activities, both civil and military, in Washington and on the high seas, etc.). Virginia's resources are not only the product of the local population's exploitation of the natural endowment; they are much more the product of the Virginians' decisions as to their role in national and international systems, as to their relations with the outside world.

The people of a given area always have choices among different possible ways to utilize the resources enshrined in the land, climate, and position, just as they have a choice among the resources offered by the markets open to their products. Our description of the variety of the economic regions and the modes of life within Virginia has shown the diversity of the choices made at different times by the people of the various regions. Rockingham County made choices different from those of Botetourt County; Roanoke made choices different from those of Lynchburg; and the physical conditions of their locations and endowment did not necessarily impose these differences. Within the same area and the same industry people make different decisions regarding their choice of attitudes and activities: thus the "plungers" and the "stayers" in truck farming on the Eastern Shore.

People must constantly make such choices in any area where the economy is not stagnant and, therefore, backward. True, backwardness itself involves the choice, stubbornly clung to, to preserve an existing system and resist any change. The attitude of the mountaineers in the hollows testifies to the desire to preserve their traditional way of life. Their forebears in the last century preferred "burying themselves," economically speaking, in the hollows of the Blue Ridge and the Allegheny Mountains, to undertaking the adventure of going west or accepting the opportunity of going to town. Resisting progress, refusing opportunities, defending a *status quo,* are attitudes expressing a choice: they are not the inescapable results of local conditions. Man is endowed with mobility to escape localization against his will and with intelligence to reform and improve conditions if and when he chooses to do so.

All these considerations have to be kept in mind in any examination of the resources and the use thereof in Virginia. Our target is the present situation, but since a great deal in the present is inherited from an active past, the historical approach will often have to be used. We shall not forget that Virginia is, in fact, a unit; thus we shall proceed by categories of resources, avoiding excessive subdivision. The forest is the first category to consider, because Virginia was mainly a vast forested area when the first Palefaces came to the Tidewater, and because its study is the one that can bring us greatest knowledge of the "natural environment." Then the tilled land is the basic resource of agricultural activities. The underground mineral resources should come next, followed by industrial development. Finally, the factor of location with its present assets and liabilities should be examined.

4. *The Forests: Use and Misuse*

LL THE EARLY WITNESSES are unanimous about it: Virginia was in the seventeenth century a land of woods. Along the Tidewater the forest reigned everywhere except in a few clearings maintained by the Indians for the purpose of growing food and attracting game. In the valleys on both sides of the Blue Ridge, wide areas had thus been cleared of trees by the Indians, probably by repeated burnings. These open lands provided good pasturage; buffalo came here across the Appalachian ridges from the western grasslands; and White settlers in the eighteenth century found it much easier to settle in the open lands of the Great Valley, opened up long before their arrival by the Indians, than to clear land east of the Blue Ridge. Small holdings could multiply rapidly in the Valley, without the original investment in slave or indentured labor necessary to open wooded land in the Tidewater and Piedmont to cultivation.[1] Early White settlers did not like the forest.

It was, however, in part because of the rich timber resources of the Atlantic coast of North America that England started to colonize this area. In the seventeenth century, Great Britain herself had been seriously deforested. The island's economic trends made necessary more open land, more pastures, and more timber for building purposes, particularly for shipbuilding, as English maritime expansion was underway. Big ships called for large-sized tree trunks; and the chemical industries of the time were largely based on wood products known as "naval stores." It was in search of these materials that the English came to Virginia, the Carolinas, and Massachusetts. In Virginia timber was abundant, but it was considered a second-rate resource, as the emphasis was early put on tobacco and

[1] See on pages 206–207 the passage quoted from Kercheval, *op. cit.*

View in George Washington National Forest, Pedlar District, with Garnet Peak on the left, Silver Peak on the right, and Route 60 in the middle distance
U. S. Forest Service

subsequently on grains and other crops. Today the great majority of Virginians would be surprised at an enumeration of the resources of their state that start with the forest, since woods are to most of them the unavoidable use for the worst kind of soil and for abandoned land. Tree growth seems so natural to them that it almost appears as a renunciation by the landowner of the chance to do something better with his ground. Few people in the area realize that of all nature's gifts to Virginia, the forest is the greatest, the best, and the most lasting as a resource.

A survey conducted in 1946 showed that woods covered 58 per cent of the total land area of the commonwealth. It is safe to estimate that this proportion is approximately true today. The forest is, therefore, still the number-one land use, and it corresponds to the normal original aptitude of the land. The advantages derived from the forest are manifold: lumbering is an important industry in Virginia; the census of manufactures for 1947 indicated that the industries using wood as a major raw material, including furniture and paper manufacturing, employed in Virginia about 42,000 persons out of a total of 216,000 for all industries, that is, close to 20 per cent. The woods also supply firewood for various purposes, including hickory for meat smoking and tobacco curing; they are an excellent recreation area; under their cover wildlife prospers and all kinds of game abound. Forest cover is the best protection against erosion on steep slopes; it regulates the run-off of water and helps rebuild a top-soil with a higher organic content. There are thus many reasons for keeping under forest cover ground that is not fitted to produce a richer crop, whether because of its chemical quality, because of its steepness, or because of the effects of erosion and depletion.

It may be said that a forest, when adequately managed, produces three crops: timber, wildlife, and a safe flow of water. However, timber is the primary, the most obvious resource obtainable from the forest; it is the most marketable; it is of direct concern to industry and trade. The other two crops are less direct results of the forest cover; they must be considered as complementary effects. We qualified our statement above with the remark that a forest produces "when adequately managed." The popular belief that all one has to do to obtain a certain kind of forest is to leave the land idle is an oversimplified one. Tree growth is a tricky process, reacting to a variety of factors: it depends on light and warmth, on rainfall and its seasonal distribution, on the length of the period of frost, on the kind of soil, on the kind of seeds, on what preceded it on the same soil. Certain species of trees are known as "pioneer" or "conquering" species: they reclaim abandoned lands that were previously cultivated; pines are an example. This does not mean that, once established on a former field, they will reproduce themselves indefinitely. After one, two, or three generations of pines, depending on the climate and the soil, some other species will come in and either mix with the pines or eliminate them.

The local conditions of land under forest can be disturbed in many ways other than clearing and cultivation. Wildlife has some effects which may contribute to a change in the predominant species in a forest: deer, for instance, graze the undergrowth and pick out the young plants they prefer, leaving the rest to grow into forest. Thus in a forest with a dense population of deer, reproduction of the species that the deer do not eat is favored. When a fire sweeps a forest, it not only kills many trees by burning them or carbonizing their roots, it also modifies the conditions that existed before it occurred: the microclimate, as specialists call it, is changed; since certain species thrive better on burned-over land and others less well, a fire determines an evolution in the previously existing vegetation. Finally, Virginia is sometimes swept by hurricanes powerful enough to uproot the higher trees and work serious havoc among the lower strata of vegetation. The disturbance they cause in the microclimate along their path is occasionally serious enough to cause a change in the composition of the forest cover. Such evolution from one pre-dominant species to another has been observed many times in different parts of the country and has been carefully studied in New England, which is periodically swept by powerful hurricanes. The kind of trees one finds in a forest does not depend only on the stable physical conditions of the area, but also on the disturbances of a long past, some of them caused by man and some caused by other factors.

There is among botanists and foresters a stubborn belief in the notion of *climax,* i.e., that there is a certain kind of growth that is best fitted to given conditions of climate, topography, and soil. Once a forest achieves its climax, it gains in beauty, in stability, and in resistance to disturbance; some believe that it is almost fireproof. But climax can be achieved only by a long period without disturbance, such as seldom occurs where people inhabit the country. It would require several genera-tions of trees reproducing themselves without disturbance to bring about a climactic forest. In fact, climax is mainly a theoretical conception: in-stead of letting forests alone, the more zealous managers, having acquired somewhere an idea of what the climax ought to be, began interfering to help it come sooner. Once something resembling a climax is achieved, its preservation would require a complete lack of disturbance, which is hard to attain, and which has hardly been possible in the recent past in Virginia. To learn what the present use and trends are in Virginia forests, a historical approach is indispensable, at least in the beginning.

The past of Virginia's forest

We do not know much about the "natural environment" of Virginia prior to the settling of Jamestown. In the first period of settlement many descriptions were provided by different observers; which concur to estab-lish the fact that Virginia was a vast forest. There were, however, some cleared areas or *savannahs* resulting from deforestation by the Indians. The first settlers tell about villages surrounded by small cultivated fields ranging in size from 20 to 200 acres. Most of the Virginia Indians were sedentary and depended upon agriculture and hunting; they cultivated their food staples: corn, beans, potatoes. Savannahs extending three to four miles in length and covered with luxurious grasses provided game animals with good feeding grounds. The Indians used fire to clear land as well as to hunt animals. The wider expansion of savannahs, particu-larly in the Shenandoah Valley, where over one thousand square miles were treeless in the beginning of the eighteenth century, probably re-sulted from repeated burning of the land.

It is difficult to tell whether in the old days there were many virgin stands, with decayed logs and windfallen trees rotting on the forest floor. However, the trees were tall and therefore old. Several witnesses stress the fact that the forest was an open one with little or no underbrush. This could have resulted from the widespread use of fire by the Indians when hunting. It is said that it was possible to ride anywhere under the trees on horseback. Such a lack of undergrowth should testify to a strong human influence on the forest before the White settlers came.[2]

What kinds of trees were then found? This was no longer virgin forest, but it could probably be described in general terms as rather close to the climax vegetation for the region. It would be quite worth while for present policies of forest management to know what species constituted the climax in eastern Virginia. Certainly there were pines along the Tidewater, but they seem to have been scattered among other species. The large and homogeneous stands of pines so favorable to the development of naval stores were found further south in the coastal plain, in the Carolinas and Georgia. Virginia never developed much of a naval-stores production in the colonial period, and this alone should bear witness to the fact that pines did not predominate. Moreover, many sources mention the fact that hogs were brought early from England to the Jamestown peninsula and that the settlers found they thrived when turned loose in the woods to feed on acorns. This means that many oaks were growing in the original forest.

As the settlers proceeded inland they reported more hardwoods than pines on the Piedmont and further west. As the cultivation of tobacco developed, rapidly depleting the soils on which several crops of the Indian weed had been successively produced, abandoned lands were turned back to forest. Land was cheap and plentiful; there was more and more abandoned land as time went on and settlement advanced further. Thus there developed a wasteful cycle of land clearing, cultivation for a few years, abandonment, and reversion to forest, but this time to *pine forest,* since pines, as we have seen, are "pioneers" at reclaiming land that has been tilled. This process created a new forest in which pines predominated in places. As time went on, pines did not regenerate themselves everywhere, and the forest, even on ground cultivated some forty or fifty years earlier, became a mixed one where the proportion of pines among hardwoods varied greatly.

In the mountains of western Virginia, white pine and hemlock must always have been mixed with the hardwoods in some degree. Deforestation of these slopes was often brought about in order to open the land

[2] See Mosby and Handley, *The Wild Turkey in Virginia,* Richmond, 1943.

A typical mountain sawmill, the property of Lonnie Clark, located in Irish Gap just south of the Blue Ridge Parkway and dependent on the George Washington National Forest for its log source. This mill is powered with the engine of a 1929 Buick automobile.
U. S. Forest Service

to the grazing of cattle and sheep rather than for cultivation. When such lands were abandoned, they were not necessarily reclaimed by pines, since they had never been plowed up. The first growth over formerly pastured soils may well have been hardwoods on many slopes.

It is said that the first sawmill in America was operated in Jamestown as early as 1608. But for two hundred years, only small sash-saws worked in Virginia, powered by waterwheels. The Civil War changed the picture greatly. Vast areas of once cultivated lands were abandoned and were reclaimed by pure stands of pines that became, some twenty to thirty years after the war, a great resource for lumber and naval stores. Big lumber operations had depleted, through careless logging, many forests of the northern states during the years 1860–1890. The nation's consumption of timber was expanding, and the lumbermen turned southwards. By the end of the nineteenth century, Virginia was equipped with enough railroads to become good lumbering ground. She was covered with vast forests that had been little disturbed since 1865 and offered stands of rather pure pines, the species that American industry preferred for its versatility and rapid growth. The official *Virginia Handbook,* published in 1893, insists on the predominance of pines in the Tidewater and their abundance on the Piedmont. It reminds us that the 1880 census reported 9,126,600 acres in Virginia under woodland and forest, and adds: "The probability is that it is about the same now as to woodland and forest, although a considerable portion of the 2,000,000 acres of 'old fields' and brush may have been converted into fair, fertile land." [3] Apparently the old fields, grown up with "field pines," were among the first cleared at that time. And the same *Handbook* adds the following note in another chapter:

Formerly the hog was one of the most profitable domestic animals; reared in the forest on chestnuts and acorns, fattened with only corn to harden flesh, this valuable staple food cost but little, and the surplus bacon was a cash product at a good price. A change has come, and while hogs are still profitably reared for home supply, the cost is greater, as well as the care and necessary attention. They are still cheaply raised in Tidewater swamps and the mountains. [4]

It would seem that raising hogs cheaply depended on the abundance of chestnut and oak trees in the forest; and the change may well have resulted from the predominance of the pine trees at that time.

The real industrial harvest of timber in Virginia thus began at the end of the nineteenth century. Never did Virginia produce as much lumber as between 1905 and 1915; and the peak was reached in 1909 with a total reported lumber production of 2,101 million board feet of which 1,315 million were pine. The same trend was true of most of the southeast, but in this particular year the Virginia production almost equalled that of North Carolina, which had not happened since 1885 (see graphs, page 255).

During this period, large logging operations developed. Large sawmills, practicing clear cutting, moved from one area to another. The softwoods were cut first, then the hardwoods. Often cutting was followed by fire; it was a scorched-earth system, resulting in an intensification of erosion. When the United States entered World War I, most of the worth-while forest had been cut on the coastal plain and in the Piedmont, the areas of easiest transportation; the mountains were still well forested. But the demand for timber was increasing. Around 1918, the forests on the ridges began to be cut. There most of the white pine and hemlock had already been cut; the proportion of the hardwoods in the total production of Virginia increased sharply by 1915 and remained impressive, though it declined until the middle 1920's; it shrank rapidly after 1929, as the de-

[3] Thomas Whitehead, *Virginia: A Handbook,* published by direction of the State Board of Agriculture, Richmond, 1893, p. 68.
[4] *Ibid.,* p. 90.

An improperly cut area in Washington County, part of the region which was really "logged out" during World War I. This devastation was caused by over-logging and then burning over the land.
U. S. Forest Service Photo, 1942

mand for timber on the market slumped considerably (see graphs, page 255).

By that time little was left of Virginia's forests. Lumbering on a large scale was no longer possible, except in areas difficult of access, like the Dismal Swamp. The large mills were replaced by the numerous small circular saws, easily movable and gasoline powered, which are still active and scattered through the Old Dominion nowadays. These mills are well adapted to the yield of small-dimension second-growth timber; it has been said, quite rightly, that they live on the scraps of the old industry. The deforestation of other regions in the United States had already worked such havoc in terms of erosion and floods that Congress passed, in 1911, the Weeks Act, empowering the U. S. Forest Service to buy and manage land as national forests where the watersheds had to be protected in an emergency. Purchases of land deforested by the large lumbering operations of the 1905–1925 period in the Blue Ridge and over the Allegheny Mountains led to the formation of the George Washington National Forest and the Jefferson National Forest, separated by the James River. In

Sawmill at Dillwyn, with stored lumber in the foreground. This mill has a
capacity of 15,000 board feet per day.
U. S. Forest Service

the 1920's, some local notables and authorities began to gather the funds
to buy out the lands that have since been consolidated under federal
ownership as the Shenandoah National Park. Thus Virginia saw, as a
result of a period of devastating exploitation of her forest resources, a new
system arising which promised to safeguard the more vulnerable areas
on the western ridges.[5]

According to the survey of 1945–1946, revised in 1950, the total forest
and wooded area of Virginia amounts to 14,832,000 acres, of which 14,-
377,000 are commercial forest, that is, able to produce timber of commercial quality. This commercial forest area is broken up as follows:

1. Saw timber: 7,138,000 acres, entirely second growth.
2. Pole timber: 3,254,000 acres.
3. Seedlings and saplings: 3,208,000 acres.
4. Denuded area: 777,000 acres.

Virginia's forests are less extensive than those of North Carolina (which
cover 18.4 million acres), but larger than those of South Carolina (about
12 million acres). The volume of saw timber standing on commercial

[5] See *Trees. Yearbook of Agriculture*, 1949, especially pp. 299–308 and 586–592.

forest land is, however, estimated at 25,320 million board feet, of which 12 million board feet are softwood and the rest hardwood. This volume is inferior to both South Carolina (29.5 billion board feet) and North Carolina (42.2). If, instead of taking account of saw timber only, which is the more valuable kind of forest product, we turn to the volume in cubic footage of all the timber which stood on Virginia's commercial forest lands in the late 1940's, we find it estimated at 11,551 million cubic feet, of which only 4,321 million cubic feet are softwoods (chiefly yellow pines), and 7,230 million cubic feet are hardwoods (chiefly oaks). Out of this total, the pole timber trees, including those between 5 inches in diameter breast high and minimum saw timber size (which is 9″ D.B.H. for pine and 13″ for hardwoods), represent 5,308 million cubic feet, of which 1,638 are softwoods and 3,670 hardwoods.[6]

These figures testify to a number of important facts to be meditated upon. They show that the forests of Virginia are, on the whole, very young indeed, as a large proportion of the stands are below the minimum saw-timber size as yet. This should not be surprising after what we have seen of the history of their use during the first half of the twentieth century. As a resource, therefore, these forests are a source of potential wealth for tomorrow rather than for the present day. While about half the older trees of saw-timber size are still softwoods, less than a third of the younger growth is softwoods. In other words, hardwoods, generally considered as a less desirable raw material for industry, are gaining against softwoods. Such a trend may be due either to the fact that softwoods are cut down at too quick a pace or to the fact that hardwoods are coming into the forests in increasing density, and perhaps to both trends simultaneously. To obtain a fuller picture of what is happening, let us look at the geographical distribution of the various kinds of trees within the commonwealth.

The distribution of trees within Virginia

Two maps give a static picture of the present distribution of woods in Virginia. The map of the proportion of wooded land in the total land area by counties (see page 240) provides a fair idea of the concentration of the forests in certain areas. County limits do not always correspond with physiographic divisions, and we have already shown in our review of the regions and sections of Virginia (see Chapter 3) how the greater proportion of forested land occurs on poorer soils and steeper slopes.

[6] U. S. Department of Agriculture, *Basic Forest Statistics for the United States*, Washington, September, 1950.

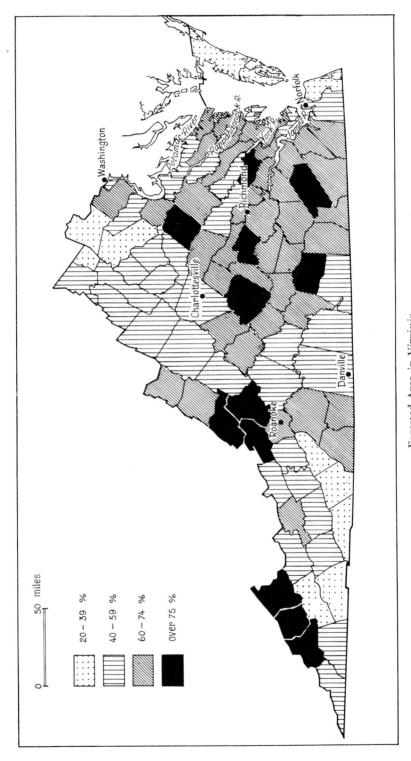

Forested Area in Virginia

(By counties, in per cent of total land area of the county, according to the figures of a 1946 survey)

Rockingham County, for instance, includes the western slopes of the Blue Ridge, the southern crest of the Massanutten Mountain and a section of the Allegheny ridges near the West Virginia line; at the same time it includes vast flatter areas of the Great Valley floor which are intensively developed and give this county the largest income from agriculture of any of Virginia's counties. Thus, though Rockingham County is 52 per cent wooded area, we know this area is concentrated almost entirely along three narrow ribbons of its territory.

In fact, the map of the proportion of wooded land shows on the whole four areas of relatively low forestation: one is in the north and northwest of Virginia, where the northern Piedmont and the Shenandoah Valley are deforested; the second one is in the southwest and includes the southern Blue Ridge (Floyd, Carroll, and Grayson Counties), as well as the Great Valley and adjoining valleys south of Roanoke; the third region is the bright tobacco belt in the southern Piedmont, plus the Lynchburg-Bedford area; the fourth region is the urbanized and agriculturally developed Tidewater area around Hampton Roads, including the whole of the Eastern Shore. All these regions have less than 60 per cent of their area wooded; their degree of afforestation is rather below the Virginia average of 58 per cent. If we remark that practically all of the Blue Ridge north of the Roanoke Gap, which is entirely forested, is included in the first of our four regions, it becomes obvious that the majority of these lands has been even more efficiently deforested than the county figures at first suggest, while the main bulk of their tree-covered space was concentrated in some fractions of territory broken up among many counties. The heaviest afforestation is found in the central section of the Allegheny ridges, in the coal-mining Cumberland Plateau, in the middle Piedmont, and in some parts of the southside Tidewater. Topography and pedology explain a great deal of this general layout; but human factors are important, too: thus the outer suburbia of Washington deforested its outside ring, the region of "station-wagon farming," while it increased the wooded area in Fairfax County (64 per cent in 1946), as much land was then kept idle there in prospect of a rapid increase in price with the expansion of suburban housing projects and shopping centers. Real estate speculation, as well as physiography, has been a factor in shaping the situation described by this map.

The second map (see page 242) shows in a simplified manner, and according to the classification of forest associations adopted by both the federal and the state forestry services, how the main species of trees are distributed in Virginia. It is apparent from consideration of the legend that there are few pure stands of one given species in Virginia. As

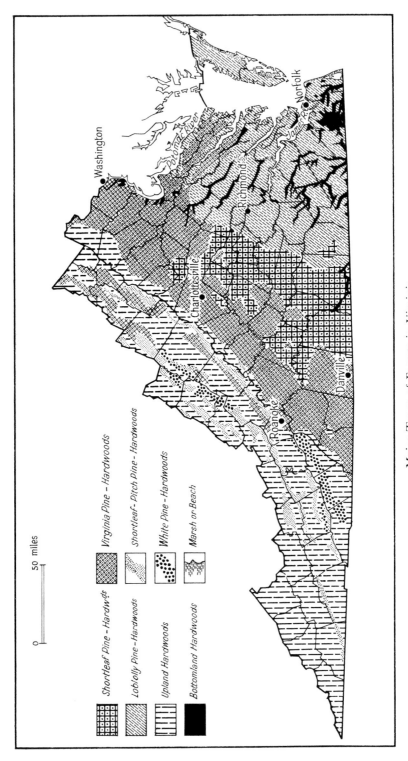

Major Types of Forests in Virginia

Simplified from the map by the Southeastern Forest Experiment Station, U. S. Forest Service, 1946

Shortleaf Pine – Hardwoods

Loblolly Pine – Hardwoods

Upland Hardwoods

Bottomland Hardwoods

Virginia Pine – Hardwoods

Shortleaf - Pitch Pine – Hardwoods

White Pine – Hardwoods

Marsh or Beach

50 miles

0

Washington

Richmond

Charlottesville

Danville

Roanoke

Norfolk

Potomac River

James River

Aerial view of the patchwork of fields and woods in Carroll County
U. S. Department of Agriculture

is the case over most of the eastern United States, Virginia's forests are mixed associations of many species within the same wood within a small area. There are exceptions, of course, and some local uniformity can be found, particularly in planted woods. However, from what we know of the trends of evolution of the stands, according to which new species come to succeed at least in part the predominance of the generation of trees preceding the newly growing one, few stands will preserve their purity unless specially cared for.[7]

The Tidewater, the Piedmont, and the western ridges do not have the same associations. The legend of the map may erroneously suggest that the white pine is as important within its association with hardwoods in the southern Blue Ridge as the loblolly pine in the southside Tidewater, when, in fact, the hardwoods increase their relative importance as one proceeds westward and gains altitude. Moreover, the trends of succession of the species are not the same throughout the whole state. It is necessary now to consider each region with its particular behavior in terms of forestry.

[7] See E. Lucy Braun, *Deciduous Forests of Eastern North America*, Philadelphia, 1950.

Aerial view in Loudoun County
U. S. Department of Agriculture

In the Tidewater, the most important forest type is the so-called pine-type, made of even-aged stands of pine trees. Resulting from the clear-cutting of the forest and from the abandonment of some cultivated fields, these stands contain generally only one species of pine, that best adapted under local conditions to reconquering idle land. The most important species in the Tidewater is the loblolly pine (*Pinus taeda L.*); however, the Virginia or scrub pine (*Pinus virginiana Mill.*) is often encountered in the Northern Necks, and the shortleaf pine (*Pinus echinata Mill.*) occurs in the southwest of the coastal plain. The loblolly-pine type of forest occupies some 14 per cent of the whole state's forested land and is found almost entirely in the coastal plain, where about 17 per cent of the total area under Virginia pine-type has been recorded and 8 per cent of the shortleaf pine-type.[8]

These stands of pine usually show a more or less dense understory of hardwoods, which have been extensively described as constituents of the type. Thus black gum (*Nyssa sylvatica Marsh.*), sweet gum (*Liquidambar styraciflua L.*), yellow poplar (*Liriodendron tulipifera L.*), red oak (*Quer-*

[8] According to Ronald B. Craig, *Virginia Forest Resources and Industries*, U. S. Department of Agriculture, Miscellaneous Publ. No. 681, Washington, April, 1949 (a basic reference work).

Aerial view in Buckingham County
U. S. Department of Agriculture

cus velutina Lam., *Quercus falcata Michx.*) and white oak (*Quercus alba
L.*) are associated with the different pines mentioned. It has recently become more apparent that they are components of a new plant association
which is preparing to take over after the pine stage. A lack of accordance
of canopy and understory is often indicative of the coming of a change
or succession in the forest's predominant association.

The pines reclaimed large areas here after the Civil War and the abolition of slavery. The secondary pine forest thus obtained was cut largely
between 1900 and 1920 and in most places a natural regeneration of the
pines followed. But the litter of pine needles was a good preparation for
a growth of hardwoods, which are now beginning their invasion according
to the laws of plant succession, laws which seem strictly enforced under the
climatic conditions of Virginia. Under the canopy of pure stands of loblolly, the mixture of hardwoods is growing more and more important in
the understory as time goes on. A mixture of loblolly with hardwoods is
becoming characteristic of the coastal plain where woodlots are mingled
with cultivated fields.

To gain a complete understanding of the process one should keep in
mind that forest fires have been very frequent in the 1900's as well as for

Aerial view in Nansemond County
U. S. Department of Agriculture

a long time before that date. The fires were certainly favorable to the
reseeding of the pines. Today, with adequate fire protection, the situation
is different. Man's early activities, such as burning and shifting cultivation, helped to perpetuate the loblolly pine for some three centuries. Organized fire protection enables dense hardwood understories to develop
in the pine stands. The present, more stabilized agriculture allows less
space to be abandoned and to revert to naturally seeded pine forest. The
existing pines are heavily cut, and each cutting opens the way for the
hardwoods to occupy the site. As the loblolly is harvested, areas formerly
devoted to pine production become converted to hardwoods; this threatens the elimination of the pines by overshading their seedlings, which
cannot grow under hardwood canopy, while hardwoods grow well under
a canopy of old pines.

Another type of forest is encountered in the Tidewater: the so-called
bottomland hardwood type. Although loblolly and other pines are sometimes present in this association, they are only a secondary species here.
Due to moist soil conditions, hardwoods predominate: black gum, sweet
gum, red maple, yellow poplar, white ash (*Fraximus americana* L.), red
and white oaks, and tupelo (*Nyssa aquatica* L.). This forest type is char-

acteristic of the floors of flat damp valleys. When cut down, it is regenerated by stump sprouts. Closely related to this type, the forest of the Dismal Swamp is a mixture of hardwoods plus a few softwoods: white cedar (*Chamaecyparis thyoides L.*) and loblolly are present; the most important hardwoods in the Dismal are black gum and tupelo, red maple, water oak (*Quercus nigra L.*), sweet gum, and sweet bay (*Magnolia virginiana L.*). From time to time it has been proposed that the great Swamp be drained completely and its rich, deep soils be turned over to agriculture. It may prove very difficult and expensive to transform the Dismal into *polders*. Virginia is neither overcrowded nor short of lands as Holland has been for a long while; and experiments conducted in the swamps of Florida and Minnesota have not been very encouraging. It may well be that well-managed forest is still the best possible use for the swamp lands. The white cedar, which is abundant there, has always been a desirable kind of timber. It was used for charcoal and gun powder, and also for shingles and saw timber. The Dismal Swamp forest could be a permanent and important resource.[9]

For trees, as for truck crops, the Tidewater has the advantage of a long growing season and, therefore, a higher rate of growth, almost double the rate of tree growth in northern New England. It ought to be an important producer of timber of various kinds. The privately owned, nonfarm, wooded area is estimated there at 950,000 acres, chiefly in large estates, many of them held by pulp or lumber companies. Another part is in the hands of insurance companies, banks, and other estates. Farm woodlots cover altogether a substantial area: over 350,000 acres in the three counties of Southampton, Surry, and Sussex alone.

The vegetation map is somewhat different in the Piedmont. Originally, oaks and hickories were probably the dominant species in the Piedmont forests; but more than three-fifths of this section has been farmed at one time or another. It was, as in the Tidewater, and possibly even more so, an extensive and exhausting kind of cultivation. Erosion developed more easily here. Lands that became submarginal were abandoned and grew pine stands. In 1940, 59 per cent of the Piedmont was wooded. The process of reclamation of old fields by a succession of plant associations is well known on the Piedmont.

Broomsedge (*Andropogon virginicus*) forms first a dense sod; then, after several years, American plum (*Prunus americana Marsh.*), sassafras (*Sassafras albidum Nutt.*), and common persimmon (*Diospyros virginiana L.*) appear. The next stage is that of the pines: loblolly seeds the lower Piedmont, Virginia pine the northern and western, and shortleaf the

[9] See Alfred Akerman, *The White Cedar of the Dismal Swamp*, Charlottesville, 1923.

Chestnut stand on Cold Mountain, George Washington National Forest
U. S. Forest Service

southside; as a general rule, loblolly occurs on a variety of soils and on all kinds of abandoned fields, but Virginia pine pre-empts fallow fields on heavy clay or sandy soils of slopes and flats, and shortleaf is most common on dry upland soils. According to Craig's report, 63 per cent of the Virginia pine stands and 64 per cent of the shortleaf stands are in the Piedmont.[10] Then, as in the loblolly stands of the Tidewater, an invasion of hardwoods develops, encouraged by fire protection and the repeated cutting of the pines. Now the forest appears to be very often a mixture of pines with many hardwoods (white and red oaks, red maple, black gum, sweet gum, yellow poplar, and hickories). Another important element in the landscape is the eastern red cedar (*Juniperus virginiana L.*), characteristic of edges, old cultivated or pastured fields, and denuded lands. Sentinel-like cedars standing in rows serve as windbreaks and partitions between fields, and line the entrance lanes and driveways of old farms in the northern Piedmont. In the bottomlands and along the streams, a typical association includes yellow poplar, red maple, sycamore (*Platanus occidentalis*), river birch (*Betula nigra L.*), willow oak (*Quercus phellos L.*), and water oak (*Quercus nigra L.*). Due to soil and climatic condi-

[10] R. B. Craig, *op. cit.* This report will be referred to subsequently as "Craig's report."

Virginia pine growing on a sand dune near the Chesapeake Bay, Westmoreland County
U. S. Forest Service

tions, the rate of growth of the pines is lower here than in the coastal plain, but the trend towards substitution of hardwoods for softwoods is at least as strong.

In the center of the Piedmont, abandoned lands were bought by the commonwealth in the 1930's and form a substantial expanse of state forests in the counties of Appomattox, Buckingham, and Cumberland. Privately owned forests are largely distributed among many small holdings and farm woodlots. In Pittsylvania County, 4,695 farms reported in 1949 a total of 280,331 acres in woodland; in Louisa County, 1,373 farms totaled 109,521 acres of woodland.[11] The Piedmont landscape seems to have achieved a balance between land clearing for cultivation and natural reforestation of abandoned fields. The proportion of woodland in the total holdings of the farms does not change much, on the whole, from one census of agriculture to another.

In the Blue Ridge, the two regions north and south of the Roanoke Gap are quite different. Both regions are covered with predominantly hardwood vegetation, but the southern section is still largely private

[11] U. S. Bureau of the Census, *U. S. Census of Agriculture*, Vol. I, Part 15, Washington, 1952.

property divided up into many farms, while the northern section is now mainly publicly owned and reverting to forest. In both cases, whatever forest can be observed now is rather young. There is no virgin stand left to speak of in these mountains. On both sides of the Blue Ridge the slopes were settled or otherwise utilized. The passerby may still notice today along the Parkway stone fences built in pre-Civil War days by slaves from large plantations in a patchwork pattern to keep in grazing hogs. Only a small proportion of the mountain acreage seems to have been cleared in early times for tilling; grazing hogs, cattle, and sheep took more space.

Most of the fields and pastures were abandoned after 1860. Heavy cuttings were regularly made to feed charcoal to the iron furnaces scattered at the foot of the hills. From 1910 to 1920 heavy cutting was done by the large lumber industry moving in from the northern and eastern areas, where all the good trees had already been felled. Railroad tracks came into the hollows to take out the timber; sections of these tracks can still be seen in the national forests. Practically all the old growth was cut down, but stumps were not destroyed and they sprouted back. Large-scale fires added, in many parts, to the destruction brought about by men. The hardwood forest showed tremendous recuperative power: it grew back, was in parts cut again or burnt, and it grew back again. Large-scale destruction by fire occurred from time to time until the early 1930's; now the forest is better protected and covers the ridges almost entirely.

Abandoned fields, where the stumpage of hardwoods was destroyed by cultivation, are covered with pure stands of Virginia or shortleaf pines. As urbanization and mechanization make small mountain farms increasingly marginal and unattractive, the process of abandonment of fields still goes on. But on most of the Blue Ridge lands there has been no stage of reclamation by the pines. The old hardwood forest, which was probably one of the finest in the world and one of the richest in number of species and in lushness of vegetation, grew back by seeds or stump sprouts; but the quality of the trees is far inferior to what the old stands must have been.

The composition of the hardwood stands differs according to soil, moisture, and exposure. On poor, dry, shallow soils we find chestnut oak (*Quercus montana L.*), yellow poplar (a pioneer species on exposed mineral soils), black gum, white and scarlet oak. The chestnut tree (*Castanea dentata Borch.*) was once a very important species, but was destroyed by the blight that spread rapidly from New York all over the eastern United States after 1904. The chestnut was a most valuable species for various uses, including the production of a tanning extract; it splits into handy

Hemlock and poplar in the George Washington National Forest. *U. S. Forest Service*

long pieces that used to be the main material for the construction of typical Virginia rail fences along the fields and around the haystacks. The blight also deprived the local population of cherished tasty nuts and the wildlife of a rich food. The harvest of dead chestnut trees still goes on in places, but the species is represented nowadays only by a few sprouting stumps. There are also a number of hickories, the most important being *Carya ovalis Sarg.,* and an understory of Rhododendrons, Kalmia, and Vaccinium.

On deeper soils or in moister locations, we find the northern red oak (*Quercus borealis Ashe.*), the river birch, the white ash, and some hickories. The most tolerant species, such as chestnut oak, white oak, northern red oak, and red hickory, are the most widespread. Black locust (*Robinia pseudoacacia L.*) grows on the most denuded slopes. Although plagued by the blister rust, the white pine (*Pinus strobus L.*) comes in old coppices and, shade tolerant as it is, is probably a constituent of the climax in many sites. One finds also in this varied forest a few beeches and American linden (*Tilia glabra Vent.* and *Tilia australis Small.*). A few stands of conifers exist at the higher altitudes or on northern exposures: red spruce (*Picea rubens Sarg.*), Canada hemlock (*Tsuga canadensis Carr.*), and balsam fir (*Abies fraseri Poir.*).

Around 1920, most of the Blue Ridge was still in small farms privately

Loblolly pine in King William County
Virginia Forest Service

owned, as it still is south of the Roanoke Gap. Relatively slow growth
and higher cost of logging made the region less attractive to large private
ownership than the Tidewater. At that time, overcutting and overgrazing
of the slopes, followed by erosion, were working great havoc. In the
1920's, the state authorities, with the help of private conservationists,
purchased large tracts in the northern Blue Ridge which were eventually
consolidated into the Shenandoah National Park and deeded to the
federal government for administration in 1935. At present the park extends over some 194,000 acres. Further south on the Blue Ridge the
George Washington National Forest and south of the James River Gap
the Jefferson National Forest have purchased most of the eroded slopes
and turned them back into beautiful forest; at least these areas are in the
reconstruction stage insofar as their timber value is concerned and also
the protection of the slopes against erosion. In its southern part, where
the Ridge widens out to become an "intermountain area," little public
ownership has yet been introduced (about 16,000 acres in Carroll and
Grayson Counties). White pine stands, somewhat more frequent here,
have attracted some lumber companies to buy land in the area; but the

An excellent stand of loblolly pine near Hopewell. *U. S. Forest Service*

larger part of the forested area in the southern section of the Ridge is in small farm woodlots.

There is little forest left on the Great Valley floor and the lower slopes of the knobs rising in the middle of the Valley. Eastern red cedar, Virginia pine and sometimes shortleaf pine are reclaiming a few mediocre or abandoned pastures. On the upper slopes there are some woodlots, rather poorly managed and often overgrazed. Hardwoods predominate there, such as oaks, hickories, black locust, ash, and yellow poplar. The larger ridges, such as the Massanutten, bear a young forest cover of the same kind as the woods on the ridges west of the Valley.

The Allegheny ridges originally supported some of the best timber stands to be found in Virginia, and they were among the last to be cut. In a way similar to what happened in the Blue Ridge, these mountains were heavily cut in the first quarter of the century and the present forests sprouted from stumps around a few old trees that were left. The vegetation here is not very different from that on the Blue Ridge. The mountain type is an association where chestnut oak usually predominates, with a mixture of oaks and black gum; beech is not infrequent, and birches occur, too (*Betula lenta L.* and *Betula nigra L.*). The cove type of forest is characterized by yellow poplar with white oak, black walnut (*Juglans nigra L.*), white ash, cucumber tree (*Magnolia acuminata L.*), and redbud, the pinkish flowers of which are the first to appear in March and April in the forest (*Cercis canadensis*). In old fields Virginia pine is generally aggressive; in some places abandoned lands are reclaimed by shortleaf or by pitch pine (*Pinus rigida Mill.*). The process of hardwood invasion of old pine stands is very rapid; the lands which now support pure stands of Virginia pines were cultivated less than fifty years ago.

In this mountainous area public lands are the most important, being part of the George Washington National Forest in the north and of the Jefferson National Forest in the center and southwest. Many small tracts, privately owned, remain mixed with the public lands; some large private holdings belong to industrial corporations. The small farms scattered through the vast forest areas are a source of grazing and forest fires; they still constitute a big hazard. In the Cumberland Plateau the coal mining companies own large tracts of woods. The forest here is of similar composition as in the Alleghenies, though beech is more abundant. Here the youth of the forest is quite striking; and cuttings go on in order to supply the mines and local populations with the timber necessary to the industrial equipment and some building.

Such is the present detailed picture of the distribution of forests by types and species associations in Virginia. It is much more complicated and more diversified than the map of major forest types could suggest (page 242). On the whole, pines are still predominant in what we called eastern Virginia in our regional breakdown of the state, while hardwoods are predominant in western Virginia. But even in the eastern parts the trend of nature almost everywhere is towards hardwoods in the long run. This poses a major problem of forest management.

Forest resources and the needs of industry

The evolution of lumber production in Virginia (see graph, page 255) since the Civil War suggests some reflections. It increased steadily up to the 1909 peak, then remained irregular, reaching its lowest point since 1890 during the depression years; then it grew again, particularly since 1939, and seems more or less stabilized at a respectable level above the 1890–1905 one. However, the production of softwoods was not much above that of the first years of the century; the hardwoods were responsible for the increase. This trend would have been, we believe, much more obvious if we had the data to continue the graphs from 1947 to 1954.

The overcutting period of 1905–1917, during which the old growth was, in fact, liquidated, was due to have a long-lasting effect. The most valuable trees of large diameter having been cut, the yield could only

VIRGINIA

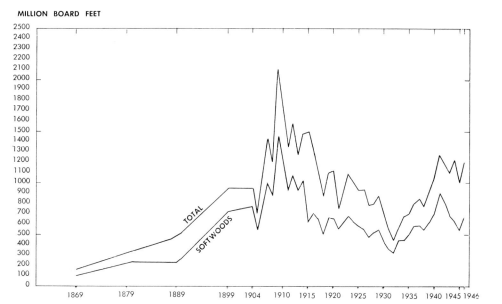

NORTH CAROLINA

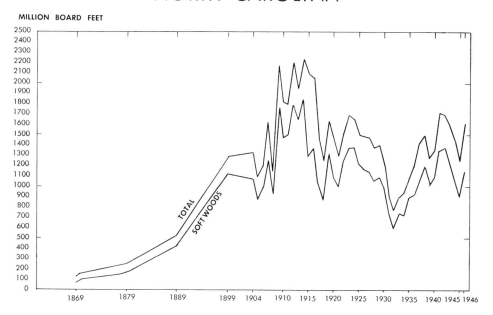

Lumber Production in Virginia and North Carolina, 1869–1945
These graphs show the evolution of the production of lumber, both the total
production and the proportion of softwoods in the total, from the Civil War to
1945 in Virginia and North Carolina. The proportion of hardwoods in the total
has been increasing.

Dense Appalachian hardwoods in Wise County, Virginia. This stand is made up mainly of white oak, tulip poplar, and beech. *U. S. Forest Service*

consist afterwards of less valuable, second-growth timber. Another consequence was that although the new stands were not all of exactly the same age, they had been cut during the same short period and the age classes could not correspond in the future to the range required by the concept of continuous yield. It was then thought possible to obtain a new crop of trees by the method of uneven-aged silviculture, with tree or group selection systems, trees being cut in each stand as soon as they attained a size of commercial value. Thanks to the tremendous rate of growth of most Virginia trees, it was possible to build up by this method a new and prosperous lumber industry which could last, provided that the annual cut is not too heavy.

The depression of the early 1930's came in good time to give the forests of Virginia a few years in which to pick up while the tendency to deforestation was moderated by the low demand on the market. In the late 1930's, the demand grew again, and a sawmill industry developed which consisted chiefly of small mills, using circular saws, scattered through the forests. By 1942, there were some 2,618 sawmills in Virginia that produced altogether 1.2 billion board feet of lumber. Only nine of them, each producing over 5 million board feet a year, all located in the coastal plain, could be termed large mills. More than 600 out of the total were idle. The industry had obviously set to work a little too fast

Pulpwood logs shipped by rail
Virginia Forest Service

before the forest had actually recovered from the period of overcutting and grown valuable stands of high-dimension saw timber. Pine sawlogs can be grown in Virginia in 30 to 40 years (a very favorable figure compared with forests of other countries), but it takes at least 60 years to obtain a yield of hardwood saw timber.

If we look for the period necessary to get a better commercial income from a forest, we find it to be around 60 years for pine stands and for some fast-growing hardwoods, such as sweet gum and yellow poplar, but in the vicinity of 80 to 100 years for other hardwoods as an average. It is apparent that hardwoods are now being felled before the age of maximum commercial return, although hardwoods are not as much in demand as softwoods in Virginia and, more generally, on the American market.

The main consumer of timber in Virginia, among many diversified industries, is the pulp and paper industry. It is an important one, although still rather young. In 1885, pulp and paper mills in the United States used only the soda process; in 1900, the mechanical and sulphite process came in, and 1910 was marked by the beginning of the sulfate process, producing kraft paper. This industry uses small pieces of wood from 5 to 10 inches in diameter. It can be built on the resources of a

Excelsior manufactured in Caroline County
Virginia Forest Service

young forest. It prefers pine wood as raw material, but it can use also, though with some reluctance, chestnut, yellow poplar, gum, basswood, and oaks. In 1952, Virginia was the ninth state in the Union (and the fourth in the southeast) in the production of pulpwood, with a total of 1,069,129 cords of pulpwood, of which 830,525 were pine, 227,883 hardwoods and 10,721 chestnut (the latter salvaged from dead chestnut trees).[12]

The trend towards utilizing hardwoods for pulp production is recent, but is increasing throughout the South. Pulp is produced by the International Paper Company at Natchez, Mississippi, from southern hardwoods by a sulphate process; this bleached pulp is used for the manufacture of rayon yarn. The short fibers of the hardwoods may be a drawback for paper-making, but they prove to be good for rayon. Pulpwood for other purposes can be made of hardwoods, too, particularly blackjack oak (*Quercus marilandica Muench.*), chestnut oak, and hickories.[13] Since 1920, the number of pulp and paper plants has increased fivefold in the

[12] W. S. Stover and J. F. Christopher, *1952 Pulpwood Production in the South* (Forest Survey Release 72), Southern Forest Experiment Station, New Orleans, La., May, 1953.
[13] See D. V. Logan, "Dissolving Pulp from Southern Hardwoods," in *Journal of Forestry*, June, 1952, and C. D. Dosker in *Journal of Forestry*, April, 1952.

southeast. There are now ten pulp mills in Virginia. The sulfate process is the most commonly used, but two mills apply the soda process. In 1954, the "paper and allied products industry" employed in Virginia 10,600 employees, 4 per cent of the state's total employment in manufactures, and its products had in 1952 a value of 180 million dollars.[14]

Some of the mills have experienced difficulty in finding supplies in their vicinity; foreseeing the possibility of slack times, many of the pulp and paper companies have acquired large tracts of forests. More than three-fourths of the present pulpwood supply is still gathered under the contract system: the company enters into a contract with farmers or dealers who supply the mill with a given amount of pulpwood, getting a fixed fee for each delivered unit. In fact, transportation costs set a limit to procurement areas. It has been estimated that 30 miles is the limit for economical truck hauling and 200 miles for railroad transportation. Generally speaking, the forests producing pulpwood must be within the proximity of the plant. When pinewood is too hard to get within a reasonable radius around a pulpmill, the production, in order to carry on, has to adapt itself to some hardwood utilization. Such has been the case of the mill of the West Virginia Pulp and Paper Company in Covington, which is using mixtures of softwoods and hardwoods in which the latter assume increasing proportions.

It must be kept in mind that pulp, paper and saw-timber industries compete for raw material so that maps of lumber and pulpwood production overlap to a serious extent. Silviculture on private lands has to be adjusted to the ultimate utilization of the wood produced, and it is dependent upon the geographical proximity of one or another wood-consuming industry. As pure stands of one species of trees are seldom found in Virginia and are very difficult to maintain, it would seem helpful for a fuller use of the available resources to have multipurpose plants, every inch of usable wood being dispatched to the machine that can make the best use of it. Too often today one sees valuable logs driven to pulpmills and converted into pulp. There is a developing trend, which should be encouraged, of large paper mills to integrate a parallel saw-timber industry to utilize to their best the larger logs delivered to their piles.

Pulp and paper are not the only sizable industries working on wood in Virginia. The commonwealth is first in the Union in the manufacture of excelsior. Over one-third of all the excelsior plants in the United States are located in Virginia, all but one in the coastal plain; in 1945, there were 17 excelsior plants, of which 14 were in Caroline and Hanover

---

[14] Virginia State Department of Labor and Industry, *Annual Survey of Virginia Manufactures*, Richmond, 1954.

Camp Lumber Company plant at Franklin
Virginia Chamber of Commerce

Counties. They used about 30,000 cords of wood, almost entirely loblolly pine, but also some yellow poplar. The species preferred for excelsior are also preferred for pulpwood. The concentration of this industry in a small section is due to an organization of marketing and to personal ties, rather than to the presence of a particularly superior supply in raw materials.

Other notable industries in Virginia using wood are tanning extracts, cooperage, veneer, pit props, poles, railroad ties and furniture. This makes for a great diversity of plants and of raw materials. The manufacturing of tanning extracts, either from chestnut wood or from chestnut oak bark, was carried on in nine plants in western Virginia in 1945; the industry used that year 5,700 cords of oak bark and 58,900 cords of chestnut wood from dead trees.

The cooperage plants produce mainly nail-keg staves made of loblolly pines from 8 to 12 inches in diameter; most of the plants are in the southside of the Tidewater, the area supplying in abundance the desirable raw material. Sixty-three plants purchased, in 1945, 76,900 cords of pine.

Veneer requires high-grade logs of large dimensions. This industry requires a grade superior to saw timber, and veneer bolts are more ex-

Pulp and paper plant at Covington
Virginia Chamber of Commerce

pensive than sawlogs; they are rather difficult to find in depleted forests, but they can stand higher transportation costs. The consumption of bolts in the state was 29.3 million board feet in 1945, three-fourths of which were sweet gum and yellow poplar, and six per cent of which were oak. Black walnut, unfortunately, has been almost eradicated from many places by ruthless cutting and is difficult to find now in important quantities. It is the most popular wood for making veneered furniture. Package veneer takes the lower qualities of available timber, the best ones being used for furniture. Virginia is a leading state in furniture manufacturing, particularly in higher quality furniture. The larger furniture plants are located in the vicinity of the Blue Ridge, mainly at Martinsville, Bassett, Roanoke, Galax, Rocky Mount, Waynesboro, Pulaski, Marion, and Bristol, but some furniture is also made in Altavista, Richmond, Petersburg, and other cities. The veneer and furniture industries definitely prefer the proximity of the hardwood forests of the western ridges.

The pole industry uses chiefly loblolly pines (it amounted to 157,000 pieces in 1945). The production of pit props is concentrated in the Cumberland Plateau area in the vicinity of the coal mines, which are the main

Rotary veneer cutter in operation at the veneer plant of the American Furniture Company at Martinsville
U. S. Forest Service

customers. The mines use any sound wood which is at least five inches in diameter at the small end; chiefly they use hardwood. Some mines receive pit props by rail from the central Piedmont; the channels of this trade are largely determined by railroad tariffs. Railroads are the customers and sometimes even the manufacturers of ties. The N. & W. Railroad had for a long time a tie-producing plant at Radford; it was announced in 1954 that this operation would be discontinued and that the N. & W., as well as the Virginian Railroad, were to be supplied by a special ties plant to be erected in Roanoke by the Koppers Company. Other manufacturers of rail ties are located near Richmond and Lynchburg.

A last use of wood to be mentioned is the age-old gathering of fuel wood. In spite of technical progress and the growing use of petroleum products, fuel wood is still important to rural people for heating, for domestic purposes, and for tobacco or ham curing. The volume used is on the decrease. The annual cut of firewood was estimated in Virginia at 3.9 million cords in 1940, 3.2 in 1945 and 2.2 in 1952. Most of this firewood is cut by the farmers on their woodlots, but mill waste is used in the proximity of the mills. Hickory is the favorite wood for the smokehouse.

Such is the variety of uses and of the species required by present wood consumption in Virginia. There is, of course, no attempt at state self-sufficiency: some lumber is being sent out to neighboring regions, and some is shipped to Virginia mills from North Carolina or West Virginia, according to proximity or rail-tariff considerations. Although a great center of rayon production, Virginia receives from the outside most of the bleached pulp necessary for the production of the artificial fibers. However, as things stand now, the drain on forest resources in the commonwealth is rather heavy.

While the drain on existing resources can be measured by the figures of lumber production (for instance, some 1,428 billion board feet in 1951), we have no precise figure for annual increment of the forests. Craig's report attempted to estimate the drain for 1945: deducting the mortality caused to trees by weather, fire, blights, etc., it appeared that the net increment on all sound trees 5.0 inches d.b.h. and larger was, in 1945, 8.4 million cords, 55 per cent of which was hardwood; the drain on the same category of trees amounted to 4.7 million cords. These figures may at first seem favorable, indicating a growth speedier than the cutting; but if one calculates the net change in total growing stock from January 1, 1940, to January 1, 1946, the increase in all species is limited for the whole state to 11.2 per cent; this increase was much more important for the hardwoods (15.2 per cent) than for the softwoods (5.5 per cent). Among the softwoods the Virginia pine scored the quickest increase: about 25.8 per cent, while the other yellow pines, mainly the much more valuable loblolly and shortleaf pines, grew only by one per cent. In other words, in the 1940–1946 period, the forests of Virginia have slightly increased their total stock; but it was by the progress of the less desirable species from the standpoint of industry: hardwoods and Virginia pines have been progressing at the expense chiefly of loblolly and shortleaf.

During the post–World War II period and even more during the period of the Korean War, the cutting of trees and particularly of pines increased in rate, as the market required more pulpwood as well as saw timber. The preference of the industries for softwoods and of the wood dealers for the pines that could be used in so many different ways led to overcutting of the best qualities of pine. The Virginia Forest Service reported in the spring of 1954, as a result of a survey conducted in 1953 on a sampling basis, that the quality of lumber was declining and that the pine situation had become critical. The survey can be summed up in two tables. The first one gives the percentage of change in the available amount of sawlogs, including all sound material in pine trees 9 inches d.b.h. and larger, and in hardwood trees 11 inches d.b.h. and larger; for

Manufacturing excelsior in a plant in Caroline County
Virginia Forest Service

these trees the survey reveals the following trend of change from 1940 to 1953:

Area	Yellow Pine	Hardwoods
Coastal Plain	−24%	+23%
Piedmont	−25%	+34%
Mountain west	+ 6%	+22%
State	−22%	+27%

Thus the net change in the whole of Virginia for saw timber was an increase of 4 per cent, which was not very much in thirteen years of recuperation after the too-heavy cuttings and burnings of the first third of the century. It was not enough, certainly, for as young a forest as the Virginia one. And the comparison of the two main categories of species demonstrates at last in a striking fashion the triumphant invasion of the hardwoods in practically all the regions of the commonwealth. The second table provides similar data for the cubic-foot volumes, including sound material in all trees 5 inches d.b.h. and larger, covering therefore smaller trees in addition to sawlog timber. The change in percentage during the 1940–1953 period appears as follows:

Area	Yellow Pine	Hardwoods
Coastal Plain	−16%	+38%
Piedmont	−18%	+40%
Mountain west	− 1%	+34%
State	−16%	+38%

The cubic-foot volume in the whole state seems to have increased by 17 per cent, but this is essentially owing to the hardwoods. The smaller relative loss in pines shown by the second table, when compared with the first one, is obviously due to the planting of young pines over vast areas of the coastal plain and of the Piedmont in recent times. Notwithstanding this endeavor, the total volume of softwood is decreasing rather rapidly. The conclusions of the survey have been formulated quite clearly by George W. Dean, State Forester of Virginia: [15]

In further examining these comparative figures between 1940 and 1953, we find that:

a). In all species a net gain of 4% in sawtimber and 17% in cubic volume indicates the forest land is better stocked even though it is with hardwoods.

b). The overall increase is in hardwoods: 27% in sawtimber, and 38% in cubic volume.

c). The loss is in pine: −22% in sawlogs, and −16% in cubic volume.

d). By comparing the pine-sawlog versus cubic-volume relationship there is indicated a larger ingrowth in the 5″ to 9″ diameter classes than in the 9″ and up diameters.

e). The hardwood percentage increase is greatest in the Piedmont region: +34% for sawlogs, and +40% for cubic volume.

f). In the coastal and Piedmont regions the decrease in pine sawtimber is more than offset by an equal increase in hardwood sawtimber.

g). The percentage of cubic volume increase in hardwoods is about one and a half times greater than for sawlogs, which indicates that the 5″ to 9″ hardwoods are rapidly replacing the 5″ to 9″ pines.

h). The industries dependent upon pine sawtimber are in bad shape.

i). The industries depending upon pine, if they are to continue on present levels of production, must immediately concern themselves more about the manner in which pine production is secured on the lands from which they cut timber.

From the report published by Craig [16] in 1949 and based on 1940–1945 figures, it was already apparent that the drain on the private forests was too heavy. In fact, most of the increase recorded for the whole state by G. W. Dean in 1940–1953 seems to be due to the cautious management of the publicly owned forests: the vast areas of national park and forests

[15] George W. Dean, "The Pine Situation Becomes Critical," *Virginia Forests* IX, No. 1, Jan.–Feb., 1954, pp. 16–17.
[16] Ronald B. Craig, *op. cit.,* pp. 42–50.

The large pulp and paper mill of the Chesapeake Corporation at West Point
Virginia Forest Service

on the western ridges, the state forests in the Piedmont. If the ingrowth of these forests were deducted (and these are very predominantly hardwoods), the depletion of the privately owned forests would become much more striking. Furthermore, specifications for saw timber are rather low. Usually in the Tidewater and Piedmont trees of 10 inches d.b.h. or more are cut. In this way the saw-timber industry seems to be working on a part-capacity basis, because it now cuts trees which tomorrow could enable it to work at full capacity. The result is a general depletion of the stands, at least on private lands.

Problems in management

Our review of present resources and their use by industries leaves no doubt as to the necessity of raising many questions about the management of the Virginia forests. The raw material is harvested too early, before the age of maximum commercial yield is reached. Timber production is a compound-interest proposition: the wood produced in a given year adds another annual ring every following year. Older trees produce more timber than young ones as far as volume is concerned, and more valuable timber because it is sawlog size. Saw-timber is usually sold at a higher price than pulpwood. Thus old stands are far more productive than young ones in terms of income, if and when the owners wait until they are built up. When understocked, the forest area is not fully used. The fact that the rate of increase in volume is higher in young stands than in the older ones shows that the forests, having been overcut, contain on the whole an excess of young or inferior material. It would seem that these stands *should now be undercut* to build up older, better trees. This would benefit all industries, whether using small- or large-dimension trees—pulp and paper mills as well as sawmills and veneer factories. However, the management of the forests is such as to make efficient conservation policies rather difficult to apply.

Animals sometimes browse the forest, cafeteria style, picking up what is best for them. Man has somewhat similar habits and cuts only certain species of trees, taking the logs of given qualities and dimensions, according to industrial traditions and habits. As less desirable species are left standing, they take over as time goes on. Virginia wood-consuming industries are nowadays adapted to the use of small-sized or medium-sized logs. Directly or indirectly, they determine the ways in which the forests are managed in the region.

Over most of the coastal plain, the mixed stands of pine and hardwoods show some variation according to type of ownership. With the increasing demand for pulpwood and the probability of slack times ahead, pulp and paper companies have acquired substantial forest acreage. Most of the time this acreage has been bought on a piecemeal basis, and the map of such an industrial estate looks like a patchwork. As a rule, pulp companies clear-cut the stands as soon as they are ready to yield good pulpwood; then comes the problem of the regeneration of the pines. To stop the invasion by the hardwoods many practices have been attempted: girdling or poisoning of the hardwoods has been applied in some areas; such operations cost $3 to $10 an acre and are too expensive to be systematically carried out on a vast scale. Controlled burning would be far less expensive and, if followed by disk-plowing, should prove a better method to insure the regeneration of pines after clear-cutting.[17] Pines always show up after a natural burn, but the problem of fire arouses many important considerations.

Fire has been man's great tool to fight the forest. To clear it and to hunt wild game in it, the Indians applied fire. For many reasons, and in part simply hazard, fire has destroyed immense areas and volumes of

[17] See Southeastern Forest Experiment Station, *Annual Report 1952* (Station Paper No. 22), Asheville, N. C., 1953.

Pine seedlings growing in the state nursery at Charlottesville
Virginia Forest Service

woods since the seventeenth century. Until the end of the nineteenth century the forest was not regarded in the southeast as a valuable resource; there was rather too much of it. Fires that burnt a good deal of it were not looked upon as really harmful. As forest industries developed and the heavy overcutting depleted practically all the wooded areas, wood appeared to be a scarce resource, and fires became the No. 1 enemy of any forester in Virginia. The first major endeavor of the State Forest Service was to fight forest fires. It still is a major theme in all forestry propaganda; the signs reading "Keep Virginia Green" are aimed at the need of eliminating the fire hazard. The Virginia State Forest Service has achieved great results in reducing the damage annually produced by wild fires. The U. S. Forest Service and the National Park Service, in full cooperation with the State Forester, have also achieved outstanding results in the organization of an efficient system of protection of the publicly owned forests against fire. This system is constantly improved. On the average, since 1940, the protection record is good: in 1942, for instance, a total of 237,400 acres burned in the commonwealth; in 1944, only 28,800 burned; the average for the five years 1940–1944 was 105,700 acres annually. In 1952, fires swept some 118,690 acres, and in 1953 only 35,197 acres; Vir-

Planting pine seedlings with modern equipment
Virginia Forest Service

ginia had the lowest forest-fire loss in the entire South during 1953.[18]

These results have been achieved through a number of means, including legislation that prohibits forest burnings. There is considerable fear among forestry authorities that if burnings in wooded areas were authorized in certain cases—as, for example, when controlled to favor the regeneration of pines—too many people might start such experiments and fire protection as a whole would be gravely impaired.[19] However, some large companies, such as Johns-Manville in Jarratt, have been experimenting with such methods. According to a report (for 1949 and 1950) of the Southeastern Forest Experiment Station, the first fires are prescribed in even-aged stands when the pines are 10 to 20 years old, or when the crowns are high enough to be safe from scorching. Proper weather conditions are needed to avoid the development of a wild fire that would wreak havoc in the forest: the elements of the forest floor should not be too dry; a winter fire can kill hardwoods up to about one

[18] Figures from Craig's report and *Richmond Times-Dispatch*, July 4, 1954; see also *Forest Fire Statistics, 1952*, prepared by U. S. Department of Agriculture, Washington, D. C.

[19] Such developments have been known in Europe, for instance, in the vast forest of pines in Landes in southwestern France.

inch in diameter. The treatment should be repeated at intervals of 4 to 10 years to keep the hardwoods small enough for continued control by fire. The best time for burning, provided the weather is right, would be September or October, before seed fall. The cost of the operation can be rather low: 25 to 50 cents an acre. Controlled burnings are, however, difficult to check in patchwork ownership; the method is not without danger, and one must consider many factors carefully before advising it.

The use of mechanical equipment has been and still is tried in attempts to take out hardwoods and prepare a good seedbed for natural reproduction of pines. Bulldozing was first used in 1945 in Virginia. The Chesapeake Corporation of West Point, a large landowner and an important kraft paper producer, has developed it on a rather large scale in mature stands just after logging, for the combined purpose of hardwood control and seedbed scarification. Another use of the bulldozer (for which large Allis-Chalmers tractors weighing 25 tons are put to work) is to reconvert to pine land recently invaded by hardwoods. The bulldozer blade is raised just high enough to clear the ground. The tractor works 0.5 to 1.5 acres per hour, and the cost is $7 to $10 per acre, after the value of salvagable merchantable trees is credited to the operation; the trash and debris are left in windrows 100 to 200 feet apart.

Other heavy equipment has been used: for instance, multiple disk plows with stump drag attached. One company used two tree tops dragged behind a tractor and several types of heavy rollers with brush-cutting knives. Many instances of a good regeneration of loblolly pine can be seen as a result of such practices, but very often Virginia pine, a less desirable species, reseeds itself, too. In some instances the method has proved a complete failure. When heavy equipment is used in wet weather, the soil is puddled, compacted, and becomes a very poor seedbed; and always some topsoil, which is the best part of the future forest soil, is removed.

A special law in Virginia orders a few trees to be left on each acre of cleared land to insure reseeding, unless the land is cleared to be converted to fields or built upon. Little provision is made, however, for the right species of trees and the proper seedbed. Moreover, the economic incentive induces the men in charge of cutting the trees to fell the more valuable, the better ones, and leave for reseeding purposes those poorer in species and in general condition. This does not prepare a better growth, because heredity is at least as important for trees as for animals; to a large extent it is the ancestor that makes the tree. Whoever has looked carefully at recently cut areas throughout the forests in Virginia and examined the seed trees left would hardly wish them to reproduce

Plantation of young pines near a chemical plant, demonstrating industry's contribution to the conservation of the site
Virginia Forest Service

on a large scale.[20] Recent legislation encourages the retaining of loblolly pines, wherever they are present, for reseeding.

In many instances it has been necessary to use planting in order to fight the natural trend towards the hardwoods. Today, one finds in the Tidewater and Piedmont many loblolly plantations 15 to 20 years old or younger. Loblolly becomes an artificially produced crop, just like peanuts. The rotation for this pulpwood is set at 25 to 35 years with one thinning in the 15th to 20th year. Sometimes the young plants have to be protected by weeding from hardwood sprouts which might overshade them. When thinned these stands produce 30 cords per acre in the Tidewater, the annual growth being, on the average, around 2 cords per acre. The pulp industry has had to take quite seriously the important job of planting trees and furnishing seedlings free to growers of pulpwood. This cultivation of the loblolly is an expensive one and founded on the upward trend in the prices of timber and paper.

The pulp and paper corporations cannot obtain as yet enough pulpwood from their own lands. They buy more from the farmers, and thus

[20] See Ernest B. Babcock and J. W. Duffield, "It's the Ancestor That Makes the Tree," *American Forests* 59, No. 11, November, 1953.

come into competition with the sawmills looking for their supply. This situation accounts for the price of forested land, which can be as high as $10 an acre, as all large wood-consuming industries try to become self-sufficient and insure their future supplies. The Chesapeake Corporation, for instance, owns an estate of about 125,000 acres; in the neighborhood the opinion is prevalent that the lands owned by the Corporation are really good for cultivation and that only such a large concern could afford to buy them and keep them under forest.

However, even the endeavors of the large companies in favoring pine regeneration and keeping loblolly stands on good soils have not been able to stop the progress of the hardwoods. As a general rule nothing has been done yet to improve the young stands of hardwoods, which are the forest of the future, besides fire control. The better protection of the forests against fires has already had some effect indirectly on the selection of species. In favoring the hardwoods, the absence of fires appears to have favored particularly the yellow poplar, which is very sensitive to burnings. As the yellow poplar is the favorite of industry among the hardwoods found in Virginia, the increase of poplars among the hardwoods is considered a substantial improvement in the commercial value of the presently growing generation of trees. It is a somewhat indirect result of improved management in terms of fire protection.

The bottomland hardwoods are important in the Tidewater because of the vast forest of this type in the Dismal Swamp. The Dismal is owned by two large industrial corporations which have begun cutting the marketable trees, leaving the others. No thinnings or improvement cuttings seem to have been carried out. The Swamp seems to have been mined as yet only on a small scale by the lumbering operations. Forest fires in it are still rather frequent and difficult to fight in the dense growth, through which traffic is restricted by the marshy nature of the soil.

Up to now only a few species of hardwoods are sought as commercially valuable. As they are cut and the others are left standing around, the reproduction of the better ones is hardly made easier. As a specialist put it: "Without utilization which permits the economic handling of silvicultural treatments, satisfactory forest practice is precluded." [21] Thus hardwood silviculture will become worth-while only when suitable markets have been created.

Silvicultural improvement cuttings are needed to augment the proportion of the most valuable species which would be left standing. But such a long-range policy is contrary to the applied principle that most of the

[21] J. A. Putnam, "The Relationship of Utilization to Silvicultural Management in Bottomland Hardwoods," *Journal of Forestry*, November, 1951.

A plantation of loblolly pines in the Coastal Plain. *Virginia Forest Service*

cut must be advantageously salable. By putting the dollar sign on the present method of management, one takes the dollar sign away from the future of the forest. It has thus been estimated recently that no more than one-third of the total bottomland forest area in Virginia could be operated under existing market conditions. This is true because past cuttings have already skimmed the cream off two-thirds of the area. In spite of their excellent growth rate and prolific reproduction, bottomland stands are made of too great a variety in form, length, and quality. As things go, the problem of making improvement cuttings, which cannot pay by themselves, will apply in a relatively short period to the hardwood stands, which are spreading. This problem has not as yet been faced.

Most of the examples we have given above in matters of forest management were taken from the coastal plain; the problems are about the same in the Piedmont. The trend towards hardwoods is stronger there, and it is more difficult to fight it. Bulldozing is not advisable in the thinner and sloping soils of the Piedmont: it would make erosion easier and increase gullying. Controlled burning is not feasible because of the patchwork aspect of most of the forest ownership. Grazing is not advisable, as it increases the possibility of erosion and hampers the growth of valuable but palatable species, such as yellow poplar and white ash, leaving weed trees to develop. Girdling or poisoning the trees means too much work

Forester and landowner confer in a scrub pine wood
Soil Conservation Service

and too high costs for small woodlot owners. For the softwood stands
there is competition, at least in some counties, between several industries;
as a result, the farmer who needs cash will first cut the most marketable
trees, the pines. Nature and men thus work together towards the same
end, which in the present evolution of vegetation means an increasing
predominance of hardwoods.

There are fewer large forest estates established by industrial corporations in the Piedmont than in the Tidewater; but in the central part of
the Piedmont are substantial state-owned forests, mainly the Lee State
Forest and the Cumberland State Forest, bought since 1930 under the
auspices of the Resettlement Policy. The office of State Forester was
created in the commonwealth in 1914 for park management and fire control. It began to deal with timber management in 1940 only. With some
60 professional foresters on the staff in 1953, it has obtained remarkable
results in fire protection for 100 per cent of the area needing such protection in the whole state. It deals with the management of the state
forests and gives occasional advice to private owners on timber sales.

The Virginia Forest Service has gone into the planting of pines on a
large scale. Plantations were made on the depleted lands owned by the

state. The service maintains two large nurseries in New Kent for the Tidewater and in Charlottesville for the Piedmont. In 1953, 11 million seedlings were produced in New Kent and 2 million in Charlottesville, mostly loblolly seedlings, which were sold at cost prices to pulp corporations, small landowners, and schools. Since loblolly is so popular among wood users, much of it has been planted in the Piedmont and even in the western mountains, although it is outside its natural range there. Planting machines are rented to the landowners, and demonstrations are organized for farmers; the Forest Service also has programs on radio and television.

The total area of state-owned forests extended, in 1950, over 107,000 acres. Outstandingly well managed and cut, they should be an excellent example to smaller landowners. The latter have rarely taken lessons, however, from the better practices of public land management. The belief seems to prevail that the management of public lands does not have to be economical, while the landowner has to manage in order to get as big an income as he can. This view may have to be reversed in the long run, when it will appear that the better forests, under public management, will bring higher revenues than the depleted and misused small woods.

The relationship of privately owned to publicly owned forest lands takes on a different but still familiar aspect in the more mountainous area of western Virginia. Here public ownership under federal management predominates in many of the mountainous parts: over the Blue Ridge north of the Roanoke Gap, over most of the Allegheny ridges except in the southwestern triangle. The Shenandoah National Park manages a gross area of over 200,000 acres in the northern Blue Ridge. About 85 per cent of the park's area supports a forest that varies in composition according to altitude, soil, moisture, and exposure, but is rather homogeneous in general appearance because of man's action: because of the cuttings and burnings before the establishment of the present management. Now the forest is as completely protected as it could possibly be. There is no commercial exploitation at all. In the long run, the evolution of forest associations freed from cutting, burning, and cattle grazing will provide most valuable information on natural trends of forest evolution in the Blue Ridge.

The two national forests include most of the publicly owned forests on the ridges of western Virginia. They cover at present in Virginia close to 1.5 million acres (i.e., 902,266 acres publicly owned in the George Washington National Forest and 536,645 acres in the Jefferson National Forest). No part of this area was in the primitive state as when first

Fighting a forest fire
Virginia Forest Service

reached by White settlers. Though such marvels may be preserved by
federal authorities in some corners of the West, in Virginia every parcel
of the fine primitive mountain forest was cut and burned at some time
within the last century. The George Washington National Forest has set
aside two "natural areas" destined to be permanently preserved in un-
modified conditions so that their plant associations can be studied scien-
tifically to learn what the natural trends in this section of the country are.
These "natural areas" cover about 3,900 acres and comprise some interesting and relatively old stands.

The Weeks Act of 1911, later amended by the Clarke-McNary Act of
1924, made possible the purchase of the tracts of lands now constituting
the national forests. Under these laws the purchasing policy aims at check-
ing the erosion on the steep slopes which causes floods. Overcutting and
burning had depleted the vegetation cover and made erosion a serious
threat throughout the Appalachians. The two national forests found in
Virginia are only sections of a vast system of land purchasing conducted
by federal authorities through the Appalachian region. To make for
efficient protection of the watersheds, it was indispensable to go also into
areas not yet devastated by erosion but seriously attacked in their upper

portions by the mountain farmers and the depredations of their cattle. Careful studies demonstrated that the preservation of an undisturbed forest cover is probably the best possible management practice to insure efficient flood and erosion control for a watershed.

It was also becoming increasingly evident that the depletion of the forests in the United States was making the nation more and more dependent on foreign imports of pulp and timber. To assure future action to build up well-stocked forests which could produce high quality timber was imperative. The past of the forests in the Old Dominion showed well enough that under private ownership trees are usually cut too young and too often. A complete rotation extending over a period of more than 100 years is hard to visualize and even harder to apply for a landowner who will not live long enough and who will need cash several times during his short life.

Therefore, several good reasons concurred to favor the establishing of national forests. In many cases purchase has been possible only of land so eroded and depleted by farming that farming was no longer profitable. An important problem still remaining is to improve the structure of the worn-out soil so that rain nourishes growth instead of scouring off topsoil. A survey of avalanche and debris areas in the Shenandoah Mountains of Virginia shows that grazing, burning, and cutting have produced slides and debris deposits in the valleys. This would be enough to justify the establishment of the system of national forests. But in some areas such devastating practices still go on in areas largely purchased by the government. However, within the perimeter that the federal authorities have earmarked as desirable for the full completion of the task entrusted them under the existing legislation, many tracts remain owned and partly farmed by small farmers. These scattered farms are a source of fire hazard and of grazing cattle, as the animals easily trespass the limit between the lands of their owners and the lands of the nation. Finally, the farms remaining within the perimeter outlined for federal purchase greatly benefit from the investment made by and the services maintained at public expense around their lands, but contribute to make these investments and services more expensive and less effective.

In accordance with the recent federal policy restricting public ownership of land, the Regional Forester for the Eastern Region of the U. S. Forest Service, which includes Virginia, recommended reductions in the gross area of the national forests in Virginia. The estimate of the eventual size of national forest holdings is based on present conditions of land use in relation to the public interest. The need for public ownership will decrease as private owners recognize their responsibility to the public in the

Selectively cutting pulpwood. The tree being cut is limby Virginia pine; in the background is good, straight shortleaf pine. *Soil Conservation Service*

management of their lands. If the future trend should be in the other direction and land abuses under private management increase, the need for public ownership would likewise increase. As things stood in the spring of 1954, after recommending some reductions in the program of eventual purchase, the regional forester still classified as "suitable for eventual public acquisition" some 515,152 acres for the George Washington National Forest and 805,382 for the Jefferson National Forest in Virginia; these recommendations still left within the perimeters of the two national forests over half a million acres that should remain under private ownership.[22] These figures show that in western Virginia the national forests have come closer to providing fully efficient protection north of the James River than south of it. It should also be remembered that these recommendations were made at a time when federal policy was oriented towards reduction of public acquisition of land.

The national forests are not financially unproductive in Virginia, though they are still young. Inventories have been made and plans laid according to annual growth. In fact, the Forestry Service can allow at present only small cuttings. Annual cuttings are lower than the annual growth owing to the fact that the Service "is not numerous enough to

[22] These figures were supplied by courtesy of the Office of the Regional Forester, Eastern Section, U. S. Forest Service, Philadelphia, in two memoranda in March, 1954.

take care of too many cuttings" and wants to build up an important lumber resource. The policy being applied is to make only small sales for improvement cuttings, the timber being sold to small operators, usually a team of three or four men with a horse and power saws. The thinnings give an average of five cords an acre. The big problem is still that these weedings and thinnings cannot pay for themselves and yield slight commercial results, although they are essential to the long-range building up of a highly productive forest. The generalization of hardwood pulping could help a lot to make the produce of such operations marketable.

The hardwood stands contain mostly a coppice of stump sprouts with a few trees from seeds. As the stumps have not been repeatedly cut, there are often one or two sprouts only. Some older trees are scattered about. The species which are the least desirable from a commercial point of view are cut; some plantings are made when necessary. The undesirable, nonvaluable species are poisoned with ammate. Openings are made in mature stands to try to get seedlings, as trees grown from seeds give better timber than trees grown from sprouts. The objective is to attain an uneven-aged forest divided into small blocks. Softwood stands are thinned from below when twenty years old. The policy appears to be very wise on the whole, though some of its details could, of course, be criticized from a perfectionist's point of view. Thus the small operators cutting the wood are not always as careful as would be desirable. For instance, big trees are cut too high, leaving a stump about one foot high. This is a waste of timber and prepares poorer sprouts. Those are, however, minor matters. As a whole, the present management of the national forests appears extremely well adapted to the purpose behind its creation: to stop the process of erosion and to put back into productivity marginal lands and depleted forest tracts.

How different things look in the private forests of western Virginia! As hardwoods predominate, large paper and pulp companies have not shown much interest in buying forest land here. Some lumber companies do their best to manage protectively the lands they own. But the methods of private cutting, as a whole, and of grazing the land are not better than what happens in the eastern sections of Virginia; they are rather worse. Outside the larger, deforested parts of the Great Valley, the small farmer on hilly land is usually too poor to engage in a long-range plan of land use, whether forested or not. Too often selective cutting amounts, in fact, to cutting the better commercial trees, with no attention to the future evolution of the forest. Wherever we look at forest management in Virginia, we encounter a shocking contrast between the conditions prevailing on the lands of the large owners and on those of the small owners.

Public ownership offers, on the whole, model management, because it is the largest in scale. Bigness seems to be a great advantage in forestry. It remains for us to see what is then wrong with the small woodlots and what could be done to improve that side of the general picture.

The farm woodlots

The woodland on the farms of Virginia has decreased somewhat in the last twenty years as a result of purchases by public authorities or large corporations, but it still covers, on the whole, a vast area: 6.7 million acres in 1950, close to one-half of the total wooded area in the commonwealth (estimated at 14.8 million acres). From what has been said about the present conditions of management, it constitutes, by its scattered pattern of distribution throughout the state, the main problem in terms of forest management as well as resources conservation.

Forestry is a complicated art and technique. It requires quite a bit of scientific knowledge and understanding to foresee the right policy for a given wood in terms of thinning and cutting, as well as the timing of all these operations. Trees grow slowly; even a loblolly pine in the southside Tidewater requires about twenty years to reach merchantable size; most others require even longer. To decide what he wants to do with his woodlot, a farmer or small owner must learn a great deal about forestry, and very few ever do. Moreover, such decisions are made by small landowners according to their material situation at the moment. Any concern as to long-range forest policy disappears when cash is urgently needed and can be provided by immediate cutting. Ignorance and the need for cash, therefore, are the two problems of almost one-half of Virginia's forest, that is, of about one-fourth of Virginia's entire land area. Even if timber and pulpwood were in abundant and increasing supply on the domestic market, the significance of this question would make discussion well worth while. As the wood supply altogether does not offer a very bright prospect, the management of farm woodlots becomes an important and serious problem.

The farmer today usually knows the higher returns brought by saw timber, which requires older trees. However, when he wants cash he sells young trees, even when he knows that they will be worth more in logs a few years hence; in some areas, such as the southside Tidewater, the farmers have often made substantial profits in recent years on peanuts, hogs, and dairy products; they keep substantial stands of loblolly growing until they can bring higher prices because of the size and quality of the logs. This is not, unfortunately, a customary pattern in other parts of the

A farm with fields interspersed among steep wooded slopes

country. During the spring of 1954, many dealers in the Piedmont especially reported a temporary "overproduction," causing a glutted market in pulpwood. The wood was piling up at the railroad sidings. A newspaper's inquiry in Goochland County showed that the farmers were cutting pulpwood to pay for the hay they had to buy as a result of the drought in 1953.[23] Some farmers were thinning in pine woods just twelve years old, instead of waiting for the fifteen-year minimum period, in order to get cash and pay debts before summer. Since, at about this same time, the output of some of the mills had declined slightly, prices went down, and the farmers did not make out so well as they could have if they had not been financially pressed.

On the farms most of the stands are either clear-cut, leaving a few seed trees per acre according to the law, or "selectively" cut. In this last method, according to the books, "the diseased or insect-infested, the limby, the crooked, or scarred trees, the old ones, and the less desirable varieties are cut to benefit the remainder. The other trees that are cut are those that are past their best growing period, or can be sold more profitably

[23] Hamilton Crockford, "Replanting of Pulpwood Pine Urged Despite Overproduction Now," *Richmond Times-Dispatch*, April 26, 1954.

now than in the future." [24] This partial cutting method has been advertised more than the seed tree method. It has the advantage of keeping the soil under protective cover, but it is not very good for pine reproduction: pine seeds, like seeds of any pioneer species, prefer bare soils. On the other hand, it is in practice difficult to sell the old, limby, crooked trees, and very often they have been left standing. What the farmer wants once a cutting is undertaken is to harvest as much revenue from the operation as possible; when an adviser is called in to help mark the trees to be felled, he knows that the final cash product is essential and that the more he enables the farmer to make out of the cutting the more his services will be valued: this is an incentive to leave the less merchantable trees standing and remove all the good ones.

The farmers have been advised to thin their pine woodlots. Thinnings are made to reduce the number of trees so as to obtain the maximum growth from the ones which are left. But there would be much to say about the methods employed. There are two ways of thinning pine stands: low and high thinning. In "low" thinning the smaller, less vigorous, diseased and unpromising trees are taken out, the material removed being used for firewood, pulpwood, or excelsior wood. This type of thinning is made with the idea of obtaining a given number of trees per acre; very often too mathematically applied, it differs in fact from the German "thinning from below" which is its origin. Furthermore, one thinning only is generally made to obtain at once the number of trees which corresponds to a complete stand, whereas thinning should be more progressive to be beneficial.

In "high" thinning, the larger, dominant trees are cut, making more room for the smaller trees to expand. In this type of thinning the most common practice of farmers is to cut out the largest trees, which are the most merchantable. What happens then is a very partial recovery of the formerly stunted trees to a normal growth. This method is, indeed, very different from the French "thinning from above" from which it originated and which consists of attending to the canopy in order to free gradually the crowns of the more merchantable trees which have the higher growing rate. One may at least say that the formerly stunted trees do not constitute the best growing stock. All the thinnings in southern pine stands favor the invasion of hardwoods. It may be observed that old southern pine stands bear a very light cover, thus preparing the way for shade-bearing species; thinning increases the speed of the substitution.

---

[24] "Managing the Small Forest," *Farmers' Bulletin No. 1989,* U. S. Department of Agriculture, Washington, D. C.

When the final clear-cut of pines is made, a hardwood forest is found growing.

In hardwood stands, cuttings are made on a commercial basis. Only the trees likely to be sold are harvested and the others left standing. This is just the opposite of the kind of selection needed. After two or three operations of this kind, the forest is made of old cull trees and, hardwood stumps having sprouted, the best species give only coppice. The inferior species thrive after the cut, and there is no improvement whatsoever in the understory, which constitutes the future forest. Weeding—that is to say, cutting off the inferior trees to give the best ones a chance, or, in other words, trying to remove the undesirable species in order to make way for something better—is not very popular in Virginia because it is not a paying proposition: it gives fuel wood at most. It is, however, the key to proper timber management because it builds up a productive, uneven-aged hardwood forest. Thus it is important to find new utilization for small-size hardwoods as fuel wood gradually passes out of the picture.

Even in the hardwood forests of the Allegheny Mountains, cuttings are made too often and in too careless a fashion, whether it is for pulpwood or timber. The State Forester has summed up the situation rather well in describing the critical situation of the pines, and it is true through the whole of Virginia and beyond:

The pulpwood mill owners are growing and cutting timber on their own lands in accordance with the best known methods. They are doing a good job. But on much other land, especially that far removed from the mills, from which pulpwood is cut, I can only suggest that you look over a dozen or so typical cut-over tracks and draw your own conclusions as to whether or not a good job of cutting has been done. However, it is believed the pulpwood mills could effectively control the undesirable methods of cutting pine which goes to their mills. They could do this by agreeing amongst themselves not to buy any wood unless it was harvested in accordance with good forestry practices. They could also do it by paying a substantial per-cord bonus where good forestry practices are used.

The question immediately arises as to why pulpwood people should initiate such a policy when a sawmill or stave mill operator might come along and make a deal to purchase the remaining timber from a landowner who is willing to have his land stripped. Many sawmill operators, and I am glad to say the number is increasing, are doing a good job of forestry on their own property and, like the pulp mills, are buying marked timber on other people's property. But again, I suggest that you inspect a dozen or so typical saw or stave mill operations on property not owned by the operator and draw your conclusions as to the type of cutting. How can the sawmill, stave mill, and mine-prop operators who destructively harvest timber be induced to use good forestry practices? It is believed that the majority of landowners are interested in growing and har-

A small portable sawmill at work in the woods
Virginia Forest Service

vesting their timber as a crop. But there are, unfortunately, all too large a number who are perfectly willing—some even insist—to sell their timber only with the thought of getting the last cent with no regard for the resulting condition of their land for future growth.[25]

Uttered by a State Forester, these are strong words indeed. The forests of Virginia were butchered a first time, *en masse,* by the large-scale lumbering operations at the beginning of the century; most of them, outside public or very large private ownership, are being butchered again piecemeal. The first result of this process is that pine recedes fast, notwithstanding constant efforts to protect it or bring it in. An improvement in the management of the farm woodlots and of the small woodlands forms the central problem of forestry in Virginia. The U. S. Forest Service has long recognized the fact that the small private holding is the toughest problem to deal with.

The Forest Economics Section of the Tennessee Valley Authority has conducted some interesting studies in southwestern Virginia, which is part of T.V.A. territory, and where farm woodlots on sloping ground occur frequently and are a permanent source of concern. The average

[25] George W. Dean, in *Virginia Forests,* Jan.–Feb., 1954, pp. 17–18.

yield of saw timber in southwestern Virginia has been estimated at 125 board feet per acre per year under prevailing conditions. If the average farm woodland were well stocked with desirable tree species, and the area adequately managed, the yield could be 300 or more board feet and the lumber value higher, bringing the annual net income up from the present $4.00 to about $11.00 per acre.[26] More striking figures of possible income increase could probably be given for the Piedmont woodlands, where transportation is easier and growth quicker.

Experiments conducted by the Southeastern Forest Experiment Station in a southern forest of 300 acres, containing average timber, hardwoods and pines mixed, show that "a farmer harvesting his wood crop and practicing good forest management can pay all his carrying charges, earn 3% interest on his investment, and receive from $.64 to $1.38 per hour for his labor." [27] Such land use is profitable and requires relatively little labor. Owners of small woodlands must be won to good management practices; they will not regret it.

Private forests are now fairly well protected in Virginia against fire and tree diseases, and grazing is not a widespread problem, many areas being fenced in against cattle. These are important steps toward sound silviculture. Regarding cutting practices, technical assistance can be provided under the Norris-Doxey Act, though it seems to have reached as yet only a few individuals, and a small part of the farm-forest owners who wanted such aid have been served. Moreover, the application of the Norris-Doxey Act is restricted to farms. The State Forest Service is very often called to give advice to farmers for the marketing of the timber they cut. This is very important, because woodland owners deal with the industry on an inferiority-complex basis; they think they are cheated before they start. As a matter of fact, if a farmer sells a timber tract to satisfy an immediate need for money, he has small chance of selling profitably. Estimates prepared by the Virginia Forest Service are thus very important to the owners.

So far, only a small fraction of the total farm woodlots has been aided by public agencies, inasmuch as the farm forestry program dates back only a little more than a decade. Technical assistance to private owners in managing their forests and selling their forest products should be made available on a much larger scale. There are a few private consultants in Virginia working mainly with the big corporations, and they cannot cover

[26] From a communication from W. W. Jolly, Chief, Forest Economics Section, Tennessee Valley Authority, Norris, Tenn., December 9, 1953.

[27] See John Frederick Preston, *Developing Farm Woodlands*, New York, 1954. See also, on the subject of New England woodlots, S. L. Barraclough and E. M. Gould, Jr., *Economic Analysis of Farm Forest Operating Units*, Harvard Forest Bull. 26, Petersham, Mass., 1955.

the field. Moreover, public aid has been found to benefit rather than to interfere with private consulting services. Basically, the management of the small woodlands is a problem in psychology; it is just one aspect of the old question of how to influence people in the way they invest their capital. It has been demonstrated that keeping young stands and allowing them to grow is a form of hoarding money; but here public welfare and the state timber output are at stake. Something ought to be done, it would seem, to encourage the small owners who are making an effort to produce with better techniques what the community needs.

When nothing is done to guide them, the farmers are tempted. There is now some competition on the farms between timber and beef. The cost of establishing year-round pastures and stocking them with pure-bred cattle is high, and farmers are tempted to cut over their woodlots and sell what they can to start the cattle business. Timber is frequently the only resource available for quick conversion into cash, and changing his investment is an inalienable right of the landowner. Then overproduction of wood may result, like the situation that followed the drought of 1953 and the heavy buying of hay by the farmers for their cattle; in the Piedmont many trees were felled early in 1954 for ready cash.

It may be somewhat daring to ask the wood-using industries to give a bonus to wood owners who follow better cutting and managing practices, at least from the industry's standpoint. Who would judge the quality of the management? And how would a bonus from the industry have gone, for instance, to the farmers who did *not* cut very young pines to sell in a period of indebtedness to get cash immediately? The problem of helping the small woodland owners manage their lands is a tough one from many standpoints. It is, nevertheless, an important one, and its consequences are not restricted to the field of organizing a better supply of raw materials for wood-using industries. Forest management is also decisive for the availability of wildlife and game, and for better conservation of water resources, all fields that cannot be neglected.

Wildlife in and around the forests

Wildlife is usually considered a product of the "natural environment." We do not know much about what this "natural" condition was in Virginia aside from the predominance of the forest cover almost everywhere, but early descriptions give us many clues as to the existing fauna. It seems to have been, until the middle of the eighteenth century, quite different from what it was in the beginning of the nineteenth. In the latter period some people became so worried at the disappearance of game and wildlife generally that arduous endeavor was applied and still is being applied to the restoration of at least some of the original wildlife, which can be done only under forest cover. At any rate, wildlife today is a product of the management of the land.

From the vague descriptions of the early travellers and settlers, let us attempt a brief summary of what was observed in colonial days. The abundance of deer was frequently mentioned, both in the forests and in the clearings made by the Indians. In the deep forests there were many birds: wild turkeys were an easy prey for the redskins. Bears and squirrels were very common. There was an abundance of fish in the unsilted and unpolluted rivers. Birds gathered in immense flocks in the marshes along the seaboard. In the ocean whales and porpoises could be seen swimming not far from the shore. Some explorers recorded having killed bison, elk, bears, deer, turkeys, and geese to feed themselves during a journey. They refer also to species now extinct. Bison were abundant in cleared areas west of the Blue Ridge. Colonel William Byrd reported a nocturnal bird, the Carolina Paroquet, which was too fond of apples to remain on good terms with the colonists, and also thousands of passenger pigeons gathering in the sky in huge clouds. Both these species are completely extinct today.

Game supplied a great deal of the Indians' commodities. They used the spurs of turkey gobblers as points for their arrows and their feathers for their caps and garments. Venison was an essential food, and the skins and furs of the animals provided many materials. The Indians lived in a kind of balance with the resources of nature; their settlements were too scattered, their population too thin to have a lethal effect on wildlife; in a relatively short time the settlers overthrew the balance. Wild animals were killed first for food, but soon also for the pleasure of hunting and for profit. Deer, elk, bears, bison, turkeys, geese, and ducks were the main items of the pioneer's subsistence. Coonskin caps are still famous. Deer hides and beaver pelts were used for clothing. Thousands of squirrels were killed with the famous long-barreled guns. Many birds and mammals approached the vanishing point: for instance, the heath-hen, martens and fishers. Beavers, trapped for their valuable furs, disappeared from Virginia in 1910; the famous Southern fox squirrel, too, a species bigger than the gray squirrel, but easier to kill, disappeared in 1895.

Predators were eliminated, considered as competitors for game or dangerous for livestock. The timber wolf once abounded throughout the state: soon a bounty was set by the authorities, and some colonists were said to make a decent living by merely trapping wolves. These bounties were paid as late as 1881. Wolf traps are still being found in the moun-

Elk in a Virginia forest. *Virginia Forest Service*

tains, attesting to the intensity of trapping in old days. The last two wolves in Virginia were killed in 1910. Another extinct predator is the cougar, mentioned by several early explorers: it disappeared between 1880 and 1900. Accompanying man, stray, self-hunting dogs have been a terrific menace to wildlife since the seventeenth century; they are apparently responsible for the decline of deer in Virginia and its disappearance entirely from many counties, having forced the last ones to find shelter in the larger forests or in the Dismal Swamp.

Even more important than hunting by men or roving dogs were the early land-clearing, forest-cutting, and cultivation processes, which disturbed the conditions necessary for the existence of many creatures. For instance, bison could not coexist with cultivated and fenced fields. While its roaming area is still marked by many names like Buffalo Gap, Buffalo River, Buffalo Forge, etc., on the map of western Virginia, the last ones seem to have been killed there in 1798. The elk, a forest-roving creature, was in danger as soon as the forest began to be cut on a large scale; the last was killed in 1855. The fisher, which haunted the dense forests of spruce and fir in the mountains, disappeared when they were cut. The cutting of woods was definitely unfavorable to forest birds like the ruffed grouse.

Soon the cultivated fields offered new opportunities to a small number of species. This new environment, devoid of wildlife, had to be filled in with highly adaptable species, according to a law of nature. For instance, cottontail (*Sylvilagus floridanus*) found a favorable habitat in farmlands, brushlands, open woods and gardens, all new environments created by the settlers. It is now abundant throughout the commonwealth. The same story is true of the other rodents, like the woodchuck, the gray squirrel, which occurs chiefly in rural districts, and the meadow mouse, which is abundant in cultivated fields and wet meadows.

One bird, the passenger pigeon, proved highly adaptable to cultivated crops, but became such a pest that man got rid of it. Another bird, the bobwhite quail, took advantage of the cultivated fields; having the habit of concealing itself in dead weeds, it found plenty of food there and was relatively secure. Like the bobwhite, a cousin of the pigeon, the mourning dove found favorable conditions in agricultural areas. Being not as much of a pest as the passenger pigeon, it was tolerated by man, though easier to kill. Many forms of wildlife benefited from the new environment. The deer developed a habit of feeding on peanuts and soybeans and wreaked havoc in cultivated fields. Only the less adaptable species, or those which could not live in relative harmony with man, were eliminated by agricultural development.

The cutting of the forests was not unfavorable to all game species. Thus the deer, whose natural winter food consists of twigs and buds browsed from young trees and shrubs, and whose summer food was grass and tender leaves of low bushes, found good conditions in the recently cut or opened forest where the canopy was not dense and where grass, brush, and sprouts could develop. Wherever settlement created large blocks of suitable young forest succession, the increase in number of deer has been noticeable, if not hampered by the presence of feral dogs.

The wild turkey has another story to tell: a typical forest bird feeding upon acorns and chestnuts, it was very abundant at the beginning of the settlement. But it was easy to kill and, due to heavy hunting combined with the destruction of its habitat, it soon disappeared from many parts of the range. However, turkeys also need clearings for their food, a large part of which comes from plants growing on the edges of the woods; and their favorite nesting grounds are small clearings. When later it was protected from wanton hunting, the turkey came back readily in the checkerboard pattern of intermingled forest and fields of the Piedmont. In a similar way, cutting and burning in the forest increased the area covered with grass and shrubs, favorable for rabbits. Fortunately, cottontails have not as yet become so overabundant that they eat young seedlings and sprouts to the extent of hampering the return of vegetation, as other rabbits do in Australia and parts of Europe.

The cutting of the forest was also unfavorable to fish in the streams. Streams were silted and choked by erosion; there were floods and sufficient fluctuation in the temperature of water to make it bad for trout. At the same time, many insects were eliminated, which meant depletion of trout in the streams.

Until the end of the nineteenth century, man's action was mainly destructive to wildlife. Then a change came about in the nature of man's influence. This change of attitude was due first to the concern expressed by hunters and sportsmen who wanted always to have something to kill, and later on to the philosophical view of a few biologists and conservationists who felt that to eradicate certain species was a grave sin, a grave loss for science, and a way of upsetting the existing natural conditions that could lead to unforeseeable material losses in the long run. Thus men began to protect a few of the surviving animals or even introduced new ones to take the place of extinct species.

The nongame birds have been protected in the United States since 1885, when the Bureau of Biological Survey was organized after a campaign sponsored by the Audubon Society resulting from the extinction of the passenger pigeon. From 1903 on, federal bird reservations began to be set aside for the protection of migratory birds. At the same time, laws and regulations for the protection of game and fish found more and more local support. The first local game law in America was enacted in New York State as far back as 1791. In Virginia, quail has been protected by law since 1879. It became normal to consider that the protection of migratory animals was a federal responsibility, while the protection of resident game was left as a responsibility to the states. This distinction remains the backbone of wildlife protection throughout the Union.

In Virginia, official action really started with the institution of the State Department of Game and Inland Fisheries in 1916, following the rise of public interest in game protection. The market hunters, illicit trappers, and poachers had obviously reduced the once plentiful supply of wildlife, and the heavy timber cuttings of the years 1900–1915 greatly deteriorated the situation for many animals. First of all, a game warden system was set up. The first reintroduction measure was taken: elks were restocked in the mountains of Virginia. The last native elk had been killed in 1855; new animals for restocking were brought from the Yellowstone National Park, which had a surplus of elk. The animals thus introduced belonged to a subspecies slightly different from the extinct indigenous one. The elks are powerful, migratory animals, apt to cover

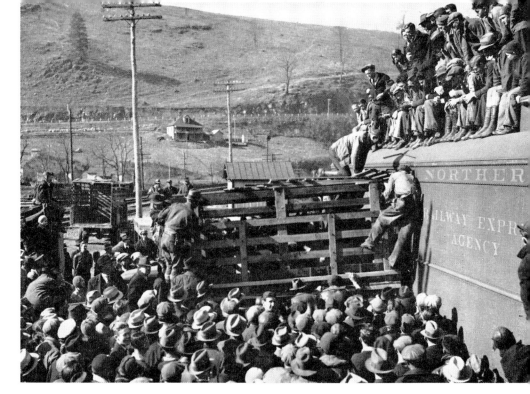

Elk from the West are unloaded in Giles County. *Virginia Chamber of Commerce*

surprising distances. Those introduced in 1917 have survived only in the wild areas of the mountains, where they find refuge in the brush. Sometimes they venture into cultivated fields, where they have developed a taste for corn. Occasionally, an isolated elk goes farther and mixes with herds of cattle, scaring the cows and causing the farmer to call for help and claim damage. It became evident in the long run that they could not be established in great number and that their depredations could cause too much damage.

In the same year, 1917, thousands of ring-necked pheasants, birds and eggs, were released in Virginia. These birds were of English origin and similar ones have been established in Oregon. Pheasant is a famous game bird in Europe, where it provides very good sport. All attempts to establish it in numbers in Virginia have failed, as the climate seems to be a bit too warm for it. In 1918, a first attempt to check the menace of the stray dogs was made by the Baker Dog law instituting dog licenses. However, the problem of feral dogs has not been solved fully as yet and has acquired local political implications, as many dogs that may be caught roving have owners. Around 1920, a state game farm was created to propagate the bobwhite quail, and some restocking of the streams with rainbow trout was started. The rainbow trout can adapt to warmer and less pure waters than the indigenous brook trout, which was becoming rare.

In 1926, the former Department of Game and Inland Fisheries was transformed into a Commission of Game and Inland Fisheries; wildlife had become by that time and has remained a question arousing public interest and sometimes stormy political debates. The restocking of the Virginian environment went on through the 1920's and 1930's. Several trout nurseries were established to avoid the full depletion of the streams; thousands of Mexican bobwhite quail were imported and released successfully; a similar attempt with Hungarian partridges failed.

White-tailed deer had been wiped out in Virginia by 1920, with the exception of a few corners of the western ridges. Thousands of deer were brought from Pennsylvania, Michigan, Wisconsin, and New York State. Released in the counties west of the Blue Ridge, they had to be protected against the stray dogs. In 1945, sportsmen at last enjoyed deer hunting in southwest Virginia, mostly in national forest land. The imported northern subspecies mixed with the Virginia one to produce a somewhat new type of deer. The restocking of beavers began in 1938. The animals were bought in Pennsylvania and West Virginia and settled at the heads of rivers in the ridges. Beavers need a precise environment: slow-running streams with stands of young aspens on the banks, which they cut to make their dams and the lodges in which they store winter food. They feed mainly upon bark and twigs of willow, poplar, and birch. The beavers released in the upper parts of the valleys came down to find more appropriate conditions and a slower flow of the stream. Then they developed a taste for apples in the orchards and corn in the fields as a substitute for twigs and bark; sometimes with their dams they flooded cultivated areas. Their development has been checked in many points. Most of their primitive habitat having been destroyed by man's land use, they will never regain it entirely.

The wild turkey, a bird almost symbolic of the environment of Virginia and the eastern United States, had been hunted to the point of almost complete extinction in the area. Until 1912, wild turkeys were sold on the markets in Virginia; then they became so difficult to find that they had to be restored artificially to their natural habitat. From 1928 on, wild turkeys were raised at the State Game Farm on Windsor Shades. At first, they were found too tame to thrive in wild and primitive conditions. A new program was more successfully started in 1936, when careful study revealed the habits and food requirements of the birds. Wing-clipped hens were placed in wire-enclosed pens within a range inhabited by native wild gobblers. Eggs obtained this way are incubated and brooded artificially. Captivity-reared young are released as soon as they are able to take care of themselves to prevent them from becoming tame.[28]

In 1935, the Commission entered into an agreement with the U. S. Forest Service to manage in a cooperative way 30,000 acres of federal forest in Augusta County. Thus was created the Big Levels refuge, very important for deer. Such cooperative management was new in the country: the game in the national forests became the state's responsibility while the environment, the forest, was managed and modified by the federal forestry service. This kind of cooperation in the management of wildlife was extended to 1,400,000 acres of federal land in Virginia. The necessary funds were provided by a charge of $1.00 for the privilege of hunting or fishing in the national forests. An excellent program of forest management for game was thus elaborated, and Virginia is rightly considered the leading state in the Union in this field.

The restocking effort was somewhat hampered by the chestnut blight, which cut down the supply of mast for many animals. For instance, bears became dependent on acorns, which is a cyclic crop, and their number was reduced. They feed also upon berries and insects, but sometimes they remember that they are predators as well and kill sheep. Though once distributed throughout the state, black bears are now confined to the rugged sections of the mountains and to the Dismal Swamp.

During the period of restocking, more and more laws and regulations for the protection of wildlife were gradually set up. The protective measures now include the institution of closed seasons restricting the legal hunting period for most game species to November and December. For elk and beaver there is no open season at all, full protection having been deemed necessary in the present state of affairs. Fox has an open season for hunting with hounds; fox hunting is a sport of long standing in Virginia. It is practiced according to a traditional ritual; no bag limit was set for the foxes. The red fox is hunted in northern Virginia and the gray fox mostly in the mountains. A few very efficient limitations have been established, however, like the prohibition of hunting on Sundays, of selling the game, and of hunting in the snow; above all, bag limits were established.

Bag limits take into account the approximate number of game animals and the number of hunters. For instance, the bag limit for deer is one male a season, or one a day and two a season according to the county. The bag limit for bears is one a season. For quail, the bag limit is eight a day,

[28] Mosby and Handley, *The Wild Turkey in Virginia,* Richmond, 1943. See also P. C. Fearnow and I. T. Quinn, "Action on the Blue Ridge," in *Trees, Yearbook of Agriculture,* 1949, pp. 586–592.

125 a season; for rabbits, six a day, 75 a season; for wild turkeys, one a day, two a season. The bag limit must be enforced with special care in areas where the game may congregate because of special opportunities offered to it, as in the proximity of wildlife refuges.

After years of depletion and destruction of game, these protective measures, allied to the effort of restocking, have proved to be efficient. A good game population was built up. According to an inventory of big game animals made by the U. S. Fish and Wildlife Service, there were in 1952 in Virginia 60,000 white-tailed deer, 1,000 black bears, and 5,000 wild turkeys. This allows for a rather heavy kill: in 1952 it amounted to more than 10,000 deer, 300 bears, and 1,600 wild turkeys. One may say that now the period of protection and restocking is over and a new era of normal game management can begin in which cropping can be adjusted to the rate of reproduction of animals. For instance, if the above figures for deer are correct, the deer population, adding about 40 per cent each year, may develop too fast and be checked by a food-supply shortage, no new range being open to them. Such has been the case in parts of Pennsylvania and Wisconsin where overbrowsing by deer is obvious and causes damage to tree reproduction in forest areas; this situation has brought about criticism of the so-called buck law, which allows only male deer to be killed. Does should be killed, too, in order to obtain a proper game management in areas overcrowded by deer. In 1951, the West Virginia Game Commission was authorized by the legislature to open a season for does. Realistic game management requires more flexible legislation, conditions for game varying from county to county and from watershed to watershed. This has been recognized in Colorado, where the territory is broken down into game management units according to physiographic divisions.

Migratory birds are protected in Virginia as part of the general pattern applied to the whole country by federal authorities. Geese and ducks can be hunted only with a federal stamp, the produce from the sale of which is used for wildlife refuges. There is, nevertheless, some poaching going on, even in Virginia. In 1951, two agents of the U. S. Fish and Wildlife Service, detailed in Virginia and Maryland, destroyed 160 duck traps and apprehended five trappers. It was estimated that some 15,000 waterfowl were killed illegally in 1952. But on the whole the protection system is fairly efficient. Two large waterfowl refuges have been established on lowlands and marshes of the Virginia seaboard along the Atlantic flyway: the Back Bay refuge, opened in 1938, covers 4,589 acres; the better-known Chincoteague refuge, established in 1943, covers 8,816 acres. (See description, page 165.) Between them a small refuge is maintained on Fisherman's Island (225 acres). A state waterfowl refuge is being organized on

Hawks and crows shot in the hunt

Hog Island near Jamestown; wheat and rice are grown there for the birds. The refuges of Virginia are shelters for many kinds of migrating birds, including the Greater Snow Goose, the Canada goose, the American brant, the black duck, the pintail, the baldpate, and the whistling swan. In the same way, areas of salt marshes are protected because they serve as spawning areas for fish, wintering grounds for birds, and breeding places for small animals and many commercial fishes.

During the period of protection and restocking, adequate measures were also taken concerning fish in the streams. Open seasons were established for fishing: from May to September for trout, from June to December or March for bass or pike. Creel limits and size limits were also set. Fishing licenses are required, and a special stamp is necessary for the national forests. It is unlawful to sell fish thus taken in the state's waters, as it is unlawful to sell game. Legal-size plantings of two- or three-pound trout are made. They offer poor sport, sometimes called "bathtub fishing," and deplete whatever food is left in the water during the short time they stay in the stream.

Stream improvement, to provide better environment for the fish, would solve the problem of fish depletion: the rivers are depleted as a result of siltation and changes in water temperature that kill the insects and microorganisms which are the staple food of the fish. Some improvement has been achieved on a small scale. For instance, logs or small dams have been placed in river channels to slow the current and provide a place where weeds and insects, which are food for the trout, can develop. Experiments are being made in a new technique of trout management: legal-size trout are stocked in short lengths of closed water along the creek; the trout are then supposed to expand from this point. The fact is that a solution to the problem of water pollution, which affects much more than wildlife alone, would provide an answer to the worries about the fresh-water fish. The State Water Control Law of 1946 was an important step ahead in water management: it gave industries ten years to cut their release of polluted waters. It is still too early to discuss its final results.

As the work of restocking and the elaboration of a complicated but efficient system of wildlife legislation are being completed, hunting and fishing have become big businesses in Virginia. Wildlife has also become a political issue, as the numbers of hunters and fishermen rise, not only in the rural areas but also among city people who like to go hunting; the view is becoming prevalent that the local administration has the responsibility of providing everyone with the opportunity to do so. Every year an increased number of licenses for state residents is sold: to hunt in the state, 155,000 in the fiscal year 1951–1952, and 203,000 in 1952–1953; to fish in the state, 105,400 in 1951–1952, and 123,000 in 1952–1953. As a result, more fish and more game are needed every year if the results achieved in rebuilding wildlife are to be maintained. Virginia is now coming into a period of game management aimed at providing a maximum crop of game animals. Ideally, there should be set for every hunting territory and for each season, according to the local situation, the number of game animals that can be killed. At present this is not feasible; the bag limit is a wholesale but realistic approach.

Virginia state authorities have cooperated most successfully with the U. S. Forest Service in restoring wildlife in the national forests. In 1951–1952, 58,028 national forest stamps that serve as hunting permits (at $1.00 apiece) were sold in Virginia and 63,712 in 1952–1953. The funds thus collected financed a cooperative wildlife program, augmented by contributions from federal funds. The program consists of various practices. Small clearings are made and sown with ladino clover and orchard grass; old abandoned fields are maintained; old logging roads are seeded to keep clearings for the game to feed. As the forest grows older and the canopy closes, there are fewer sprouts and twigs and less grass to feed the deer. Grains are sown for turkeys. In cutting, certain trees are left or planted that provide desirable food for wildlife, like oaks and Chinese chestnut trees, which give mast. White pine is favored, as it gives good cover for turkeys. For squirrels and raccoons, one den tree per acre is left wherever possible.

These efforts provide more deer, bears, grouse, turkeys, and other game for the hunters. The opinion has even been expressed, founded on the constant lowering in value of the forest production, that wooded areas should be managed mainly as hunting grounds, without concern for silviculture. This opinion represents a dangerous interpretation of the situation, since adequate concern about silviculture would greatly increase the value of the forest crop in lumber and pulpwood. The product per acre of a forest is always higher in dollars and cents than the product of an acre of hunting ground. On the other hand, very intensive forest management precludes over-abundant wildlife. If one takes into account the moderate hunting pressure in Virginia today, it seems possible to set up a good forest management that would include a good game program, keeping a balance in public forests between timber production and recreation. Such multipurpose management is now working well in both national and state forests.

Improving the habitat of wildlife should be done only on public lands. Resident wildlife, in general, is a responsibility of the commonwealth, and this means dealing with the farmers and small woodlot owners. A game farm program has been initiated by the Commission of Game and Inland Fisheries to induce farmers to plant trees and shrubs and maintain hedges or coverts on the borders of their fields to benefit quails, rabbits, and mourning doves. All these animals are well adapted to cultivated areas and are popular for shooting. In the old days, hunting used to be a "free for all" proposition. Now that hunting is more popular and the country is heavily populated, hunting can become a true nuisance to the farmer, as some hunters feel too much at home on his land. The relationship between farmers and hunters reveals the need for education of the general public on the subject. When the land is posted with a no-hunting sign, it generally means that the local farmer has lost any interest in wildlife through bad personal experience. A realistic trespass law would perhaps help. Only if well protected from trespassers will the farmer help to protect wildlife; he has to be interested in it and perhaps get a revenue from it. Up to now hunting is generally free on farmland or can be practiced for the price of a bottle of whiskey.

In some areas, restocking of rabbits and quails has been made by the Commission. The control of predators is also their responsibility, in connection with the U. S. Fish and Wildlife Service. There is no control of foxes, as fox hunting is so popular; but bounties are paid for hawks and skunks. There remains the difficult problem of feral dogs, often called the "free-running dog menace." These are sometimes dogs without licenses, but often licensed dogs on a spree, which shows that the license approach is not the answer. These dogs wreak havoc in the forests, killing or wounding deer and flushing turkeys or ruffed grouse from their nests.

It is apparent in conclusion that relations between man and wildlife have undergone several changes at different periods and that they are again in transition. While changing the landscape, man exerts a tremendous influence on wildlife, the living conditions of which are thus related to the distribution of population, type of agriculture, industrial activities, and existing legislation. At present, protection, reintroduction, and habitat improvement are working well and still can be developed. All such endeavors can be ruined if the hunting pressure becomes too great: in many European countries, where there are too many hunters, game is raised on farms and released for hunting. This provides a highly artificial type of hunting. By sound techniques, Virginia has been able to create artificially a balance which can be maintained through the ways of nature if not again interfered with.

The story of the past and present of wildlife in Virginia, particularly in the forests, is a fascinating one. People are too often inclined to consider wildlife, the fauna of an area, as the characteristic product of the natural environment, as an unaltered gift of God. It must be realized that in Virginia, as in many other parts of the world, wildlife today is as much the result of systematic restoration as restored Williamsburg is. And just as the present town of Williamsburg is different even so from what it used to be in the eighteenth century, the present tableau of wildlife in Virginia is also quite different from what it used to be.

Water resources and vegetation

Water is in some respects, like wildlife, a crop of the forest. The U. S. Forest Service was established and the purchases of land for the national forests were started under the Weeks Act mainly as a measure of flood control. The vegetation cover is a capital factor in determining the circulation of water on the ground and in the soil. Thus land use and land management directly influence the whole vast problem of water resources.

The vegetation cover is particularly important where the slope of the land is steep, which is the case in the whole of western Virginia and in a good part of the Piedmont. From the Appalachian ridges come most of the waters that run across eastern Virginia. Some of the streams origi-

Floodwaters of the Shenandoah River covering a Virginia farm
Library of Congress Photo by Arthur Rothstein

nating at least partly in Virginia, especially in its southwest, belong to a basin feeding some other great rivers; thus the New River and the Clinch River flow towards the Mississippi through a series of intermediaries. Thus water resources and forestry both came, and one through the other, into the realm of responsibilities of the federal government. But what is done on federal land alone cannot determine all that happens on the surrounding lands, however cleverly public property is situated.

The effect of the forest on water circulation is manifold. An abundant literature has been devoted to this subject. In arid regions of the West, during periods of drought and strong evaporation, people have deplored the fact that some of the water that reached the ground was lost for the downstream inhabitants and their crops through evaporation by the canopy of trees in the forests upstream. However, this extreme view was inspired by critical circumstances. It has been demonstrated by many experiments in various parts of the country that the forest cover over steep slopes contributes to storing more water in the ground, keeping the run-off from being too violent, keeping the soil in place, and preventing, therefore, erosion and the silting of streams.

A specialist, concluding a detailed study of water yields and the possibility of controlling them, writes:

Certain land uses and vegetation treatments have clearly defined hydrologic consequences. . . . It has been repeatedly demonstrated that fire which lays the soil bare, and agricultural practices which leave the soil exposed during seasons of high intensity rain, must be avoided if surface flow and erosion are to be kept low. . . . The clearing of wooded slopes or the breaking of native sod for agricultural use of the land has often been accompanied by seriously increased surface flow and erosion. Hydrologic consequences of these kinds are most severe in steep lands where the soil is easily compacted or eroded, and in those places where rains are heavy.[29]

After conducting minute studies in the southern Appalachians, another specialist in the relationship between forest and water remarks:

When stream conditions in undisturbed forests are observed, one is convinced that good forests, good soils and good water go hand in hand. Soil conditions under undisturbed forest encourage storage of water and make possible the control of erosion. It is reasonable to believe that through the ages there has developed harmonious adjustment of vegetation, soil and water. This natural adjustment, however, appears to be a delicate balance. It is impossible to disturb the forest without disturbing this equilibrium.[30]

The more depleted the forest cover in soils on steep ground, the greater the quantity of water that flows down on the surface towards the streams. In such conditions infiltration and storage of water are reduced; the flow of the streams draining these slopes immediately becomes more irregular, determined to a greater extent by rainfall or the thaw of snow. The waters are bound to flow downstream more rapidly and carry more silt; as a result they are more difficult to use because of both irregularity and content. The increased siltation of the rivers means, besides a threat to navigation, to industrial uses, and to the thriving of fish, less good soil left upstream. Management of the watershed should be conducted in such a way that erosion is reduced and the largest, cleanest, and steadiest possible flow in the streams is insured. This assignment is not easy to execute, given what we know of the past and present of Virginia soils and vegetation cover.

Within the last twenty-five years, the amount of water used in Virginia has tripled, perhaps quadrupled. Such a rapid increase in requirement is to be explained by industrialization, urbanization, general increase of the population, and particularly the rise of this population's standard of living, that is, of its consumption of many diverse goods and services. In-

[29] E. A. Colman, *Vegetation and Watershed Management*, New York, 1953, p. 355.

[30] Robert E. Dils, *Influence of Forest Cutting and Mountain Farming on Some Vegetation, Surface Soil and Surface Runoff Characteristics*, Asheville, N. C., Southeastern Forest Experiment Station, Paper No. 24, June, 1953, p. 52.

This small stream carries a quantity of pebbles and stones, even in its level downstream sections, amounting almost to an avalanche. These rocks came from the steep slopes and ridges upstream, which were deforested.
Virginia Forest Service

dustry has an enormous thirst for water: the generation of electricity at steam plants, for instance, requires huge quantities of water for cooling purposes; a steam plant using 1,000 tons of coal per day needs also about 600,000 tons of water daily, and preferably cool, clean water. Textile and chemical mills consume water on a large scale also. As the industrialization of Virginia develops, the problem of water supply will grow more and more important, more and more upsetting. The proper authorities are cognizant of this in the commonwealth, especially as the droughts of 1953 and 1954 created acute water shortages which disturbed the whole rural population.

Most of the present water supply comes from surface water: in early 1953 it was estimated that about 11 billion gallons of surface water were used per day in Virginia and only 0.3 billion gallons of ground water. The surface waters come from the Appalachians and the Blue Ridge, flowing in a general southeasterly direction along many channels organized into several watersheds, some outside the state. Those of the James River, the Potomac, and the Roanoke are by far the larger. In southwestern Virginia, the New River and the streams forming the head-

Looking up South River towards its junction with Irish Creek, George Washington National Forest
U. S. Forest Service

waters of the Tennessee River flow in different directions and each drains over 3,000 square miles of Virginia territory. The practice of keeping stream-flow records is not very old, nor have many been kept; it was only in 1925 that a statewide program was started with a network of gauging stations.[31]

The intensity and distribution of rainfall, the topography, geology and vegetation cover are the main factors determining the way water behaves when it reaches the ground. Virginia's rainfall pattern often includes long dry spells followed by very heavy rains. Normally the months of heaviest precipitation—June to August—are also the months of heaviest transpiration, which is for farming a very advantageous coincidence. This means, however, that the light rains from late fall to early spring contribute most to the annual upkeep of surface-flow and ground-water supplies. The average annual runoff over Virginia approximates 15 inches, i.e., about one-third of the annual rainfall. During a very dry year this runoff may subside to 3 inches, about 10 per cent of that year's rainfall.

[31] Donald S. Wallace, "The Surface Water Resources of Virginia," *The University of Virginia Newsletter*, Charlottesville, April 15, 1953. Engineers have prepared many detailed technical reports on the various rivers of Virginia, mainly concerned with water-power and navigation problems.

In a very rainy year, on the contrary, runoff may amount to 35 inches, or 50 per cent of that wet year's rainfall. In an average year, two-thirds of the runoff occurs from December to May, leaving only one-third for the warmer half of the year. The streams with the highest annual runoff are those of southwestern Virginia, particularly the tributaries of the Tennessee and the New River; this is easy to understand, as steeper slopes and a heavier average rainfall combine here to accelerate runoff. The lowest annual runoff is found in the Shenandoah Valley, owing to both lighter rains and greater infiltration into the ground of the limestone valley. According to the records of the James River flow at Cartersville since 1900, the history of the runoff in the largest watershed of Virginia has been a most irregular one; the highest runoff was observed in 1949 and the lowest in 1930–1932, a very dry period.

As the demand for water for municipal and industrial uses is increasing steadily, new measures must be considered to provide for it. A network of adequate storage reservoirs which could be used in a multipurpose way, and from which the water could be distributed by pipelines, is being advocated at present.[32] The people of Virginia are slowly growing "water conscious." Their concern is not limited to surface water resources. As an increasing number of farms in the Tidewater and the Piedmont are turning to irrigation for certain crops, more ground water is being tapped by wells. As dry years occur, like those of 1930, 1936, 1941, 1952, 1953, and 1954, more people may turn to supplementary irrigation in order to obtain higher and more regular yields. As recreation develops in importance in the mode of life of the average Virginian and as a commercial activity for the whole state, more lakes and clean streams will be needed. Hence water resources have begun to attract the attention of the local government.

In 1952, the Advisory Council on the Virginia Economy had its committee on water resources study the situation. The detailed report that ensued[33] discussed at length the uses of water, the existing legislation and the recommendations to the federal government of the President's Water Resources Policy Commission of 1950. It concluded that a constructive water policy for Virginia should be rapidly worked out:

Clearly, in a rapidly expanding industrial and urban society, such as Virginia is experiencing, water resources take on an ever rising value. Virginia and the federal government have taken many legislative and administrative steps in recent years to bring about a more effective utilization of the water resources of the state. One measure on the state level, the State Water Control Board established

[32] Donald S. Wallace, *op. cit.*
[33] The Advisory Council on the Virginia Economy, *Water Resources of Virginia*, Report of the Committee on Water Resources, Richmond, April, 1952.

The Shenandoah River seen from the Woodstock Tower overlooking the Shenandoah Valley, with the town of Woodstock at the left.
U. S. Forest Service

in 1946, has been strikingly successful in abating pollution in Virginia waters. The effectiveness of this program has increased the quantity of water available for municipal and industrial users as well as increased the quality of water—this latter effect contributing to the benefit of recreation and commercial fishery users. . . . It is recommended that watershed management and conservation programs be integral parts of multi-purpose developments determined during the initial studies and executed in coordination with work on downstream projects. . . .

More action is needed regarding water-pollution laws. Although much progress has been made, many large industrial plants still pollute the waters of the neighboring rivers. Many large cities, including Richmond, although major consumers in need of increasing quantities of clean water, still add greatly to the pollution of the streams on which they were built and which should remain essential sources of water.

The problem of water conservation is too vast to be considered entirely within the realm of the consequences of forestry management; but the Committee on Water Resources could not help being impressed by such reports as this, which it quoted:

Mr. George W. Dean, State Forester, reports that the average forest topsoil at one inch depth absorbs fifty times as much water as bare silty loam. Carefully conducted experiments over a number of years in Mississippi show that between a scrub oak forest and an adjacent open field with the same per cent of slope and soil type the surface runoff from the open, cultivated field was 127 greater than from the adjacent forest." [34]

The studies made in Virginia did not pay enough attention perhaps to the problem of grazing the slopes, which is still being done in many parts of the valleys-and-ridges section of the state. In explaining how to care for watersheds, leading specialists of the U. S. Department of Agriculture remark:

The chief thing to avoid is overgrazing. When the livestock overcrop the herbaceous and shrubby forage, the ground surface is bared to the direct impact of the rain. This condition opens the canopy, permitting the sun's rays to hasten the disintegration of litter on the ground. Consumption of the forage, though it puts pounds on the grazing animals, robs the soil surface of its normal annual accumulation of dead grass stalks and leaves. Continued over the years, this further exposes the soil surface. In addition, the hoofs of the grazing animals compact the soil or push it down hill. All these effects lower the capacity of the land to soak up and store water and therefore favor destructive overland flow, accelerated erosion and greater sediment loads in the streams. Overgrazing results in progressively serious stages of watershed deterioration.[35]

Whoever has travelled through western Virginia recently has seen many disastrous effects of overgrazing—river beds filled with pebbles and stones, swollen with heavy rains and advancing like lava towards the Valley to the southwest of Harrisonburg; deep erosion on the meagerly wooded slopes of the obviously overgrazed ridges to the southwest of Lexington; and many other such landscapes in southwestern Virginia. Effective legislation must begin where the flood and the erosion begin, that is, in the upstream sections of the watersheds, where too many small mountain farmers still appear to be unaware of the need to conserve water and soil, as if they did not intend to cooperate with the public services endeavoring at great cost to insure a better water crop for the community.

The greatest of Virginia's resources

The use or misuse of the forests affects much more than just the timber crop. However, even when limiting ourselves to that product of the forest, we may claim for the forests of Virginia the first rank among the resources with which nature has endowed the state. Trees can be grown

[34] *Ibid.*, p. 105.
[35] G. W. Craddock and C. R. Hursh, "Watersheds and How to Care for Them," in *Trees, Yearbook of Agriculture*, 1949, pp. 603–608.

almost anywhere in the state; they grow relatively fast owing to the warmth and dampness of the climate. Over half of the land area is today under trees. From all that has been said about the present state of forestry, it seems fairly obvious and conservative to suggest that the value of the tree crop could be about doubled in the Old Dominion if adequate management were provided for a sufficient period of time in both public and private wooded lands.

Why has the forest of Virginia been so mismanaged for long generations? Many factors have been at play. For some three centuries the American people have had too much woods throughout the country. The early settlers did not like the forest: they came here in part to cut it down. In Virginia they were somewhat disappointed by the fact that local tree associations were not so favorable to the needs of naval stores and shipbuilding as forests further north or south in America. The necessity of clearing trees and stumps from the land made agricultural settlement more difficult. The forest seemed to favor the richer planters who could command the labor of indentured workers or slaves for land clearing. The poorer people were limited by the trees in the endeavor to expand their farms.

In addition, these people came from England, where for several centuries the forest had been an enemy of the people. William the Conqueror had brought from Normandy and France a feudal legal system deeply resented by the Anglo-Saxon people, and one aspect of it, the "Forest Court," was, according to Trevelyan, "more odious to Norman and Saxon alike than any private jurisdiction." "The forest law and the forest courts of Normandy were transplanted to England, with lamentable results in human suffering and servitude . . . The special courts of the forest deprived all who dwelt within their jurisdiction of many of the ordinary rights of the subject. . . . The gradual deforestation of district after district marked the economic and moral progress of the country." [36] Fighting the woods for the Englishman had been for hundreds of years fighting for liberation; the fight may not have been forgotten by those who emigrated to Virginia. In the seventeenth century the forest question was again a great political issue in England, as the Crown was trying to set up more new forests. The British disliked the forests so much that nowadays Great Britain must import about 97 per cent of her needs in forest products. Some of this attitude may have been carried over to the Virginia shores and kept alive by the obstacles raised by the trees to settlement in the East.

[36] See G. M. Trevelyan, *History of England*, London, 1926, Book I, Chapter VIII. The game laws were also deeply resented, and the Anglo-Saxon chronicler bitterly complained about them.

As the American economy grew, however, trees became a valuable raw material, especially at the end of the nineteenth century.

At first, timber was a nuisance, something to be rid of, so the land could be used for other purposes. Then, as the people moved in, came the demand for lumber, and much of the remaining accessible timber was cut: the all-time peak of lumber production in the United States was reached in 1907. The fires which followed did terrible damage. And all of these factors together reduced the area of forest land from the original 900 to 622 million acres, of which about 460 million acres are today rated as commercial in character. And they reduced the standing timber volume from the original 8,000 billion board feet to about 1,600 billion board feet.[37]

The supply of wood is rapidly falling short of the demand, although per-capita consumption has greatly decreased; the population continues to grow, and the deficit in the domestic procurement of forest products threatens to increase.

The quantity of wood available is only part of the story. American forest industries definitely prefer certain species to others, and they put conifers (pines, firs, spruce) at the top of their requirement list. This is easy to understand. The pattern of procurement of these industries was set during the last third of the nineteenth century and the beginning of the twentieth, when they developed on a large scale. At that time there were vast areas of pines in the eastern United States, largely on abandoned fields, as agriculture had receded after the Civil War in the southeast and also in the northeast because of the triumphant competition of the rising agriculture in the Great Plains. The industrial techniques were geared to the use of softwoods. These species grow faster anyhow, and handling them is certainly easier. Moreover—and this detail may be a fairly important one—most of the foresters who went to study silviculture abroad and then established the traditions in teaching it in most of the American schools of forestry, went to Sweden, Norway and northern Germany, all countries in which softwoods uniformly predominate. To the American forestry tradition, hardwoods became largely a nuisance, as were all trees two hundred years ago. Then came a bitter disappointment: after the great crop of softwoods was cut, in most parts of the East, softwoods had great difficulty regenerating themselves, and their retreat began before the invasion of the hardwoods.

The trend towards hardwoods is not exclusively Virginian. The Harvard Forest in Massachusetts has experienced in its endeavor to regenerate white pine difficulties similar to those encountered in eastern Virginia

[37] From an address entitled "Forestry in Transition" by Charles L. Tebbe, Regional Forester, Eastern Region, U. S. Forest Service, at the winter meeting of the New England Section, Society of American Foresters, March, 1953, in Boston, Mass.

A National Parks Service lecture on botany

in the regeneration of loblolly or short-leaf pines. As industry cannot avoid adjusting itself to the available supply, many wood-using plants, especially of the larger size, are beginning to use hardwoods even for pulp-making. The plant of the West Virginia Pulp and Paper Company in Covington, Virginia, manufacturing different kinds of sanitary and wrapping paper, has for some time now been using mixtures of softwoods and hardwoods, the latter sometimes constituting 80 per cent of the raw material out of which the paper is made. Covington is situated in a valley amidst Allegheny ridges where hardwoods have indisputably predominated for some time. In southeastern Virginia, at Franklin, the large mill of the Camp Lumber Company has been equipped to utilize the greatest possible variety of species, producing lumber, pulp, paper and chemicals from wood in the same plant. On an even larger and fuller scale, some large mills in New England and California are adopting a system under which their plants can utilize to best advantage all kinds and sizes of woods shipped to them. A dispatching system directs the various logs to the section of the mill which can use them most efficiently. A great deal has yet to be done to achieve such ends in Virginia, as one can still see there, where hardwoods are used, oak logs of impressive size, which could be valuable material for furniture or veneer, dissolved into pulp.

The majority of the wood-using industries in Virginia are still very far from renouncing their exclusive preference for softwood. As recent surveys have shown that the pine situation is becoming critical, more measures to favor pines and eliminate hardwoods have been suggested. The Virginia Forest Service has done a most creditable job of fighting forest fires; it is engaged now in a much more difficult fight against the hardwoods. The action of men and the trends of nature concur at present to favor hardwood growth *versus* softwoods over most of Virginia, even in the Tidewater. Opposing such a combination of factors is a hard task with little hope of success. The State Forester would of course be in a difficult position if he opposed the measures requested by the wood-using industries. But it would also be rather hard for him in the long run to encourage the wishful thinking that the invasion of hardwoods can be easily prevented.

In a resolution adopted in 1954, the General Assembly cited the "alarming rate" of decline of merchantable timber in recent years in the state, and called for a study of the forest resources. In July, 1954, a legislative study commission appointed by the Governor began to consider the various problems involved. The Assembly's resolution stated:

The commission shall investigate the supply of timber remaining in Virginia, with particular reference to softwood timber; determine the areas of the State in which timber resources have been most drastically depleted; consider whether present cutting practices are extravagant or wasteful, and result in excessive depletion of timber; and develop information as to practices which should be put into effect to produce the largest returns to owners of timberland including consideration of price trends during recent years for stumpage of various kinds, including sawmill and pulpwood. The commission shall determine what regulatory measures, if any, are needed to provide adequate supplies of timber for industrial use and to maintain stable income for owners of timberland, and develop information and recommend educational programs, if needed, to increase the returns to landowners from timber resources and to advise landowners as to how best to develop the same.[38]

The attention given to this major problem of land use and resources-management by the General Assembly of Virginia should be heartening. It ought to give much greater results than just encouraging measures aimed at fostering the production of softwoods. The state government has at present an opportunity to start a program that would generously benefit the regional economy, landowners as well as industries, and could set a pattern for the rest of the nation.

[38] *The Richmond Times-Dispatch*, July 14, 1954.

Observation towers provide a measure of protection against forest fires.
Virginia Forest Service

A great deal could be achieved in forestry through wise legislation. The management of privately owned woodland is a major problem throughout the state. Public control of cutting on private land meets with opposition in the land of the free, even though many benefits would result for the community. A compulsory system of cutting, as in the United Kingdom, France, or the Netherlands, would not work in America, as it could be made effective only by severe penalties. Any compulsory intervention of state forestry officers in the management of private forests, as in Sweden or Norway, would be rather unpopular too.

It has been proposed that a federally sponsored credit system be established to make long-term loans under conditions encouraging forest improvement, for instance, to enable owners to consolidate holdings or adopt more efficient protection and management practices, and to facilitate forest plantings and weedings. But many owners may hesitate to contract debts to improve their forests. Furthermore it is difficult for the agency involved, as far as forestry is concerned, to see that the loan is properly used, especially when the landowner is poorly educated in forestry.

Some system of credit could perhaps be devised to help the woodlot owner spare his forest until it is fully mature even though he needs an immediate cash crop. There is little doubt that the community benefits when more forest properties are acquired by companies or corporations with more ready capital, longer life, and greater interest in the future than the majority of the present individual owners. In forestry this is true the world around: but the individual owner resents this trend; and instead of eliminating individual ownership, which is quite unthinkable in a region like Virginia, owners should be helped to adopt an attitude toward the forest more nearly like that of the larger owners, and this attitude could be brought about by provision of capital and credit.

The small landowner is often afraid of loans from the banks, and the national banks do not like long-term loans. Moreover, as a tree grows, it rarely adds more than 3 per cent annually to its value. Therefore it is not difficult nowadays to find more profitable and safer investments for capital. If a system of credit could be worked out which would mortgage the stands and the growth of the stands, without mortgaging the land, it might prevent woodlot owners from cutting down young forests when they need immediate cash. However, commercial banks would hardly undertake such transactions unless some official guarantees were provided. Such an investment could perhaps be suggested to insurance companies or to tax-exempt institutions which can finance long-term loans. Nevertheless the return therefrom may be smaller to the investor than if the investment were made in a more orthodox fashion. There is always the possibility of a rise in the prices of timber or pulpwood to encourage such investment, but prices might remain stable, and some slight decline might even occur. How much the motive of better resources and land management, of providing for the future of the national materials supply, might influence capital to go into such a credit scheme remains to be studied and discussed.[39]

In any case, the forest owner, unless he has organized his forest property on a grand scale, needs in Virginia more help and advice as well as more education than he has been getting and, often, than he is willing to accept. In the present situation, as the industries and the nation grow more and more concerned about the future of the wood supply, Virginia may take the lead in solving her own problem and establishing a new pattern. One possibility is an optional management of private forests by a technical agency such as the State Forest Service, under conditions made attractive for private ownership—something like an adaptation of

[39] See the paper "The Functions of Capital and Credit as They Apply to Forestry in Transition" given by Edgar C. Hirst, President, First National Bank of Concord, N. H., at the winter meeting of the New England Section, Society of American Foresters, in Boston, March, 1953.

the British dedication system, according to which the forest is permanently managed by a public agency; American conditions, however, might favor contracts for shorter periods with less control by the public agency. Or something like the Portuguese system might be considered, in which tax reductions are granted to forests managed by a public agency.

A simple solution might be to induce small owners to enter into cooperative agreements with the Virginia Forest Service. Such agreements should be long-term ones and should provide that the forest be managed, and if necessary planted, according to principles that insure continuous yield and stand improvement under the guidance of officers of the Forest Service. Under such agreements the owner could not cut more than allowed by the plans of the Forest Service. Such a program would of course involve some sacrifices by the owner, who would not be able to cut during the time necessary to build up fully stocked stands. As a counterpart, it might be advisable to allow the owner some tax exemption. Banks might then find it safer to give him long-term loans based on the growth of the stands, as they would trust management by an institution like the Forest Service more than management at will by an individual.

To fit such a purpose, special legislation would be needed. Such a system would have the advantage of being by no means compulsory, the forest owners being induced to use it by the prospect of getting a better return from the property in the long run, even if it benefits their heirs rather than themselves. Obviously such a program would mean a considerable increase in the staff and competence of the Virginia Forest Service, with heavy expenses at first for weedings, thinnings, and all kinds of improvements of the forest. From the experience of many foreign countries, we know that these expenses pay in the long run. It takes time and money to build up a good forest resource, but when it is built and properly cared for, it yields high returns. Forestry is worth putting money into. Besides producing more raw materials for industrial use, some such plan would increase the wildlife resources, improve the water supply, add to the beauty of the country, and augment its value for recreation. It should also be remembered that expansion of the area of land under other, more profitable, farm uses is highly unlikely. No better utilization could be found at present for half of Virginia.

Better management of private forests would benefit the public in Virginia within some thirty to forty years. The expenses of the work done on private land might, if necessary for the commonwealth's treasury, be accounted for and refunded at the time of the first timber sale by preemption of a small percentage of the product of the sale. Many systems might be arranged for making of such agreements between landowners

Smokey rides the mail truck.
Virginia Forest Service

and public authorities something like a long-term credit system controlled by a state agency.

There are about 170,000 small forest owners in Virginia. Not all of them could be expected to participate in such a program of contract agreements if it were established. The Virginia Forest Service would have to advise private owners on the management of their forests and educate them as the first indispensable step to achieve good forest practices. The education program should include systematically all the major problems of forest management in addition to fire protection and softwood encouragement. It is a difficult task to get in touch with so many people scattered throughout the territory, but personal contacts are the most valuable. The farmers could be prepared by systematic campaigns and courses over the television networks, perhaps demonstrating the operations on model or experimental woodlots. In the summer of 1954, federal authorities offered to turn over to the State of Virginia the Lee experimental forest in Buckingham County, a tract of oaks and pines about 2,600 acres wide, on condition that the state authorities would take up and pursue an experimental research program. In cooperation with the officers of the national forests and of the Shenandoah National Park, Virginia could show a great deal of diversified forestry within her lands; and it would be a worth-while lesson for the whole country east of the Mississippi.

A program is easy to draft; it is less easily put to work. Education in forestry is needed at least on three levels nowadays: the level of the forest owner, for better management; the level of the wood-using industries, for more efficient use of the available supply; the level of the technical staff in forestry, which is certainly not large enough at present to meet the task ahead. To obtain any actual improvement, through education and through legislation, public opinion must be won to the side of the need for better forestry, and this requires more education at the level of the common man and of the children in the schools. It is a curious and striking fact that in Virginia, one of the important forested states in the Union, so little forestry is taught in institutions of higher learning. Aside from undergraduate courses at the Virginia Polytechnic Institute, the offering is quite slim. Almost all the foresters in responsible positions throughout the State have had all or most of their training in forestry at schools outside Virginia, perhaps Michigan or Pennsylvania, Yale or Harvard. The commonwealth appears to be so situated, by its geography, its past and present problems, and its industrial activities, as to have a special stake in forestry and therefore, it would seem, in a large, well-endowed center of teaching and research in this field. As more concern is being expressed in responsible circles throughout the nation about forestry matters, such centers are bound to come into being. Virginia now has a good chance for assuming national leadership.

The study of forests and the use thereof brought us in touch with a variety of questions and fields: the biological and geological environment, recreation and industry, banking and education. It is too often believed, even in the more enlightened circles, that the forest, like wildlife, is just one of those gifts of God that man can enjoy but about which there is not much he can do. The review of the past and present of forests in Virginia demonstrates how artificial is the actual status of these resources as of most other so-called natural resources. Man has the forests he has deserved in any area he has occupied for a long period of time. Resourcefulness is essentially a human quality and function: more of it can and will be displayed in connection with the Virginian forests.

5. The Use of Farmland

THE PAST HISTORY of agriculture in Virginia is a more complicated and diversified one than that of the forests. We reviewed it briefly in our study of three and a half centuries of change in the Old Dominion. The days of the large plantations, of the manorial farms, have long since passed. Virginia is today a country of many small and medium-sized farms, with a small number of large farming units. The census of 1950 recorded 151,000 farms in the state; this meant a substantial decrease since 1935, when the number had reached 197,632 units. Of these total numbers, in 1950 only 12,227 had more than 260 acres each and only 828 more than 1,000 acres each. In 1935 there were 12,153 farms of more than 260 acres and 691 of more than 1,000 acres. The figures for 1935 were not very different from those of 1920. But the farmland has shrunk in area in this period: it came down from 18.5 million acres in 1920 to 17.6 in 1935 and 15.5 in 1950. The farmland occupied 72.0 per cent of the total land area in 1920 and 61 per cent in 1950. There is less and less land tilled in Virginia, and it is concentrated in a slightly smaller number of somewhat larger units on the average.

These statistics raise a few questions: Is agriculture declining in Virginia? Was it broken up into too many small units in the beginning of the century? Should such a trend be interpreted as signifying a social evolution? Agriculture has certainly not declined in Virginia since the beginning of this century or since 1920. The trends shown by the figures quoted hint at the same kind of evolution as farming has demonstrated throughout the United States: the number of all farms decreased and the number of large farms increased. But in the whole country the total area of farmland expanded (from 955 million acres in 1920 to 1,159 in 1950), while in Virginia it decreased. Since 1920, Virginia has seen large purchases of land by the state and the federal government for the creation of national forests and parks or military bases and camps. The rapid expansion of urban residential and industrial property took away from farming rather important areas. Altogether, many factors contributed to bring about some shrinking of the tilled land acreage in Virginia. In most cases it was the cheaper kinds of land, the marginal or submarginal kinds of farms, that were in this way turned over to other uses. What remained of agriculture kept the better lands or those dedicated to the more profitable crops.

The question of whether there were too many small farm units cannot be answered in a simple way. While a trend towards consolidation of a number of farms into larger units has been observed in Virginia, it was slower than on the national scene as a whole, which witnessed almost a doubling of the number of farms over 1,000 acres each from 1920 to 1950. On the other hand, the number of very small farms, under 30 acres, has been rather stable; the number of farms under 3 acres has even increased, witnessing to the growth of outer-suburbia residences, with a little farming around these homes. The statistics for a diversified area the size of Virginia are difficult to interpret; the regional breakdown may teach us a few more facts as to trends.

The picture of the crops has also been changing in recent years. Since the beginning of this century, the areas sown in corn, wheat, and oats and those planted in cotton and Irish potatoes have gradually shrunk, while the areas in hay, soybeans, and barley expanded and those under peanuts and tobacco remained relatively stable. The general trends of livestock figures correspond rather well to the preceding ones: horses and sheep are definitely on the decrease; hogs, although their number changes quite a bit from year to year, seem on the whole stabilized (in the vicinity of 800,000 head); but the number of cattle has been steadily on the increase. This latter trend seems to be the most sustained one over a long period: Virginia had 600,000 head of cattle in 1870, about 800,000 in 1910, 896,000 in 1940, and 1,410,000 in 1954. The expansion of cattle husbandry explains the growth of the requirements of hay, and these requirements have exceeded the local production in many a dry year.

The total area of the farmland as quoted above is much larger than the land tilled, i.e., the land under crops or pasture. More than one third of the total acreage in farms is under woods; we have dealt with this woodland while studying the forests. The tilled and pastured land which produces the annual harvests covered in 1950 some 8,841,584 acres—35 per cent of the total land area. It was less important therefore in the land-use picture than the forested land, which occupied some 58 per cent. The income annually secured by the tilled land is of course much more important than that provided by the forests. Even if better management practices and the gradual average aging of the Virginia woods should double, as seems reasonably possible, the present returns from the forests, agricultural production would still remain more profitable than silvicultural income. This 35 per cent of the land area is the essential part of the traditional Virginia economy; although agricultural income payments do not represent in recent years more than 5 to 10 per cent of the total income payments in the commonwealth, the rural farm population in 1950 amounted to 22 per cent of the total population in the state. The agricultural income is not necessarily the only source of revenue of the rural farm residents; nor does this whole income go to people residing on the farms: many landowners live in town; but it remains that about one fifth of the people of Virginia depend on agriculture for their means of living. As can be seen from the part of agriculture in providing the total income, the farmers are not the better-paid section of the population. However, they enjoy on the farms many material advantages which are not available to townsfolk and which do not appear on any payroll.

To better understand the present land use, we must examine now the geography of the farms and then the geography of the crops before studying in greater detail the principal problems of the tilled land.

The geography of farms

Farms may be classified in many different ways, according to a variety of characteristics. The size of the farm is one of the important features in the pattern of land use, and it is interesting to look at the variation in the average size of farms in the counties of Virginia. We have already used this feature in attempting to describe the regional aspects within the commonwealth. Let us look now at a map of the counties, on each of which the average size of the farm is indicated by a graduated symbol; to indicate the economic importance of the holdings, we have set these measures on the general background of shades corresponding to the main categories of values of an acre of farmland (see map, page 319).

The extreme case of the urbanized county of Arlington, where 24 farms of an average size of 18 acres still subsisted in 1950, has been deleted from this map as being practically nonagricultural. This exception being made, let us note where the extremes in average sizes are located: the column symbolizing the size of the farms is graduated up to 250 acres; the highest average acreage is found in Highland County with 248 acres in 1950, and it is followed by neighboring Bath (223 acres) and by hilly Clarke County (209 acres); the lowest average acreage is found in the bayside county Mathews (30 acres), closely followed by hilly Wise County in the southwestern triangle (with 38 acres). Other small average acreages are found in several of the southwestern counties. The largest continuous area with a low average acreage is to be found in the south of the commonwealth: most of the counties in the vicinity of the North Carolina line have farms of an average size below or just above 100 acres. On the contrary the largest group of counties, six of them, where the average acreage is consistently above 150 acres is to be observed in the north of the Piedmont, west and southwest of the District of Columbia.

Relating the size of the average farm to the average value of an acre of farmland makes one realize the complexity and multiplicity of the factors involved. The smaller sizes are found in areas of very different land values: high values in Mathews and Wise, in Arlington and Roanoke Counties; relatively low values in Dickenson and Buchanan. On the whole the lower land values, particularly in the Piedmont, correspond to average farm sizes, chiefly between 50 and 150 acres, but in the Alleghenies lower values of farmland mean larger-scale farming units (as in Highland, Bath, and Craig Counties). The price of the land interprets a demand. It is higher of course around the large cities, as a result of the expansion of metropolitan areas and of the proximity to consuming markets: thus it is high around Hampton Roads, even more so around Washington, and on a much smaller scale around Richmond and Roanoke. The price of land being very high in the immediate vicinity of the expanding suburbs brings the size of the farms down in Arlington and Fairfax, York, and Warwick. But in the outer suburbia of Washington, as both price and distance go up, farms are more and more bought by wealthy people or organizations that can afford to invest in this land and prefer to do so on a large scale: in Loudoun, Clarke, and Fauquier the average size of the farm goes up. Sizes similar to those of the latter counties in Washington's outer suburbia are then found in only one other corner of Virginia—in the poorer and much cheaper lands of the middle Allegheny counties. Relatively high prices for farmland are also found in the Shenandoah Valley (particularly Rockingham and Augusta Counties) and in overpopulated sections of the southwestern triangle: here they produce average or very small sizes.

The relationship between the size of the farm and the price of the land appears rather complicated in Virginia; one does not determine the other. The higher land values and smaller farms of Mathews County, for instance, have nothing to do with a similar relationship that can be observed in Fairfax: Mathews is not a suburban area; it is rather out of the way of the major traffic; but it is on the Chesapeake Bay and con-

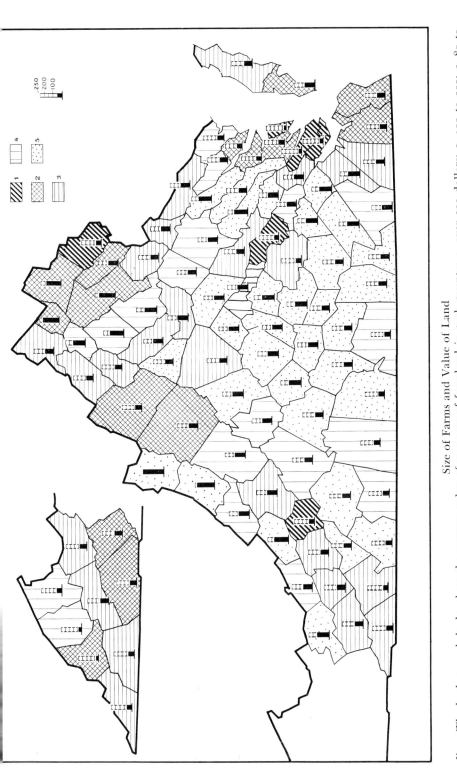

Size of Farms and Value of Land

Key: The background shades show the average value of one acre of farmland in each county: 1, over 200 dollars; 2, 100 to 200; 3, 80 to 100; 4, 60 to 80; 5, 40 to 60. The column-shaped symbol in each county shows, according to the scale in the top right corner of the map, the average size of farms in each county up to 250 acres (no county in Virginia has an average above this figure, according to the 1950 Census of Agriculture).

ducts active oystering and fishing; it is the only county in Virginia where the major source of income is fisheries. Thus, the value of the farmland and the size of the farms reflect a composite picture greatly influenced by the proximity to cities, the presence of nonagricultural activities, the pressure of population, and many other factors. The proximity to industrial plants employing scattered rural manpower may help keep the small farms going, as it may also induce many former farmers to reduce their agricultural activities to a kind of gardening. Similar trends are generally observed in the vicinity of cities. Certain types of landownership and certain crops greatly affect this picture, too, for some important landowners divide their properties into farms operated by tenants according to family tradition or the type of land utilization; this happens often, for instance, in the tobacco belt.

The kind of tenancy is a very important social and economic feature. There are sharp contrasts in the number and importance of tenant-operated *versus* owner-operated farms. The map (see page 321) showing the distribution of farms operated by tenants in proportion to the total number of farms reveals a vast area, crossing the commonwealth from the Appalachian ridges to the shores of the Bay, where the percentage of tenants is low, under 10 per cent of all farms. This vast area covers almost one half of the state but does not correspond, curiously enough, to any one of the major physiographic divisions. It encompasses almost all of western Virginia, but for a few counties at its two extremities, north and south. It also encompasses most of the northern and central Piedmont and the eastern part of the Northern Necks in the Tidewater. In most of this area tenants operate between 4 and 10 per cent of all farms; in seven counties only does this percentage fall below 4 per cent, and the lowest percentage is again Mathews County (with 2.5 per cent). Quite a varied gamut of land values and average sizes of farms is found within this area, which curves over the state from the Cumberland plateau to the estuary of the Potomac. North of this belt there are two islands with percentages higher than ten in which owner-farmers predominate absolutely. One is made of three northern counties: Loudoun, Clarke and Frederick, where the percentage remains between 10 and 20; the other, somewhat larger in area, consists of the western part of the Northern Necks, where the percentage stays between 10 and 14. Another island of such moderate percentages of tenants is found in the southwestern triangle, south of the coal fields: the percentages here range from 15 to 21 per cent. On the whole, the areas where the percentage is higher than 20 are all found in the south of Virginia.

The main concentration of tenant farming is in the southern Piedmont

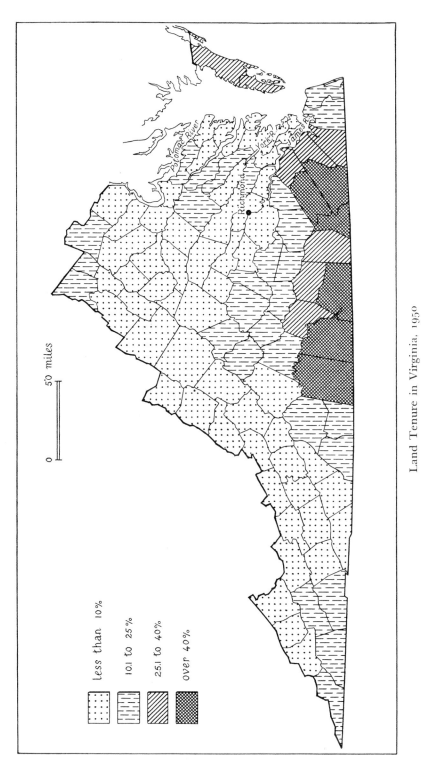

Land Tenure in Virginia, 1950

Per cent of all farms operated by tenants, by counties, according to the 1950 Census of Agriculture

and the southside Tidewater, with an extension on the Eastern Shore. The highest proportions are in Southampton (61.8 per cent) and Halifax (51.8), the only two counties where tenants are in the majority. In Mecklenburg, Pittsylvania, Greensville, and Sussex the percentage is still above 40. Tenants are concentrated today in the more deeply rural areas, with such traditionally "southern" crops as tobacco, cotton, and peanuts. These row-crops require more manpower, especially in harvesting; they are also high-priced, chiefly due to government support and limitation of acreage. The abundance of tenants is an inheritance also from the old plantation system. It seems to belong to an earlier economy, rapidly receding in the present evolution. In 1945, the proportion of tenancy in Virginia was 20.3 per cent; in 1950 it had come down to 17.1 per cent. The decrease was particularly sharp in parts of the Piedmont where the proportion used to be quite high; thus from 1945 to 1950 the percentage of tenants went down in Pittsylvania from 56.4 to 47.5, in Henry County from 24 to 11, in Amherst from 26 to 15, in Appomattox from 41 to 18, in Halifax only from 57.4 to 51.8. It went down also in many Tidewater counties such as Accomack, Nansemond, and Northampton, but went slightly upwards in a few cases, such as Surry. The main area where the proportion of tenants seems rather to have increased is in the mountainous west, where it has remained on the whole rather low.

The distribution of the farms operated by tenants is somewhat related to the distribution of Negroes, especially in fully rural areas. However, some of the counties with the highest proportion of Negro people in the population do not belong to the belt of concentrated tenancy—for instance, Charles City County, where many Negroes own their lands and where the main source of income is derived from urban jobs. The tenancy system provides a rather scanty living, and nowadays high-priced crops such as those mentioned above are required to make it possible to take two successive profits from the land. The great majority of the tenants are share-croppers or croppers; less than ten per cent of all tenants operate on a cash or share-cash system.

The whole trend of farming in Virginia points towards a smaller number of somewhat larger farms, more and more operated by owners, or in some cases by specialized managers; it is a healthy trend which promises to increase the rentability of the farming unit and bring larger average profits to the farm population. These different trends have forged ahead rather quickly in recent years. The 1945 census of agriculture enumerated in Virginia about 173,000 farms of which only 40 per cent were classified as commercial farms. The 1950 census enumerated some 151,000 farms of which 51 per cent were commercial, despite the proliferation of small suburban farming units, partly residential. Farming is becoming more commercialized, a fact which means more profitable business for the Old Dominion. Not only did the average size of the farm increase, but it is apparent that the beneficiaries of this trend were actually fairly large, well-managed farms. Looking at the breakdown by categories of sizes, we find that in numbers as well as in acreage all categories of farms lost between 1945 and 1950 except the 500-acres-or-more category. The decline was insignificant for the farms between 220 and 500 acres in size, but all size categories below 220 acres registered a substantial drop. At the same time the number of farmers working part-time off their farm increased by about ten per cent, and the number of farm operators not residing on the farm was cut almost in two. All these trends concur to reduce the problem of marginal and submarginal farming in Virginia.

Another way of approaching the geography of farms in Virginia is to consider the land use within the farmland by county. There are about three main possible uses of farmland: for crops, for pasture, and otherwise, the latter meaning chiefly woodland and shrubland. To present this, the map (see page 324) reprsents as a half-circle the total land area of the county. On that half-circle, sections represent the proportion of the total area in farmland, and within the latter, in cropland and pasture. In the great majority of counties, farmland covers from one-third to two-thirds of the total area. In a few cases the proportion of farmland is much higher, chiefly in the southern parts, such as the rich tobacco-growing counties of Pittsylvania and Halifax and in the deeply rural intermountain area of the Blue Ridge (Floyd and Grayson Counties). Another corner with a high proportion of farmland is found in the extreme north of the state (Loudoun especially). The lowest proportions are located in the urbanized, history-devoted peninsula between the James and York Rivers, as well as in the hilly and forested counties of Alleghany and Bath.

Within the total farmland the proportion of tilled land (crops and pasture put together) offers other variations reflecting the general proportion of woodland (compare with map, page 240). That proportion is particularly slim in counties occupying the Great Valley floor, and also in Clarke County. Whatever woodland there is in those counties is on the ridges and not usually included in farmland. On the contrary, farm woodlots play an impressive part in the middle and southern Piedmont, and in many Tidewater areas. The importance of cropland and of pasture varies greatly too; however, this is not at all indicative of the relative part of animal husbandry on the farms. A good deal of the cropland is devoted to hay or livestock feeds; in many cases animals are allowed to

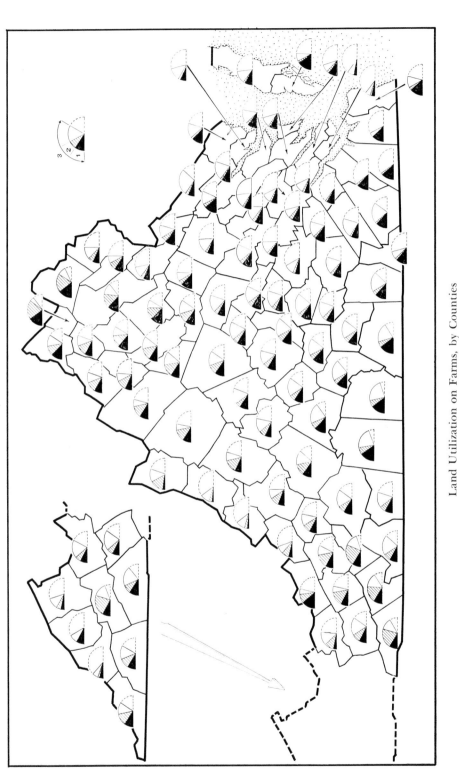

Land Utilization on Farms, by Counties

Key: Each symbol in the shape of a half-circle represents the total farmland in the county. The shaded subdivisions of the half circle represent the approximate proportion of the total farmland which is: 1, in cropland; 2, in pasture; 3, under cultivation (total). Source of data: Virginia Farm Statistics, Bulletin No. 16, Richmond, 1952.

pasture parts of the cultivated fields. However, it is interesting to observe the variability of the proportion of cropland within the area of the various counties. This feature of the map provides a schematic view of the relative importance of farming in the region. The southside Tidewater, the Eastern Shore, and a few counties in the north and southwest have impressive proportions of their land area in crops. This impression must be corrected to account for the fact that some farming activities, although substantial sources of profit, such as poultry raising in the Shenandoah Valley, do not appear on the map, and the rich agricultural counties of Rockingham and Augusta, expanding over ridges covered with national forest land, seem to have a moderate part of their area under crops. This fact underscores the concentration of rich farming of the Great Valley as against the much more scattered and diffuse cropland of the southern Piedmont.

To better understand land use on the farms, this general review must now proceed to an analysis of the distribution of major crops throughout Virginia.

The geography of crops

The fields of Virginia are scattered amidst woods and pastures over most of the land. Only on the Eastern Shore and on the flatter parts of the Great Valley floor does one get the impression of a continuous predominance of tilled land. To portray such a patchwork, which changes from year to year, some systematization was needed. A simple method has been devised (see map, page 326) by which the figures of the 1950 census of agriculture by counties have been recorded on a small map. For each county a checkered rectangle symbolizes the total area of farmland. Each of the eight vertical columns in every rectangle corresponds to 12.5 per cent of this area. They have been marked by different symbols representing eight major crops: corn, hay, annual legumes, Irish potatoes, sweet potatoes, cotton, tobacco, fruits, and vegetables.

The tableau thus obtained testifies to a few interesting features of farming in Virginia. The crops of the Tidewater have a greater variety and are of greater importance in space than those west of the fall line. The greatest variety and the largest share in area of the crops is to be found on the Eastern Shore. In other parts of the Tidewater the picture would have been even more diversified if wheat and peanuts could have been indicated too. On the Piedmont, the better and more diversified farming of its northern and southern parts as against the central section becomes striking. Grains and hay appear the two major crops everywhere west of

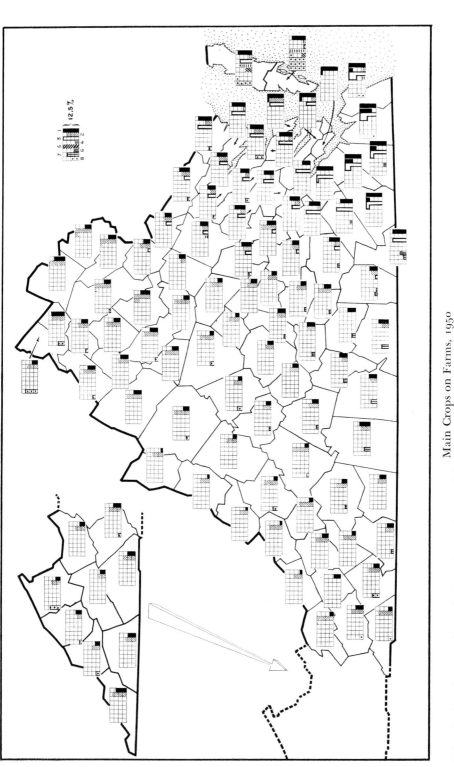

Main Crops on Farms, 1950

The checkered rectangle symbolizes the total area of farmland in the county. Each of the eight vertical divisions of the rectangle corresponds to 12.5 per cent of the area. Each of eight principal categories of crops has been indicated by shades in a vertical column according to the legend in the upper right-hand corner of the map: 1, corn; 2, hay; 3, annual legumes; 4, Irish potatoes; 5, sweet potatoes; 6, cotton; 7, tobacco; 8, fruits and vegetables. Thus the relative importance of each crop in each county is shown.

the fall line, with some addition, small in space but usually big in profit, of tobacco in the southern Piedmont and of fruit orchards in the Valley and the Blue Ridge foothills. Hay is quite important everywhere but in the southside Tidewater and on the Shore; in the two latter areas annual legumes and corn take a lot of land. The two classical examples of Southern agriculture and of the plantation economy, cotton and tobacco, are very little present, cotton particularly, and both are restricted to a small section of the commonwealth. Cotton has never been a predominant crop in Virginia, but tobacco certainly was at one time. Tobacco is now herded into the southern Piedmont, with a secondary producing area in the southern Blue Ridge. As the dictum describing the recent evolution of Southern farming has it, "cotton goes west and cattle comes east." This certainly applies fully to Virginia, where the cultivation of cotton will probably almost completely disappear in a not too distant future, and where the main line of development is towards cattle in almost all parts of the state.

The tableau of land use provided by such a sketchy map is of course incomplete and must be supplemented with more detailed sketches of the distribution of crops. Since animal husbandry is becoming the leading occupation of the majority of Virginia farmers, let us look now at the distribution of livestock in the state (see maps, page 328). All cattle distribution changes somewhat every year, and the 1950 count is already superseded by a substantial growth of the herds since. Still basing our conclusions on the general pattern of the 1950 statistics, we find that western Virginia, the Valley especially, is the area of main cattle concentration. This is an old trend, as grains and pastures have always been more important west of the Blue Ridge, where neither tobacco nor cotton were usually grown. However, the northern Piedmont shows a most impressive cattle density in a half ring around the Washington metropolitan area, and the cattle invasion of the upper Piedmont is quite notable also in such foothill counties as Albemarle and Bedford. If figures for 1954 were fully available, more Piedmont counties would have darker shades on such a map.

Map II on the same page gives the distribution of milk cows, which follows approximately the same lines as the map of all cattle, but, of course, in lighter shades. However, it is remarkable that the difference seems smaller in the Tidewater and lower Piedmont. Although milk cows are rather well distributed throughout the state and achieve greater densities along the Great Valley and in the northern Piedmont, western and northern Virginia seem definitely more specialized in beef. This is also apparent in the landscapes as one rides around the country: there is

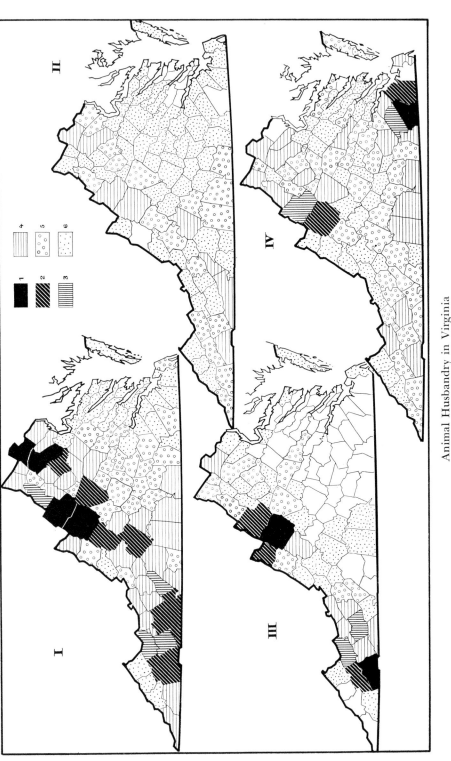

Animal Husbandry in Virginia

Key: These four maps show the distribution of livestock in Virginia. Map I: all cattle; Map II: milk cows; Map III: sheep and lambs; Map IV: hogs and pigs. Scale of shades (common to all four maps), in thousand head, by county: 1, over 50; 2, 25 to 35; 3, 20 to 25; 4, 10 to 25; 5, 5 to 10; 6, 1 to 5. Source of data: 1950 Census.

Registered Shorthorn cattle grazing on native pasture of bluegrass, Orchard grass, and white clover
Soil Conservation Service

definitely more black Aberdeen-Angus and White-Face Hereford cattle in the west and the north, and more black-and-white Holstein on the Tidewater pastures. The Tidewater and the lower Piedmont are closer to the large cities of the fall line and of Hampton Roads, and dairy farming benefits more by the proximity to urban consumers.

The map of the distribution of sheep and lambs (Map III on page 328) points up a massive concentration west of the Blue Ridge, chiefly on the limestone valleys and surrounding ridges. On the whole the pattern of distribution in the state is not very different from that of cattle, particularly of beef cattle. Finally the map of hogs (Map IV) shows them scattered everywhere, with the exception of the immediate suburban areas (such counties as Fairfax, Norfolk, York, Warwick, etc.). The area of heaviest concentration is by far the southside Tidewater, the land of the Smithfield hams, of peanuts, and of the corn-hog-peanuts association. The second area with many hogs, where a good many Virginia hams are also produced, is again in the Shenandoah Valley, particularly in Rockingham and Augusta Counties, outstanding for their richness in livestock of all kinds. Sheep are an old tradition with western Virginia, as are hogs with eastern Virginia. Cattle is a relatively new trend and a rapidly ex-

A pasture of seventy acres on an island in the Little James and the James Rivers grazed by sixty animals. Later in the season it will be clipped for seed.
Soil Conservation Service

panding one. In 1950, cattle already constituted by far the most important branch of and investment in animal husbandry throughout Virginia, as the darker coloration of Map I as against either II or IV well demonstrates. And cattle is moving in because Virginia, like most of the Southeast, has been discovered to be extremely well endowed as a grassland although its natural vegetation would be forest.

Grass grows easily and quickly on practically all the soils of Virginia. It is the product of the warm, damp climate. The brevity of the cold season and the rarity of heavy frost and deep snow in the Tidewater, the Piedmont, and the Great Valley are among the reasons for a good perennial grassy cover, and among the inducements for an all-year-around pasturing of cattle. Thus farm buildings can be reduced to a minimum despite the presence of large herds. The climate is considered just right in Virginia. The hot season is neither so hot nor so prolonged as to cause any of the trouble occurring with cattle bred in tropical regions. The climate is favorable to hay as well as grass; grass, a crop like any other, can be seeded, and selected species and seeds of grass will produce a much better pasture of forage crop from lands that may have brought poor yields otherwise.

Pastureland badly eroded
Virginia Forest Service

In a country where grass grew so plentifully and where such immense
expanses of grassland existed naturally, this resource appeared also to be
a gift of God and something men could harvest through livestock, without having to bother much about its production. As the United States
economy grew bigger, more demanding, and more complex, the need for
human intervention in the process of grass growing became apparent.
Careless pasturing can cause a great deal of erosion and depletion of the
soil. Erosion is one of the consequences of grazing on steep slopes, which
occurs so frequently in western Virginia. The South as a whole was not
considered an area for grass nor for cattle until recently. Within the last
thirty years, Southern farmers became conscious of the advantages of their
mild climate (which is not hotter during the summer heat than the Great
Plains are at that same season) for animal husbandry and for growing
grass. They had to learn, however, about the techniques and the economy
of an agriculture centered on grass: "Good pastures can do great good
in the South," wrote two specialists in government service a few years ago.

Every farmer knows why. His aim is to provide a large yield of nutritious forage
over a long grazing season. If he does so he has a cheaper source of minerals and
vitamins and other nutrients for his stock, a tool against erosion, a way to revive
abandoned land, a chance to raise more cows and pigs, an opportunity to

stabilize his income by getting away from too much row-crop agriculture. He needs them all. But to get a good pasture started he must remember two points: his pastures must include both grasses and legumes; he must fertilize his fields.[1]

A cardinal principle of pasture management is that grasses that grow themselves, of the bluegrass kind, should not be allowed to eliminate legumes, such as clover. A number of legumes grow naturally in the area and provide better feed for animals as well as better soil conservation. As the cattle economy develops in Virginia, pasturing on the ordinary kinds of grasses, of which bluegrass is the most popular, becomes more and more inadequate to feed the herds. Fields of alfalfa, clover, and other special grasses or legumes such as lespedeza have to be maintained.

The distribution of these valuable forage crops in Virginia is therefore an important aspect of farmland and will be increasingly so if the present trend towards cattle lasts, as it probably will. The maps (see page 333) indicate that the southern Piedmont has a concentration of lespedeza, while the acreage in alfalfa is scattered through the Valley and Piedmont lands, more of it towards the north than in the south of the state. On all three maps the Tidewater seems little interested in these three crops, except for the Northern Necks, where some lespedeza and clover are found. The southside Tidewater has almost none of the three. But we know from the general map of the crops that annual legumes are quite important in these areas (see map, page 326). However, the preferred legume in this category throughout the Tidewater is the soybean; moreover the area left blank on the three maps of legumes is also the country of the peanuts-hogs-corn system, where cattle is scarce as yet and where soybeans are quite frequent (see map, page 328).

There remains still a great deal to be done in the elaboration of a good grass-legume system in Virginia. Serious research on this problem was started rather recently. The inspiration came largely from lands of different climates and soils, either in the United States or in Europe. More must be done, found, and experimented with locally before a good rotation of grasses and legumes can insure to the farmer a satisfactory supply of hay to feed his cattle all year round without having to buy much hay from afar. The recent drought years of 1952, 1953, and 1954 have caused concern among the farmers about the capability of their cattle economy to survive. Hay shipped by rail for long distances comes at high prices and cuts down the farm income considerably. Federal aid for this purpose in 1953–1954 did not make up for all the losses. More and more one hears discussion in the commonwealth of the usefulness of

[1] H. W. Bennett and R. L. Lovvorn, "Starting and Maintaining Good Pastures," in *Grass, Yearbook of Agriculture, 1948,* Washington, 1948.

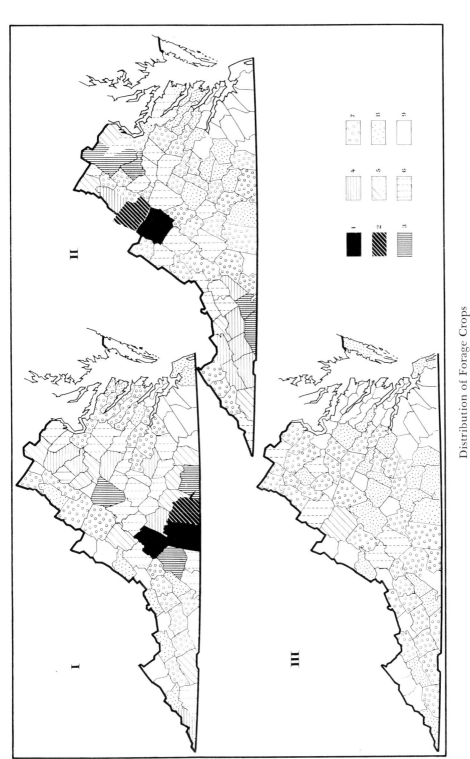

Distribution of Forage Crops

Key: Map I, lespedeza; Map II, clover; Map III, alfalfa. Scale of shades (common to all three maps), in thousand acres cultivated, by counties: 1, over 25; 2, 20 to 25; 3, 15 to 20; 4, 10 to 15; 5, 7 to 10; 6, 4 to 7; 7, 1 to 4; 8, 0.5 to 1; 9, less than 0.5.

supplementary irrigation. This would be an expensive solution, not always nor everywhere adequate. In the fall of 1954, so many wells and small streams temporarily dried up, completely or almost so, that they could have supplied little water for irrigation purposes just when the vegetation needed it most. When the drought is not too prolonged, irrigation does not seem to help more than do good cultural practices and a good choice of grasses and legumes, as experiments conducted in 1953–1954 seemed to show at the Experimental Station in Blacksburg.

More research should be carried on, since "we do know enough about the available plants, however, to build a fairly satisfactory pasture and forage program for most Southern farms and to realize that other plants are urgently needed to fill gaps in the program for certain sections." [2] But the farmers have to be educated and persuaded to follow the better practices now known to the specialists. Several experimental farms are working on this problem of pastures and forage in Virginia. Progress in the field is relatively rapid, because interest in cattle raising is very high. The 1950 Census of Agriculture showed that cattle and calves sold alive amounted to an annual value of $52,617,564, to which should be added a total sale of dairy products reaching $46,242,771. Thus cattle raising has brought Virginia farmers close to a hundred million dollars annually. This figure does not of course represent net revenue, especially as a good part of the young stock was bought and imported from other states. Nevertheless, returns from cattle have been approaching the total value of all agricultural crops sold (133.6 million dollars according to the 1950 census). Among the crops, tobacco ranked first in value of the harvest (55 million dollars), almost entirely sold on the market, and was followed by corn (51.3 million), a large part of which was consumed on the farms.

Poultry was also, according to the value of the produce sold, among the leading activities of Virginia farmers. In 1954, some statistics ranked it second only to tobacco; in 1950, the whole value of poultry and poultry products sold amounted to 45.8 million dollars. In both years it was far behind cattle as a source of income, if dairy products are considered together with cattle. Moreover, large-scale poultry husbandry is heavily concentrated in the Shenandoah Valley and on the Eastern Shore; it does not seem to be a major activity in other parts of the commonwealth. The economic structure of poultry raising in the major producing areas makes of it (see the discussion of poultry in the Shenandoah Valley, pages 207–208) a speculative production bringing back to the farmers only a small part of the cash product of the sales. In 1954 Virginia produced 314 eggs

[2] W. W. Woodhouse, Jr., and R. E. Blaser, "This Is Our Unfinished Business" in *Grass, Yearbook of Agriculture, 1948*, Washington, D. C., 1948, pp. 472–476.

per inhabitant; this was less than one egg a day per capita and less than the national average of 406. It does not seem sufficient to meet the growing demand both for human consumption and for hatching eggs. Poultry could still be developed in Virginia.

The agriculture of Virginia has been at some periods oriented towards the production of grains for export outside the state. Such was the case at the end of the eighteenth and in the beginning of the nineteenth centuries. Then, as the large-scale production of cereals developed in the west with the settlement of the Great Plains, Virginia farmers knew they could not compete, and grain cultivation was aimed only at the local or regional supply. While the acreage in corn and wheat has decreased somewhat, the yields of these crops per acre has gone up rapidly. The present distribution (see maps, page 336) shows the relative importance of the four main kinds of grains, corn, wheat, oats, and barley, in the various parts of Virginia.

Corn is of course the most popular and the most generally cultivated. No county, except the urbanized ones, had in 1950 less than 1,000 acres in corn. The greater acreages are, as could be expected, in the southern sections of the state, particularly the southern Piedmont and the southside Tidewater, but the acreage is impressive also in the northern Piedmont (Loudoun and Fauquier) and the richer parts of the Shenandoah Valley (Rockingham and Augusta). The two latter areas also show the more important acreages in wheat; the southern Piedmont, particularly Pittsylvania, shows on a lesser scale some interest in wheat. The Tidewater as a whole devotes little area to grain production other than corn. Barley, although its acreage has been on the increase, remains a secondary crop limited chiefly to the Great Valley and the northern Piedmont and linked to the areas of older cattle raising. Oats have been declining with the decrease in the number of horses at the beginning of the century, but their acreage and production have risen somewhat since 1940. They are nevertheless of some importance in Virginia, where horses are still raised on many farms, and where the northern Piedmont is an important center of fine horse-breeding. The number of these valuable animals, however, remains rather small and does not much affect the total number of the work stock of both horses and mules, which continues to decrease slowly. The number of horses declined from 171,000 in 1940 to 137,000 in 1950 and 95,000 in 1954; the number of mules followed a similar trend, from 94,000 in 1940 to 50,000 in 1954.

The case of grains testifies to the difficulties experienced at present by Virginia farmers in a rapidly changing economy. While the acreage under cereals decreases, the yields increase steadily, barring adverse weather con-

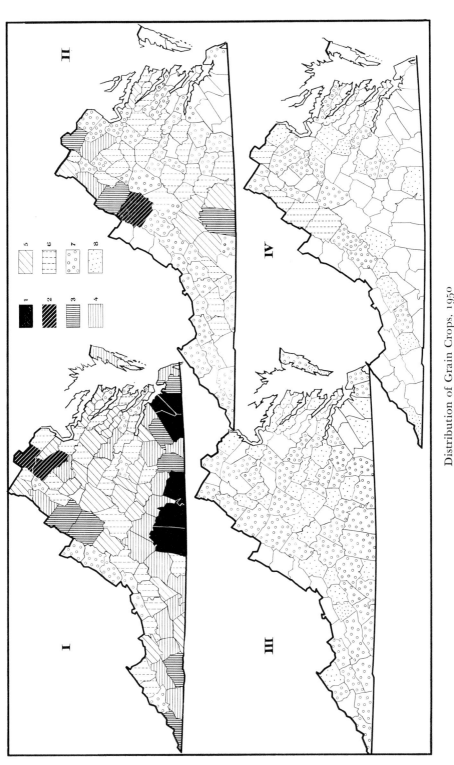

Distribution of Grain Crops, 1950

Key: Map I, corn; Map II, wheat; Map III, oats; Map IV, barley. The scale of shades applies to all four maps, in thousands of acres, by county: 1, over 25; 2, 20 to 25; 3, 15 to 20; 4, 10 to 15; 5, 7 to 10; 6, 4 to 7; 7, 1 to 4; 8, 0.5 to 1.

Butter beans being processed at Accomack on the Eastern Shore. *Virginia Chamber of Commerce Photo by Flournoy*

ditions. The production of corn, for instance, went up in the state from an average 33 to 36 thousand bushels in 1940–1944 to 41 to 44 in 1948–1951; only unfavorable weather brought it down to 24,800 bushels in 1953. The acreage, meanwhile, had steadily decreased from 1.3 million acres to 0.96 in 1940–1952; but the average yield per acre harvested went up from 25 to 27 bushels in the early 1940's to 45 to 46 in 1950–1951 and was 27 even in the very poor harvest of 1953. The average yields for wheat, oats, and barley also show a steady increase, though not as spectacular as in the case of corn; the volume of the production of wheat has been maintained around 7 to 8 million bushels; the production of oats has been rather on the increase. In short, Virginia has produced more and more grain in recent years. As both the population and the livestock herds increase, more food and feed are needed. The development of poultry raising expands the demand for grain on a large scale. Virginia finds it very difficult to store the grain at the time of harvesting, since very few large silos exist in the commonwealth. The more centrally situated, in Richmond, although impressive looking, is far from filling the needs of the present. And little new storage has been built recently on the farms. Norfolk is expanding its facilities for grain, and this development should help the southern parts of the state, from which transportation is well organized towards the great seaport. More storage facilities should be built inland and scattered throughout the state.

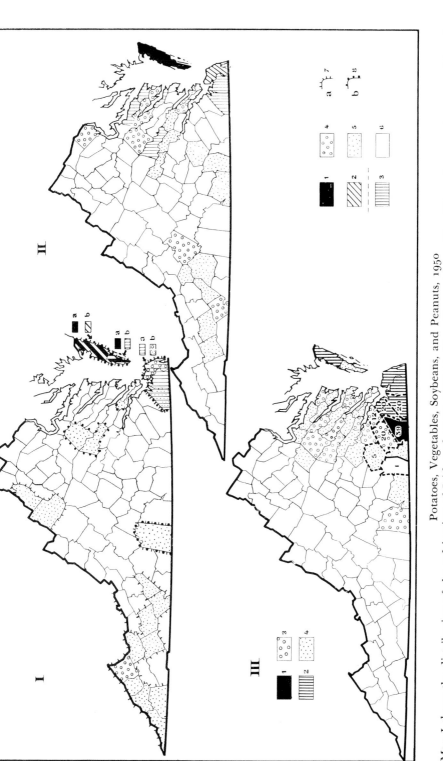

Potatoes, Vegetables, Soybeans, and Peanuts, 1950

Map I shows the distribution of the cultivation of Irish and sweet potatoes; Map II, vegetables; Map III, soybeans and peanuts. Maps I and II have a common scale of shades (see lower right corner) indicating the areas devoted to each crop in thousand acres, by county: 1, over 10; 2, 5 to 10; 3, 1 to 3; 4, 0.5 to 1; 5, 0.2 to 0.5; 6, less than 0.2; 7, areas under Irish potatoes, and 8, areas under sweet potatoes, on Map I. Map III has its own scale of shades for the areas in soybeans: 1—over 20,000 acres; 2—10,000 to 20,000; 3—5,000 to 10,000 acres;

Peanuts in a plant at Suffolk
Virginia Chamber of Commerce

A survey was conducted by the state authorities in 1948 because it had
been recognized that increased production of corn and small grains created certain marketing and storage problems in Virginia, and the farmer
was thus not getting as good a price for his grain as he might have. As
there is within the region an increased need for grains, it would have
been wise to foster conditions that would encourage farmers to expand
their production of these crops, instead of letting storage and marketing
facilities lag behind a rather slow and gradual growth. Prospective plantings in 1955 indicated an increase of the acreage under oats, barley, and
sorghums. Yields in Virginia and their progress are far behind what has
been recently happening in the Midwest. The trends on the farms are
nevertheless encouraging and will receive better coopration in time.

Grasses, legumes, and grains are the only groups of crops grown over
the whole state. Other productions are limited in their expansion to
certain sections of Virginia; but they may be extremely important to the
farming within this smaller compass. Vegetables are still grown through
the whole territory but their commercial role is clearly restricted to a few
areas, as can be seen from two maps (Maps I and II, page 338). It may
be well to look first at the distribution of potatoes, Irish and sweet.

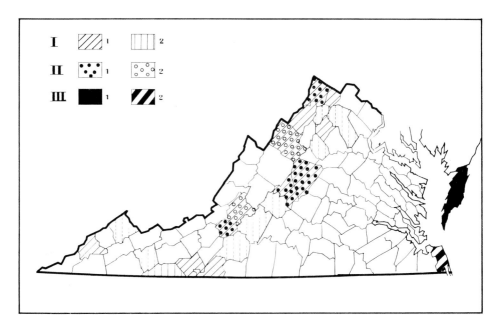

Fruit Crops in Virginia, 1950
Key: I shows the distribution of apple orchards by counties, indicating in Shade
1 counties with more than 100,000 trees and in Shade 2 those with 50,000 to
100,000 trees.

II shows the distribution of peach orchards, indicating in Shade 1 counties
with more than 100,000 peach trees and in Shade 2 those with 50,000 to 100,000
trees.

III shows the strawberry-growing areas, with Shade 1 for the two Eastern Shore
counties having over 1,000 acres under strawberries and with Shade 2 for Princess
Ann County with less than 1,000 but more than 500 acres.

In Virginia, the Irish potato, a northern kind of vegetable, is found
chiefly in the western counties and particularly in the southwest, but its
large scale commercial production is on the Eastern Shore and around
Norfolk, the great truck-farming areas of Virginia. Here the Irish potato
coincides with the sweet potato, a typical southern vegetable which is
otherwise little grown except in Pittsylvania County and in the vicinity
of Fredericksburg. Vegetables of all other sorts are a specialty of the Tidewater, but mostly of the low, flat, damp soils and long growing season of
the Shore and Flatwoods.

The Tidewater is again the region producing soybeans and peanuts
(see Map III, page 338). Soybeans are cultivated throughout the whole
Tidewater and even in the Piedmont county of Halifax, but the main
acreage is in the southside Tidewater, where it coincides with peanuts.
The latter crop is almost entirely limited to seven counties between the

Packing apples in Clarke County
Virginia Chamber of Commerce

Dismal Swamp, the James and the fall line. As regards soybeans, Virginia is a minor producer among the states; but for peanuts it is one of the leading areas: only three states (Georgia, North Carolina, and Alabama) have produced a greater quantity of peanuts than Virginia in recent years, and Virginia's rank was particularly high in 1950–1952, when this crop decreased rapidly in Texas. Moreover, Virginia specializes in the bigger sizes of peanuts, largely for human consumption; its yields are the highest in the United States and probably in the world: 1,254 pounds per acre as an average for 1941–1950, but 1,950 pounds in 1952. These yields do not include the unknown but substantial quantities of nuts rooted out of the ground by hogs.

Fruit crops are also restricted to certain parts of Virginia. Apples, peaches, and strawberries are the three kinds commercially grown on a large scale. Strawberries belong to the larger family of truck crops and are produced, as are most of the vegetables, in Accomack, Northampton, and Princess Anne Counties. Orchards of apple and peach trees are located at higher altitudes, in the Valley or on the Piedmont foothills of the Blue Ridge. There are three main areas of orchards: the Shenandoah Valley from Harrisburg northwards, the Piedmont foothills from Charlottes-

Packing apples in Clarke County
Virginia Chamber of Commerce

ville to Lynchburg, and the hills around Roanoke. Although the peach trees seem to be more concentrated in space and the apple orchards more scattered, they are found on the whole in the same general locations. Both kinds of orchards have been receding in area in recent times. A survey conducted at the end of 1952 showed that almost one fifth of Virginia's commercial apple trees and nearly one fourth of its peach trees were uprooted or abandoned to the birds and bugs in the three years prior to 1953.

In 1937 there were in Virginia 4,153,000 commercial apple trees; in 1949 there were 2,766,000 and in 1952, 2,389,000. Peach trees went down from 1,116,000 in 1949 to 938,000 in 1952. The rate of felling or abandonment seems higher in the Piedmont and southern Shenandoah Valley; the northern Valley and the Roanoke districts are concentrating more and more on orchards. Peach trees are also pushing eastward in the Northern Necks, closer to the city markets and into an area where frosts are less severe. The loss of trees has been largely the result of the abandonment of fruit growing by smaller growers. The remaining orchards are mostly in the hands of big growers who can afford modern grading and packaging plants. Some smaller growers are joining in groups to run modern packing sheds cooperatively. There has also been a marked trend away from green apples in favor of the red strains, particularly the "Red Delicious," which enjoys great popularity with consumers.

The last two specialized crops of Virginia, to a large extent the inheritance of the plantation past, are cotton and tobacco (see map, page 344). Cotton is limited to the counties where peanuts are a predominating cash crop and extends somewhat westward to bridge the area between peanuts and tobacco. The acreage in cotton is no longer important, unless for the rural Negro laborers in a few localities. It may be expected that as more Negroes leave the farms of the southside Tidewater, the acreage under cotton will shrink further. The fields of cotton are not continuous nor vast enough to warrant the mechanization of its picking. They are little more than a hangover from the past history of the area.

The situation is quite different with tobacco. The acreage of it is much more important and more stabilized. All of the southern Piedmont is highly interested in bright leaf tobacco, and many farmers of the southwestern triangle have an investment in burley tobacco. Most of the counties concerned have from 500 to 6,000 acres in tobacco, but two counties, Pittsylvania and Halifax, have more than 18,000 each. These two counties are the very heart of the tobacco growing region, the "Old Belt" of flue-cured tobacco. We have already stressed the very curious and special part of tobacco in the economy of the southern Piedmont (see page 178); only cattle raising is today an activity of greater importance to Virginia farmers. The southern Piedmont depends financially on the tobacco crop as much as the Eastern Shore depends on its truck farming and the southside Tidewater on the peanuts-corn-hog system. The prosperity of the tobacco growers is definitely artificial, maintained by means of government support of prices. This was strongly felt during the slump on the cigarette and tobacco market in 1953–1954. How well this crop can be maintained is a problem of great importance for the whole of Virginia agriculture.

The case of tobacco

Tobacco was the precious resource the early settlers developed in Virginia. The name of the commonwealth is probably better known through the world for a certain kind of tobacco than for anything else. At the same time, tobacco was, because of its success, for some three centuries a major weakness in Virginia's economy. To start with, tobacco was not processed or manufactured into the finished product in Virginia. Colonel Byrd is known to have been ordering smoking tobacco for his pipe from

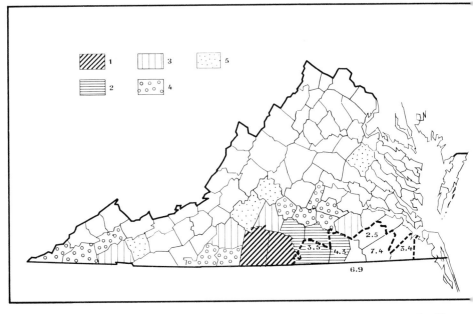

Distribution of Tobacco and Cotton in Virginia, 1950. The shades show the distribution of the cultivation of tobacco by county, in thousands of acres; 1—18 to 23 (only two counties, Pittsylvania and Halifax); 2—5 to 6; 3—3 to 5; 4—1 to 3; 5—.5 to 1. The broken line limits the counties of Virginia in which cotton was still cultivated in 1950; the figures written on each of these counties indicate the area under cotton in thousands of acres.

London around 1700. The mixture prepared for him in England was probably made with a great deal of the "Indian weed" grown in the Old Dominion. It was only in the nineteenth century that tobacco manufacturing developed in Virginia. Richmond, Lynchburg, Petersburg, and Danville made plugs of chewing tobacco as well as snuff and pipe tobacco; then cigars became fashionable. Cigarettes came into favor in the twentieth century; they accounted for only 2 per cent of the total consumption of tobacco in 1900; the per-capita consumption in the United States in that year averaged 32 cigarettes. In 1951, cigarettes made up three-fourths of the national consumption of tobacco; per-capita annual consumption then reached 2,607 cigarettes.

Today Virginia has a powerful industry processing tobacco and manufacturing cigarettes and other kinds of finished tobacco products. Cultivation is strictly regulated in acreage, but minimum prices have been guaranteed in exchange since the great depression. This situation came as a temporary solution of a very old problem. The area for which tobacco provided the main source of income in cash found itself constantly de-

A tobacco field with an irrigation sprinkler in action. There are eleven sprinklers in this five-acre field.
Soil Conservation Service

pendent on two variables: the weather and the market, both of which fluctuated a great deal. Neither the weather nor the market could be controlled by Virginia. When Virginia came into being in the seventeenth century, the modern economic system was already being organized, according to which the area producing raw materials is bound to be poor, somewhat underdeveloped country, especially if the production is limited to one raw material and if the area commands no monopoly of that product. Virginia depended too long on tobacco sales as its only important source of income; and, indeed, the monopoly never existed, even for the so-called Virginia tobacco. Often bad weather conditions helped the planters by reducing the crop so that previously accumulated surpluses could be absorbed, raising the prices. However, such a solution may have pleased the merchants, and later the economic historians, more than it pleased the producers at the time.

The market fluctuated all the more as tastes and fashions in tobacco consumption evolved. The same kind of tobacco does not serve for both chewing and cigarettes, or for both cigars and pipes. Every time the emphasis of the demand changed, it meant changes in methods of curing,

One rain caused erosion in this tobacco field because the rows were not planted
on the contour and the field was not terraced.
Soil Conservation Service

in the strains of the "weed" cultivated, in areas fitted for production.
Virginia had much more tobacco in the central Piedmont when the demand for sun-cured tobacco for chewing plugs was high. Fire-cured was
more popular when snuff was in great vogue. Flue-cured in the southern
Piedmont expanded greatly with the fortunes of the cigarette. The "Old
Belt" in Virginia's southern Piedmont extended early into the North
Carolina Piedmont. Then the cultivation of flue-cured tobacco went
further south. Not only did it straddle the fall line in Virginia and in-
vade the coastal plain of both Carolinas, but it is now found on a large
scale in Georgia and northern Florida. Further south, tobacco matures
earlier in the year and the season of auctioning opens earlier. The chant-
ing of the auctioneer can be heard in Georgia as early as July, in South
Carolina and eastern North Carolina beginning in August, in Virginia
only in September. True, the season in Virginia lasts longer, often until
Christmas, sometimes until early January. But prices for the same qualities are usually a bit better early in the season than they are late, when
the main buyers have already built up their stocks. In December, prices
obtained at auctions will be, as a rule, lower on the average than those

Planting tobacco seeds
Virginia Chamber of Commerce

obtained in July and August. Virginia's position northernmost among flue-cured producers is not an advantage. If an expansion of the authorized acreage of the types of tobacco produced in Virginia were to occur, it seems probable that it would occur further south, increasing the competition of Southern markets. This competition does not always cause lower prices for Virginia producers; whether it does or not depends on the quality of the crop through the country and on the demand during the season. When the demand on the Southern markets is light, however, as it was in 1954, Virginia markets prefer opening later and shortening the season.

The harvest of tobacco in Virginia has substantially varied from year to year. The total acreage of all types of tobacco in the state was quite low on the morrow of the War Between the States, as a result of the disorganization in the traditional supply of manpower. In 1866, only 70,-000 acres were harvested; by 1873, this acreage had risen to 118,000; then it oscillated from year to year but continued a slow upward trend. It never fell below 150,000 acres from 1890 to 1931, and it reached an average above 200,000 acres for the peak period 1918–1925. Having come down to 92,600 in 1931, it has oscillated between 100,000 and 175,000

Taking tobacco seedlings from the plant bed
Virginia Chamber of Commerce

acres since the depression and the passing of legislation attempting to stabilize the crop; it was expected to be 125,900 acres in 1955, that is, 4 per cent below the 1954 acreage.

Yields have varied from year to year much more than the acreage. The state's average yield in tobacco leaf remained between 500 and 750 pounds per acre from 1866 to 1933. Then, legislation having restricted the acreage but not the yields, it became worth while to improve them. In 1935, the average yield reached the unprecedented figure of 874 pounds per acre; since 1940, it has remained above 900 pounds per acre; in 1952 it reached 1,348 per acre. Production increased with the average yield. The 1952 harvest scored a record with 185 million pounds. Virginia is no longer, and has not been for some time, the leading producer among the states. North Carolina harvested 918 million pounds in 1952; its production has been systematically above Virginia's since 1911. Kentucky achieved in 1952 the figure of 478 million pounds, of burley tobacco essentially; it has produced in weight more than Virginia since before the Civil War; but burley is heavier than flue-cured and usually cheaper.

Thus Virginia is, today, the third state in the Union in terms of tobacco production, and the second for flue-cured tobacco. North Carolina

Setting out tobacco seedlings in the field. *Virginia Chamber of Commerce*

has achieved an enormous supremacy in quantity on both counts. Virginia does not produce only bright, flue-cured tobacco, although it is her specialty; the commonwealth has also a substantial crop of burley in its southwestern parts and some fire-cured and sun-cured in the central Piedmont and Carolina County. The main types produced go into mixtures for cigarettes (which nowadays use 50 to 55 per cent of flue-cured and 30 to 35 per cent of burley) and for pipe smoking (25 to 30 per cent flue-cured and 45 to 50 per cent burley). The prices obtained by Virginia tobacco were greatly improved by the price-support policy instituted since the New Deal, and by the rising consumption of tobacco, which resulted from the vogue of cigarette smoking, from the growth of the population, and from the rise of the average standard of living. In recent years the average price obtained did not go below 40 cents per pound; before 1942 it had reached above 40 cents only in the fabulous year 1919 (it went to 43.8 then) when the harvest was small. It usually stayed below 20 cents a pound until 1941.

The total value of Virginia's tobacco production never reached 10 million dollars from 1866 to 1906; it never reached 50 million until 1944, which was also the first year when the average yield per acre went over 1,000 pounds. The crop of 1952 brought the producers about 90 million dollars. In 1951, North Carolina made over half a billion dollars on

J. A. Hines and his son in their tobacco field. The field is planted on the wide-and-narrow row system, which conserves soil and moisture and prevents drowning of plants in case of excessive rains.
Soil Conservation Service

tobacco sales. The few states (there are six of them) that are large producers of tobacco make an enormous profit on the well-supported prices of the "weed"; few crops pay as well. It may be argued that the consumer is thus induced to spend more than perhaps he may otherwise have had. Nevertheless, the cost of the raw material is only a part, and not the decisive one, in the cost of a cigarette or of smoking tobacco to the consumer. The small difference that the support of tobacco prices makes in the price of the finished product is compensated by the prosperity thus brought to the growers—to a small but still significant section of American agriculture.

The prosperity of the tobacco belt in Virginia is substantial if one compares the present standards of income and of living in the southern Piedmont or in the burley growing areas with the standards that obtained before stabilization by federal intervention. This intervention in the field of flue-cured tobacco has been constantly felt since 1939. The Commodity Credit Corporation financed loans and purchases of tobacco in order to maintain the price and supply foreign countries during World War II;

The two leaves being displayed differ in size and quality because the one on the left is from a plant that was irrigated. Both were seventh leaves on the plant. From the farm of E. W. Cooke (at left) near Chatham.
Soil Conservation Service

after 1948, a good part of the exports of tobacco was financed by ECA funds. Moreover, parity for flue-cured was 23.1 cents per pound in 1941, but rose, because of the general increase of prices paid by the farmers, to 56.3 cents in 1951; the support level rose along with parity from 19.6 in 1941 to 50.7 cents in 1951. The support price reflects not only prices currently paid by farmers, but also average flue-cured prices in the previous ten years.

The government's control of production is less strict than the obligation to support prices, for the control is aimed at acreage but not at yield. This has been an incentive, with the results already mentioned, for the growers to improve the yields and get more out of each acre of base allotted to a farm. This usually means better agriculture, but also more expensive cultivation. Tobacco is an exacting crop in terms of soil and toil. Higher yields mean better practices, more fertilization, better protection of the plants against possible diseases, better selection of the plants, more labor all around, and sometimes also irrigation (see photos, pages 345 to 354).

E. W. Cooke displays a good stick of tobacco which has been in the barn for three days. It will be completely cured in another day.
Soil Conservation Service

An average farm in the southern Piedmont has about 100 acres. Such a farm may have no more than 30 to 50 acres cleared, and of these only a small fraction, perhaps 3 to 6 acres, in tobacco. From these few acres nearly all the cash income is derived. Tobacco reigns supreme in the minds of this area's farmers. On many farms not even a single milk cow for family use is maintained, though the soils and climate are quite favorable to hay and pasture. Tobacco fully occupies the labor of the farmer and his family from the time it is transplanted to the field in May until the picking of the final leaves around October 1st. Other crops receive little attention. The tobacco grower feels that the good prices now brought by tobacco, which has been an important raw material since Virginia was founded, must be taken full advantage of. Compared with returns from other crops grown in Virginia, the profit on the small acreage of tobacco is especially high. Some farmers calculate the costs of fertilizer and labor amount to $200 per acre planted in tobacco. The average return in recent years on yields of 600 to 2,000 pounds is approximately $300 to $1,000. Most of the farms in the tobacco-growing areas of Virginia would be unable, in their present condition, to support their

E. W. Cooke adding fuel to the fire in one of his three curing barns. Eventually
he intends to install oil furnaces in each of his three barns.
Soil Conservation Service

operators if prices were to fall; a free increase in acreage would not help
in that case as it could only depress the market further. Price support
helps maintain many farmers who otherwise would have been chased off
their lands.

The land is, therefore, overdivided, and the small farmers could not
withstand the present situation, if the prices of tobacco were not supported, unless the whole system of local land use were reorganized. In
Halifax County, for example, 51.8 per cent of the farms were operated
by tenants in 1950; over half of these belonged to absentee landlords who
received one-fourth or one-third of the returns from the tobacco harvest.
The landlords do not expect the tenants to do more for the development
of the farm than produce the crop, and the tenant rarely does feel like
contributing to the long-range improvement of a farm on which he has
a short tenure, often a one-year tenure. If the tenant has more than four
acres of tobacco allotted, he is usually assisted by "croppers," who receive
one-half of the tobacco they produce, the tenant retaining one-quarter
and the landlord another quarter. While trying to get the most out of
the land they cultivate, neither tenant nor cropper is much interested in

Hogsheads of tobacco in a warehouse in Richmond
Virginia Chamber of Commerce

maintaining its fertility for the future or applying any conservation practice. The majority of these farmers neglect to plant any cover crops of winter grains to prevent erosion and maintain a little humus on the tobacco lands. In fact, during the periods of idleness in tobacco cultivation, the farmer could, with a little more labor and not much expense, plant cover crops in November, plow them under in April, and do some terracing on the hilly slopes of the Old Belt. One wonders to what extent the price support of tobacco maintains a type of land utilization and social organization that seems to belong to a disappearing past. The same division of land and some social changes could insure better conservation and more benefits if the farmers were educated to it and if the tenants had greater stability in tenure.

What has been achieved on some well-run small farms shows the way for the possible general increase in this region's prosperity. Let us take the example of one farm in Halifax County studied by E. C. Higbee in 1953. It was a 51-acre farm purchased by its owner, Mr. G. W. Hudson, at Clover, in 1946, for $4,500. In seven years, and particularly since 1949, the productivity of the land has been so improved as to double at least the value of the farm. There is on it a four-acre tobacco base on which the yields went up from a previous average of less than 1,000 pounds to the 1953 capacity of 2,000 pounds per acre. Whereas there was neither hay nor pasture at the time of purchase, there is now enough of both to carry three cows and their calves. Corn yields have more than doubled and now average nearly 60 bushels per acre. The mortgage on the farm has been paid off and some $2,200 worth of pine timber was sold from 15 acres of woodland. There is one tractor and one horse on the farm. Most of the soils of the southern Piedmont are heavy loams: the once fairly light and friable topsoils have, under cultivation, been so eroded that much heavy subsoil is now incorporated with what is left. Animal draft power is inadequate to do a good job of field preparation. In the hands of an intelligent and industrious operator a tractor proves a good investment even on a fifty-acre farm, as this example indicated. This is a family farm. Father, son, and grandfather do the work and occupy the same household. There is no tenant and no cropper to share the labor or the income. The farm carries 50 laying hens and always a number of fattening pigs bought from others who had not enough corn to feed them. All the tobacco land is terraced and each winter has a green cover crop of rye which is turned under in the spring. There is no show of special affluence about the homestead, but its occupants may well feel a deserved contentment and pride.

The year's work with tobacco begins with the preparation and planting of a seedbed in late January or early February. The spot selected is usually a clearing at the edge of a wood where weed seeds are fewer and yet where sunlight can penetrate. The soil is generally more friable in these locations. In April the cover crops of winter grain are plowed under to rot before the fields are prepared for the transplanting that is done in the middle of May. Weeding is done by hand hoeing and plowing. As the plants put on their leaves, suckers in the axis of petiole and stem are removed so that the principal leaves will be more fully developed and of better quality. The leaves are picked as they reach their maximum size, so that harvest of the bottom leaves begins in late July or early August and the picking then continues into the middle of September. As the leaves are gathered they are taken to the mud-chinked log curing sheds equipped with a stove and an extended flue. The stove is fired on the outside, the heat travelling through the flue, which is inside the shed. In this way the leaves are dried and preserved until the harvest is complete. Then, on damp days when the previously dried leaves have become limp with atmospheric moisture, they are removed, sorted, tied, and taken to the local auctions. This is the season of the year the average tobacco farmer lives for. It is the only time when farmers who have not diversified their operations have any cash to spend. Yet even then a note of sobriety is introduced into the general levity, for debts on the crop must be paid by those who have had to borrow through the previous year. A man must wipe his accounts clean after he sells his tobacco, or there will be little if any credit afforded him in the year to come. He may, if the auctions have not been favorable, obtain some cash by felling the best timber available on his land. This, however, cannot be repeated very often on small farms. With the existing organization of the regional economy and society in the tobacco-growing country, price supports of their produce perform a most desirable task. They keep away the time of the too-lean kine.

The general economics of tobacco cannot be discussed on the basis of Virginia's stake in it alone. In 1951, there were in the United States about 211,000 allotments to individual farms for flue-cured tobacco. The number of people throughout the nation who depend on the tobacco crop is impressive. There is good reason to help them improve their standards of living. These standards would be much improved if the farms were larger, if less tenancy and "cropping" existed, if the activities of each farm were more diversified and more labor and attention were devoted to livestock and dairy production. No such reforms can be expected to occur unless these farmers are given some means by a longer period of relatively prosperous years.

The market of flue-cured tobacco is affected by many factors, among which supply is only one and seldom the decisive one. The flow of the supply is regulated rather efficiently by the existing legislation.

The production of flue-cured followed a long-run upward trend in the 1919–1951 period, and in 1951 total production was three times the 1919–1924 average. On a year to year basis, production throughout this period usually increased following increases in price and declined after price declines. But government acreage controls since 1934 have reduced the upward response of production to rising prices and increased the downward reaction to falling prices. Before government controls on tobacco, the production trend was up, while the price trend was down, but since government controls have been in effect both production and prices have followed an upward trend.[3]

It would be erroneous to ascribe to government controls alone the maintenance of the upward trend. From 1934 to 1952 the number of

[3] *Flue-Cured Tobacco, An Economic Survey,* by the Research Department of the Federal Reserve Bank of Richmond, Richmond, 1952, p. 106. An excellent analysis. We also have made steady use in this section of Charles E. Gage, *American Tobacco Types, Uses, and Markets,* Washington, 1942, U. S. Department of Agriculture, Circular No. 249; and the following periodical publications by the Department of Agriculture have been most helpful: *Agricultural Statistics; The Tobacco Situation; Flue-Cured Tobacco Market Review;* and *Tobaccos of the United States: Acreage, Yield Per Acre, Production, Price, and Value, 1866–1945,* Washington, July, 1948. See also *Business Week,* January, 1955.

consumers rose with the population; the average consumer's capacity to buy cigarettes increased, too; and government funds financed a large part of the exports of tobacco. Considerable amounts of flue-cured are exported. Export buying seems even in the long run to be the most variable factor on the demand side. It is responsible for much of the short-run variation which has occurred. Exports have accounted for over a third of the total production in the last few years and they are important in determining the price. As a per cent of the total American production, the exports have nevertheless been on the decline. The major importers abroad have done their best to save dollars that go into smoke. The British Commonwealth especially has been supplied with increasing quantities of flue-cured tobacco from Southern Rhodesia and India. Canada, once a sizable importer, has become almost self-sufficient in flue-cured. Despite this competition, Western Europe remains the principal foreign market and, if purchases by the United Kingdom have decreased, those by continental countries have been rising. For further expansion of the demand, however, the producers should rely more on domestic buyers than on exports.

In 1953–1954, the domestic market of flue-cured underwent a scare. Consumption of cigarettes dropped. The 1954 consumption stood at 371 billion tax-paid cigarettes, or 114 packs per capita, 6 per cent below the record figure of 1952 (and almost 10 per cent less in terms of per-capita consumption). This was attributable partly to statements by medical authorities as to the probability of a higher incidence of lung cancer among heavy cigarette smokers. This was the worst counterblast Virginia tobacco had had since King James. It appeared also that the consumption of tobacco had not risen in recent years as rapidly as population figures rose; of course, the rapid rise in population since World War II could not yet affect tobacco consumption, for babies do not smoke, and even the number of children who chew plugs in Virginia and elsewhere has been on the decline. Moreover, the generation now reaching the respectable age of 60 years is more numerous than it used to be; beyond that age people generally show enough concern about their health to give up smoking when advised to. The consumption of tobacco will probably rise steeply again in the 1960's, as the more numerous young generation comes of age; it is not impossible, however, that before that time the vogue of the cigarette may have passed its peak and some new fashion in tobacco consumption, perhaps with different proportions of flue-cured and burley, may have reoriented the market.

The long history of tobacco cultivation in Virginia is being readied for more changes in the future. This is a crop with a rich and turbulent past.

It is probably better protected today than it ever was, but still is not fully secure. It used to be practically the whole of the agriculture of Virginia, at least during the first one hundred and fifty years of the colony. Now tobacco is just one of many crops, though responsible for the agriculture of an important section in the Old Dominion. It has been a matter of regret for all competent authorities who studied this case that the farming of the tobacco belt has not been more diversified. Now that cattle is coming into Virginia, it will probably move into the southern Piedmont, too. The tobacco grower must give up his traditional agricultural "one-track mind" and learn to share his attention before diversification can successfully be brought about. The present trends of the tobacco belt are encouraging: the average size of the farms is slowly increasing, the per cent of tenants among all farmers is decreasing, and the number of tractors is quickly rising, too. It would indeed be a curious paradox if the crop best supported by the public were to contribute mainly to maintain on a scanty subsistence level small farms ill-fitted otherwise for survival in modern conditions.

Small farms and the problem of land management

Virginia is at present a region of small farms; the tilled land area on each farming unit is much smaller still. This arrangement is the result of the evolution of rural life since the War Between the States. The old plantation system was one of rather large estates, particularly in the Tidewater and the Piedmont. Western Virginia knew little of the vast estate system of the eastern parts of the Old Dominion; nevertheless, in many western counties the size of farms shrank during the latter part of the nineteenth and the early twentieth centuries. The war ruined many Southern landlords, even among those who did not have many slaves; and the larger estates in eastern Virginia were all dependent on Negro manpower, with the result that after the emancipation the land had to be divided. In the southwestern section, where there never were many Negroes, the white population multiplied so fast that the farms had to be subdivided to provide means of living to more numerous rising generations that wanted to stay in the area.

The large number of small farms that barely subsisted on the products of their soil caused concern. Earlier in this century most of the farms did not depend on some marketing or commodity exchange system. Tobacco and cotton were grown by a minority of the farmers only. The problem was that of the isolated subsistence farms, and these were many. The too-small farm was a problem to the South as a whole, and was a worse prob-

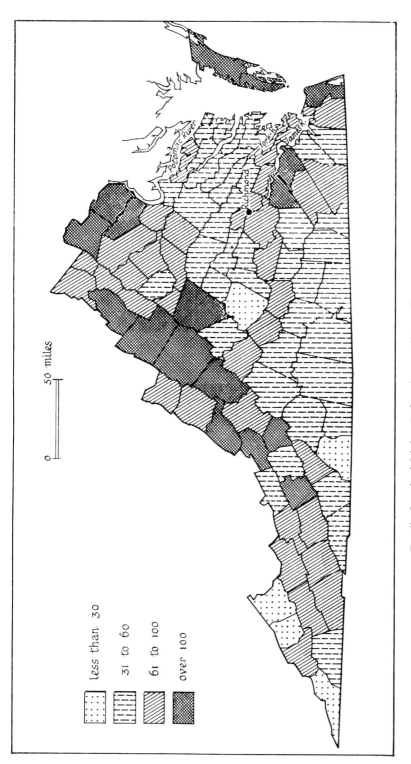

Family Level of Living Index Among Farm Operators, 1950

Alternate contour strips of corn and recently mowed hay crops seen from the windows of the home of T. G. Ragsdale at Brandy Station near Culpeper
Soil Conservation Service

lem further South than in Virginia: in 1900, about 70 per cent of all farms in the whole Southeast were below 100 acres each; by 1930, this proportion had reached 80 per cent. The proportion of small farms was high also in the far West and was increasing with the small irrigated plots of intensive gardening; but this was the sign of a rich agriculture with impressive profits to the acre. Such was not the case in the Southeast or in Virginia. The submarginality of a large part of Virginia's population was a source of weakness and of trouble. The problem was well exposed for the whole Southeast in the middle 1930's.[4]

Since 1930, the maps of the United States have undergone many changes, and the evolution of the Southeast is responsible for a great deal of them. Though Virginia was not the worst off of the Southern states, she nevertheless gave some attention to rural poverty as well as to urban. Local authorities sponsored some excellent studies of the problem. A sociological survey conducted in 1940 [5] showed that approximately 100,-

[4] Howard W. Odum, *Southern Regions of the United States*, Chapel Hill, N. C., 1936. See especially Chapter VIII.

[5] W. E. Garnett and A. D. Edwards, *Virginia's Marginal Population: A Study in Rural Poverty*, Virginia Agricultural Experiment Station Bulletin 335, Blacksburg, Va., July, 1941.

This land near Orange is planted to a four-year rotation of corn, small grain, and two years of hay, wheat, barley, oats, alfalfa, clover, and grasses.
Soil Conservation Service

ooo rural White and 65,000 rural Negro families in the late 1930's could be classed as marginal, i.e., as having less than a net $600 income from a farm, or less than $750 nonfarm. In this marginal group the subsistence farm owners were more numerous in the mountain counties, and the tenants and wage laborers in the southern and eastern parts of Virginia. Many historical, economic, and psychological factors have contributed to bring about the marginality of such an important part of the population. The authors of the survey went on to point out the significance of the facts observed:

The disadvantaged conditions under which most of the marginal group live tend to retard personal development. The vitality and efficiency of much of the state population are lowered by the inadequate nutrition prevalent among marginal standard families. Furthermore, with the crowded and unattractive housing conditions under which many of the marginal group live, the chances are against a good home life, good habit formation, and a full utilization of educational opportunities. Thus, the whole cultural life of the State is lowered. . . . The small buying power of the large group with low living standards and low incomes diminishes the volume of the State's potential business by many millions of dollars annually. When a large portion of the market demand for a given product

The landscape produced by poor farming features, bad housing and eroded soils. The steep slope of this land has not been properly managed.
Virginia Forest Service

is supplied by workers with low standards, the standards of those on a higher plane also tend to be lowered. Controlling groups have been extremely short-sighted in not more generally recognizing this principle.[6]

Since 1935 things have changed, and by 1950 a number of improvements had already been registered. There were fewer small farms and more large ones. There were more tractors, better fertilization on the whole, and better tilling and conservation practices on many farms. The development of the livestock and poultry-raising economy in many regions, particularly in the Shenandoah Valley, has given much greater rentability to small farms. Many farmers learned how to better operate their farms. This is and must be a slow and gradual process. The small farmer remains, however, in the majority of cases, still a problem within Virginia's economy and rural organization. Even with the prosperity of recent years he often lacks the financial means to invest the indispensable funds for improving efficiently his land and the use thereof. Money, however, is only one aspect of the problem. It would be a great mistake to assume, for instance, that buying a tractor would renovate a worn-out

[6] *Ibid.,* pp. 152–153.

farm. It is the use to which the tractor is put and the skill in managing the land which are the first essentials; these cannot be purchased—they must be learned. It is learning how to do a better job of farming that is the prime necessity in the areas of small farms. The commonwealth has some good agricultural schools, beginning with the Virginia Polytechnic Institute in Blacksburg, situated in the midst of the western section where the greater number of small subsistence farms is still concentrated. It has been observed, however, that the majority of the graduates of that school do not return to the family farm or even to their native area; they find better jobs on bigger farms, often outside Virginia.

The small farmer is usually under-equipped, rather incompetent, and ill prepared for competing on the highly organized national or regional market; he is largely responsible for land exhaustion, gullying, erosion, overgrazing of slopes, and other ills in southern and western Virginia. The commonwealth authorities have grown more conscious of all this in recent years. The Advisory Council on the Virginia Economy released in January, 1951, a substantial report entitled *Improving the Economic Conditions of Farmers in Virginia*. The main emphasis of the report is on the farmers' income as an easy measure of land management and an area's prosperity. It was pointed out that owing to the high level of prices for agricultural products since the beginning of World War II, farmers have enjoyed a fair degree of financial prosperity, which may not continue if no measures are taken to counterbalance in the future some probable decline in prices.

"Agriculture in Virginia," according to this report, "has become increasingly specialized within the last fifty years. During this period of time the live-at-home frontier type of farm has yielded to one in which the major part of the farming operations center around the production of commodities for sale." Then it stresses the need for community services, for further electrification and development of the network of telephone communications in rural areas, especially towards the small farms, and the possibility of expanding the acreage of pastures and farm woodlands, as about five million acres were lying idle in the state. In conclusion, a number of practical recommendations were made for private action by the farmers themselves, for private business to aid in the maintenance of farm prosperity, and for governmental action. It was not always clearly recognized in this report that what remained of the old "live-at-home frontier type" of farming was one of the worst features of the rural landscape. This is not always true, of course, in terms of the spectacle presented: such backward farming areas are not always unpleasant to look at—they are sometimes truly picturesque. But they depress the

John D. Ferguson and his son in a tobacco wagon
Library of Congress Photo by Marion Post Wolcott

regional economy permanently. The fact that they suffer less proportionately from an economic depression or recession does not make them more attractive: they simply could not recede further without disappearing. Agriculture is better protected nowadays against slumps in business than it ever was; it is probably better protected than any manufacturing industry could be, for the same soil may produce a great variety of different crops once the farmer knows how, while a factory can hardly manufacture goods very different from those it has been devised to make.

It is often contended in Virginia, and more generally in the Southeast, that the large proportion of Negroes in the population and the survival today of a social structure still reminiscent of eighteenth-century Virginia, and perhaps of eighteenth-century England, are the factors that keep the rural areas from progressing and the number of marginal farms so high. The question of the Negro people and of their lower levels of income and education has been studied many times in these areas.[7] There is no doubt that such lower levels have constantly depressed the general level

[7] See G. Myrdal, *An American Dilemma*, New York, 1944; and in the Virginia Writers Projects series, *The Negro in Virginia*, sponsored by The Hampton Institute, New York, 1940.

of Virginia's economy. But recently a steady current has been carrying Negroes out of the rural areas toward the cities or suburban areas. But Negroes have tended to remain on the farms in regions specializing in better-priced or supported crops, such as the tobacco belt in the southern Piedmont, the peanuts-hog belt, and the truck-farming area of the Tidewater. The real problem area in Virginia agriculture is the category of small farms operated, and often owned, by White farmers in the west and southwest. Negro people would have had much more difficulty obtaining better jobs and better living conditions than these Whites. If in many western counties the social hierarchy is still the same as many generations ago, if small, poor farms, seldom adequately equipped, are scattered around the manorial home of some large landowner whose family may have some larger revenue from other sources and from outside the area itself, this situation is not attributable to the autocracy of the landlord or to the presence of many Negroes in other parts of the country. The will to preserve the old regime, or at least to avoid changes, is effective if and when it is shared by the great majority of the small White farmers of the area.

Some of these counties have been sympathetic to certain innovations; it may seem surprising (see map, page 366) that a high percentage of farms are equipped with telephones in Craig County, one of the more backward counties in many other ways. Adopting the telephone did not cost much, owing to the Rural Electrification Administration, nor did it bring immediate changes in the local economy. Craig remains an area slow to progress, with old ways of tilling and living. Bringing a single opportunity to the people in an area does not always make them take advantage of it. Some owners of small farms have achieved excellent results in improving their lands and making a good living on what may have been, according to averages, inadequate acreage; we have already described some successful small farms. But these examples did not necessarily determine their neighbors to follow a similar pattern.

What is important for the prosperity of a country is not the size of the farm but a wise management of the land. There is no optimum size for farms, given a certain soil and a certain climate. Marketing, labor supply, and technical knowledge are even more decisive factors in determining the benefit that an acre can bring. Returns from a larger farm will probably, though not necessarily, be higher, but small farms, too, can provide a decent standard of living. What has been said about the past and the present of agriculture in Virginia seems to stress the fact that too often small farms have meant a poor, backward kind of subsistence farming or some highly specialized land use focusing on one crop which enjoys spe-

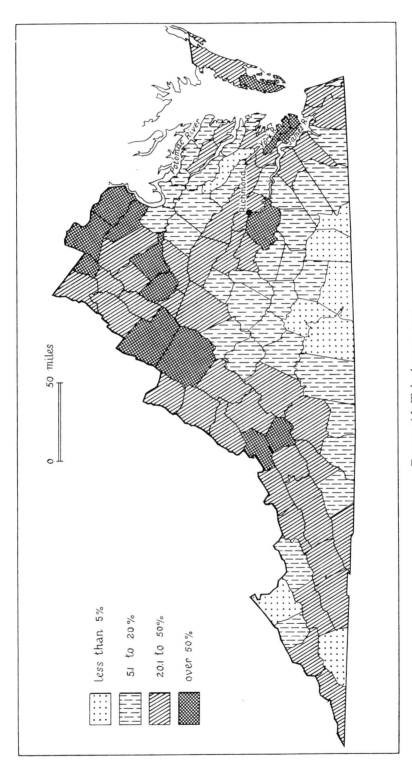

Farms with Telephones, 1950
(By counties, in per cent of all farms)

less than 5%

5.1 to 20%

20.1 to 50%

over 50%

Potomac River

York River

James River

Richmond

50 miles

0

cial marketing advantages. Not all small farms are marginal, of course, but many are. Such is the problem: Virginia could still achieve great progress by accelerating the pace at which the small subsistence or too-specialized farms are receding today. The advances scored in the last twenty years by the larger farms, growing in number and in area, must be considered a healthy and desirable trend.

New versions of the plantation

The term *plantation* suggests to the imagination a large rural estate with impressive looking residential quarters for the owner and with abundant manpower. Today the labor supply need not be large: the mechanization of agricultural work has reached a point where a few men, adequately equipped, can manage a vast acreage of cropland and pasture, unless some special handiwork is necessary, like picking tobacco leaves as they mature. Such land use is becoming increasingly advantageous as it becomes generalized over the American scene. Full employment, on the other hand, demands a labor market capable of absorbing most of the people who leave the farms because their functions are taken over by machines; this need is strongly felt in Virginia.

The result of such a process is not only an increase in the average size of the farm, but more definitely an increase in the number of farms having over 500 acres each, farms that may claim to be the new kind of "plantation" in the Old Dominion. In 1925, the number of such farms reached a low point with the total figure of 3,041, of which only 623 had over 1,000 acres. In 1950, the number of farms of more than 500 acres had risen to 3,705, of which 828 had over 1,000 acres. Only 1,187 farms reported in 1950 having 200 acres and over of harvested cropland, and 1,632 farms reported five or more hired workers. Pasture and cattle, which require much less labor than crops, play an increasing part on these large farms.

In 1950, farms of 500 acres and more occupied about 21.5 per cent of all land in farms in the whole of Virginia. The relative part of farmland in such large units of operation varies greatly from one section of the commonwealth to another and even from county to county. The lower figures are found in some of the southwestern coal-mining counties, such as Dickenson and Wise, with about 5 per cent; the highest figures are found also in western mountain counties, where pastures and woodlands covering vast stretches are owned as farms by individual owners or by corporations for the purpose of showing small incomes and sometimes losses resulting from such agricultural operations for fiscal purposes. This may be the explanation for the high percentage of farms of over 500 acres in

Barn on a farm near Radford
Library of Congress Photo by Post Wolcott

the total area of Bath (almost 50 per cent), Highland (48 per cent), and Tazewell (48 per cent) Counties, as well as for the abundance of investments in large, well-kept farms which may serve both this purpose and that of suburban residence in the outer western rim of Washington's metropolitan area. The percentage of the area in such farms reaches 33 in Loudoun, 47 in Fauquier, 40 in Rappahannock, and 34 in Culpeper. It is 38 in Albemarle County, where Charlottesville is a center of elegant living. It is high also to the east of Richmond, in New Kent (47 per cent) and King William (45 per cent), but must be explained there by vast woodlands more than by suburban estates. Large farms are less important on the whole in the southern and even in the middle Piedmont, as Appomattox County shows only 16 per cent and Bedford 10 per cent.

A detailed map of the distribution of large farms would be a complicated puzzle and a somewhat confusing one unless the reasons for maintaining such large units were well understood. There are several reasons which we have already suggested: a large farm, well run, is a good investment. If the owner has a large income from other sources, he may disregard the usefulness of profit and sometimes even accept lightly the idea of losing small sums while improving a well-situated estate. Such farms are often owned by corporations or groups of people, or by owners who reside on them but work at least part-time in town. The suburban estate around Washington, particularly towards the Blue Ridge on the northern Piedmont, appears to be an excellent position for the development of such new versions of the plantation. It produces a region of what local wits describe as "station-wagon farming," of fox hunting, and of elegant living. The same area, however, is one of the leading areas in the United States for breeding horses of famous pedigrees, which requires space and large capital investment. It is also an area of beautiful pastures and high-grade beef cattle. Fauquier and Loudoun Counties have more farms operated by managers, i.e., by highly trained specialists, than other counties in Virginia. They have also a high proportion of farms operated by people who fully own their lands. Through Culpeper, Orange, and Albemarle Counties a stretch where such "plantations" abound extends from the vicinity of Washington to Charlottesville.

Large farms specializing in cattle, either for dairy production or for beef, are scattered throughout the commonwealth; they are more numerous perhaps along the Great Valley than in the Piedmont. In the western ridges section large holdings are used for pasturing cattle, but also for the recreation of the customers of famous hotels in the vicinity. A large part of these lands may still be run officially as farms. The woods on these lands, whether or not they serve the purpose of recreation, may also be used as timber land or farm woodland when the trees mature. Wood growing is also an important aspect of the larger farms of the Tidewater, particularly in the Northern Necks. Around Richmond and Norfolk, some large farms may also serve the same residential-suburban purpose for those among the moneyed city folk who can afford the investment. Dairy farms in the proximity of such larger cities can easily be profitable businesses.

Thus the present-day plantations grow trees and raise cattle rather than tobacco or cotton. Some landowners residing on relatively large estates close to town or to a good road own besides substantial lands broken up into several farming units and operated by tenants. This has become a general trend since the abolition of slavery and can always be suggested for areas with a high percentage of tenants among farmers. The operation of these lands, however, is left to the tenants and obeys the dynamics of the small farm, more or less well managed, rather than the economics of the large farming unit suggested by the term *plantation*.

Another version of the plantation, remarkable by its immediate dependence on a consumers' market, is found on the Eastern Shore. In Northampton County the recent trend showed rapid progress in the area occupied by farms of 260 to 1,000 acres, at the expense of both the smaller and larger sizes. This middle size, a substantial one, covered about one-third of all land in farms in the county in 1950. In Accomack the trend away from small farms and towards farms of more than 220 acres has recently been quite clear: in 1945, farms of more than 220 acres aggregated 29 per cent of the county's farmland, and farms of more than 500 acres only 16 per cent; in 1950, these two percentages had risen to 45 and 27 per cent respectively. Such a rapid trend towards consolidation into larger farms is due to the prosperity of the area, to the greater rentability of units big enough to pay rapidly for the investment needed to prepare the land and run the business, to the availability of migrant labor at harvest time. The organization of the Shore's truck farming helps to explain the consolidation into this kind of farm, perhaps closer to the traditional plantation by both the employment of large numbers of Negro laborers and the strict dependence upon a marketing system controlled from the outside.

Such plantations, whether based on cattle, on truck farming, or on fruit orchards, no longer suffer from the two major ills of the old-time Southern farming unit. They do not dispose of a practically unlimited supply of land which could be used up and exhausted without much concern because more fresh land was available within the estate. Now these new versions of the plantation signify in almost all cases better land management, more careful agricultural practices, greater willingness to invest in improvements, and more concern for soil conservation, drainage, and occasionally irrigation. In these various respects the trend away from the small farm and towards these new versions of the plantation is a definite indication of progress. The other bad feature of the old plantation system was its exploitation of numerous laborers, either Negro slaves or poor Whites; this situation no longer exists. The only case reminiscent of this old weakness of the South is perhaps found in the scenery offered by the migratory labor camps of the Eastern Shore; these laborers, however, come here of their own will, from the deep South and chiefly from Florida, because they choose to come to look for higher wages and better opportunities. This summer work is for them an improvement over the conditions in their native region. For most of them the Eastern Shore of Virginia is just one of a series of places along the Atlantic seaboard where they work for short periods. With this exception, the new kinds of plantations or large farming units pay good wages and often provide for quite comfortable living conditions, much better in many cases than what the subsistence farmer, the cropper, or tenant may afford on small submarginal farms.

Holstein yearling steers grazing on a farm near Goochland
Soil Conservation Service

These new large farms have perhaps retained a few traits of the old-time plantations. The beautiful old houses, either well-preserved or restored, still often serve as the homes of the landowners. In the social structure, some of the quiet, well-established order prevails, with better relations between the head of the enterprise and his subordinates than in many other rural areas. As the number of larger farms increases, as the new system of crops and extensive pastures expands and becomes better organized, fattening better cattle and bringing in larger profits, a sort of calm enthusiasm about the present and future of Virginia agriculture rises over the land. There is more talk here about the better farming and brighter prospects opening before the people of Virginia, as well as some other parts of the Southeast, than there is nowadays in the Great Plains or the northeastern states.

A new trilogy: trees, grass, and water

If one tried to put into a brief formula the present trends of land use in Virginia, one might come up with a new trilogy of concerns, which would be also a trilogy of hopes: trees, grass, and water. Trees are of

Registered Hereford cattle grazing on land which was recently retired from crop and put to pasture. Bare spots and broomsedge covered the field before it was planted with Ladino clover, orchard grass, and bluegrass.
Soil Conservation Photo

growing importance as crop-bearers in the Old Dominion. This is true primarily because of the demand for all kinds of wood products; we dealt with this aspect of the rural economy in discussing the use and misuse of the forests. But trees are also important in the parts of Virginia where fruit orchards produce apples and peaches. They are important to give shade and charm to the landscape. Groups of large trees often tower above the farmer's house; smaller ones, such as red cedars, line the alleys leading towards the house from the main road.

Grass—and for our present purpose we shall include under this term what specialists call annual or perennial legumes—grass symbolizes the newly developing cattle economy. Virginia here puts to use her mild climate, long growing season, and the good aptitudes of her soils for grasses and legumes. Land once cropped into sterility and laid idle is being brought back into production by new types of exploitation which promise enduring productivity rather than ephemeral prosperity followed by collapse. In general, the conversion from soil-exhausting annual crops of corn, wheat, cotton, and tobacco to perennial grasses and legumes is more advanced in Virginia than in most of the Southeastern states. The advantages of grassland farming, long appreciated in the grazing country of southwestern Virginia, have now been realized to some extent in every section of the Piedmont and the coastal plain.

The widespread knowledge that most of the exhausted, idle, and abandoned lands east of the Blue Ridge can be made into excellent pasture and hayfields has already greatly raised their real-estate value. If the renovation of idle or scrub forest lands outside the boundaries of operating farms does not now proceed at an accelerated pace, the cause will be in part their increasing speculative value. The time when the quality of land was dependent upon its native fertility is past. It was partially this dependence, in the days when commercial lime and mineral fertilizers were little known and seldom used, which contributed to the "clear, crop, and abandon" cycle that undermined the livelihood of planter, small farmer, and tenant. As the density of the population and the quantity of its consumption rise, as no more good free land is available in plenty, new cycles must be applied, maintaining the land's fertility and even improving it. The use of adequate fertilizer is one aspect of modern management needs; crop rotation that helps the land regenerate its own fertility is another need. Grasses of various kinds must play a decisive part in the new cycles being worked out in experimental stations.

Trees and grass profit by a longer growing season every year if and when water is abundantly supplied to them during that period. Other crops, like corn and tobacco, which are so important to the welfare of Virginia's farming, suffer greatly from droughts, too. Water is becoming an increasing concern to the farmers who have improved their yields and their equipment and have come to rely more on capital and credit than on the physical gifts of the environment. Droughts have plagued Virginia, as they have almost all other agricultural areas in the world, since early colonial times.

As early as 1680, William Fitzhugh wrote from Westmoreland County, "I believe no great crops will be this year made, by reason of our great drought . . ." William Beverley from his home on the York River wrote, August 8, 1737, "We have had and it still continues such a drought that has not been known here by any man alive and indeed I believe we shall not make corn serve till April in this colony.". . . In 1782 there was reported a great scarcity of tobacco, hemp and flour "arising from the late general and deplorable drought." [8]

A severe drought occurred in 1869. Better weather records were kept from 1882 on, and drought years since then have been recorded and their effect on the production of crops measured. Thus the years of bad

[8] T. L. Stuart and H. M. Taylor, "Virginia Droughts and Their Effect on Agricultural Production," *University of Virginia Newsletter*, Charlottesville, October 1, 1954.

droughts were 1869, 1883, 1900, 1914, 1921, 1924, and 1925; and this tight series culminated with the disastrous drought of 1930, when the average yield of corn per acre fell to 11 bushels, i.e., about 47 per cent of the preceding five-year average. That same year, pasture conditions were reported to be 75 per cent of normal on April 1, 56 per cent on July 1, and 30 per cent on September 1, 1930. On that date corn was near failure in the northern Piedmont and over most of the Great Valley; pasture was failing in the same areas, and the drought was severe over the whole Piedmont.

Later on, 1932, 1936, 1944 and 1952 were dry years. The drought continued severe in 1953, making two successive years that threatened pastures. The situation on September 1, 1953, was second only to that in 1930 in terms of ill effects of the drought. That year the average yield of corn went down to 27 bushels per acre (65 per cent of the preceding five-year average), and the average yield of tobacco was substantially diminished also. The pasture condition was 89 per cent of normal on July 1, 1953, but 37 per cent on September 1 and 23 per cent on November 1. Hay had to be rushed by truck and rail into the Old Dominion. To make matters even worse, 1954 turned out to be at least as dry through most of the growing season. In many areas pastures were parched; the cattle economy was deeply affected by these three dry years in a row. Many problems were discussed, including a better system of grass and legume rotation to better resist dry years, and the need for the expansion of irrigation. After long dry periods, as in the early fall of 1954, irrigation may be difficult to apply even on farms equipped for it, as many small streams and wells went dry or nearly so. But such severe water-supply conditions seldom occur. Irrigation for pasture, hay, and truck crops is expanding. It has been shown that irrigation can increase the yields and quality of tobacco leaf also when wisely applied. Irrigated land on farms, in the whole of Virginia, amounted to 687 acres in 1940, 1,419 in 1945, and 2,817 in 1950. It has expanded since and probably will go on.

Drainage and irrigation are a permanent problem in the trucking areas; such as the Eastern Shore and the Flatwoods. Many schemes are at present being promoted, including plans for draining the Dismal Swamp. Smaller projects will probably succeed better and earlier, expanding the good cropland and the yields of the Tidewater. Water is becoming a matter of greater interest to both public authorities and public opinion. As industries and cities consume increasing quantities of it, their interest in clean water coincides with that of the rural areas. It may be that pollution of the streams will soon be better controlled. Underground resources are also being carefully studied.

The farmland of Virginia is undergoing great changes.[9] The trends on the whole are good: they show steady improvement and promise more and more of it in terms of land management as well as in terms of profits from farm work. Most of these trends mean, however, fewer people on the land to live from its harvest, even though the harvest may grow and the returns increase. The present evolution is, therefore, a welcome one, on the condition that other means of making a living are made available to the people of Virginia, preferably within the commonwealth. In other words, these tendencies must be complemented by more urbanization and industrialization in Virginia. Both are proceeding apace, and their rhythm has already contributed much to hasten change in the use of rural land and labor.

[9] The main source of statistics in this chapter is the U. S. Census of Agriculture, 1950. For a general review of the changes between 1930 and 1950, see W. L. Gibson, Jr., "Farmland Utilization in Virginia," *University of Virginia Newsletter*, January 1, 1955.

6. *The Resources of the Underground*

VIRGINIA is traditionally a rural state. The first groups of settlers in and around Jamestown looked eagerly for precious minerals and pearls to send to England. The spectacular finds of gold and silver by the Spanish conquistadors in Mexico and Peru stimulated the hopes of most of the settlers who opened up new lands in early America. Every gold or copper bracelet worn by an Indian chieftain served to fire new hopes, and the settlers were proud of being able to ship some pearls to London in order to demonstrate the probable riches of Virginia. Tobacco, however, rapidly took over the export trade, and the expectation of precious minerals was quickly given up.

Virginia nevertheless proved to be richly mineralized. The vast expanse of old crystalline bedrock under the soils of the Old Dominion from the fall line westward yields in many places a variety of valuable materials, from stone for building to diamonds. Stones of different kinds are quite abundant, and diamonds are rare, as is natural. Few Virginians, even among those who are quite proud of their land, know, for instance, that the largest gem found in the United States until 1884, the "Dewey" diamond, weighing 23¾ carats in the rough, was picked up in Manchester, Chesterfield County, in 1855 by a man grading one of the streets. Other large diamonds, purer than the "Dewey," were found in Orange and Tazewell Counties. A more famous diamond, the "Punch Jones," came from just northeast of Rich Creek, Giles County, already in West Virginia territory. Gold in small nuggets has been found in many places all over the Piedmont. Moonstone and Amazonstone have been produced in substantial quantities in Amelia County; but these stones are not as precious as diamonds or gold, and no finds of precious gems or minerals have led to systematic extraction. The quantities found were not important enough. The only exception was, in the middle of the nineteenth century, the Vaucluse Gold Mine of Orange County.

The commonwealth's mineral endowment

The mineral heritage of Virginia turned out to be more important in other productions which have been the modern basis of greater power and prosperity than gold or gems: coal and some metallic ores, particularly iron and manganese ores, have been at different periods of considerable importance in the regional economy. The settlers in Virginia started shipping out samples of their mineral resources quite early: some bog iron went out to England in 1609. A small iron works was established in 1619 at Falling Creek, seven miles south of the present site of Richmond; the furnaces were destroyed during the great massacre of 1622. Published records refer to sources of minerals in Virginia many times after 1669, and exploitation became continuous in the beginning of the eighteenth century. Coal from the Richmond basin on the James River was mined and used locally; iron ore began to be mined on the lower Piedmont at Germanna, where Governor Spotswood hoped to develop a spectacular iron industry on the ores of the Rapidan River with German immigrants. Lead was mined in the 1750's at the Chiswell mines, Wythe County. Copper was mined at the Phoenyx Mine in Fauquier County in the 1760's. Coal extraction in western Virginia started around 1768 near Blacksburg. Salt, marble, mica, limestone, and greenstone were already used at the time of the Revolution and probably somewhat earlier.

At the beginning of the War Between the States, Virginia was the major mineral-producing state of the Confederacy. Her main contribution was lead and iron, although salt, saltpeter, and coal were also important. "Oriskany iron ore from the Grace Furnace Mines, Botetourt County, was used by the Tredegar Iron Works of Richmond for making the armor of the iron-clad *Merrimac,* which was fueled with coal from the mines of Montgomery county."[1] Since the Civil War, the utilization of Virginia's mineral resources has gradually increased; new iron mines were opened in 1878 and the iron smelting furnaces scattered all over western Virginia. Manganese was discovered in Augusta County in 1867; new zinc and mica mines were started in the years following. The Crimora mine, at one time the largest open-pit mine in the eastern United States,

[1] Richard V. Dietrich, *Virginia Minerals and Rocks,* Bulletin of the Virginia Polytechnic Institute, Engineering Experiment Station Series No. 90, Blacksburg, January, 1954.

Soapstone quarry near Schuyler
U. S. Bureau of Mines

has produced more high-grade manganese oxide ore than any other mine in the country. It has been estimated that more than 25 million tons of iron were produced in Virginia, chiefly west of the Blue Ridge, until 1940, when extraction virtually ceased. The rutile mines at Roseland, Nelson County, have supplied substantial quantities of titanium oxide.

Many materials found in Virginia are used in the building industries—limestone and dolomite, slate and granite, sand and gravel, brick clay and shales, etc. In recent years these materials became more diversified, as quartzite is being produced in the Blue Ridge area of Rockbridge County to be used in steel refining. The major new finds were located in the southwestern triangle: natural gas from Scott County has been used since 1938 and a small oil field has been worked since 1941 in Lee County; since 1943 large deposits of high calcium limestone near Kimballton, Giles County, have been mined, transformed locally into chemical lime, and shipped from there to many points in the eastern states. New zinc ore deposits were discovered in 1952 in Smyth County and an active search for more manganese ore is being conducted in various sections of the commonwealth.

The major resource, however, produced in the depths of Virginia is

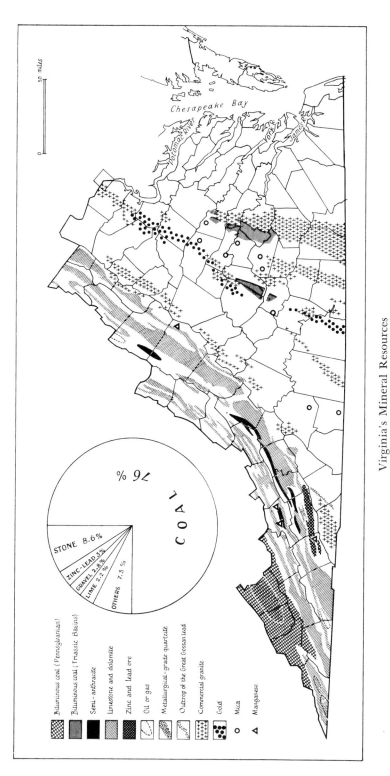

Virginia's Mineral Resources

The inset graph in the circle shows the distribution of mineral production in per cent of value in 1952. From the map "Virginia's Mineral Resources, 1953" prepared and published by the Virginia Engineering Experiment Station, V.P.I., Blacksburg.

coal, particularly bituminous coal from the Cumberland Plateau, in the southwestern counties. In 1950, Virginia ranked twelfth among the states in value of mineral production, which was estimated at about $150,000,-000; of this total, 76 per cent was coal, 8.6 per cent stone, 3 per cent zinc and lead ores, 2.8 per cent gravel, and 2.2 per cent lime. Building materials are found in abundance, of course, over most of the country. The most interesting and important aspect of the mineral endowment of Virginia is therefore coal.

The coal fields

Coal occurs in three distinct areas in Virginia: the southwestern fields are a part of the larger Appalachian field extending from western Pennsylvania and eastern Ohio through West Virginia, southwestern Virginia, eastern Kentucky and Tennessee, into northern Alabama; the Valley fields are scattered in narrow beds through the southern section of the Great Valley of Virginia; and the eastern fields are small basins located west of Richmond and in the vicinity of Farmville. In recent years about 99 per cent of the state's coal production has come from the southwestern fields. They lie in northern Tazewell County, all of Buchanan and Dickenson Counties, most of Wise and parts of Russell, Scott, and Lee Counties. Here are found medium and high volatile bituminous coals occurring in a strip of some 110 miles in length and 30 miles in width at the widest point in Buchanan County. In Lee County the strip tapers to less than one mile in width at one place. The other fields scattered through the south of the Valley or the center of the Piedmont have at present mainly an historical interest; they contain some other kinds of coal than the southwestern fields; often these small basins have somewhat higher quality, semi-anthracite, varieties; the size of these mines is so small, however, for present operations that we shall give them only the indispensable minimum of attention in this brief review.

In old times the eastern two small coal fields have been of great import. The Richmond basin, which supplies a bituminous coal of relatively high sulfur content, was the first coal field to be mined in North America and the principal source of American coal until the canal era in the 1820's. There are references to the discovery and limited local use of its coal as early as 1701, but no reliable record of production before 1748. In the middle of the eighteenth century standard mining methods were introduced in the area around Midlothian, south of the James River, on the eastern edge of the basin. Production increased from 50 tons in 1748 to around 400 or 500 tons in the next three years. In 1763, the output had

Conveyor belt and steel tipple of Jewell Ridge Coal Corporation Mine No. 2,
Jewell Valley, showing six sizes of coal being loaded simultaneously
Virginia Chamber of Commerce Photo by Flournoy

risen to 1400 tons; then it declined and dropped back to around 500
tons until 1794, when approximately 1000 tons were again mined. In
1798, after improvements, the output of the Richmond basin area climbed
to 22,000 tons and steadily increased for the next thirty years until nearly
100,000 tons per year were being mined. Coal from the Richmond basin
was exported to distant points, such as the West Indies, Philadelphia,
New York, and New England, and some shipments even came to London
in the 1760's.

Then came the development of the Pennsylvania anthracite fields and
the opening of the canals linking them with the seaboard. After the
1830's, competition from these higher quality anthracites and also from
lower priced British coals began to squeeze Richmond coal out of the
more distant markets. A general decline set in and mining in the area became erratic, despite improvement in methods and the sinking of deeper
shafts on the western side of the basin. Along with the fields of Alabama,
the Richmond basin proved to be a principal source of fuel for the Confederacy during the Civil War, but the production never fully recovered.
After the 1870's, the opening of the New River and Pocahontas fields re-

Setting timber inside a mine under the direction of a safety inspector before proceeding to cut
Virginia Chamber of Commerce Photo by Flournoy

duced to very little the part of the Richmond basin in the economy of Virginia. The census for 1870 listed six active coal mines in Virginia, four of which were located in the Richmond basin, which accounted for more than 60,000 tons of the total output of 61,800 tons of coal mined in Virginia that year. The two other coal mines were then situated one in the Farmville basin and one in Montgomery County. Coal fields were going west: the first find in Tazewell County was made in 1873; the town of Pocahontas was established in 1882. The Richmond basin could not compete with the great Appalachian fields. Continuous production there stopped in 1904 and operations have been only intermittent since.[2]

Although scattered coal pits were worked in the Farmville basin, they were largely for local consumption and could not be expected to be large undertakings. The coal in this basin is of low volatile bituminous quality

[2] See E. N. Eavenson, *The First Century and a Quarter of the American Coal Industry,* Pittsburgh, 1942, and also Joseph MacFarlane, *The Coal Regions of America,* New York, 1875. A great deal of the material in this chapter has been borrowed from *Coal Resources of Virginia,* by several authors, U. S. Geological Survey Circular 171, Washington, 1952, and from *Minerals Yearbook,* annually published by the U. S. Bureau of Mines in Washington.

and of the same geological age as that in the Richmond basin, i.e., both are of Triassic age, and Triassic rocks, amongst which coal beds are interstratified, have been preserved in a trough on both sides of which much older, pre-Cambrian rocks are exposed.

The Valley fields are scattered from Botetourt County to Smyth County along the Great Valley of Virginia. The main deposits are situated along a few major faults between the towns of Blacksburg and Bland. Some coal mining for local purposes seems to have been carried on in the Valley, especially in Pulaski and Montgomery Counties, as early as 1782; until the time of the Civil War there was no record, however, of shipments from these basins to outside areas. The area is drained mostly by the New River, which flows northwestward towards the Ohio. Transportation to outside markets could not be undertaken until the railroads came to the coal basins. Mining in Tazewell County and around Pocahontas developed before this area, but the Valley fields supply another quality of coal: this coal, which appears in the Price formation of Mississippian age, just overlying some Devonian formations, is usually of a semi-anthracite quality, much superior for certain uses to bituminous coal. Beginning in 1904 the Virginia Anthracite Company began to develop these fields on a comparatively large scale. Markets were built up for this "Virginia Anthracite," the production of which exceeded 100,000 tons for the first time in 1916. Heavy demand for fuel during World War I enabled Valley producers to compete for a time in distant markets with Pennsylvania anthracite and cheaper coals from other regions.

The total output from the Valley fields amounted to about 174,000 tons in 1920. The following year it dropped to 89,146 tons. Since then it has remained at more than 100,000 tons each year, reaching a record of 272,000 tons in 1926. In 1951, production amounted to 156,000 tons. The greatest part of this output has come from the Merrimac bed in Montgomery County.

Commercial production of coal in the southwestern fields of Virginia began in 1881 with the location of the 12-foot thick Pocahontas seam in Abb's Valley, Tazewell County. In 1883, Tazewell County produced 119,-000 tons of low volatile bituminous coal. In that year the first coal from the southwestern fields was shipped to the Tidewater over the Norfolk and Western Railway and the region was becoming the leading coal producing area of the state. Ten years later coal was mined commercially in Wise County, and by the end of World War I the total output of the southwestern fields was around 10,000,000 tons annually. It was not until 1932, with the opening of branch railway lines into Buchanan County, that commercial production of coal started there. Currently the largest single coal producing county in Virginia, Buchanan contributes between four and six million tons each year towards a total for Virginia fluctuating around twenty million tons (the oscillation has been between 15 and 22 millions since 1940).

It was estimated that the reserves of coal remaining in Virginia amounted, on January 1, 1951, to about 11,119 million tons, of which about 3 per cent were semi-anthracite in Valley fields and the rest bituminous coal in southwestern fields. About 932 million tons had been at that date already removed or lost by mining. Out of the reserves left, some 7 per cent is classed as measured coal, 52 per cent as indicated coal, and 41 per cent as inferred coal. This may seem disappointing to whoever is not familiar with the indispensable approximation in estimating underground reserves. Compared to other coal-bearing areas in the country, where "inferred coal" usually makes up more than half of the reserve estimates, Virginia's coal fields are relatively well explored. These reserves are classified according to the thickness of the seams as follows: 47 per cent are classed as thin (14 to 28 inches) coal; 35 per cent as intermediate (28 to 42 inches) coal; and 18 per cent of the total as thick (more than 42 inches) coal. The thickness of the seams is an essential factor as mechanization of operations and extraction of a higher proportion of the coal are much easier in thicker seams; thin coal is more difficult to mine and more costly.

The southwest field, which represents almost the whole of Virginia's important coal endowment, extends over about 1,552 square miles, one-third of which is in Buchanan County. All parts of the coal-bearing area belonging to the Appalachian plateau are highly dissected and characterized by steep slopes, narrow ridges and stream valleys which seldom contain enough flat land to permit farming. Differences in altitude of about 1,000 feet within the radius of one mile are not uncommon. The coal-bearing rocks belong in the "Pottsville group of the Pennsylvanian series of Carboniferous age," according to the present classification. Beds of sandstone, shale and coal alternate in a rather irregular fashion, having been folded and faulted in many places. This area is drained by many small streams belonging either in the basin of the Ohio River through the Big Sandy River, or in the Tennessee River basin through the Clinch and Powell Rivers. This hydrographic network supplies enough water for the present needs of the area, but it consists of too small and rapidly flowing streams to serve any kind of transportation. Railroads command the transportation of coal and the story of the fields started when they came.

Coal transportation and marketing

The coal fields of southwest Virginia appear rather well situated on the map of the United States for easy transportation of coal to the major markets on the national scene, to the heavily industrialized northeastern Atlantic states, to the southeastern states, which are beginning to consume coal in increasing quantities, and to markets abroad. The coal field is adequately served by the rail network. The greater part of the trackage in the area belongs to the Norfolk and Western Railway, which serves also the area of the principal Valley fields. It carries the coal towards the main industrial centers within Virginia—Roanoke, Richmond, Norfolk—and through the latter's seaport ships it conveniently overseas. Other railroads active in the southwest field are the Clinchfield Railway, which handles most of the coal extracted in Dickenson and Russell Counties; the Interstate Railway and the Louisville and Nashville Railway, which come to Norton; the Southern Railway, which operates a north-south line passing through Appalachia and Big Stone Gap; and finally a spur of the Chesapeake and Ohio Railway enters Lee County from Kentucky and hauls the coal produced in a small part of that county. The Norfolk and Western and the Chesapeake and Ohio are the leading railroads specializing in the function of coal carriers from the fields to the great centers of consumption and shipping of the eastern seaboard.

In recent years about 75 per cent of the coal produced in Virginia has been shipped directly by rail, something over 20 per cent by truck to railheads, and less than 5 per cent by truck to its final destination. The railroads have handled therefore some 95 per cent of the total output. The percentage of truck-hauled coal in Virginia was about one-third of the national average; this reflects probably both the efficient organization of rail service and the final destination of Virginia coal. Very little of it can be consumed locally for lack of large industrial consumers; much of it is shipped to distant points in the United States for special purposes, and large tonnages are shipped overseas through the ports of Hampton Roads.

The total output of Virginia has shown much more stability in recent years than that of most of the other states which are large producers of coal. In 1949, Virginia ranked eighth among coal-producing states; in 1952 and again in 1953, she ranked sixth, after West Virginia, Pennsylvania, Kentucky, Illinois, and Ohio. In 1953, her output amounted to 19.5 million tons and supplied 4.3 per cent of the national production of bituminous coal. Recent years have seen a rather rapid decline in the

Twenty-ton locomotive pulling coal out of the Jewell Ridge Mine No. 1
Virginia Chamber of Commerce Photo by Flournoy

national consumption and output of coal. The decline affected Virginia, too, of course, but more slowly than it affected the larger producers, partly because of geographical position and accessibility to markets, partly because of concentration of the production in large and better-equipped mines. Thus from 1952 to 1953 output declined somewhat, but the tonnage produced by mobile loaders in rail-connected deep mines increased from 41 to 57 per cent, while the amount produced by the hand-loading method decreased from 35.7 to 22.2 per cent. The number of seams worked was also reduced from 18 to 16, according to a circular of the Virginia Coal Operators Association.

The size of coal mines in Virginia does not compare favorably, however, with the national average. There were in 1949 only four mines in Virginia with an annual capacity of more than 500,000 tons, and they produced 18.8 per cent of the total output, while mines of such size supply 29.3 per cent of the national production. Mines capable of an annual output between 100,000 and 500,000 tons numbered 34 in 1949 and produced 47.5 per cent of the state's coal as against 43.4 per cent as a national average. Since 1949, substantial progress has been achieved in better equipping the larger mines. However, Virginia was not the only coal-producing area to seek to improve mining methods. The relative stability of her production must be largely due to a better system of marketing, slightly helped by the geographical position of the field.

Distribution channels within the state are generally as varied and complex as elsewhere in the coal industry. There are loosely three principal methods of coal distribution: they are direct sales, sales through agents, and wholesale distribution. In the case of direct sales, the mining company has its own sales organization or controls a separately incorporated sales company. Sales agents are either individuals or organizations normally affiliated with the mining company or a group of mines, and they sell on a commission basis. Finally, these agents may be wholly independent of the mine and act as distributors buying wholesale to resell to retailers or to the ultimate consumer. The greatest concentration of coal-selling organizations is in the Norfolk–Hampton Roads area, from which the bulk of the incoming coal is sent out in shiploads towards the east coast industrial centers and to foreign ports. A good part of the coal output of West Virginia is handled here. Next comes Richmond, where there are agents and distributing companies for the movement of coal in practically all directions, including the Middle West. Other important distributors are located at Roanoke, Lynchburg, Covington, Wise, Tazewell, and scattered points on or near the principal rail routes throughout the state.

Although there are many small producers in Virginia, several of the mining companies are important producers owning several mines each and producing, even in the lean year of 1953, over one million tons of coal; such are especially the Pocahontas Coal and Coke Company, controlled by the Norfolk and Western Railway, the Clinchfield Coal Corporation, related to the Clinchfield Railway, the Stonega Coke and Coal Company, the Jewell Ridge Coal Corporation. Smaller but still important are the Blue Diamond Coal Company and the Blackwood Fuel Company. They are just medium-sized producers, however, on the national scale.

A number of the larger coal-distributing companies in Virginia are actually branches of nationally operated companies which ship to practically any point in the world where coal is consumed. In some instances the control of these companies is vested in holding companies which, in turn, own steel mills, steamship lines, public utilities or any number of different enterprises consuming coal. The larger companies among the Virginia producers and distributors are usually represented in Washington, either directly through their own office or through an association representative. It is in Washington that representatives of the industry

Jewell Seam coal entering the tipple. It will then be washed, sorted for size, and loaded on railroad cars.
Virginia Chamber of Commerce Photo by Flournoy

watch pertinent legislation affecting production, prices and movement of coal, as well as new technological developments in fuel uses. That they attempt to influence legislation favorably for the industry and keep a close eye upon the movement of foreign fuels is generally not denied. The extent to which the coal industry can deter the importing of foreign oil into the United States is, perhaps, very small. It may have obtained government credit or a guarantee to develop during and after World War II the export of American coal to friendly countries requiring fuel. The evolution of the market in the United States and abroad depends largely on factors beyond the sphere of effective influence of the coal industry.

The role of the railroads in developing coal fields and helping to get the coal to the market could hardly be overemphasized. Building tracks towards mine tipples scattered through the Appalachian valleys, and supplying the necessary rolling stock, is an expensive proposition; no railroad will undertake it unless it has good reason to believe that it will have a great deal of freight to carry and that the market will quickly absorb the goods. On the other hand, a mining company needs a considerable investment in the building and equipment of the mines: this is worth while only when good transportation, under competitive conditions, to the final consumer is insured. Thus cooperation and community of interests between mining operators and railroads has been intimate. Often long-range contracts are signed between the mines and the railroads serving them. Sometimes railroads have participated directly or indirectly in financing the mining. The Norfolk and Western Railroad is the most important carrier in southern Virginia generally and in the coal-field area in particular. It is closely linked with many mining companies; it owns, in fact, the Pocahontas Coal and Coke Company, which is an important producer in Virginia, West Virginia, and Kentucky. In 1951, bituminous coal represented 73.5 per cent of the total freight tonnage and 63.6 per cent of the gross freight revenue of the N. & W. This railroad originated 47.3 million tons of bituminous coal in 1951 and carried 52.7 million tons. Other great railroads, such as the C. & O. and the Virginian, also carry large quantities of bituminous coal from West Virginia towards Hampton Roads. Virginia benefits to some extent from this coal traffic in transit, often larger in bulk than the output of the mines located in Virginia proper. One of the advantages of these mines is their position about halfway between the great shipping terminal of Hampton Roads on one side and the great consuming terminals of the Midwest, such as Columbus, Cincinnati, and St. Louis, on the other side.[3]

Among the complaints voiced by Virginia coal producers, one that is frequently heard concerns unfavorable rail rates applied to their coal moving within the state along certain routes in competition with coal from West Virginia and Kentucky; another complaint concerns the loss of New England markets formerly served over a combined rail-water route, now served by Pennsylvania producers who ship via a direct, all-rail route at lower cost. There is perhaps some justification for the Virginia producers' complaints in a few instances. But the more serious problem is the steady trend toward an increasing use of substitute fuels, particularly oil. This poses a serious problem not only for the Virginia producers, but for the entire coal industry. Conversion of railroads, steamship lines, many industrial plants, and domestic users continues at a rapid rate. The N. & W. Railroad was, perhaps, the one to fight the most stubbornly in America against the use of Diesel-powered locomotives. For a long while it insisted that only coal-burning engines could be used on the N. & W. tracks, regardless of the origin of the train or the length of the run. But the national and world wide trend is against the use of coal in many applications.

[3] See the excellent volume by Joseph T. Lambie, *From Mine to Market: The History of Coal Transportation on the Norfolk and Western Railway* (Business History Series of the New York University Press), New York, 1954.

Tipple, water storage tank, and filtration plant at the Jewell Ridge Mine No. 1. *Virginia Chamber of Commerce Photo by Flournoy*

Consumption of bituminous coal by Class I railroads in the United States has been steadily declining since 1944, when it reached over 132 million tons. It fell to 94.8 million tons in 1948, 54 in 1951, 27.7 in 1953. Bunker coal used in foreign-trade shipping went down from 1,785,000 tons of bituminous coal in 1945 to 611,000 in 1953. Retail deliveries of bituminous coal mainly for heating purposes decreased also from almost 125 million tons in 1944 to 61.3 million in 1953. On all these scores 1954 seems to have brought about further reductions of consumption. True, coal consumption has recently been increasing for such uses as electric power production, cement mills, coke ovens, and certain chemical industries. But the use of coal by steel and chemical industries depends largely upon the general level of industrial activity in the country. As 1954 was not marked by greater industrial production on the whole, even these industrial uses of coal showed signs of reducing a total consumption which was already steadily falling due to the constant decrease in the demands of transportation and heating consumers. While there will continue to be many industrial uses of coal, it may not be too long before many of the marginal mines will be forced to close down for lack of orders. And while there are considerable numbers of Virginia mines richly endowed with relatively thick seams of high-grade coking and steam coals, there are a greater number whose future is limited by outmoded operations and nearly exhausted seams. The year 1954 brought a sense of alarm not only to the operators, but also to all those interested in the prosperity of the coal industry and of the coal-fields areas. To the unfavorable trends on the national scene are to be added those resulting on the world market from both the rehabilitation of coal mining in western Europe and the greater abundance of petroleum products and natural gas over the whole globe.

Yet the producers and distributors in the Virginia coal industry were no less guilty than those elsewhere of relaxing their efforts in technological research and marketing techniques as long as world demand was strong and the union was kept at arm's length. Traditionally a "sick industry," the coal industry must find new ways of cutting costs, improving its product and doing a better selling job. Those in Virginia who have come to grips with these manifold problems have sent their representatives abroad to do a better job of selling in foreign markets. They have brought in younger and better-trained management at all levels, and they have sought for improvement of their products through laboratory research.

The expanding chemical industry in the state offers considerable encouragement for greater consumption of Virginia coal. Similarly, the movement of other industries southwards in the East should benefit the Virginia coal industry, for, despite the inequality in rail rates for a very small area, the over-all rate structure, the strategic location of the fields, and the comparatively high quality of its products are all favorable to the competitive position of the Virginia coal fields.

By September, 1954, unemployment in Virginia's southwestern coal-mining counties reached the impressive figure of ten thousand, jumping up as one mine after another shut down. Both state and federal authorities have been concerned over the growing unemployment and unrest in the coal-mining regions. There is no use in attempting to win back to coal those markets that have been so successfully conquered by oil and natural gas. New uses have to be found for coal. Scientists and technicians have been at work on these problems for some time; many of them believe that future hope for coal may lie in the process of "low temperature carbonization," which makes low-grade coal into a much better fuel. A recently developed method of *coal reduction* has fired new hopes for increasing the calorific value of coal without increasing the costs much. Virginians would like to see their coal fields provide the proving grounds for this new method. A group of Lee County businessmen have been considering experimenting in the new direction. Another possibility that has been considered is putting the coal fields to better use by avoiding the costs of transportation of coal and transforming bituminous coal on the spot either into electricity or into synthetic liquid fuel. Although these ideas still belong in the realm of experimentation, if not dreaming, the debates around them show the seriousness of the present situation, which arises from the shrinking of markets.[4]

The coals from Virginia still belong to some of the better qualities of the low volatile bituminous kinds. They have a better chance of keeping a position on the remaining markets than those of some other coal fields throughout the country. But the mines and the marketing must organize to meet severe competition. There appear to be considerable opportunities for improving productivity through greater mechanization of underground operations, especially with cutting machines, mobile loaders, and mechanical cleaning plants.

Virginia's coal-mine operators are reputed to be highly individualistic and single-minded. Supposedly, the tendency to cling to tradition and employ the methods one's father employed simply because they are at hand still persists among many of these operators. Assuming that such a handicap actually exists, and it can be observed in some cases, the present depression on the coal market provides a good opportunity for inducing the operators to try new methods and for "natural selection" to operate through economic pressure.

The labor force and population pressure in the coal field

The opening of the coal mines in southwestern Virginia was a godsend to an overpopulated area inhabited by stubborn mountaineers, most of whom did not want to migrate outside their native valleys and ridges. Appalachian Virginia, and the southwestern triangle especially, has for some time experienced serious population pressure; it was and still is to a large extent a region of subsistence farming and surplus manpower. Coal mines opened up new perspectives for the local people employing thousands in mining operations and connected activities. When many mines began to shut down because of a shrinking market, serious problems again arose in this area. In the coal-mining counties alone, unemployment jumped from an estimated 2,000 in January, 1953, to 10,000 by September,

[4] See "Seeking New Uses for Coal," *Virginia Economic Review,* published by the commonwealth's Division of Planning and Economic Development, Richmond, issue of October, 1954, pp. 3–4; and the report prepared for the Bureau of Mines, U. S. Department of the Interior, Washington, D. C., on *The Synthetic Liquid Fuel Potential of Virginia,* by the Corps of Engineers, Department of the Army, and the firm of Ford, Bacon & Davis, April, 1951.

1954. So serious did the situation become that the Governor of Virginia authorized the State Department of Welfare to arrange for the distribution of relief commodities and funds in that area.

The wages and conditions of work for the coal miners are rather comfortable when mining goes on. Labor is strongly organized here: the district local of the United Mine Workers of America is a powerful union and the most strongly organized labor body in Virginia. The U.M.W. represents virtually all of the organized union members in coal mining in Virginia. Its District No. 28 (southwest Virginia) maintains headquarters and a representative in Norton, Wise County. While that organization does not, as a matter of policy, disclose the number or extent of its membership in a given district, it is variously estimated that between 55 and 60 per cent of the 17,000 to 20,000 production workers in the bituminous coal mines of Virginia belong to the U.M.W. Because of the relatively large number of small truck mines in Virginia operated by small producers employing anywhere from two to a dozen miners, union membership is believed to be somewhat below the national average.

Due to persistent efforts of the United Mine Workers to increase the wages of every category of coal-mine workers, average hourly rates for all categories of workers have increased by approximately 220 per cent since 1939. In that year the average hourly rate for bituminous coal miners in the Appalachian area (including Virginia) was approximately 75 cents; in 1951 it was around $2.20. Moreover, the operator's contribution to the Miners' Welfare Fund has increased from 10 cents to 40 cents per ton of coal produced. This was the outcome of collective bargaining between a very strong union and a loosely organized, highly individualistic group of operators. Many of these advantages were won by the union in negotiations on a national scale. The regional relations between the union and the mines' management appeared to be rather good and less strained than in some other mining areas.

Who are these coal miners of southwest Virginia? The typical coal miner might well be the descendant of immigrants from Scotland, Northern Ireland, Wales, Germany, or practically any country of western Europe whose sons and daughters landed in Pennsylvania, Tidewater Virginia, or some other point of the Atlantic seaboard and moved westward first by ox-drawn wagons and then in larger numbers on the iron horse. Mass migration really came to this part of Virginia beginning only in the 1830's. It penetrated deeper into the folds of the plateau only at the end of the nineteenth century. The town of Norton, which now plays the part of a small capital of the coal fields, since it houses the offices of the U.M.W. representative, of the Virginia Coal Operators Association, and of the engineer representing the U. S. Bureau of Mines, was started in 1891 "when the trains came." [5] The town was named for a president of the Louisville and Nashville Railroad. The whole population of Wise County amounted to only 9,345 people in 1890; it reached 56,336 in 1950, when the town of Norton alone accounted for 4,315.

While a good number of Virginia coal miners, such as leading-machine operators, coal dullers, timbermen, sproggers, and bottom cagers, may receive straight-time hourly earnings in excess of $2.25, the majority of them seldom realize annual earnings of more than $3,000. Census data indicate as the median income in 1949 for rural non-farm families in Virginia's southwestern coal field a figure in the vicinity of $2,000. Average family income ran by counties from $1,347 in Russell County up to $2,257 in Tazewell County; the percentage of families with annual incomes above $5,000 remained below 10 in the coal-mining counties. As this is an area of relatively high birth rate, where families are numerous, the per-capita income was low indeed. While coal mining accounted for something under 50 per cent of all non-agricultural wages-and-salaries employment in this area, and while data prepared subsequent to the December, 1952, wage increase of $1.90 daily to Appalachian coal miners would probably reflect slightly higher medium incomes among employed miners, the growth of unemployment and the reduction in the number of working days in many mines has of course set back the total cash income available to the local people. The activity of the mines determines also the activity, and to some extent, the employment of the regional transportation services, including the railroads. True, many families of miners live on small subsistence farms and derive therefrom some material advantages which do not appear in the official income figures. Nevertheless, the population of the coal field does not give to the visitor an impression of prosperity (see pages 221–225).

Notwithstanding the comparatively low annual wage, the typical coal miner is likely to spend a good part of his cash on consumer items, such as an automobile, a television set, and a radio. He may travel some twenty or thirty miles over mountainous roads to work in the mines. It is natural, therefore, that with the requirement of going and coming over such distances each day he should be inclined to place a somewhat greater value on items that will afford him material comfort and diversion when he is not cutting coal underground or picking slate in the mine tipple.

Due to the predominance of coal mining and agriculture, neither of which employs large numbers of women, the size of the labor force as a

[5] See *When the Trains Came to Norton, Wise County, in Old Virginia in 1891,* compiled and edited by Pres Atkins, reprinted from *The Coalfield Progress,* Norton, 1941.

A mining village of the Jewell Ridge Coal Corporation. The predominantly hardwood forest in the background is typical of the area.
Virginia Chamber of Commerce Photo by Flournoy

percentage of the population in southwest Virginia is relatively small. In 1950, only about 27 per cent of the total population aged 14 years and older of Buchanan, Dickenson, Lee, Russell, Tazewell, and Wise Counties was in the labor force. Comparable data for all of Virginia in the same year indicate a labor force amounting to 54 per cent of the total population 14 years and older. The average for the coal field is almost exactly one-half of the Virginia average in this respect: very few women are able to find employment in that area.

The majority of miners' houses in the southwestern field are in need of some kind of repairs, and they are frequently overcrowded. Generally, houses owned by the miners themselves are in better condition than company-owned or rented houses, although there are frequent exceptions. There is notably better housing in the more progressive company-owned towns, especially in Tazewell and Wise Counties. Too frequently, on the whole, sanitary conditions are inadequate, with a stream in the back of the miner's house serving as the only running water in the neighborhood!

It is interesting to observe that in Buchanan County, where the coal field was developed more recently, the condition of the dwellings is not

Miners at a safety-bonus presentation
Virginia Chamber of Commerce Photo by Flournoy

generally above the average for the region. The greater number of houses in Buchanan County were built in the 1930's after the opening of the coal seams in this area, whereas in Tazewell and Wise, where coal mining got an earlier start, the houses are generally older and larger. The Census for Housing for 1950 shows that the proportion of dwelling units "with hot running water, private toilet and bath and not dilapidated" stood at 14.1 per cent in Russell County, 26.3 in Wise, 29.2 in Tazewell, 13.2 in Buchanan, 12.3 in Dickenson, 14.6 in Lee. It was 49.7 per cent for the whole of Virginia. If dwellings for Whites alone were counted, the southwestern triangle would be the worst area for housing in the whole of Virginia. If some areas of the southside are not much better, it is due to the poorer (but not much poorer) housing conditions of the Negro people. The higher percentages of well-equipped dwellings found in Wise and Tazewell Counties are to be explained largely by the presence of more towns in these two counties: Big Stone Gap, Norton, Appalachia, Coeburn, and others in Wise; Bluefield, Richlands, Pocahontas, and Tazewell in Tazewell County. There is no doubt that in Virginia the towns have, on the whole, much better housing than the rural areas.

The median number of persons per room in dwellings is well below one as an average for the commonwealth. It is slightly above one in Buchanan County, one in Dickenson, and slightly below one but still above the state average in the four other coal-mining counties. The crowding, therefore, is worst in Buchanan, perhaps because the benefits of coal mining to the population have been felt there for a shorter period, and perhaps also because there are fewer agglomerated townships in that county. True, housing statistics are not much more encouraging in southwestern counties outside the coal field. The mountain folk definitely attach less importance to their houses, particularly to outside appearance and to plumbing, than do most Americans and most eastern Virginians. This might be explained by the amount of time spent away from home by long-distance commuters, if it were not true that they usually leave their families at home and the non-employed members of these families rarely have occasion to go out. Television sets are often seen in rather dilapidated dwellings, the occupants of which do not feel it is important to have modern bathrooms. Expensive cars are often owned by people housed in wretched conditions. Tastes are curious and vary greatly from region to region (see maps, page 147).

The conditions of housing witness, nevertheless, to a rather low percapita income. The people in these areas who can easily afford both good housing and other necessities, such as a good car and television, have both. Population pressure in the southwestern triangle has been somewhat eased for a while by the prosperity of coal mining. As these times seem gone, new solutions must be found for local problems. What is needed is not only new uses for coal, but also, and preferably, new uses for the local potential manpower. The southwestern triangle is a bit out of the way and aside from the main arteries of traffic across Virginia. Nevertheless, it is well served by railroads and also by highways. Industry is highly desirable for this area, which is both underdeveloped by present American standards and overpopulated. Besides the need for transferring to other activities a good part of the labor that worked in the now-closed mines, there has been for some time a need for employing on a larger scale other elements in the population, especially the women.

Many coal-mining areas in the Old World, particularly in Great Britain, have known a similar evolution. As the original economy founded on coal mining aged and became obsolete around Newcastle-upon-Tyne, near Glasgow, and even around Birmingham, new industries were brought in. "Industrial estates" were created, attracting a variety of lighter industries that needed a great deal of trained manpower rather than bulky raw materials. It was the exhaustion of the coal fields that caused most of this evolution in England; it is rather the shrinking of the markets for coal that causes similar problems in Virginia and a few other areas in the Appalachian region. In Birmingham local planners pointed out the desirability of creating light industries capable of employing women on a large scale in an area too specialized in coal, iron and steel, and chemicals, which employed essentially men. Such precedents may well be studied by people duly informed of conditions in southwest Virginia and looking for inspiration to improve the rapidly worsening local situation.

The significance of Virginia's mineral resources

Mineral resources have never been of essential importance in the economy of Virginia. Nor did any of the mineral productions of the Old Dominion in the twentieth century play a great role in the American economy as a whole. The most important of these resources recently has been bituminous coal, and even there Virginia did not produce more than 3 to 5 per cent of the national total. Coal mining was terribly important indeed only on the regional scale of the southwestern triangle.

Metallic ores are produced only secondarily and in modest quantities. Nor is any iron worth mentioning being worked today. Manganese, which has become so important in modern steel making, is produced chiefly at the Glade Mountain Mine in Smyth County, which ships ore containing 44 per cent manganese. The Crimora Mine, north of Waynesboro, is no longer as active as it used to be. Manganese occurs in many parts of the Blue Ridge and the Appalachian ridges in Virginia; the total production of the state consisted, in 1950, of 56 tons of ore containing 25 tons of manganese, a very small fraction of the national output, most of which comes from Montana. Prospecting still goes on in Virginia, as considerable efforts are exerted at present to find more domestic sources of manganese.

Virginia's contribution is slightly more important in another metal, the supply of which threatens to grow short in a few years: the production of lead in the Old Dominion stood at an average of 3,269 tons annually in 1941–1945; it reached 4,703 tons in 1948 and went down again to 3,254 tons in 1950. Although Virginia is the leading producer of lead among the states east of the Mississippi River, the state's output usually stays slightly below 1 per cent of the national production; and most of the national supplies of lead now come from recuperated metal. Zinc, which is usually associated with lead in the ores, is also produced in Virginia, particularly at the Austinville mine of the New Jersey Zinc Company. From an average of 18,650 tons of zinc annually, Virginia's output

The Mathieson Alkali Works at Saltville
Virginia Chamber of Commerce

decreased to 12,396 in 1950, still only about 2 per cent of the total mine production of recoverable zinc in the United States. Finally, among metals, titanium is worth mentioning: the rutile mine at Roseland was once among the world's important centers of production. In 1950, ilmenite was produced at Piney River, Nelson County, by the Calco Chemical Division of the American Cyanamid Company. This was again a small quantity when compared to the national output, which came mainly from New York State and Florida.

Among the interesting non-metallic productions of Virginia's underground are mica, found often in the Piedmont, slate, abundant also in the Piedmont, and quartzite, from the Blue Ridge. In recent years the availability of natural gas and some oil has been ascertained, particularly in the southwesternmost corner of the commonwealth. High-gravity paraffin base oil has been produced in the Rose Hill field, Lee County, since 1941. Natural gas from the Early Grove field, Scott County, has been used since 1938. More recently, a daily potential production in excess of 50 million cubic feet of natural gas appeared possible according to exploratory drillings in the Cumberland gas field (Wise, Dickenson, and Buchanan Counties). Gas might thus make up somewhat in this area for the decline of coal mining, but it would then accelerate the latter's downward trend. Some gas has appeared, in such a way as to suggest commercial quantities, in the buried Oriskany sandstone near Bergton, Rockingham County.

Building materials are available in large quantities in all parts of Virginia. In the coastal plain, of course, one would not look for stones; there are, however, plenty of clays for brick and tile, as well as marls chiefly for use as agricultural lime and grit, but also for the manufacture of cement (near Norfolk). We have mentioned previously the large lime production in the southwest.

Ground water is another abundant resource in the depths of the Virginia land. In the Piedmont and Blue Ridge it is relatively scarce. Among the areas of crystalline rocks, the abundant ground water is practically confined to shear zones and fracture systems, and to permeable sandstones within the Triassic basins. In the Valleys and Ridges province, it is more frequently found in such places as fault zones and solution holes in the limestone. In the Pennsylvanian coal measures, ground water is generally scarce and of inferior quality. Its relative scarcity there is often an advantage, as it diminishes the threat of flooding in many mines.

The sediments of the coastal plain yield huge quantities of ground water. It is rather soft and of low mineral content in the vicinity of the fall line; then it turns to soft sodium-bicarbonate water, hard bicarbonate water, and high chloride water gradually eastwards, as one approaches lower-lying sediments closer to the sea and to the sea level. In some localities salt water occurs. In the coastal plain ground water is used by most small communities and for almost all rural purposes. Yields of from 350 to 2,000 gallons a minute are obtained at depths of from 350 to 500 feet. Too-active daily pumpage has lowered the water levels in some localities (such as Franklin and West Point, where paper mills consume large quantities); such observations, as well as recent decreases in the yields of wells in the northern Piedmont, near Washington, may signify that "maximum development of available supplies has been reached in that area." [6] Additional withdrawals of ground water could certainly still be developed in many areas of the Tidewater, but these places ought to be carefully chosen from now on to avoid creating depletion and local shortages.

Yields from wells are much lower in the Piedmont and Blue Ridge, where large volumes of water of high purity are not to be generally expected. But west of the Blue Ridge the prospects are better again and

[6] *Water Resources of Virginia*, A Report of the Committee on Water Resources of the Advisory Council on the Virginia Economy, Richmond, April, 1952.

large volumes of ground water for industrial uses have been developed from belts of limestone near Elkton, Waynesboro, and Roanoke. Springs are relatively widespread and some yield large volumes. Much of the water, particularly in areas with limestone underlays, is hard. Some of this abundance of water in the Great Valley has helped the establishment there of large rayon and acetate plants.

By 1951, the total quantity of ground water consumed or used in Virginia was estimated at about 295 million gallons a day, of which about 200 million went to industrial uses. As the demand is constantly increasing, some concern may be shown for the future of the supply in some areas threatened with shortages. The Report of the Committee, quoted above, states:

> Although water is a replenishable resource, and thus not exhaustible in the same sense as are our mineral resources, the quantity recoverable and usable is neither constant nor continuous, but variable. There are definite limits to the quantity that can be safely withdrawn or developed and used continuously, year after year, from both surface and underground sources in any area or locality.[7]

Such thoughts must be carefully pondered, especially in periods when dry years recur, as they did in 1952–1954. We have already stressed the possibility of soil and vegetation conservation for better water supply in connection with our study of the forests. We may expect this resource of the underground to cause much concern and perhaps some action and legislation in years to come.

Ground water use and conservation are causes for concern in parts of almost every state in the Union, much more so, of course, as one proceeds towards the arid West. On the whole, Virginia has few original problems arising from the use of the state's underground potential. At present the worst of these problems is the shrinking market for bituminous coal, but that market is not controlled by Virginia and even less by her underground. This situation serves as a good example of the consequences for Virginia, as for any other country, of being a large-scale producer of some material consumed on a vast outside market. Some parts of Virginia have known such worries for another staple raw material, tobacco, many times in the past and once again quite recently. Tobacco and coal have the common feature of being burned, in their principal use, and going into smoke. Tobacco is the safer product today as it has less competition than coal and more government protection. Coal is undergoing a severe crisis. It affects mainly one corner of Virginia, because of the production concentrated there, and perhaps another corner, that of Hampton Roads, because of the vast quantities of coal in transit handled by the ports of that

[7] *Ibid.*, p. 13.

area. The crisis is serious, however, and suggests problems of policy for the whole commonwealth, because the coal-mining region belongs to that crowded, overpopulated and underdeveloped southwestern section which has been a problem area for some time.

Virginia is not an essential mineral-producing area. Agriculture, industries, and services are much more important in her economy, and as the relative part of mining tends to decline, the part of manufacturing steadily rises.

7. The Manufacturing Industries

ANUFACTURING was not part of the Old Dominion's tradition or endeavor until the twentieth century. Thomas Jefferson was a true exponent of the traditional feelings of Virginians when he wrote in his *Notes on Virginia,* answering Query XIX, as to "the present state of manufactures":

During this time we have manufactured within our families the most necessary articles of clothing. Those of cotton will bear some comparison with the same kinds of manufacture in Europe; but those of wool, flax, and hemp are very coarse, unsightly, and unpleasant; and such is our attachment to agriculture, and such our preference for foreign manufactures, that be it wise or unwise, our people will certainly return as soon as they can, to raising raw materials, and exchanging them for finer manufactures than they are able to execute themselves.

Jefferson was again a true Virginian in his preference for a rural society, for scattered settlement by partially self-sufficient units. He believed the rural society to be morally healthier and politically preferable. "Carpenters, masons, smiths are wanting in husbandry; but, for the general operations of manufacture, let our workshops remain in Europe." This general statement expressed an opinion prevalent in the South until the War Between the States. And the Southerners felt there was a very good explanation for it apart from the social advantages of the rural society: "The political economists of Europe have established it as a principle, that every State should endeavor to manufacture for itself," Jefferson wrote, answering the query about manufactures in his *Notes;* "and this principle, like many others, we transfer to America, without calculating the difference of circumstances which should often produce a difference of result. In Europe the lands are either cultivated, or locked up against the cultivator. Manufacture must therefore be resorted to of necessity not of choice, to support the surplus of their people. But we have an immensity of land courting the industry of the husbandman. Is it best then that all our citizens should be employed in its improvement, or that one half should be called off from that to exercise manufactures and handicraft arts for the other?"

Jefferson, and almost all of Virginia around 1800, chose to follow the first suggestion in this dilemma: land improvement, which, as we know, was a rather wasteful "improvement" as a rule. But such was not the choice of the people in Massachusetts and Pennsylvania. Even in neighboring Maryland at the time of the Revolution, Baltimore was proud of its manufactures and of having manufactured the first umbrellas made in America. The weakness resulting from the lack of manufactures was bitterly felt by the Confederacy during the Civil War. Economic studies of the shortcomings of the South in the twentieth century express resentment of the Jeffersonian advice and doctrine of letting "our workshops remain in Europe," especially as these workshops have moved to this side of the Atlantic to the great advantage of other states in the Union.[1]

Some Virginia historians may disagree with the general statement that Virginia lacked manufactures in early times. They may point out that in 1609 the settlers in Jamestown were already producing glass ornaments for the Indian trade and that the glass house erected in the woods was the first manufactory in this country. In the same year, boards and clapboards began to be made; in 1609 probably the first brick was made. Works for smelting iron ore were erected in 1620 and destroyed by the Indians in 1622. The list of these early endeavors, little of which survived a short, almost experimental stage, could become quite long. It is significant, however, that some 170 years after the historical glass house was erected, Jefferson was able to take a definite stand against any large kind of manufacturing and boast of the virtues of raw-material production alone.

One careful survey of the past of Virginia's industries remarks as follows:

Only in tobacco manufactures, such as leaf stemming and making plugs, did Virginia take leadership in volume and value of product. This industry centered at Richmond, where shortly before the Civil War 2,500 slaves were employed in some forty tobacco houses. As early as 1815, Virginia was outranked only by Pennsylvania and New York in tobacco manufactures.[2]

[1] See Howard W. Odum, *Southern Regions of the United States*, Chapel Hill, N. C., 1936, particularly pp. 425–426.
[2] *Virginia: Economic and Civic*, prepared in the Virginia Polytechnic Institute, Richmond, 1933, quot. p. 16.

The latter two states were small tobacco producers, but large consumers and highly industrialized. In 1850, the total product of manufactures, mining, and the mechanic arts in Virginia was given as 29.7 million dollars, while it amounted to 237 million dollars in New York State, 155 in Pennsylvania, and 151 in Massachusetts. At that time the population of New York was only double that of Virginia and the population of Massachusetts equalled two-thirds of Virginia's.[3] The difference in favor of the northern states was much greater, of course, in the 1870's.

Growth of both manufactures and cities really started in Virginia in the 1870's. Much of the growth is still due to tobacco, local flour production and other food needs, and the requirements of the railroads. But there are also some iron works and textile mills. Richmond, Danville, Petersburg, Lynchburg, and Roanoke were the only urban centers of consequence by the end of the century. In cotton manufactures, Virginia's advances were far less spectacular than the achievements at that time of regions further south. In 1899, Virginia had 3,142 manufacturing establishments, the products of which were valued at 108 million dollars and which disposed of a total energy of 136,696 horsepower.

Recent development

During the first twenty years of this century few new industries came to Virginia. Those that expanded most were cigarette manufacturing, as this new way of smoking gained vogue, and furniture making, as woodcutting flourished on the western ridges. The most remarkable date of that period was 1917, when the first large rayon mill was established in Roanoke. Virginia thus became the first rayon-producing state in the Union, and the manufacture of rayon was to take an important place in the commonwealth's economy in the 1920's and 1930's. This date marked also the coming to Virginia of a forerunner of the chemical industries, which became the most important category of manufactures in Virginia. The textile plants that came to the state more recently often specialized in man-made fibers and were partly attracted here by the proximity of the mills producing these fibers. The coming of rayon to Virginia was therefore an important event worthy of study.

Why did this rayon mill, then called a "silk mill," come to Roanoke? And why did another smaller such mill establish itself shortly afterwards at Covington? A few years later the Du Pont Rayon Company erected two plants in Virginia, one at Richmond using the viscose process, the other

[3] See J. D. B. de Bow, *Statistical View of the United States, Being a Compendium of the Seventh Census,* Washington, D. C., 1854.

Du Pont de Nemours rayon plant at Amphill, near Richmond
Virginia Chamber of Commerce

at Waynesboro using the acetate process; then the Tubize-Chatillon Corporation built a rayon plant at Hopewell applying the nitrocellulose process. Around 1930, Virginia produced about one-third of the total United States rayon production—about one-ninth of the world production. Such concentration of rayon manufacturing cannot have been the result of mere accident. Most of the sources consulted quote as a decisive advantage of Virginia as a location for rayon plants the availability in certain sections of an abundant supply of water with a low dissolved iron content and a year-around temperature close to 50–55° F. Water supply of similar quality can be found in North Carolina and South Carolina, and in some other states. Large industries are rarely established without careful planning and the consideration of many factors. In this case as in others, many more considerations than water supply alone were involved.

Labor supply is at least as important as water supply. Virginia has, especially in her western parts, an abundant, expanding, and easily trained labor supply. The population is rapidly growing. It has been estimated that in the decade 1950–1960 the state's labor force will increase by more than 200,000 as a result of natural growth, provided the out-migration current is not accelerated. Many families of small farmers have supplied and still could supply substantial numbers of hands for industrial employment. The distinct feeling of attachment to the home locality so common among Virginians is a stabilizing factor: even when better opportunities develop far away, most Virginians would prefer avoiding a move if they have the possibility of making a living at home. Nevertheless, the conditions of labor supply were about as good, especially in the 1920's and 1940's, in most of the southern Appalachian and Piedmont areas. Water and labor for rayon could have been had just as well in many parts of North Carolina and Tennessee.

Next comes, in the question of locating a plant site, the factor of transportation. The plant has to pay the freight on raw materials purchased, and rayon is sold on a delivered basis, the freight paid by the manufacturer. Thus it is necessary to attempt a balance between costs of transportation of raw materials supplies on the one hand and cost of delivery to customers on the other. In the first years of the American Viscose Corporation's operations, the raw material consisted of bleached pulp imported mainly from Nova Scotia. The first plant of American Viscose started producing in 1911 at Marcus Hook, Pennsylvania, on the Delaware River. When the company looked for another site, they needed a good connection with a port on the Atlantic coast from which pulp could be brought to the plant inexpensively. The N. & W. Railroad provided a good link from Norfolk inland; as its main traffic was to carry coal down to the seashore, taking empty trains back towards the coal-mining areas, this railway was interested in having some freight to haul westwards, and it could do so at a cheap rate. Roanoke was a young town, just beginning to develop in the 1910's. It was developing fast, however, as was the traffic of the N. & W., during the years of World War I. At times rayon manufacturing requires cotton linters, and today it uses also bleached pulp from the deep South; the Roanoke site was close enough to the Southern producing areas and well linked to them by rail. Finally, the main consuming region was in the large industrialized area along the northeastern seaboard. The first customers of the American Viscose Corporation had been in Brooklyn, N. Y., Philadelphia and Chester, Pa., and Riverton, N. J.; the new plant had to be located not too far away from this string of industrial towns and consuming markets and within the northeastern territory for rail rates. Roanoke was about as far south as such a location could then be found. It had many advantages in transportation, with that of the vicinity of the South, to which textile industries, potential customers, were increasingly moving.

Shortly after the American Viscose plant developed successfully in Roanoke, the Industrial Rayon Corporation from Cleveland, Ohio, chose Covington, on the C. & O. Railroad line from Newport News to the Midwest, for the site of another "silk mill." Then Du Pont came to Richmond and Waynesboro, both of which offered similar advantages regarding water, labor, and transportation. It may be said that while the two former factors could have been had on similar terms further south, the transportation equation was less favorable south of the N. & W. main line: rail rates were different; distance to the northeastern consumers was greater; and, especially, east-west rail communications from the seaports inland were definitely less well organized. Virginia was the southernmost state providing good transportation conditions to rayon manufacturing in the 1915–1930 period, and the northernmost state providing "Southern" advantages in terms of labor, water and taxation. This combination seems to explain the remarkable development of this particular industry in the Old Dominion. More rayon and acetate plants were built in the state after 1930, notably the large plant of the American Viscose Corporation at Front Royal and Celanese's plant at the Narrows, on the New River.

Most of these rayon mills preferred sites in western rather than in eastern Virginia. This is probably to be explained by water and labor supplies to a large extent, as well as by a definite policy of the large manufacturing companies favoring small or medium-sized towns rather than crowded cities for the sites of their plants. The Du Pont plant in Richmond's suburbs is the main exception to the western location of rayon plants. As more textile industries went south, more large rayon and acetate mills were built south and west of Virginia. The share of the Old Dominion in the national output of rayon seems to be lower in the 1950's than in the 1930's. Nevertheless, it is still important.

The case of rayon is a curious one and worth some examination. It led us to conclude that the position of Virginia as the "northernmost of the Southern states" was in many ways a most advantageous one for industry. Many other industries have come and are still coming to the commonwealth for the whole complex of reasons in transportation, labor, climate, and taxation policy that this formula suggests. The South became quite aware in the recent half-century of the usefulness and even necessity of becoming more industrialized. Local businessmen and state governments are endeavoring to attract industry. Active and fruitful rivalry has thus developed among many of the southeastern states. Virginia has exerted her share of effort and has attracted a share of incoming industries.

The average number of wage earners employed in manufacturing in Virginia rose from 66,000 to 105,000 from 1899 to 1909, then oscillated mainly between 100,000 and 120,000 from 1909 to 1929, with highs in

1919 and 1929 and a low in 1921 (when some of the activities spurred on by World War I were ended). Employment then climbed steadily from 120,000 in 1929, after the depression years, to 179,000 in 1940 and 252,-000 in 1943; it receded to 222,000 by 1945, then climbed again, despite another low in 1949, to 248,000 in 1952 and 255,000 in 1953. The recession which followed World War II was less serious than the one following World War I, and the end of the Korean War in 1953 was not followed by a recession, but rather by an increase in employment, as the figure for 1953 established a new record surpassing that of 1943. The spring of 1954, however, brought about a substantial, though temporary, reduction of employment in manufacturing; the average for the year 1954 stood at 242,000.

Ups and downs of Virginia's manufacturing employment curve have followed in a general fashion those of the national trends. But the increase in this category of manpower was more rapid in Virginia than in the nation as a whole: the number employed in manufactures more than doubled in Virginia from 1929 to 1952; it increased only by some 60 per cent in the same period for the United States. The national figure for 1929 was just slightly below that for 1919, while in Virginia it was very slightly above. Thus it might be inferred that the rhythm of industrialization in the 1920's was not much quicker in the Old Dominion than the national average; but after 1930, Virginia's pace definitely became quicker than the national one, particularly during the 1930's. Figures on employment, however, cannot tell the whole story: they are just one index among many others.

If the value added by manufacturing (i.e., the value of the products manufactured less cost of materials, supplies, fuel, and electricity) is considered, one finds that this index grew by 7 per cent from 1919 to 1929 for the whole country and by 350 per cent from 1929 to 1952, while in Virginia it rose by 40 per cent in 1919–1929 and by 280 per cent in 1929–1952. The "value added by manufacturing" is not an entirely reliable index either, as its precise calculation changed from place to place and from year to year within the country. However, a comparison of the pace at which it rose in Virginia and the average national pace seems to indicate better progress in Virginia in the 1920's and slower progress since 1930. This is not necessarily in contradiction to the indications supplied by the figures on employment: the rationalization of Virginia manufactures may well have been conducted in the 1920's (when Virginia was more belated in the industrial field) at a quicker pace there than in the nation as a whole, but this situation no longer obtained after the 1920's and particularly since 1939.

Machinery in the Dan River Cotton Mill at Danville
Virginia Chamber of Commerce

There is no simple index of industrialization. The picture is a complex and manifold one. What is certain is that the absolute value and volume of the output of manufacturing industries has been steadily growing in Virginia, as have the number of the employees in this branch of economic activity and the profits therefrom to the local population. Manufacturing employment has been fast growing in relative importance as a percentage of total employment in the state, but not as fast in recent years as the per cent employed in trade and in construction industries. The commercial and residential functions of the Old Dominion have expanded more than the manufacturing function. Nevertheless, manufactures employ today more people than any other category of occupations usually considered in the counts, with the exception of government service. Since 1943, manufacturing employment has exceeded agricultural employment, but during 1954 it has been threatened by the advance of employment in trade, which would even have surpassed it already if the "trade" category included that of "finance, insurance and real estate." Comparisons between these various categories of employment suggest the general trends of Virginia's economic evolution. The growth of manufacturing remains one of its essential features.

This growth does not develop in a free economy along lines planned in advance or aimed at some particular specialization of the area. We insisted on the case of the rayon industry because it was a curious one and because the first large rayon plant in Roanoke can be considered as opening, in 1917, a new period in Virginia's industrial history. But many other dates and industries must be mentioned before a general picture is ready. These industries have sometimes sprung out of the initiative and capital of local people: such was the case of the Dan River Mills in Danville; but sometimes they came when an industrial organization from the outside chose a Virginia site for a new plant: such was the case when the American Viscose Corporation came to Roanoke and later Front Royal, when E. I. Du Pont de Nemours built plants at Richmond, Waynesboro, and later near Martinsville, when General Electric made a recent decision to establish one plant in Waynesboro and another in Roanoke, and Westinghouse planned a plant in Staunton. All these examples refer to large corporations and large plants; the same variety exists among smaller mills or plants: many of the pulp and lumber mills are owned and operated by local people (such is Camp in Franklin, and many others); but some small plants are controlled from and supply industries at some distance; this is often the case with textiles and the garment industry. It is true for the large mills owned by Burlington Mills, as well as for a small plant making pajamas in Newcastle, Craig County, for New York interests.

The variety of the industries is considerable, too. It ranges from manufactures of locally produced materials, such as tobacco and wood, to plants in the electronics field that import practically all their raw materials or parts from outside the area. The complexity of the recent development of manufactures in Virginia appears more clearly as one considers either the distribution over the commonwealth's territory of the various kinds of industries, or the industries group by group.

The geographical distribution of manufacturing

Manufacturing is scattered all over Virginia, with a greater density in the Tidewater and the Great Valley. The map (see page 412) showing its geographical distribution by main categories emphasizes some concentration in the main cities or in their vicinity. Thus symbols of various industries congregate in the metropolitan areas of Washington, Richmond-Hopewell-Petersburg, Hampton Roads, and Roanoke. There is also a variegated constellation in the Danville-Martinsville area. A string of symbols follows the Great Valley all the way from Winchester to Bristol,

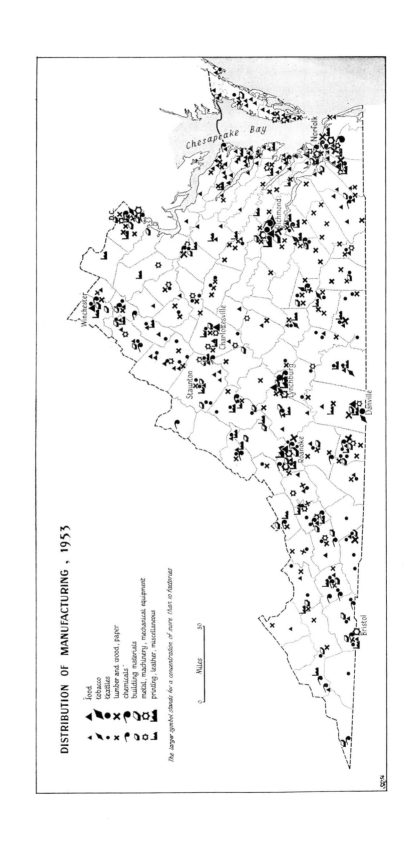

DISTRIBUTION OF MANUFACTURING, 1953

food
tobacco
textiles
lumber and wood, paper
chemicals
building materials
metal, machinery, mechanical equipment
printing, leather, miscellaneous

The larger symbol stands for a concentration of more than 10 factories

Miles
0   50

Chesapeake Bay

Norfolk
Richmond
D.C.
Winchester
Charlottesville
Staunton
Lynchburg
Danville
Roanoke
Bristol

indicating the presence of some manufacturing in each of the many smaller towns along this great axis. The towns in the area of contact of the Piedmont and the Blue Ridge have some impressive concentrations, too, particularly Lynchburg and Charlottesville.

Two symbols on the map are most often found scattered in between the cities: the sign (in the shape of an X) signifying wood-using industries, which include paper and pulp and furniture as well as sawmills, and the sign (in the form of a triangle) indicating food industries. In a wooded and agricultural area like Virginia one would expect such a wide scattering of these plants. Many of them are rather small, of course, and do relatively little processing. It is, however, difficult to draw the line as to which establishments are not important enough to be put on the map. We preferred showing too many to leaving out some significant plant. The fishing industry and truck farming on the Eastern Shore are largely responsible for the density of food industry symbols all along the Tidewater on both sides of the Bay. The importance of the forests in the southside Tidewater and all over the Piedmont explains the frequency of the symbol showing wood-using industries in these areas. If we disregarded these two categories of industries, and the symbols representing them on the map, we would get a picture of much greater concentration in and around the main cities, particularly in eastern Virginia. But the Great Valley would remain a ribbon of scattered industries. This sketch provides us with a general picture of the distribution of manufacturing.

The main congregations of industries in the principal urban centers are remarkably lacking in specialization. Besides the unavoidable food and wood industries (which include a considerable variety between them), each of these congregations has at least five other symbols showing five other categories of industries. Tobacco is found often, of course, within the Richmond-Lynchburg-Danville triangle, the main tobacco-growing area. Textiles are scattered over the Piedmont and the Valley, but are practically absent east of the fall line. Textiles thrive in areas with surpluses of manpower in rural areas and with good north-south connections for easy access to the raw materials and the consuming markets, both at a distance. These are less frequently available in the coastal plain than on the poorer soils of the Piedmont and ridges; the surplus of local manpower along the Tidewater is usually absorbed by activities linked with the sea, travel trade, or food industries based on agriculture. Metal-working industries, including machinery and mechanical equipment, are represented by a whole string of works along the main axis of the Great Valley; there is none west of U. S. 11, and very few on the Tidewater, besides the big centers of Richmond and Hampton Roads. Their importance in the Valley is growing with the completion of plants built since 1953. Chemical industries are probably less scattered than any of the other categories, since they are usually located in the main urban centers, with the exception of some scattering along the Valley and in the southwestern triangle, where they are located on underground deposits of raw materials. The scarcity of manufacturing establishments in the coal-mining counties is striking. The two areas in Virginia least invaded by manufacturing seem, however, to be two long and narrow ribbons of land oriented generally north-south. One of them follows the highly wooded Appalachian ridges west of the Great Valley, north of the Covington–Clifton Forge vicinity; the other is the lower Piedmont, between the fall line and Blue Ridge foothills, north of the tobacco belt. These two areas are not well served by north-south transportation lines, either rail or road; in them the advantages of being northernmost among the southern states are little felt.

The relative importance of manufacturing in the economic activities of different parts of Virginia is even better demonstrated by a map of the percentage of the total labor force employed in manufacturing. Such a map, by counties and independent cities, as of 1950, confirms approximately the general picture presented by the map of the distribution of establishments (see page 429 and compare with page 412).

The Appalachian ridges beyond the Great Valley, with the exception of two counties (Alleghany and Giles, where important railways cross on their way westward), and most of the lower Piedmont are areas of relatively small importance in manufacturing, as are also parts of the Tidewater and Northern Necks and the whole of the Eastern Shore. Many of the establishments working wood and many of the food industries occupy little personnel, a very small percentage in the labor force. Even Charlottesville and Albemarle County are thus included in areas where manufacturing employs less than one-fifth of the labor force. On the other hand, counties with few or no industrial establishments at all show in some cases a high percentage of their employment in manufactures, because they may be residential areas drained by employment offered by a mill situated in another county or in the next city. Such is obviously the story of Charles City County, next to Richmond and Hopewell, where about one-third of the labor force is in manufacturing, while practically no establishment worth mention is located in that county.

The regions which on this map appear to be heavily industrialized are mainly the areas at the foot of the Blue Ridge on both sides of it, the region along the fall line south of Fredericksburg, and the region of

Hampton Roads. Here another inconsistency with the map of the distribution of establishments is worth being stressed: the very low percentage of employment in manufactures in the vicinity of Washington and over the northern Piedmont. What may appear by the number of the establishments to be a substantial group of manufactures in Fairfax County and Alexandria comes to very little in percentage of the local labor force, which is considerable, but employed essentially in government and trade.

In fact, the main groupings of manufactures in Virginia are few: Hampton Roads is one, the Richmond-Hopewell area another, then the Roanoke-Radford area, the Danville-Martinsville area, the Waynesboro-Staunton group, and finally Lynchburg. Otherwise there remains a scattering of industrial works and mills of various sizes and specialties tapping the great reservoir of scattered rural manpower throughout the state, with greater densities in certain areas than in others. Certain single large plants like the wool carpets mill at Glasgow or the rayon mill at Pearisburg employed enough workers, especially in 1950, to modify the distribution of the neighboring area's labor force. In some cases a scattering of four or five small mills can have the same result as the neighborhood of a single large one. Industrial centers with more diversity and concentration of manufacturing, labor, and transportation facilities are limited at present in the Old Dominion to the "Big Six" manufacturing groups enumerated above. They aggregate some two-thirds of the total manpower employed in Virginia's manufactures.

It is important to recognize the variety of the industries gathered in each of these six centers; while Hampton Roads is the most specialized of all, being centered on the needs and activities of a great seaport and naval base, it is not restricted to the shipbuilding and repairing industries. But Richmond and Roanoke are centers of a great diversity of manufactures. In Danville, besides the group of cotton mills of the Dan River, there are some mechanical industries and a great deal of tobacco processing; around neighboring Martinsville there are more chemicals, furniture, and machinery plants. On a smaller scale, Lynchburg associates many other kinds of manufacturing with its famous shoemaking specialty, and in the Waynesboro-Staunton group, chemicals, textiles, and electronics offer another diverse collection.

To the diversity of the associations can be added the diversity of the sites chosen by smaller congregations of plants or even by isolated mills. What is always needed, of course, is good transportation facilities: a highway crossroads and usually a railway line (unless the materials are light enough to travel by truck only); but plants often need also the proximity of a clear stream. What is often least apparent is the agglomeration of workers. The endeavor to avoid the "mill-town" has been quite successful since the triumphal advent of the motorcar and of the improved secondary highway. This is particularly true in the upper Piedmont and in the Valley, as we have already seen in describing these areas.

Manufacturing remains rather concentrated in the case of some industries, such as shipbuilding, located for obvious reasons on both sides of Hampton Roads and, more particularly, at Newport News, and tobacco, with Richmond by far the greatest cigarette-making center, Danville the chief leaf-processing center, and Lynchburg and a few smaller towns as satellites. But other categories of no less importance, such as textiles and chemicals, are rather scattered, as are the mechanical and wood-working industries. Some of these categories of manufactures deserve closer reviews.

The principal kinds of Virginia manufactures

The *Annual Survey of Virginia Manufactures* prepared for 1952 by the State Department of Labor and Industry provides an interesting breakdown of the Old Dominion manufacturing picture in some seventeen categories. Among them tobacco manufactures come first in terms of value of the products manufactured: a little over a billion dollars in 1952, more than one-fourth of the total for all manufacturing industries. This industry employed, however, few people (about 15,000, or 6 per cent of the state's total); the amount of salaries and wages paid was among the lowest of the categories listed; but the raw materials used by the tobacco manufactures are expensive and the ratio of value added by manufacturing rather high.

The industry manufacturing chemical and allied products came second as to value of the products (775 million dollars), second also, but to textile mills, as to the number of all employees (about 40,000), and first as to amount of salaries and wages paid, the value added by manufacturing, and the capital invested (the latter being one-third of the total capital of Virginia manufactures). It may well be considered, therefore, as the leading group of industries in the state, for it has invested and is annually spending much more money than any other category of manufacturing in Virginia. It also brings high profits, but these in large part do not remain in Virginia, as most of the chemical plants are owned by large corporations, the headquarters of which are outside the commonwealth and the shareholders scattered all over the nation.

The chemical industries include the manufacturing of man-made fibers (rayon, acetate, nylon, etc.), which constitutes the most impressive part

Paper plant of the Chesapeake Corporation at West Point
Virginia Chamber of Commerce Photo by Flournoy

of the industry, accounting for six plants, each employing over 3,000 people in 1952. Associated with this branch of the industry is the manufacture of cellophane carried on by the Du Pont plant in Richmond and an American Viscose plant in Fredericksburg. Cellophane is used for many wrappings, but the vast cigarette industry of Richmond is here the leading consumer. Virginia also has large sulfuric acid plants, mainly in the Norfolk area, and impressive works making explosives (chiefly the Hercules Powder Company's cellulose department plant at Hopewell and the arsenal at Radford). Also produced are caustic soda, soda ash, bicarbonate of soda, ammonia and nitrogen materials, iron sulfide, calcium carbide, sodium hydrosulfide, sulfur dioxide, synthetic solvents, carbon bisulfide. A substantial industry of fertilizers is located chiefly in the Norfolk-Portsmouth and the Richmond areas, with a few other works inland. The pharmaceutical industries are not negligible as, besides some local small factories, large firms such as Merck and Monsanto have large plants in Virginia. Dyes and color lacquers, soap and glycerine, cleaning and polishing preparations, paints and varnishes, titanium pigments, wood turpentine, tanning materials, vegetable and animal oils and fats, cosmetics and insecticides, rubber sponge, and heels and soles are all pro-

Smoking hams at Smithfield.
Virginia Chamber of Commerce

duced in Virginia. It is hardly necessary to mention coke ovens processing some of the coal mined in the southwest. A large oil refinery is being built near Hampton Roads. If paper and pulp, which are usually considered a separate category or included with the wood-using industries, were added to the chemicals, they would raise this group of manufactures to the first rank in Virginia with even less doubt.

The plants of the man-made fiber industry are rather scattered; however, the Richmond-Hopewell area on one hand and the Hampton Roads area on the other are definitely the two major concentrations of chemical industries. The rest are scattered, though a number of them are found in the Great Valley. The locations of some are quite isolated, like the Celanese plant at the Narrows, or the large plant operated by the Mathieson Chemical Company at Saltville, which processes salt into many products.

The rayon yarn industry seems to have reached in 1951–1952 a peak of growth, at least for some time. Activity and employment in the huge plants of Virginia decreased somewhat in 1953–1954. This is true of the whole industry on the national scale. The total production of rayon and acetate in the United States reached 1,294 million pounds in 1951, decreased to 1,135 in 1952, and went up slightly in 1953 to 1,197; the first nine months of 1954 indicated a new decrease somewhat below the 1952

A lumber company near Ashland
Virginia Chamber of Commerce Photo by Flournoy

figure. Meanwhile, the production of non-cellulosic man-made fibers (nylon, orlon, dacron, etc.) has been steadily on the increase: 144 million pounds in 1950, 209 in 1951, 263 in 1952, 300 in 1953 and certainly more than 300 million pounds in 1954. These newer non-cellulosic fibers may develop as serious competitors to the rayon and acetate products. They are represented in Virginia mainly by the Du Pont nylon plant at Martinsville; they may develop, but it does not seem probable at this time that Virginia will achieve in this field an eminence comparable to that she has held in the manufacture of rayon yarn: the complex of factors favorable to the coming of large rayon plants to the Old Dominion in the period 1917–1940 does not appear to be duplicated at present for the new kinds of man-made fibers.[4]

While the manufacture of man-made fiber yarn or staple and tow is classified with the chemical industries, the weaving and finishing of materials from these fibers belong, according to the official classification, in the textile industries. The link between the two is not, however, purely

[4] A good source of statistics and trends in the man-made fibers field is the monthly review, *Textile Organon*, published by the Textile Economic Bureau in New York. See also Thomas William Douglas, *The Rayon Yarn Industry in Virginia,* Bureau of Population and Economic Research, Charlottesville, Virginia, 1950.

technical. Among the factors determining the location of textile mills, the proximity of yarn-producing plants is of some importance. The concentration of man-made fiber production has, therefore, favored, although not necessarily determined, the coming to Virginia of textile mills weaving or knitting goods made entirely or partly of these fibers. Thus the man-made fiber industry has, besides its immediate profits, contributed to attract to Virginia more manufactures, especially in the textile category.

Textiles are a third category of important industries in the Old Dominion. In 1952, they were the leading one, slightly ahead of chemicals, in the number of employees; they were second in the amount of salaries and wages paid, as well as in the value added by manufacturing, and third in the value of products manufactured. They would hold these same ranks, but in a more impressive manner, if to the textile mill products was added the category of "apparel and other finished products" in the textile field. Two firms have a very special and leading role among the textile mills: Dan River Mills and Burlington Mills. Dan River is of local origin and is concentrated in Danville. If the several mills belonging to this firm, located within the same city, are considered as one unit, this unit would be the largest single manufacturing establishment in Virginia. It has employed at times over 12,000 people in Danville. No other Virginia unit employed as many as 10,000, with the exception of the shipyards in Newport News (15,000 employees listed in 1952). Very few went above the 5,000 mark (as did the E. I. Du Pont de Nemours rayon and cellulose plant in Richmond). The Dan River Mills dominate the economy of Danville and claim to be one of the largest cotton mills in the United States and perhaps in the world. Burlington Mills originated in neighboring North Carolina; it does not have any single establishment comparable to the Dan River Mills in Virginia, but it does have, scattered through the Old Dominion south of the James River, some ten important mills out of a total of 72 plants in ten states. The Virginia plants of Burlington Mills employed a total of almost 4,000 people in early 1954.

The concentration of Dan River Mills in Danville and the scattering of the plants of Burlington Mills provide a curious contrast. True, the kind of work performed is not quite the same: cotton and man-made fibers are not processed in quite the same way; and Burlington starts with a more advanced stage of semi-manufactured rayon or nylon, while the beginning of the work at Dan River is much closer to the raw material. Finally, the two concerns did not start at the same time; while Dan River is one of the oldest among the important cotton mills in the South and began in the 1880's, Burlington Mills was founded in 1924 and first came to Virginia in 1933. Several factors concur to make the planning of each development quite different from the other.

Dan River Mills began to produce yarn and cloth in 1883. It then had 2,240 spindles and 100 looms; about 100 men and women were employed in the mill; six Virginia stockholders had raised the initial capital of $75,000. Some 70 years later, in 1954, Dan River Mills occupies about 100 acres of floor space in Danville, employs about 11,000 people, and operates approximately 440,000 spindles and 9,000 looms. The company is proud of its continuous plant-modernization program, of its extensive research laboratories and of its up-to-the-minute finishing plants. A large general sales office in New York City deals with customers throughout the United States, and a subsidiary company handles sales in eighty foreign countries. This is indeed one of the best and most impressive successes in the upbuilding of Southern manufacturing, largely the achievement of regional initiative and endeavor.

Burlington Mills is, perhaps, an even more impressive achievement of North Carolina's initiative on the national scale. Its specialization in textiles from man-made fibers was bound to link it with Virginia. The oldest plant of the company in the Old Dominion is the Altavista weaving plant, an old cotton mill bought in 1933 and converted to the weaving of synthetics, near the large rayon-making centers of Roanoke and Richmond. In a suburb of Altavista, the Hurt finishing plant is the company's newest and largest of its kind. Further south in the Piedmont, Burlington Mills owns a ribbon plant at South Hill devoted to the weaving, dyeing, and finishing of narrow fabrics. Most of the other plants are in the southwestern section of the Great Valley: a weaving plant at Vinton in the suburbs of Roanoke and a nylon hosiery plant in Salem; then a weaving plant at Radford, a dyeing and finishing plant at Dublin, and other nylon hosiery plants at Chilhowie and Marion; finally, a large mill of the company's decorative fabrics division located at Galax in the intermountain section of the Blue Ridge, originally launched with the support and financial assistance of local citizens interested in attracting new industries to their town.

The heaviest concentrations of textile and apparel workers as a per cent of total employment in Virginia are found chiefly in the western part of the southern Piedmont and in the Great Valley, largely because the two leading corporations in this field have all their plants south of the James and west of the fall line. Many other firms have scattered their mills throughout Virginia, the majority of the sites being in the Great Valley. Most notable among them are the vast mill of the James Lees and Sons Company making wool carpets at Glasgow near the James River water gap, and the groups of mills and finishing plants at Staunton, Waynesboro, Bristol, and other towns, as well as the Roanoke metropolitan area. Many important mills have gone, however, to the Piedmont at the foot of the Blue Ridge—to Lynchburg, to Fieldale (Henry County), and others. Some are also found in the Richmond-Hopewell area. Virginia manufactures on the whole a wide variety of fabrics, apparel, and other finished products made from fabrics and similar materials; in the textile field its products run the gamut from yarn making and all kinds of clothing and awnings, to automobile seat covers and flags.[5]

Chemicals and textiles are certainly the two major specializations of Virginia, besides the manufacturing of tobacco and wood products (including pulp and paper). Large shipyards naturally came to the Hampton Roads area with sea trading and the naval establishments at the gates of the Chesapeake. Newport News is one of the largest shipbuilding centers in the country and one of the better situated according to the logic (if there ever was an operating logic) of geography. The shipyard of the Newport News Shipbuilding and Dry Dock Company, which employed 15,000 people in 1952 and even more in wartime peak periods, is the largest unit of manufacturing employment in Virginia, just equalled at times by the Dan River Mills. Shipbuilding, carried on at Norfolk as well as at Newport News, is chiefly responsible for the importance of the transportation-equipment industry, notably the Norfolk assembly plant of the Ford Motor Company. Plants processing food and kindred products are again scattered over the state, but with strong concentration at the principal centers of consumption and distribution—the major metropolitan areas (Hampton Roads, Richmond, Roanoke, and to a lesser extent the Washington area, which draws from a much larger radius of supply than the smaller, purely Virginian urban centers). Lynchburg, with adjoining Campbell County, and the Danville and Winchester areas are three other smaller but appreciable areas of concentration of food industries.[6]

We have thus rapidly reviewed the relative part of the various industries in the tableau of Virginia manufactures. There are really few very large manufacturing units in the Old Dominion, and most of these, being

[5] A. M. Whitehill, *Textile and Apparel Industries in Virginia*, Charlottesville, Bureau of Population and Economic Research, University of Virginia, 1948; we have often utilized in this chapter the data included in *Directory of Virginia Manufacturing and Mining, 1953–1954*, published annually by the Virginia State Chamber of Commerce in Richmond, and we have been able to supplement our information with data and materials kindly supplied to us by the headquarters of Dan River Mills, Burlington Mills, American Viscose Corporation, and the E. I. Du Pont de Nemours Company, in 1954.

[6] See Arthur M. Whitehill, *Food Industries in Virginia*, Charlottesville, Bureau of Population and Economic Research, 1950.

in the fiber-making or textile field, could be classified as "light industries." Producing some raw materials, transforming them to some extent, Virginia is still not essentially a manufacturing area as such areas go in America. It has at present, it may be said, an economy rather well-balanced between industrial and agricultural pursuits. Industries came rather recently to the Old Dominion, most of them since World War I. They are continuing to come, and although this growth knows, like any other, its ups and downs, it may be asserted that in recent times manufactures have developed in size and importance more rapidly than did either agricultural production or mining.[7] As this trend goes on, it becomes important to examine more closely the process of industrialization, its factors and effects.

The process of industrialization

Mr. Jefferson favored letting "our workshops remain in Europe" mainly because of a deep distrust of the many ills resulting from the crowding of workers in towns.

It is better to carry provisions and materials to workmen there (in Europe), than bring them to the provisions and materials, and with them their manners and principles. The loss by the transportation of commodities across the Atlantic will be made up in happiness and permanence of government. The mobs of great cities add just so much to the support of pure government, as sores do to the strength of the human body. It is the manners and spirit of a people which preserve a republic in vigor.[8]

The belief in the greater perfection and happiness of the rural societies and in the many dangers inherent in urban agglomeration was quite common in the good society of the eighteenth century. Jefferson was a true Virginian in setting forth such an opinion; but, more than that, he reflected the prevalent belief of the stratum of Western society to which he belonged in the 1780's. The industrial revolution was just starting in Western Europe, and it threatened to have revolutionary consequences. Virginia, moreover, had remained faithful to her original tradition of scattered settlement and few townships. This had been deplored, how-

[7] A recent survey, *Trends in Hours and Earnings in Virginia*, Richmond, 1955, prepared by the Virginia Department of Labor and Industry in cooperation with the U. S. Bureau of Labor Statistics, deals with manufacturing employment in the five years 1950–1954. It shows that for all manufacturing the annual average of hourly earnings of production workers went up from $1.18 in 1950 to $1.42 in 1954 and the average weekly earnings went up from $47.55 in 1950 to $56.66 in 1954. Thus manufacturing adds a great deal to the steady improvement of the standard of living in the area.

[8] Thomas Jefferson, *Notes on Virginia*, "Query XIX," last paragraph.

ever, by many British and Virginia authorities, including such early observers as Robert Beverley and the Commissioners Hartwell, Blair and Chilton.[9] New England and the Middle Atlantic states, meanwhile, had not adopted the same attitude: they followed the trend of urbanization so early apparent in England, Holland, France, and other countries. New York, Philadelphia, and Boston were cities of respectable size, according to the scale of the time, by the end of the eighteenth century. We saw while reviewing the economic past of Virginia what consequences the lack of cities and manufactures had for the Old Dominion and the entire South in the nineteenth century. But the kind of industrialization experienced by Virginia in the twentieth century still seems to bear the imprint of Jefferson's opinion.

Virginia is gradually becoming urbanized, but not as a direct effect of industrialization. The larger urban agglomerations are mainly caused by the development of government services (near Washington, around Hampton Roads, and in Richmond) and by trade activities (especially in Norfolk and Richmond). The more industrialized communities (such as Roanoke, Lynchburg, and Danville) are far from achieving sizes comparable to the larger metropolitan areas. In 1947, when the most recent Census of Manufactures was taken, the Richmond-Petersburg-Hopewell area accounted for 20.4 per cent of the state total manufacturing employment and the Hampton Roads area for 17.6 per cent; both together represented thus 38 per cent of the Virginia total. The two areas next in importance were the western southside (i.e., mainly the Danville-Martinsville area) and the Roanoke-Radford area, which then aggregated 20.7 per cent, but extended over an expanse of land that went far beyond the cities' limits.

We have already noted the endeavor of manufacturers to avoid establishing "mill-towns." Many plants in the Piedmont or in western Virginia were located so as to avoid a too great concentration of industrial employment and so as to tap the reservoir of rural manpower around the site without attracting workers' residences to the immediate vicinity of the mill. Such policies aim at industrializing Virginia while preserving the scattered and largely rural character of her population. Thus the commonwealth is spared the inconveniences of the "mobs of great cities," and the workers in the factories are given the opportunity of preserving at least in part their old way of life and the advantages they may derive from rural residence and part-time farming. This situation should, according to the usual interpretation in Virginia, contribute to the greater happiness of all: employees, employers, and local government. It should

[9] See Chapter 2, pp. 70–76.

make for greater stability in the people, in income, and in industrial relations.

Such a system of industrialization has been possible indeed only since a good system of highways, including the secondary highways, was made available to the scattered crowds of commuters who live at some distance from the plants where they work. The improvement of the secondary highways after the state took over their administration and maintenance made possible an accelerated rhythm of industrialization after 1932. These policies explain to some extent the lack of too great concentrations of manufactures in the commonwealth. The scattering of the plantations in the seventeenth century and the scattering of manufacturing in the twentieth result curiously, in both cases, from a determined preference of the Virginians for such a distribution rather than from any feature peculiar to the natural environment.

Avoiding too much industrial concentration has been in recent times the policy not only of Virginia authorities, but also of large industrial corporations operating many large plants. One of the attractions that the southeast offered for such a policy of dispersal was the availability of scattered manpower, of a low density as yet, for large industrial establishments. Industry, however, attracts industry: this is a principle of long standing in studies of the geographical distribution of manufacturing. The successful development of industries of some size necessitates a site where the equation of location conveniently combines the factors of transportation, access to raw materials and markets, labor supply, and others. The organization of these factors thus established is apt to serve the purposes of other plants or industries, perhaps not at the same precise site, but within the vicinity. More plants will tend to flock to regions where other industries are already prospering. We saw, for instance, how some textile mills came to Virginia partly because of the proximity to rayon yarn producers.

The process of industrialization encompasses conflicting trends in the case of the southern United States: some working for dispersal, others making for concentration. It could probably be argued that concentration results mainly from a kind of economic force of gravitation, while dispersal results from deliberate policies aimed at avoiding some of the consequences of such gravitation. Dispersal requires, of course, a good network of means of transportation covering the land with adequate density. This requirement is more easily fulfilled in a country of intense motorcar traffic, now that trucking has developed on a large scale. In a country with few railroads and few good highways, dispersal of industrial plants is hardly possible at all.

The state government of Virginia claims to have been doing its best to attract more manufactures to the Old Dominion. The Southeastern states, Virginia included, were fully convinced by the end of the nineteenth century that the great workshops of the Atlantic realm were no longer, and should not be, in Europe only. The rapid and impressive industrialization of the northeastern United States and of the southern banks of the Great Lakes suggested that the land of the Yankees was soon going to become one of the greatest manufacturing regions of the world. This industrial expansion brought both more prosperity and more power to the northern states. The South, now conscious of these advantages, strove, especially after World War I, to attract more industry to its territory. Virginia was particularly well situated in this respect: close to the great markets of the northeastern area, included for the most part within the district of northeastern rail rates, and endowed with an abundant coal supply and easy access to the sea lanes of the Atlantic.

Government policies are important in putting these geographical advantages to work. Measures taken by federal and state authorities may cause management to prefer certain areas to others for the location of plants—measures affecting power and water supply, transportation rates, state and local taxation, labor legislation, etc. One method used by chambers of commerce of Virginia cities to attract industries is to advertise that, among other advantages, Virginia offers the favorable conditions of "conservative government," of "authorities friendly to corporations." This factor, it is explained, can be of importance to management in many ways. Though this may be true, one wonders at the results achieved in recent years. Virginia authorities often hint that the Old Dominion is a more conservative state, for whatever may be meant by the vague term *conservative,* than many of the states further south. As one looks at the recent changes in the geography of industrial employment in the Union, Virginia does not appear as one of the leading states in the process of industrialization. Nonagricultural employment rose from 1939 to 1952 by 58.2 per cent in the United States and by 64.7 in Virginia; but this percentage stood at 70.5 per cent in Georgia, 73.3 in South Carolina, 105.7 in Florida, 113 in New Mexico, 193 per cent in Utah! In size of nonagricultural employment, Virginia improved her rank among the states, rising from seventeenth in 1939 to fourteenth in 1952. But most of this progress does not seem to be due to the growth of manufacturing. Neither in 1939 nor in 1952 did Virginia rank among the fifteen first states in size of manufacturing employment; in the South, North Carolina, Texas, and Georgia outranked Virginia by a wide margin. Out of all civilian workers 14 years and older, some 20.5 per cent were employed in manufacturing in Virginia in 1950 (and 20.7 per cent in 1940); the same per cent rose from 16 to 18.4 per cent in the South and from 23.6 to 25.3 per cent in the whole nation.

In the 1940's, Virginia thus benefited more in other branches of her economy than in manufacturing despite the special advantages that government and geographical position may have offered. The most impressive growth, when compared with national and regional achievements, occurred, curiously enough, during the 1930's, a decade deeply marked by economic depression throughout the nation. The industrialization of Virginia seems to have been more regular, though less spectacular, than in most of the other parts of the Union which benefited by the recent developments.

Some of Virginia's manufactures are established on locally produced raw materials; such is the case for tobacco, wood-using industries, pulp and paper mills, most of the food industries, and some of the chemical plants (for example, the products made at Saltville from local salt deposits). Coal, the largest of the resources with which nature seems to have endowed Virginia for industry, appears to have caused little local development. Virginia has, of course, some coke-oven production, and industries all over the state use some of the state's coal, but neither the southwestern coalfield nor the concentration of coal-shipping facilities at Hampton Roads has determined the location there of any of the industries so often found on sites where coal is abundant. Rumors were heard around 1950 in Virginia that when the United States Steel Company, looking for a location for a new and large steel mill, considered favorably a site in the Hampton Roads area, the state and local authorities responded with so little enthusiasm that the mill was finally established on the Delaware. Perhaps the Jeffersonian aversion for the "mobs of great cities" still influences the Virginians enough to make them prefer "light" industries to heavier concentrations. The Hampton Roads area already has large shipyards and the crowds of workers unavoidable in a large seaport. A big steel mill would have increased the crowding in that area and probably would have brought there thousands of members of the powerful steelworkers' union. So many factors interplay in the process of industrialization of a region that no safe statement can be made now as to the decisive reason determining the present distribution and specialization of manufactures in Virginia: it may have been geographical position, the dynamics of inter-regional competition, or social policy. In fact, all three sets of factors must have been constantly at work.

This rapid analysis of the ways and means of industrialization must caution us against too simple or one-sided explanations of such a complex phenomenon as the geography of manufacturing. In every place, local authorities and local patriotism plead, quite normally, a simple cause, defining simple and definite reasons for things to be as they are and better. The facts are seldom in full accord with such explanations, however well informed they may be. We shall have the opportunity to return to a more careful examination of two aspects of the factors involved: the geographical position of Virginia and her labor supply.

Virginia's labor supply

When Virginia is called the "northernmost of the southern states," what is generally meant is that Virginia is closer to the northeastern markets than any other state offering employers the advantages of the South, particularly in terms of labor supply. The main characteristics of Southern as against Northern labor can be summarized as follows: labor in the South is plentiful, it works at wages usually below the national average, and for the most part it is not organized.

For at least half a century before 1930, Virginia regularly lost population by out-migration to other states; the rate of increase of Virginia in the period 1880–1930 was low as compared to the other states, although her natural increase was rather high; out-migration took away more than one-third of this natural increase. The majority of those who migrated were Negroes going west or north; but many Whites were leaving, too. Since 1930 the trend has reversed; although a substantial out-migration of Negroes, especially women, still leaves Virginia, the Old Dominion seems able, for the first period in a long time, to absorb her natural increase and even some in-migration. The 23.9 per cent increase in population from 1940 to 1950 was the highest since the first census was taken in 1790.

The expansion of government services has been a decisive factor in the regional increase of the labor force; but the progress of manufacturing has helped it greatly, too. Summarizing the findings of a careful survey of potential labor resources, Edwin E. Holm, Jr., stated as follows the trends in the early 1950's:

In general, during the decade of the 1950's there will continue to be greater flexibility and expansion possibilities in the labor force in Virginia than in the nation. In the first place, agriculture, which has been a source of supply for non-agricultural sectors of the Virginia economy in the past, reported in 1950 some 31,500 more low-income farmers than was normal—using the non-South as a standard. Suitable nonagricultural employment could probably draw these workers into the nonagricultural labor force. Secondly, on the basis of national norms Virginia has 30,000 females that could be drawn into the labor force if employ-

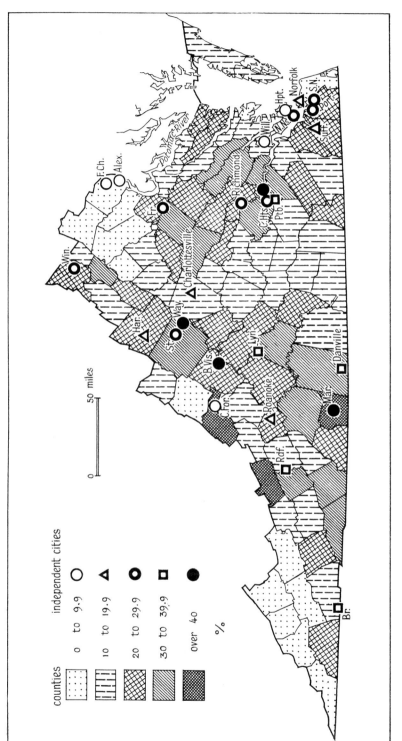

Labor Force Employed in Manufacturing, 1950
(By counties and independent cities, as per cent of total labor force)

ment opportunities develop for them. Thirdly, the white population of Virginia is younger in age than in the nation [as a whole], even after adjustment is made for the young-aged armed forces personnel stationed in Virginia. The age distribution of Virginia's population is such that during the 1950's Virginia will have a larger proportion of its population entering the labor force and a smaller proportion leaving the labor force than has the nation.[10]

The labor supply is, therefore, plentiful and has been for some time. Industry came south largely to meet the worker. Virginia offers such opportunities, too, although during the 1940's, because of the dramatic expansion of government employment in the Old Dominion, manufacturing employment declined here in relative importance, a trend contrary to what statistics show for the whole nation. To attract industry, however, it is not enough that a region offer plenty of workers; it is necessary to consider what kind of workers they are. Many Chamber of Commerce officers, particularly in western Virginia, insist on the racial qualities of the Virginians; they speak of the Anglo-Saxon stock and the Germanic races who settled the commonwealth and who are more "stable," "less emotional" people than the more recently immigrated people from southern or eastern Europe who form such an important part of the labor force up north. Psychology is always an important factor, and for generations Virginians have been in the habit of explaining a great deal through heredity. Naturally, the industrial planner who looks for a good manpower supply will not disregard the fact that wages and salaries are lower in Virginia than further north among "less stable" people.

The Southeastern states have long had the advantages of offering low wages, low benefits. Comparing general statistics does not always make things quite plain. A part of the Virginia labor force in government service is well paid, according to a scale established on a national basis. In manufacturing, however, wages were definitely below average in the Old Dominion.

In almost every line of employment for which an average annual earnings per worker in Virginia and in the nation could be computed, average earnings per worker were substantially lower in Virginia than in the nation. . . . In 1950 . . . per worker earnings in manufacturing in Virginia [were] 19.5 per cent below the national average.[11]

Similar differentials existed also in other categories of employment; they were estimated in 1950 at −17 per cent in mining, −5 per cent in federal government service, −26 per cent in services, −16 per cent in agriculture.

[10] From the excellent report by Edwin E. Holm, Jr., for the Advisory Council on the Virginia Economy, *Labor Resources and Labor Income in Virginia,* Richmond, July, 1953, Vol. I, p. 6.
[11] Holm, *op. cit.,* Vol. II, p. 31.

Thus to the accounting of an industrial payroll Virginia offered a substantial advantage.

Richard A. Lester writes as follows: [12]

Wage differentials between the South and the North, and within both regions, vary widely and irrationally from industry to industry, from locality to locality, and from firm to firm. In most industries, the differential is greatest for unskilled workers; it practically disappears for skilled workers in such lines as iron and steel, paper and pulp, and building. However, in cotton textiles and some other low-wage industries markedly affected by minimum wage determinations, the differential is greatest for skilled occupations.

The special importance within Virginia of such low-wage industries as textiles has contributed to a general lower average in earnings. The abundance of available manpower has, of course, helped maintain the differences between these regions and those where labor was less readily available.

The financial advantages that an industry could win by establishing itself in Virginia were not limited to the scale of wages and salaries. As with wage rates, unemployment compensation benefits in Virginia have been consistently lower than in most of the states. The employer's contributions to unemployment compensation funds were in 1953 below the level for 1938–1940—considerably below if the rise of the cost of living index is taken into consideration. The employer's average contribution rate (which fell to an all-time low of 0.6 per cent in 1953) is among the lowest in the country. In 1952, only four states had averages slightly below Virginia's average.[13] Virginia was the last state in the Union to join the social-security program.

Social legislation and the way it is applied add to the possible advantages an employer may gain at the expense of the employed. Virginia has no state minimum-wage law. Legislation relating to the employment of children and women dates back to the 1890's. The commonwealth's Department of Labor and Industry has recently grown worried about the way in which this legislation too often is applied:

Unfortunately there are many unscrupulous employers whose only aim is to profit by the health and even the lives of women and children, working them long hours, in dangerous jobs and at very low wage rates. . . . Thirty years ago this Department reported that the employment of children was diminishing and

[12] Richard A. Lester, "Must Wages Differ North and South?" in *Virginia Quarterly Review*, Charlottesville, Winter 1946, p. 21.

[13] Unemployment Compensation Commission of Virginia, *Annual Report for the Year 1953*, Richmond, 1954, p. 5; and a leaflet of same Commission, "How to File for Benefits"; also *Trends and Prospects of Unemployment Compensation in Virginia*, Bureau of Population and Economic Research, Charlottesville, Sept., 1953; M. N. Trued, *Digest of Virginia Labor Legislation*, Charlottesville, March, 1953.

that the enrollment record of the schools of Virginia was the largest in the history of the State. (Less than 4,000 employment certificates were issued in 1924.) Today the child labor picture is somewhat reversed. There has been a rapid rise in the employment of teen-agers; juvenile authorities report an alarming increase in delinquency and most of our schools are faced with attendance and "student drop-out" problems. . . . The commonwealth's attorneys are obligated by law to represent and prosecute violations of the law which it is made the duty of the Commissioner of Labor to enforce, yet we come in contact with a few who, despite their oaths of office, openly admit their unsympathetic views of the laws and even fail to appear as our Inspectors' counsel at scheduled court cases. Apathetic attitudes in prosecuting as well as court convictions in which penalties are suspended are ineffectual as deterrents to violators of Labor Laws and only tend to break down the standards we are trying to maintain." [14]

This is indeed strong language for an official government report.

In other parts of the United States, higher wages and better social laws have often been achieved in the past under pressure from organized labor. In Virginia, labor unions are weak and generally frowned upon, all the more so as many Virginians feel that the weakness of the unions contributes more than any other factor to their chances of attracting industry from areas where labor relations are growing more difficult. Virginia has had very few strikes in comparison with more unionized parts of the country. There have been some, of course, in the coal field, where the United Mine Workers have organized about half of the mines' employees. In terms of idle man-days caused by strikes in Virginia in 1941–1950, about 76 per cent of the loss came from the mining industry and 8 per cent from transportation, communications, and other public utilities where nationally organized unions are rather strong. Manufacturing suffered little on the whole from strikes in Virginia, much less, at any rate, than the national average.

It was generally estimated that in the United States about 26 per cent of the total labor force was organized in unions in 1950. In Virginia, the more favorable estimates of organized labor for 1950 set the figure at 170,000 persons in all unions—about 13 per cent of the labor force. A more realistic estimate of the membership (regularly paying dues) of labor organizations would be somewhere between 100,000 and 120,000, probably less than one-tenth of the labor force. In 1953–1954, the CIO reported some 34,000 members, the AFL about 35,000, the UMW about 10,000; and membership in the Brotherhoods and Independent Unions hardly surpasses 20,000. A few thousand more belong to company unions. By average American standards, such numbers indicate a weak labor movement with its strongholds outside the field of manufacturing.

[14] Commonwealth of Virginia, Department of Labor and Industry, *Labor and Industry in Virginia: Fifty-Fifth Annual Report,* Richmond, 1953, pp. 35–37.

The four o'clock shift leaves the shipyard, Newport News
Library of Congress Photo by John Vachon

The labor movement in Virginia still appears by and large as an import, an unwelcome and little-reckoned-with participant in local affairs. It has very little electoral or lobbying power in Richmond; in fact, it is anathema to a clear majority in the General Assembly. A "right to work" law was approved by the extra session of the General Assembly in 1947 and amended to make it even stricter in 1954. Only some members representing the southwestern coal field, where the UMW is influential, had much to say against it in the House of Delegates. The "right to work" law prohibits both closed shop and union shop. Not only is the union violating the law when it tries to obtain such advantages in a contract, but the employer himself is violating it and is punishable if he consents to such preferential employment clauses. Another provision in the Code of Virginia limits the strength of unions: Paragraph 40–71 provides that "no employer shall require any person, as a condition of employment or continuation of employment, to pay any dues, fees or other charges of any kind to any labor union or labor organization." This destroys the possibility of "check-off" clauses in union contracts, leaving to the union the heavy burden of collecting dues from all members individually. The decrease in union membership at the Dan River Mills, after the "check-off" clause was barred from the contract in April, 1953, is but one illustration of the impact of that measure on union organization.

Legislation and politics cannot be held responsible, however, for the weakness of a labor movement: such a movement can be strong in politics only if it is strong at the grass-roots. Virginia, as one member put it during a discussion in the House of Delegates, "is not the state of Michigan, it is not New York, it is just Virginia." [15] Labor unions in the commonwealth are up against a definite resistance on the part of the average individual worker. The Virginian does not feel the need, nor does he like the idea, of participating in a professional organization. Industrialization and urbanization are both quite recent in the Old Dominion. The great majority of the Virginians have been brought up in a rural environment and always instinctively look back to the farm.

The farm from which he, his parents, or his grandparents came still explains a great deal in the Virginian's behavior. The millworker may still live on the farm and go to the plant because the land will no longer provide the kind of livelihood he wants; or he may have left the farm, but with the intention of going back there once he has made enough money. Though generally he is no longer a farmer, the Virginian has not yet become an industrial worker. He has not yet acquired the spirit of opposition between social classes which often develops in the immensity and loneliness of the big city. He has kept some of the peasant's individualism and much of the peasant's acceptance of social hierarchy with the rendering of respect due from small farmers or tenants to the occupants of the manorial house on the hill. He has his pride and the belief that he can solve alone the problems the union offers to solve for him. He has a sense of brotherhood in the community, which regards a certain amount of social hierarchy as good, rather than a sense of brotherhood in the mill. His reaction to unionization may perhaps be a defense mechanism, an attempt to resist social changes that he does not desire and of which he is somewhat afraid.

A union leader familiar with the psychology of the workers in the Blue Ridge region was heard once saying: "They are still clannish, suspicious, not social. They are no 'mixers.' Through the times, they stick with their particular little group, and show no interest for the outside." They have a great fidelity to Virginia, to their region, to their community. Many natives of the southwestern valleys and ridges come back home after having spent long years working in the large industries not only of Newport News and Roanoke, but also of Baltimore, Pittsburgh,

[15] A. L. Boothe, Delegate from Alexandria, House of Delegates, in a debate pertaining to labor in Virginia, March 11, 1954.

and Detroit. Virginians have the feeling, partly as a result of education and partly because there was so little immigration into the Old Dominion for a long while, that Virginia is a large family and that almost all Virginians are related to one another. In many of the western valleys we heard the allegation advanced that the people in this valley were "all cousins." While in the big northern or western cities the union may give to the individual worker lost in the crowd the feeling of "belonging," the Virginian needs this feeling much less as he knows that he belongs to Virginia, to a certain local community, to a certain social stratum of that community. Moreover, he has less desire than many other people for social climbing; he is strangely, and perhaps wisely, more satisfied than so many of his neighbors with the group he belongs to.

Such well-integrated communities as those of Virginia's countryside and small towns distrust outsiders. Many of the organizers the unions sent among the workers were obviously of foreign origin, some of them bearing "names that even a high school teacher could not pronounce." Rather than follow such organizers' appeal and advice, the workers will turn to the managers or owners of the plant, to the "town-folks." These attitudes greatly vary, of course, from locality to locality and from profession to profession. The coal miners were organized perhaps because their work was more dangerous and exacting or perhaps because the union leadership was more skillful.

The Dan River Mills, created by "town-folks" in 1882, have a long history of labor relations. At various times in recent years the prevailing bargaining power shifted from the company to the union and from the union back to the company. Their relations throughout the last fifteen years have been dominated by a spirit of fairness. Management remained as neutral as possible in the face of union organization drives. It has been the policy of the company not to take stands for or against the union in such instances, even refusing to answer questions raised by employees as to the suitability of their joining the union. This has not been the case of all industrial managements in the commonwealth; bitter struggles have at times placed labor and management in opposition, as sometimes happened also at the Dan River Mills.[16]

In some cases company unions have been successfully organized and run. A well-known example is the company union at the plants of E. I. Du Pont de Nemours. Always one step ahead in its wages and benefits of the current demands of CIO and AFL unions, Du Pont has had no difficulty in maintaining its company union. The company has found it

[16] B. and G. S. Mitchell, *The Industrial Revolution in the South,* Baltimore, The Johns Hopkins Press, 1930. See also George T. Starnes and John E. Hamm, *Some Phases of Labor Relations in Virginia,* New York, 1934.

worth while thus to escape some of the too-strict rules of other unions. The development of such practices would further weaken national unions in Virginia, but might nevertheless profit the employees. On the whole, it may well be claimed that the history of labor relations in Virginia is a rather good one and at present there is less tension than in many other manufacturing areas.

The behavior of the Virginia industrial workers has been well described in a study of two chemical plants, one situated at Elkton and the other at Scottsville.[17] This study shows that in choosing their jobs the workers give most thought to two decisive factors: "more money" is the first and, of course, universal consideration; "closer home" is the other, more particular to Virginia. The Virginian is not a hard bargainer in ordinary times, nor is he very demanding. This can be partly explained by his traditional lack of drive to climb upward, and partly by the situation on the labor market where there has more often been a scarcity of jobs than a scarcity of hands.

The Negro problem does not play so great a part in this situation as one might expect in a Southern state. Negroes have been leaving Virginia for other regions continuously since 1880, and the outmigration continues. This steady flow out has reduced the competition between them and the "poor whites," although the latter still seem suspicious on this score. The statement is often heard among them that the competition of the Negroes contributes to depress the level of wages. This is certainly exaggerated. There is little evidence that the Negroes are paid less than Whites for the same job. It may be that the Negroes are not in a good position in Virginia to organize and claim raises successfully. But the general situation of the labor market and the attitude of White labor on the matter of organization are much more potent factors in keeping wages down. Negroes are still discriminated against in terms of the kinds of jobs open to them; these vary also from place to place. During the period of tighter labor supply in World War II, more opportunities were opened to them because there were not enough Whites to fill them.

Given the local traditions and prejudices, the unions have often been very moderate in their opposition to race discrimination. In some instances they have even been among the first to discriminate, forgetting the general principles set at the national headquarters and taking locally popular and strategic measures. At times, even during the wartime shortage, unions opposed the training of Negroes for skilled jobs in some professions. It is certain that union leadership would like to put an end

[17] Starnes, Wilkins, and Wisman, *The Labor Force of Two Rural Industrial Plants,* Bureau of Population and Economic Research, Charlottesville, 1951.

to all discrimination in labor's ranks; but the time has not yet come when local labor leaders will be able to publicly oppose discrimination without determining stronger resistance to unionism on the part of the "poor whites," who are really the strongest component of the labor force in Virginia, as in other northern states of the Southeast.

Present trends and prospects

Manufacturing has now come to Virginia to stay, to play an important part in the regional economy, and to continue its development. More plants are being built in different parts of the Old Dominion, and more new categories of industry are coming in. The announcement since 1953 that several plants manufacturing electrical machinery and electronics will be built in Virginia rang a new bell. It meant growing diversification on the list of leading industries in Virginia and the development of a manufacturing branch that requires many skilled workers and takes a role of ever-increasing importance in modern life. Early in 1955 it was announced that a large plant will be built near Lynchburg by the Atomic Energy Division of the Babcock and Wilcox Company to manufacture many types of special equipment for the nuclear power industry.

The distribution of manufactures as it appears on the map for 1953 may slowly change. The particular role played by the Tidewater, especially along the James River from its falls down to Hampton Roads, may decrease in relative weight. This area has benefited more than others from the industrialization boom of World War II, and it shows signs of crowding and of a less easy labor market than inland areas. "The significant effect of World War II in the field of labor relations in the Hampton Roads area was to accelerate the development of collective bargaining in a region which had been predominantly an open shop and individual bargaining area." [18] The Great Valley and the southern Piedmont will probably receive most of the new manufacturing to come in the near future. The policy of dispersal can be easily applied to these areas, and one would also wish to see it extended towards the less well situated valleys of the southwestern triangle.

The labor market will certainly remain for quite some time in the same general conditions we have described. At the basis of the situation is the psychology and the geographical distribution of the workers, and their abundance, which are not liable to change rapidly. Psychological attitudes will be the last to evolve. As Virginia becomes more urbanized

[18] Charles F. Marsh (ed.), *The Hampton Roads Communities in World War II*, Chapel Hill, University of North Carolina Press, 1951, p. 227.

and more industrialized, however, the labor supply will grow less plentiful as against the demand; and it may gradually lose some of its rural, peasantlike character.

Remarkable things are happening already. A startling experiment developed in 1954 in the historical town of Appomattox. A local plant, the Appomattox Garment Company, employing about 375 workers, refused to negotiate a new contract incorporating a wage increase and other benefits with Local 236 of the International Ladies Garment Workers' Union, AFL. The union called a strike against the company and was followed by about one-half of the employees. The company had no trouble finding new workers, though it had to train many of them and raise the minimum wage. But the national headquarters of the ILGWU stepped into the picture and decided to build a new plant at Appomattox, a few hundred yards away from the Appomattox Garment Company, to employ the striking workers. The new plant was leased by the ILGWU to a New York manufacturer who signed a union contract and got an option to acquire ownership of the plant after three years of operation. The new plant, operated by the Lin-Bar Dress Corporation in competition with the Appomattox Garment Company, intended to introduce to the area higher wages and benefits in an attempt to raise the local level. The future will show how great an impact such an experiment may have. Setting aside the historical symbolism of the town where it occurred, the Appomattox case of 1954 is indicative of the great power of national unions today and of the greater attention they give to such areas in the South, where they have had relatively little success as yet, but where more industries are moving in. The Appomattox case is all the more interesting as the ILGWV was fighting there an apparel manufacturer who moved his plant from New York City to Virginia in 1953. It was a response from New York to Southern endeavors to induce manufacturers to abandon unionized plants in the North and move South.[19]

As more jobs are made available and fewer subsistence farmers are left on their lands, the labor supply is bound to slowly tighten up. As more large national industrial corporations, such as the General Electric Company and Westinghouse, move into Virginia, following others like American Viscose and Du Pont de Nemours, the scale of wages is bound to be improved and more attention is sure to be paid to the area by large national unions. Virginia may thus gradually become less "provincial" than it used to be as regards industrial conditions. It must and will become more industrialized, developing further as a center of manufacturing. Its geographical position at the gate of the South will force such an

[19] Articles in the *New York Times,* July 27 and August 11, 1954.

evolution upon the Old Dominion even if the state resists. But the spirit of resistance to the usual main consequences of industrialization will remain alive for quite a while, all the more so as industrialization is coming to Virginia largely independently of urbanization. The two processes are curiously distinct here.

8. *Assets and Liabilities of Location*

THE PRACTICAL VALUE to a community of the geographical location of the land on which it lives is always difficult to determine. It is an ever-shifting value, as the same coordinates do not mean the same advantages or disadvantages in changing conditions and for different purposes. The process of history produces constant fluidity in the distribution of people, resources, and values in space. One of the main purposes of geography is to show, concerning any phenomenon located in the space accessible to men, what outside influences are brought to bear upon it and how this network of outside influences shapes up on the map, on the surrounding lands.

During our review of Virginia's main features, past and present, and of the use made of her resources, we encountered at every step the determinant influence of relations with markets, competitors, and points from which supplies came, as well as many more less obvious relations in terms of collective psychology, of comparative law, and of faculty of access to the potential resources, human as well as natural. The length of the Tidewater near the entrance to the vast Chesapeake Bay was a great asset at the time when all trade was overseas trade and when navigation was the best and easiest mode of transportation. As settlement progressed inland we saw the fall line become the preferred, the more advantageous location. Later the Great Valley gained a privileged position because it was the easiest and best-organized route from the better-developed Northeast to the main centers of settlement in the Southeast.

The forest resources of Virginia were put to use and depleted mainly when the national market needed them and after the more easily accessible possibilities of the northeastern states had been largely exhausted, but before the exhaustion of the less accessible forests of the Deep South or Northwest. The cultivation of grain in Virginia depended on how well the accessible markets were supplied from elsewhere: at one time an important supplier of cereals for the northeastern consuming centers, Virginia lost this function when the Midwest undertook the production of grain on a much larger scale and at lower cost. When the needs of the market and the evolution of techniques began to favor the raising or fattening of cattle on the Piedmont grasslands, Virginia put that resource to work. Data on local potential cannot be of much use until the potential can be made to function in an organized network of relations integrating it with a wider system.

Virginia has always functioned as part of a broad and loosely organized economic system, first as part of the vast colonial empire of His Britannic Majesty, then as a state in a great Union which was rapidly expanding and within which internal economic barriers were prohibited. Thus her geographical location was always of the utmost importance to the economic life of Virginia, much more so than if the Old Dominion had had an opportunity for isolation. Relations with the outside were essential. This position on the map carried with it many assets and some liabilities.

Can location be a liability?

Any land, regardless of location, can be developed when properly integrated with a congenial surrounding system. Isolation has always been a hindrance to the full blossoming of the potentialities enshrined in any land and any people. This is why conditions of access and transportation are decisive in determining at a given time the value and significance of a position in space. This is also why location can be a liability when an area is not well linked to the outside world. Would isolation be a constant liability even to a vast country, let us say to a whole continent? Such a question can have no logical answer because there is no clear or constant meaning for *liability* as it pertains to a vast geographical unit. Whether the kind of life a vast country can develop, once isolated by a blind wall, is better or worse than the life the same people would have in this same country while participating actively in relations with the outside is a question of taste for the people concerned. Was Japan happier before it was opened by the insistent pressure of the Western powers to international trade and cultural exchanges about a century ago? Historians and philosophers may debate such problems at length. They

The ferry on the James River at Scotland, across from Jamestown. In the background can be seen the monument commemorating the first settlement.

border on philosophy and are not actually within the realm of geographical research. Geographers who have a smattering of history know that peoples who may have enjoyed the conditions of isolation for a while have always seen this isolation broken by outsiders, and often to the temporary advantage of the outsiders: such were the stories of China and Japan, who tried to enclose themselves behind high walls, of many smaller peoples of Africa, and of the Indian parts of America.

History teaches us that people who were curious about the outside and willing to explore beyond their own horizons have usually been stronger and more prosperous than those who attempted isolation. Have they been happier? The answer depends on what makes people happy. The people in the hollows of the Virginia mountains may prefer their isolation, at least until they have tasted something else. Western civilization has based its behavior and a great deal of its strength on the struggle for free movement, for the privilege of roaming at will on the vast open seas and over the immense continents and of opening new frontiers beyond what was already known. Some scholars have suggested that the Western nations have been able to carry on this ever-expanding exploration because they were the strongest and the most blessed of nations. The

Tide mill in Mathews County near Poplar Grove
Virginia Chamber of Commerce Photo by Flournoy

theory might just as safely be submitted that they were strongest and most blessed because they were willing to undertake these endeavors and endure the hardships involved, by the sweat of their brow.

No location in this world is forever a Garden of Eden. Every geographical position has at least the liability that another can be at least as well organized for the needs of the moment. Few positions have as many assets as a narrow low pass across a long and lofty range. Such a position, however, will carry with it many liabilities: it is narrow and confined, it is threatened by positions on the heights framing it, it will be coveted. Some of the old tobacco plantations on the Tidewater had fortunate locations for trading with lands overseas and expanding inland; but many of them communicated with the outside world only through their river landings until the Civil War and, in a few cases, even after. But at the end of the nineteenth century this was already a pretty bad link with the outside world; it was a shortcoming not to have a rail track or a decent road passing nearby. Access is a matter of organization according to the techniques of the period, not a mere question of distance or natural endowment.

Location, in other words, can be a liability if and when connections with the outside are not properly organized. The proper form of organization varies with the changes in the conditions of the outside. For Virginia, the "outside" has meant, from the earliest period of her history to this date, both the United States and the world overseas. Virginia was born a daughter of Atlantic navigation, of transoceanic traffic, and of the settlement of a continent. From what followed the early period, when the Tidewater was the whole of Virginia, it would seem that the Old Dominion did not remain much attached to its oceanic parentage.

The continentality of the Old Dominion

The export of tobacco and at times of grain has remained throughout Virginia's history a necessity and a good reason to look towards the sea. But the more important horizons were westward. Virginians were mainly settlers, pioneers, rural people who wanted more land and who went in large numbers to settle beyond the Appalachians. Although they navigated along the Tidewater and went fishing at sea, their maritime horizons were limited to the proximity of their coast. No large-scale commercial maritime activities developed from Virginia. The trade in tobacco was largely carried on by people from abroad, although some of them settled for a while in Virginia and may even have remained there. The great endeavors in navigation so characteristic of American settlers from early times had their origin on the Atlantic seaboard further north: the Delaware Bay, New York, New England. When the planters of Virginia built ships and sent them to Britain filled with tobacco, they usually sold them in British ports, as they were not interested in bringing to the plantation all the worries and troubles connected with ship ownership and operation. From Baltimore northwards the idea of taking advantage of the ocean lanes to trade, get rich, and even engage in privateering was very much alive. In Virginia the people were more firmly rooted to the continent.[1]

This does not mean that at times Virginia merchants did not covet the role of the great center of exchange on the Atlantic seaboard, at least as an outlet for the raw materials produced inland. Great efforts were made, inefficiently and without much success, to capture the trade from the west in favor of Richmond, Alexandria, and Norfolk. The results of these efforts were slight before World War I. The canals and turnpikes built from the Tidewater westward were rapidly superseded by railroads or better roads leading to Baltimore, Pennsylvania, and New York. The

[1] See A. P. Middleton, *Tobacco Coast*, Newport News, The Mariners Museum, 1953.

Erie Canal was opened and favored New York long before the canals planned by the Virginians had crossed the Blue Ridge.[2]

Nevertheless, Virginia looked inland. At first it was inland that the surplus of Virginians could find what they wished for most ardently: free land. Then it was inland that Virginia could find more and more markets for her products, for the Negro slaves she sold in the nineteenth century to the expanding cotton country, and even for tobacco, as consumption by the continent increased. Some maritime activities developed in Richmond and Hampton Roads largely in order to ship the products of Virginia or of a hinterland which produced raw materials.

In the *Notes on Virginia*, Jefferson expressed great hopes that the development of the James–Great Kanawha route towards the Ohio and Mississippi Rivers would open up, settle, and then drain the interior. Virginia for the Virginians extended then as far as the Mississippi and the Great Lakes. Even much later the interest in transcontinental development rather than in the maritime assets of the geographical location of the state was still apparent. We are indeed justified in stressing the continentality of the Old Dominion.

The rural character which most of the commonwealth possessed until recently, and the deep attachment to the land and the farm felt by many Virginians, are other symptoms of continentality. A country can hardly be deeply agrarian and engage actively in the adventures of the high seas at the same time. Of the two calls any inhabitant of a seaboard area can hear, the Virginian definitely listens to the call of the land. The outline of the Old Dominion's territory clearly stresses this preference: the southwestern triangle, jutting out to the west as far as the Cumberland Gap and made familiar to all because of the story of Daniel Boone, symbolizes the direction in which Virginia looked. There are no legends of sea navigation and of clippers that can match in popularity in Virginia the tradition of Daniel Boone. Territorial outline and folklore concur to emphasize the fact that Virginia had her back to the sea.

On the map of the United States (see page 446) Virginia stands in the middle of the eastern seaboard and extends far inland. Its southern boundary measures almost one-sixth of the total width of the continent at that latitude. Several easy axes of traffic cross this territory: one follows the fall line, another crosses the Piedmont close to the foothills of the Blue Ridge, a third follows the Great Valley. Other axes of traffic extend in an east-west direction: from Winchester towards Wheeling and Pittsburgh; from Lynchburg and Roanoke towards the great coalfields of West Virginia, and beyond them the valley of the Ohio; then from Roa-

[2] See above, Chapter 2, pp. 105–108.

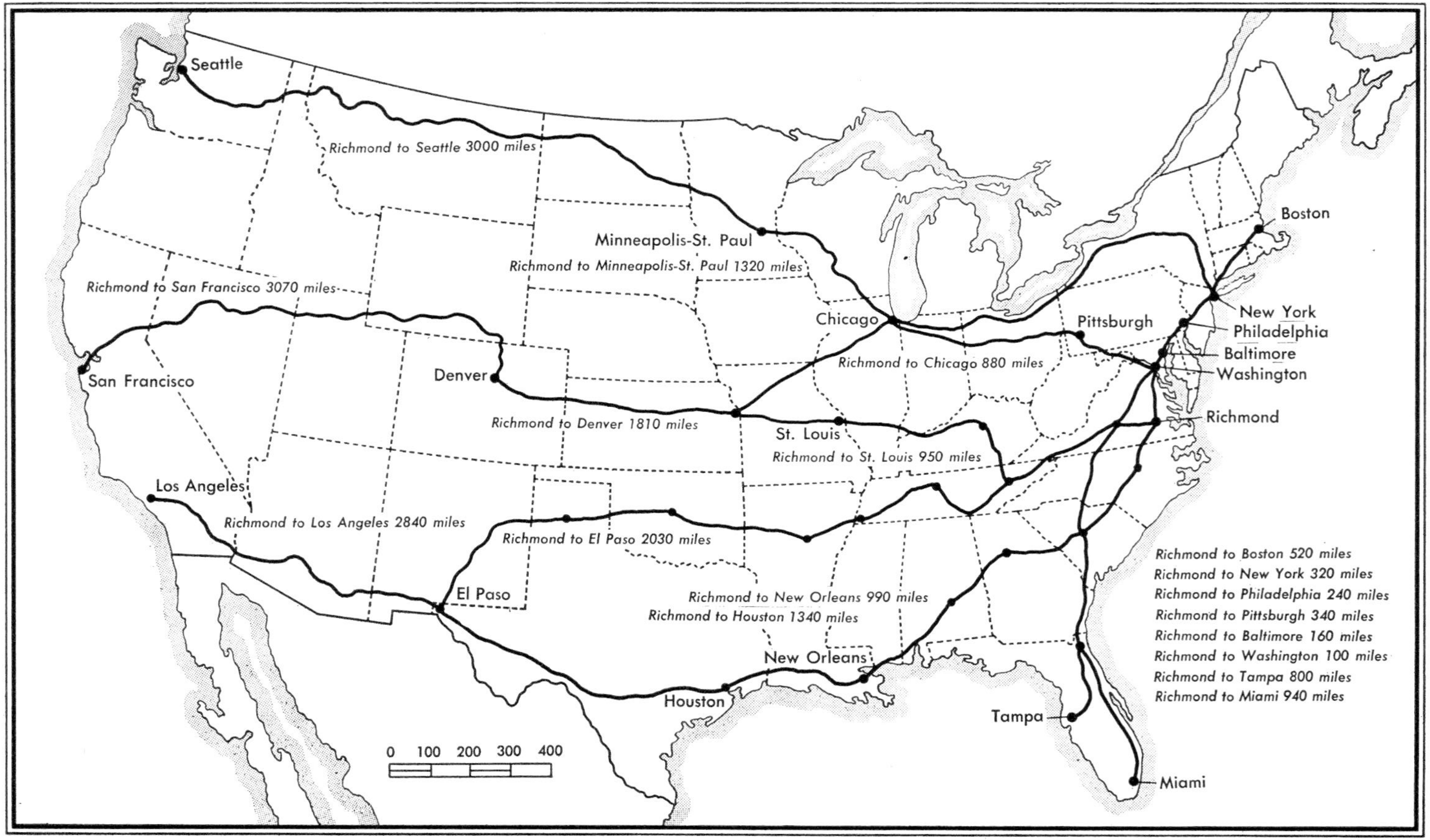

Major Distances from Richmond

Richmond to Boston 520 miles
Richmond to New York 320 miles
Richmond to Philadelphia 240 miles
Richmond to Pittsburgh 340 miles
Richmond to Baltimore 160 miles
Richmond to Washington 100 miles
Richmond to Tampa 800 miles
Richmond to Miami 940 miles

Richmond to Chicago 880 miles
Richmond to St. Louis 950 miles
Richmond to New Orleans 990 miles
Richmond to Houston 1340 miles
Richmond to Denver 1810 miles
Richmond to El Paso 2030 miles
Richmond to Los Angeles 2840 miles
Richmond to Minneapolis-St. Paul 1320 miles
Richmond to Seattle 3000 miles
Richmond to San Francisco 3070 miles

Boston
New York
Philadelphia
Baltimore
Washington
Richmond
Pittsburgh
Miami
Tampa
Chicago
St. Louis
New Orleans
Houston
Minneapolis-St. Paul
Denver
El Paso
Seattle
San Francisco
Los Angeles

0   100   200   300   400

noke through southwestern Virginia to the Cumberland Gap and Kentucky. None of these possible ways of crossing the Appalachian system has turned out to be very important in the twentieth century. In terms of topography the advantage of one valley over another in crossing a mountainous system can always be debated. But in terms of organization of access the railroad companies of the Baltimore and Ohio, of the Pennsylvania, and of the New York Central accomplished more during the last third of the nineteenth century than had the Virginians. The tariff wars of the 1870's and 1880's between these great railroads helped them win most of the traffic and improve the organization of the access of the trans-Appalachian regions. Later the Chesapeake and Ohio, the Norfolk and Western, and the Virginian railroads channelled towards the ports of Hampton Roads, chiefly after 1914, when these became adequately equipped, a large part of the coal extracted in the Appalachian fields.

Altogether Virginia appears as a great continental crossroads, but not so great in terms of traffic as one might expect after looking at the map. The northern states and seaports won and retain most of the functions of the great North American Atlantic crossroads. In a way, Hampton Roads is only a southern extension of this great maritime and commercial system; it developed later, and then chiefly because of the overcrowding of the seaboard to the north.

The gates of the Chesapeake Bay

The position the Virginia Tidewater occupies is a commanding one on the eastern seaboard. South of Norfolk the Atlantic coastline is a rounded, rather low and sandy one, an immense mud or sand bank that does not favor navigation, especially by the larger ships of our time. The easy penetration by seagoing ships into the depths of the continent, made possible by the Chesapeake and the tidal estuaries of such rivers as the James and the Potomac, has long been a great advantage. Baltimore took great advantage of it. When Washington was first built in the early 1800's, many specialists ventured to predict that it would become the great sea-trading center of the east coast. These hopes did not materialize. The large-scale trade was entirely retained by the ports of the area north of Washington until the immense development of Hampton Roads, which resulted largely from the needs of World War I and later of World War II, and also from the fact that the growing size and cost of operation of ships favored harbors situated as close as possible to the open seas.

The gates of the Chesapeake Bay are the southernmost point on the

An oyster boat off the Virginia shore
Virginia Chamber of Commerce

North American Atlantic seaboard to which physical access is easy—all
the more so as the climate is warm and the water rarely freezes along the
coast—and which is at the same time well linked today by rail and road
with most of the eastern United States. The distances from Norfolk or
Richmond to many points in the southern and central parts of the country are shorter than from Boston and New York. It is paradoxical to observe that Hampton Roads is now more favorably situated than Boston
and even perhaps New York, as communications go, with respect to the
rapidly developing parts of the country. Even Richmond still has some
activity in its deep river port, although navigation is difficult and slow up
the James. Hampton Roads has another advantage as a result of its position at the gate of the largest bay that penetrates the east coast of the
continent: the proximity or easy access through the bay to other great
ports, particularly Baltimore, and beyond it, via the Chesapeake and
Delaware ship canal, to the Delaware group of ports. Great harbors not
only compete among themselves, they also cooperate. In many cases a
ship's cargo is not entirely debarked or entirely loaded in one port; often
ships endeavor to complete their loads in neighboring ports, if there are

Dredging oysters from private beds near Norfolk. *Norfolk Ad. Bd.*

any. The proximity and easy access of great ports like Baltimore and Philadelphia turn out to be assets for Hampton Roads.

Its position at the gates of the Chesapeake was decisive for the establishment at Hampton Roads of a major naval base. Its central location on the United States east coast was a favorable one for the headquarters of the Atlantic Fleet; the necessity of defending the vast inland system of navigation of the Chesapeake, which includes the national capital, the large cities of Baltimore and Richmond, and the proximity of Annapolis —these points contributed in the choice of Norfolk as the greatest American naval base on the Atlantic. Such a base had to be at the gates of the bay in order both to protect its entrance and to permit sailing out in any direction to sea.

Finally, the Chesapeake has contributed in another way to increase the variety of Virginia's resources. The sea and the vast expanse of the bay with its tidal estuaries are the realm from which come the resources of fishing and especially oystering. It is estimated that from 50,000 to 125,000 pounds of finfish and from 35,000 to 70,000 pounds of shellfish are landed annually in Virginia. The catch varies substantially from year to year. It has brought to the fishermen of the Tidewater, and particularly of the Eastern Shore, about $20,000 per year since 1945 (the pre-1942 catch was

Dredging crabs in Chesapeake Bay
Virginia Chamber of Commerce Photo by Flournoy

usually $3,000 to $5,000 each year, hence the progress in the last decade
has been quite important). Careful studies of marketing conditions and
methods have recently been made in order to enable Virginia to develop
this resource of her offshore waters.[3]

The Tidewater is of little service today as a coastwise waterway, although its utility in this respect is not entirely gone. Maintenance of the
main channels for seagoing ships and the organization of navigation facilities are taken care of by federal authorities, largely because of the
strategic importance of the place and also in order to facilitate interstate
and foreign trade. While decreasing in significance for coastwise navigation, the Tidewater is gaining in importance for recreational purposes,
particularly as large urban agglomerations have arisen near the gates of
the Bay and immediately behind it. Thus the position at the gates of the
Bay carries many advantages, some of purely local importance and some
of great national scope. It was only in the middle of the twentieth century
that this enormous asset of Virginia's location was actually put to work.

[3] See the reports prepared for the Advisory Council on the Virginia Economy in
Richmond by Charles L. Quittmeyer, *The Marketing of Virginia Seafood,* March, 1950,
and by the Committee on Water Resources, *Water Resources of Virginia,* April, 1952.

A bayside wharf in Mathews County
Virginia Chamber of Commerce Photo by Flournoy

The gateway to the South

Perhaps more important in the long run than the Chesapeake gates will
be Virginia's position commanding access to the South from the highly
urbanized and industrialized areas of the Northeast and of the Middle
West between the Great Lakes and the Ohio River. More than any other
state to its west, Virginia commands the entrance to the South, as well as
the South's access to the great markets of the North. It is remarkable that
the main traffic and the better organized roads go from the northeast
towards the southeast in terms of highways and from the northwest to
the south or southeast in terms of railways (see the maps on pages 527
and 532–533).

As Virginia extends all the way from the ocean shore to the difficult
maze of Appalachian ridges to the west, traffic between the southeast and
the northeast has to cross it in order to avoid long and unnecessary detours. This transit function of Virginia is at least as obvious as the function of guarding the entrance of the Chesapeake. The two motoring itineraries in the Old Dominion with the heaviest traffic are U. S. Route 1
(partly paralleled by U. S. 301) following the fall line and U. S. Route 11

Dredging oysters in Chesapeake Bay
Virginia Chamber of Commerce Photo by Flournoy

following the Great Valley. The frequency of trucks on both these routes at any time of day and night is impressive. The through-traffic brings some trade to the towns and travel-trade establishments along the main routes and has forced the building of detours around the main cities, avoiding the business sections where crowding is great even without the through-traffic. Richmond and Petersburg have had to renounce the little advantages brought to some of the merchants on their main streets by the transit traffic and, despite some resistance, a new turnpike taking U. S. 1 around the more congested parts of this metropolitan area was decided upon in 1954.

We noted in describing the Great Valley [4] the variety of trades encouraged along U. S. 11 by the passage of such good customers as the Texans driving to or from Washington and New York. Until the late 1930's, the traffic on U. S. 11 was more important than that on U. S. 1. The latter took the lead in a decisive way with the recent and rapid development of South Carolina, Georgia, and especially Florida. The routes along east-west directions have much less traffic at all times than the north-south itineraries, a fact which again stresses the role of Virginia as a gateway to

[4] See Chapter 3, pp. 200–215.

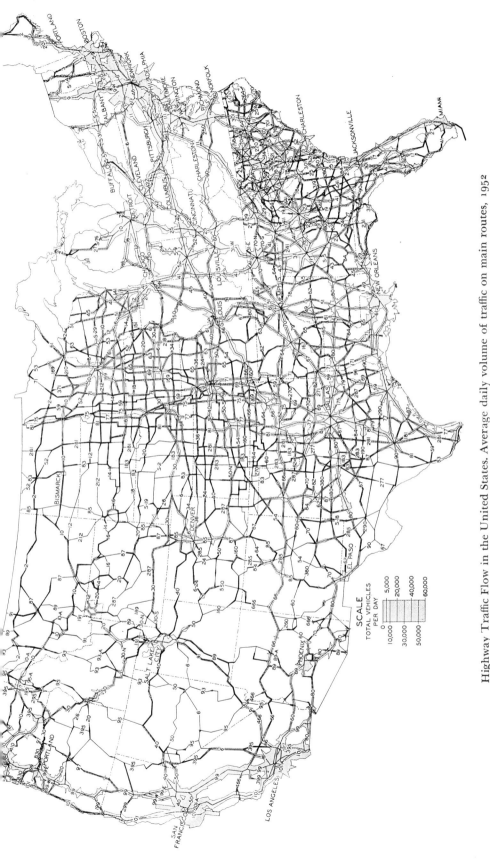

Highway Traffic Flow in the United States. Average daily volume of traffic on main routes, 1952
Bureau of Public Roads, U. S. Department of Commerce

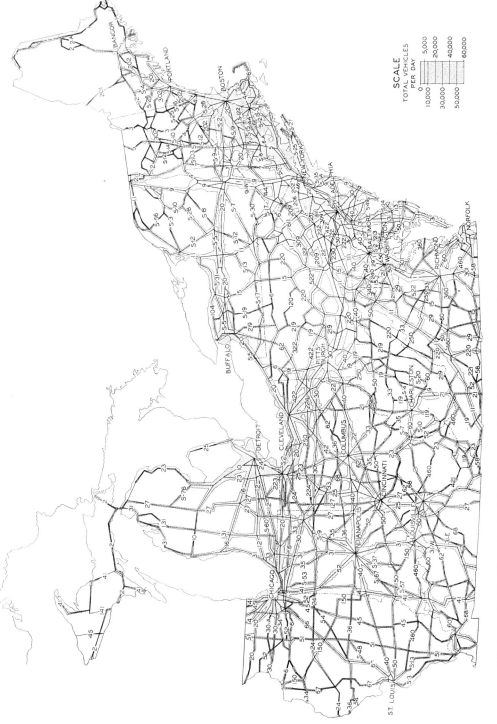

Highway Traffic Flow in the Northeastern United States. Average daily volume of traffic on main routes, 1952

the South. But what is true for highway traffic is not true for the flow of railway traffic, because the main mass of freight carried by the railroads consists of coal (as we have seen for the N. & W., and it is true as well for the C. & O. and the Virginian). The roads going south and southwest across Virginia, mainly the Southern System and the Atlantic Seaboard, do not have any comparable amount of freight to carry. Passenger traffic is more important in this direction, of course. More and more the long-distance passenger traffic takes the airlines; thus Richmond and Norfolk are both important commercial airports with a very active traffic, but even more traffic passes above the land of Virginia without stopping there.

The study of manufacturing in a previous chapter has shown the importance of the proximity to the great northeastern markets in the industrialization of Virginia. The "northernmost of the southern states" has substantially benefited by this position as the gateway or the façade of the South. This fact again makes a great crossroads of Virginia. From the triangle of Washington-Richmond-Winchester, highways and railways fan out in many directions, with little competition in servicing the communications between the northeastern markets and cities on the one hand and the states to the southeast on the other. Another set of routes has a powerful hub at Norfolk with itineraries radiating from there towards the sea lanes on the one hand, and inland toward the south and west on the other. As the economy of the Southeast develops, the function of its gateway northwards cannot help growing and developing.

Virginia has a great advantage conferred on her by the relief of the land in that both the Great Valley (with U. S. 11) and the fall line (with U. S. 1) are fairly close to each other on her territory. This is repeated to some extent northwards in Maryland and Pennsylvania, a fact which probably played a great part in the early and, for the time, phenomenal development of Philadelphia in the eighteenth and early nineteenth centuries. In the Virginia area this proximity is at present especially vital. Farther south the two great thoroughfares diverge in different directions. Topography has indeed helped Virginia with regard to both major contemporary assets of its geographical location: the gates of the Chesapeake and of the South.

The proximity to the national capital

The position of Virginia in the eighteenth century as the largest of the Southern states and one of the northernmost had something to do with the selection of the site for the District of Columbia and the national capital on the Potomac just below the falls, on the outskirts of the Old Dominion. To some extent this proximity to Washington, D. C., may be interpreted as an inheritance from Virginia's great past. It might not have been so if she had not been the first English colony in America, if she had not been the most densely populated of the thirteen original states, if she had not produced such an astounding number of American leaders in Washington's generation.

The effects of this proximity were little felt until the Civil War; Washington was not yet a great city in that period (40,000 inhabitants in 1850), and many Virginians had been prominent in the capital's life for the first half century of the city's existence. It was in the twentieth century, when the capital and the federal government's bureaus and activities expanded as a result of three wars and one depression, that Virginia felt the full impact of this neighbor.

The population of the District of Columbia grew to 131,700 inhabitants in 1870, 278,700 in 1900, 437,000 in 1920, 663,000 in 1940. Then as the urban agglomeration grew by leaps and bounds during World War II, the residential and even the bureaucratic sections spilled over the District's boundary into Maryland and Virginia. The metropolitan area of Washington counted 927,000 people in 1940, of whom 173,400 lived in Maryland and 90,500 in Virginia. The Virginia section of the metropolitan area at that time included only Arlington and Alexandria; its population had grown by 78.4 per cent between 1930 and 1940, while the Maryland side of the metropolitan area increased only by 58.6 per cent.[5]

From 1940 to 1950, Washington's metropolitan area expanded in space and even more in population. For the whole area the intercensal period brought an addition of population of 51.3 per cent, but this growth was quite unequal according to sections: the District of Columbia saw its population augmented by only 21 per cent, the Maryland part of the area by 106.8 per cent and the Virginian section of it by 130.7 per cent. In addition to Arlington and Alexandria, Fairfax County and the city of Falls Church had been included in the metropolitan area, within which Fairfax had a record growth for the period of 140.8 per cent.[6] There is no doubt, although detailed statistics are not yet available, that the same trends of growth continued in the early 1950's and that more of Virginia's territory and more of her people will have been absorbed in the suburbs of Washington by the time the next census is taken.

The impact of the proximity of Washington should not, however, be

[5] See U. S. Bureau of the Census, *County Data Book, A Supplement to the Statistical Abstract of the United States*, Washington, 1947.

[6] See U. S. Bureau of the Census, *County and City Data Book, 1952*, Washington, 1953.

estimated only in terms of metropolitan growth as registered by population statistics. With the wars and with foreign commitments, the military responsibility of the federal government grew. Despite the American tradition of decentralization, a concentration of much of the high command of the Armed Forces in the national capital or its immediate neighborhood was unavoidable. The Pentagon was built during World War II on the Virginia bank of the Potomac; many more military establishments mushroomed to the south of the capital's metropolitan area. The location of Washington on the Potomac was not alien to the decision to make Norfolk the major American naval base on the Atlantic. Thus the proximity of the capital was still indirectly responsible in part for the importance of naval installations and personnel in Virginia.

Underlying the dramatic growth taking place in the Virginia economy in the late 1930's and 1940's was the increase in federal government employment. Without this federal activity there is left only the more gradual changes that had been under way in Virginia for half a century. Federal employment in Virginia numbered in 1950 214,000 persons, 106,000 of whom were federal civilian employees and 108,000 were armed forces personnel stationed in Virginia. In proportion to the size of its labor force and population the impact of federal employment was greater on Virginia than on any other state in the nation. One-twentieth of the federal civilian employees and one-eighth of the military of the nation lived in 1950 in Virginia.[7]

This statement in a report prepared for the state government emphasizes the employment aspect of the proximity of Washington. It must be realized that military installations and civilian residences meant a great deal of spending in terms of construction and retail trade. The remarkable prosperity of the construction industries in Virginia is largely to be explained by expenditure from federal budget funds, whether directly or indirectly. The two metropolitan areas that expanded most impressively in Virginia in the last twenty years were those of Washington and Hampton Roads, under the influence respectively of the federal government and the navy.

Thus the proximity of the national capital has deeply affected Virginia and her economy. Beyond the limits of Fairfax County, with which the metropolitan area of Washington stopped according to the census of 1950, the suburbs have gone farther south and west. Loudoun and even Fauquier Counties count many commuters to Washington, and the same is true of the area around Fredericksburg. The expansion of federal influence through military employment and establishments progressed

---

[7] Edwin E. Holm, Jr., *Labor Resources and Labor Income in Virginia,* Richmond, The Advisory Council on the Virginia Economy, July, 1953, Vol. I, p. 3; see also pp. 50–57.

Ashland, on the main north-south rail line in the Coastal Plain
Virginia Chamber of Commerce Photo by Flournoy

chiefly southward, down the Potomac and U. S. 1, and towards Hampton
Roads. West of Washington the expansion was more residential and on a
higher level of income and society. The blossoming of the "station-wagon
farming" area is related to the social life and to the politics of Washington. The same reasons may explain, at least in part—for the charm of
the local way of life and the mildness of the climate have their influence,
too—why so many retired people with some means, especially high-rank-
ing officers of the armed forces, former businessmen, government officials,
and even professors, choose to retire in northern or central Virginia,
where they can buy some acreage and still feel close to the heart of the
nation.

Virginians may argue also that the closeness to the national capital,
coupled with the old traditions of national leadership still alive in the
commonwealth, have caused many young Virginians, some of the most
able of their people, to go north to engage in the service of the nation,
leaving their native state and thus depriving it of some of the elements
that could have assumed improved leadership in many communities. The
potential resources of Virginia might have been better used and developed if more of these active, more adventurous people had stayed at

home. This is possible. However, Virginia lost even more people by out-migration westward than by attraction to Washington. Some of its best elements went into the world of business and made remarkable contributions, establishing careers that made them leaders in New York or Chicago. The proximity of the capital certainly cannot be held responsible for this. In fact, many of those who went into federal service were often able, especially after they achieved positions of some importance, to live in or near Virginia and participate in regional activities in a degree impossible to those who, very numerous until 1930, migrated to more distant parts of the country. If this out-migration has been slowed down since the 1930's, particularly among the Whites, the proximity to a rapidly expanding seat of federal government has been one of the responsible causes, perhaps the determinant one.

If all income payments by government services are combined, including those made by state and local government services, they make up the greatest single source of income payments to individuals in the state. Virginia is unique among the states in this regard. Thus government has been, at least since 1950, the major source of income payments in Virginia —about 26 per cent of all such payments in the state in 1953, when trades and services accounted for 25 per cent and manufacturing for about 18 per cent. The proximity of the capital benefits Virginia's economy more each year than the year before. This may be inferred from such remarks as this: "Per capita income payments in Virginia during 1953 were $1,361, a gain of $23 or 1.7 per cent over 1952. More than 60 per cent of the increase in income payments available for per capita calculation came from larger allocations of income originating in the District of Columbia to Virginia residents." [8]

It is hardly necessary to add that Washington and Norfolk with their suburbs are important markets for food and consume some of the agricultural produce of Virginia, their proximity making possible better prices on the farm as transportation costs are low. These markets also have their importance for manufactured products as well. In this respect the capital plays a much greater role than can be precisely estimated statistically. It may be even partly responsible for the fact that Virginia has not gone into manufacturing in a greater degree, at least in some parts of the commonwealth: there is little manufacturing in the vicinity of the District of Columbia because government and the trades and services attached to the capital's functions pay better than industrial employment would.

How far into Virginia the influence of the capital's proximity goes is

[8] "Changes in Major Sources of Fifth District Income, 1953 vs. 1952" in *Monthly Review* of the Federal Reserve Bank of Richmond, October, 1954, p. 5.

hard to estimate. On the whole it seems to be limited by the James River to the south, but it is no longer limited by the Blue Ridge to the west; the Shenandoah National Park has become one of the favorite playgrounds of the national capital, and, with a slack period in the winter season, thousands and thousands of Washingtonians drive on week ends on the scenic parkway and hike in the relative wilderness of the park. As highways are enlarged and improved in this direction, more and more traffic may be expected. In another direction, Williamsburg and Yorktown are becoming almost classical targets of week-end trips from Washington. Therefore the travel trade of Virginia is indebted, too, to the neighborhood of the capital.

Virginia and the South's progress

Could the progress of the South bypass Virginia? Such a question may seem highly paradoxical after our description of the location of Virginia as the gateway to the South and as the northernmost of the southeastern states. The gateway, however, is something different from the workshop. The advantages in terms of a transportation formula may be equal or somewhat inferior to those found further south. For instance, in manufacturing, the lack of which was one of the main economic shortcomings of the South, other states, such as North Carolina and Georgia, have made quicker progress, although Virginia started earlier in some industrial activities. The travel trade of Florida eclipses that of Virginia. The cattle-raising development of Georgia and Florida exceeds Virginia's. And, of course, Virginia has nothing to match the fabulous industrial and commercial boom of Texas and Louisiana. On the other hand, Virginia's economic progress has been steadier and more diversified, if slower, than that of many other Southern states. True, diversification of manufacturing has been going on in most of the industrialized areas of the South where a combination of textile, chemical, and light mechanical industries has been growing faster than heavier types of industry. On the whole, Virginia has not been bypassed as yet, but one wonders whether the state's featured characteristic—a dispersed, inexpensive manpower—will not change soon to resemble that of the regions up north. And, while it is moving south, why should industry stop halfway, now that transportation is well organized all over the region?

Such things may happen. The industrial development of Virginia can hardly be called spectacular by American standards, though it gives an impression of solidity. But economic progress does not necessarily mean winning a race with the neighboring areas in numbers of employment

The Ashland station
Virginia Chamber of Commerce Photo by Flournoy

and amount of production. Virginia has progressed more in urbanization than in industrialization; this has not been achieved in the same degree in other Southern states. In the Southeast, only Florida had in 1950 a higher proportion of urban population in the total: Florida owed this largely to the travel trade, for which the peninsular state enjoys some exceptional assets granted by nature. The urbanization of Virginia, added to the state's industrialization, gives a wider foundation to its economic development. This urbanization is likely to continue, as Virginia has been invaded in her northern parts by the southern extension of the great string of northeastern seaboard cities which we called "Megalopolis." This "megalopolitan" aspect of her growth may be the result of the closeness to the northeast rather than the result of appurtenance to the southeast, but it is a tremendous and powerfully developing phenomenon.

Thus the progress of the South is not quite similar as an economic and geographical process to what has been happening in Virginia. The Old Dominion can hardly be bypassed, since it is a great crossroad, but the organization and use of resources of the crossroad area may well be quite different from those of the areas served by the roads that cross here. The geographical position of any area of some size (even of a size smaller than

Virginia's) in our inhabited world is unique in many respects. It is unique in the whole tableau of its present resources and outside relations; it is always unique in its past and in its prospects for tomorrow.

Virginia's location has some liabilities and many assets as the situation appears today. The future will depend on what the Virginians make of the potential enshrined in the present. Now that the Old Dominion has become a land of in-migration, the coming evolution depends also on what these newcomers will do with the local opportunities. In the last quarter of a century so many changes have occurred, such optimism has come to prevail, and so much more initiative has manifested itself that Virginia looks with a sort of youthful confidence to the future.

PART THREE

The Old Dominion Grows Young

By many standards Virginia deserved her title of "Old Dominion" until recently. In a way, by her strong attachment to tradition and to the past, Virginia still merits this designation. Sir William Berkeley was recommissioned by King Charles II as governor of the Old Dominion apparently as a reward for the Virginian's loyalty to the Crown during the Civil War in England. Two hundred and fifty years later the Commonwealth of Virginia still displayed many of the features associated with the concept of an "old" country: an essentially rural society and economy, low standards of living, abundant and cheap labor, emigrating surplus population, predominance of a peasantlike psychology resisting innovation. All of these traits still are to some extent present today, but they have retreated in a degree into the background or to some out-of-the-way parts of the state.

The changes in the recent twenty-five years testify plainly to a rejuvenation. From an old, tired land with depleted soils and an impoverished population, a large part of which was looking for a better living elsewhere, Virginia has changed into a land of rapidly rising indexes, of constant improvements in the standards of living, of in-migration and of many new developments in agricultural as well as industrial pursuits. In the preceding chapters we reviewed one by one the major fields of economic activity, describing the present use of the available resources with their past background and their new trends. Among these main fields, the only one in which progress did not seem to be as encouraging as might be expected was forestry, with which we dealt at length. Even there the trends were toward improvement and a better realization of the necessary task ahead. Elsewhere rejuvenation was on its way; even the present plight of the coal mines reflected a general modernization trend and forced upon the mines a selective evolution of ways and means of production. Virginia, in brief, seems nowadays much better integrated than she used to be into the American economic system, an amazing system which refuses to show any of the usual signs of age and maintains a fluidity that combats sclerosis.

The geographer believes in the cartographic method: he needs to see what modifications have resulted from the recent changes in the distribution of people within Virginia's area. These modifications are shown on the map of population changes from 1930 to 1950 by minor civil divisions (see page 465). While the total population increased substantially, from 2.4 to 3.3 million persons, the shades indicating local decrease and an increase of less than 10 per cent cover most of the area. Increase of more than 10 per cent appears in a patchwork pattern over the map. Increase of more than 50 per cent is found in an even smaller number of patches and often over small nuclear areas only. Nevertheless, there can be no doubt as to the fact that these small areas with an increase superior to 50 per cent are responsible for the commonwealth's total growth in population, some 38 per cent in twenty years.

The patches showing rapid increase are centered on cities in almost all cases. Charlottesville offers a striking picture of a rapidly growing town, with its immediate neighborhood increasing, too, while the surrounding area, which covers all of Albemarle County and some of the adjacent lands, is losing population. Such concentration in the urban nucleus is no longer common, however. Virginia's larger cities have already passed this stage, and the downtown sections do not increase in residential population as rapidly as the suburbia does, especially the outer suburbia within a radius of some twenty miles. This is quite clear around Washington, D. C., where Arlington grew much less than Fairfax County did, as well as around Richmond and Hampton Roads. In these three major metropolitan areas of Virginia the main tentacles of population growth follow the better and wider highways, so that the trend of the three nuclear areas is to grow one toward the other. From Washington the main extension of the shades representing over 50 per cent of increase follows U. S. 1 southward toward Richmond. From Richmond the main tentacles extend to the north and south along U. S. 1, but even more to the southeast, along U. S. 460, toward Norfolk. Around Norfolk and Portsmouth

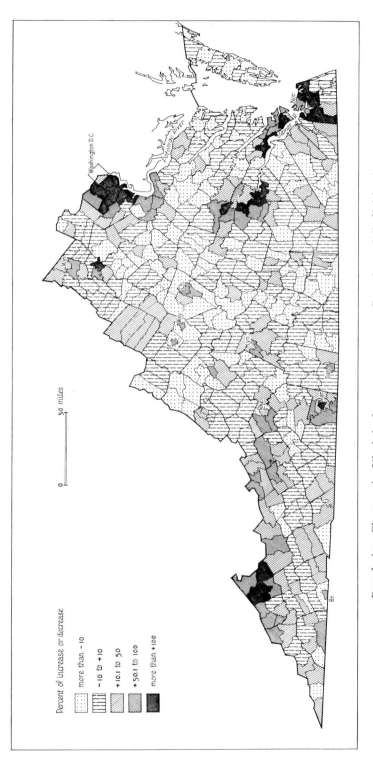

Population Changes in Virginia from 1930 to 1950 (By minor civil divisions)

the increase describes as yet a half-circular aureole, but from Newport News and Hampton the expansion is definitely up the James towards Richmond.

The predominant influence of urbanization in the pattern of population increase is again emphasized by the presence of patches signifying rapid growth at Lynchburg and Danville, around Martinsville, at Winchester and Front Royal, Staunton and Waynesboro, Harrisonburg and Roanoke. The main expansion of Roanoke, partly dictated by topography, occurred along U. S. 11 to the southwest toward Radford. However, west of the Roanoke-Martinsville longitude the pattern of growth tends less toward urbanization. Scattered industries of important size have attracted new population or have at least kept the growing population on the spot. Such is obviously the case in the southwestern coal field and in such smaller patches as that around the large plants at the Narrows. The lesson taught by this map could be summed up by saying that urbanization is responsible for the population growth of Virginia all over the state, with the exception of the southwestern triangle, where people have been piling up for other reasons and without the benefits provided by urban growth.

We have elaborated at some length on the regional problems of southwestern Virginia both in the regional description and in connection with our study of the coal resources.[1] The major factor of change in Virginia is not regional: despite the innovations resulting from the period of prosperity of coal mining, the southwestern triangle remains a rather "old" section in both economic and social terms. It is a problem area, producing chiefly raw materials, such as coal or salt, and in the last few years some gas and oil, and it is plagued with many small subsistence farms. It has yet to be rejuvenated, and measures to this end could be quickly planned and applied. But the main present problem of Virginia, the leading one, which is for many reasons the significant factor in rejuvenation, is the problem of urban growth. This trend, so obvious on the map and in the statistics, threatens to transform the Old Dominion. At the time when this is being written, the rural and urban populations in Virginia must be about equal. With the continuation of the present trend, a majority of the population will be living in urban territory from now on.

This fact signifies a break in the old tradition among Virginians, well maintained until recently, of pride in their rural background; they are psychologically and socially just off the farm. But with the continuation of the movement that severs this connection, the psychology of the majority of the people and their social structure are bound to change. Virginia

[1] See Chapter 3, pp. 221–225, and Chapter 6, pp. 392–398.

is today still a land of scattered settlement, though it is no longer as completely scattered as it used to be; and what, after all, does scattering mean in this day of the commuter, when the city population is moving out, not only in Virginia but all over the country? These are grave problems: they announce an evolution, the consequences of which may reach very far, especially as more outsiders come into Virginia to stay and as the next generation will have grown up in an environment quite different from what Virginians have known for over 300 years.

The old Virginia way of life is gradually undergoing considerable change. This change is not so brutal as the corresponding change may have been in Maryland, for instance, because of the stupendous development of Baltimore with its immense seaport, its large plants for heavy industries, and its mushrooming suburbs swallowing almost half of Maryland west of the Bay. The Virginia evolution is of a more subtle quality. The rural areas are being slowly industrialized, while even the scattered pattern of habitat is largely preserved. Urbanization is proceeding without bringing about the crowding of industrial plants so frequent elsewhere. In some sections the development of suburban functions has even caused a revival of agricultural activities, of bigger and better farming. Centers of concentration of population are dispersed across the state. A great deal of diversity in the principal sources of income results from these two parallel and not always coinciding processes of urbanization and industrialization. Economic development is thus manifold and differentiated from area to area. Many of the old rural pursuits are still being carried on and are rather well protected by legislation, as is the case with tobacco, peanuts, and other products. Hog killing still goes on all over Virginia, and never have there been as many hams produced in the Old Dominion as in recent years.

Nevertheless, the evolution goes on. Every year, metropolitan growth conquers more space and more people, a larger share in the regional system. More industries are coming in and more and better means of transportation are being provided. More "foreigners" come to the state, either to travel through or to settle there. The old partitions are being broken despite internal resistance and the weight of inertia. For centuries the necessity of more and better education for the people of Virginia has been the subject of debates and resolutions. Now more action has been taken and still more may be expected to come.

The tradition of national leadership is still alive in Virginia, but as the commonwealth becomes better integrated into the whirlpool of modern economics, of the constant readjustments of the national market and industrial system, Virginia is becoming better aware of the road to be followed to gain greater recognition within the nation. As the contacts with the outside are multiplied, the problems of the internal situation become more obvious. More windows open on the neighborhood throw more light inside. The present evolution is sure to continue, but which way it will turn is not yet clear. The whole personality of Virginia is at stake.

9. *Metropolitan Growth*

IN DAYS of yore the city was a clear-cut compartment, distinct from the surrounding country. To make the separation more effective, towns used to enclose themselves behind barriers or even walls. New York still remembers its beginnings behind the wall now marked in the downtown business section by Wall Street. From the ancient Latin heritage there comes to Western countries of the twentieth century the notion of a distinction between the city and its suburbs: *intra-muros* and *extra-muros,* within the walls and beyond the walls. However, the trend of cities to expand far beyond any such physical limit to their development seems also to date back to antiquity. "When are men living in the same place to be regarded as a single city?" said Aristotle: "What is the limit? Certainly not the wall of the city, for you might surround all Peloponnesus with a wall. Like this, we may say, is Babylon and every city that has the compass of a nation rather than a city; Babylon, they say, had been taken for three days before some part of the inhabitants became aware of the fact." [1]

The phenomenon, therefore, is not as new or as exceptional in history as it may have been thought, that the expansion of cities far beyond their old limits made them into entire regions, the people of which did not need necessarily all to meet daily within the downtown section to belong to the same urban body. As the city-dwellers conquered more space for their residences and professional occupations, the notion of "urban territory" had to be revised; it was revised several times by the Bureau of the Census, once for the Census of 1950. Moreover, the concept of metropolitan areas has been created, *metropolis* meaning in Greek central or mother-city. The metropolitan area has been compared to a cell with its nucleus, the old, densely built-up city being the nuclear center. To the city is added the whole suburban area, in which the type of land use

[1] Aristotle, *Politics,* III, 3, 1276a, 25.

which is urban gradually changes as one moves away from the center to a rural kind of space organization. Where this happens the metropolitan area stops; its limits are thus constantly on the move and often hard to define with precision. The Bureau of the Census provided the definition and revised it many times as the phenomenon to be measured was evolving. It is this metropolitan growth rather than the increase of population in cities that counts in Virginia. It has to be studied first in its present expansion and then in the trends bound to develop in the foreseeable future.

The Tidewater becomes urbanized

The examination of the changes in the distribution of population between 1930 and 1950 has led us to stress the concentration of population and of three principal metropolitan areas of Virginia in the Tidewater (see map, page 465; and commentary, page 464). Maps of the density of population either by counties (see page 142) or by minor civil divisions (page 36) testify to the same effect: the agglomeration of population is occurring chiefly in the Tidewater, but not equally over the whole of it. It is no longer the possibility of easy navigation on inner waters of the Bay and tidal estuaries that attracts people here. The attraction of the Tidewater is its concentration of employment opportunities and transportation facilities. The maritime vocation so long resisted by Virginia has at last crystallized at Hampton Roads at the gates of the Chesapeake. The two agglomerations of Norfolk-Portsmouth and Newport News–Hampton are closely interconnected by a complex of commercial, industrial, and military functions; the whole system is founded on the seaport. Washington's metropolitan area at the other end of the Tidewater is founded on government activities; it bestrides the fall line, and its development inland over the northern Piedmont is extensive. In the middle part of the Tidewater the Richmond-Hopewell-Petersburg area is also on the fall line, but the greater part of its development is along the Tidewater. Fredericksburg, between Washington and Richmond, creates a relay on the fall line which may help in the not too distant future to cement the approaching continuity of the metropolitan areas developing around the two capitals—of the nation and of Virginia.

The present development stems from a historical background rooted in the eighteenth-century economic geography of this area, with the steady growth of a few small urban centers established near the falls of the main rivers and at the head of tidal estuaries (which was the case for Richmond, Petersburg, Fredericksburg, and Washington), and of sea-

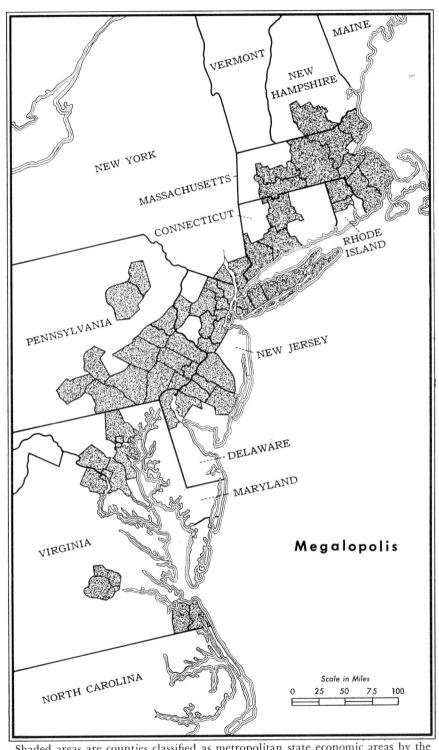

Shaded areas are counties classified as metropolitan state economic areas by the
U. S. Bureau of the Census in 1950

ports at the entrance of the great Bay (Norfolk and to some extent New-port News). As these few agglomerations had crystallized much earlier, urban activities were naturally attracted towards them or their immediate vicinity when the present process started in the twentieth century. We saw how the enlarging of the scope of some of the manufactures of Virginia, of trade and business activities, and even more of government services, has brought about the expansion of a few cities into vast metropolitan areas, while many smaller towns were built up to look like cities in their own right. This type of development occurred throughout Virginia and to a large extent throughout the Southeast, which, following the Virginia tradition, was not urbanized to any degree until World War I. As it occurred in Virginia, however, this development was more the result of factors acting from the outside than of those stemming from the local ground. It may be worth while, therefore, in order to better understand what is happening on the Tidewater, to have a look at the situation north and south of the Virginia sector of the east coast.

The Bureau of the Census has produced a most interesting map of the metropolitan areas of the United States, based on the 1950 census. It has also elaborated a more detailed map on which each county is indicated as metropolitan or non-metropolitan according to its role in the economy of the state to which it belongs. The distribution of "state economic areas" thus achieved is founded on a group of carefully worked out statistical indexes.[2] The map (page 471) of the Northeastern seaboard, including Virginia, reproduces the network of counties differentiated according to the metropolitan or non-metropolitan quality of their economy: any map of standard metropolitan areas and this map of counties with a metropolitan economy will show an impressive congregation of "metropolitan" spaces—of urbanized and suburbanized areas—extending from the north of Virginia (Fairfax and Arlington Counties) rather far to the northeast, without any break. On the map of standard metropolitan areas the continuity is clearly established from Washington's metropolitan area to that of Hartford, Connecticut. It makes up by far the largest patch of metropolitan territory in the country; the only one to rival it, the Los Angeles–San Bernardino agglomeration, expands on the map far beyond its actual limits because one of the counties included covers eastward an immense section of California desert.

The map (page 471) based on the state economic areas is even more

[2] See U. S. Bureau of the Census, *State Economic Areas*, by Donald J. Bogue, Washington, 1951. The map of Megalopolis is taken from the pertinent section of the United States map of this publication. Maps of standard metropolitan areas in the country are found in the *Statistical Abstract of the United States, City and County Data Book*, and other publications of the U. S. Bureau of the Census.

interesting. Here the counties recorded as "metropolitan" extend from the north of Virginia to the south of New Hampshire. The continuity is quite clearly shown. If some sections of eastern Connecticut and a few corners of eastern Massachusetts and of New Jersey are not included, it may be attributable to the season at which censuses are taken; this census was taken on April 1 in 1950. If the census were taken in the summer, it might well show many of these relatively empty sections of the seaside between Boston and Washington thickly settled by city residents who own or rent summer homes in these not yet too-urbanized sections, close enough to business sectors to commute daily. However, let us remain satisfied with the data based on permanent residence and other permanent economic ties with the cities. This is the largest and probably the longest continuous area of a "metropolitan" character that exists in America and even in the world today. A unique phenomenon at present, but one which shows the way in which other areas may develop, it deserves a special name and was called *Megalopolis* a few years ago when its unity became evident. Megalopolis accounts for close to thirty million inhabitants, almost one-fifth of the nation. It has grown in a curious elongated fashion along the northeastern seaboard and was obviously built up on the network provided by the early mushrooming of towns along the coast from Boston to New York and then along the fall line from New York to Washington. As the metropolitan areas that sprang up at many points on this American Tidewater expanded one toward the other, often along U. S. Route 1, they finally came to form this extraordinary Megalopolis.[3]

The Virginia Tidewater extends from the falls of the Potomac southwards. Its northern extremity is already annexed to Megalopolis. This annexation means, perhaps, much more than just the proximity to the national capital and to a unique conglomeration of great markets of consumption and centers of business and manufacturing.

Megalopolis in Virginia

The expansion of Megalopolis to reach its present form has been determined by many factors. When we tried to list all of them we counted more than forty elements important in the process. The two most important, however, are polynuclear origin and the immense amount of business of all types resulting from the role played by the string of north-

---

[3] For an analysis of the growth of Megalopolis, see Jean Gottmann, *L'Amérique,* Paris, 2nd ed., 1954, and "La région charnière de l'économie américaine," *Revue de la Porte Océane,* Le Havre, March–April, 1951, pp. 9–14 and 11–20.

eastern seaboard cities as a *hinge* of the American economy. The poly-nuclear origin results from the early establishing of many competing cities and seaports, from Baltimore to Boston, to which the federal capital was later added. The federal organization of government and the division of the Atlantic seaboard into so many states that engaged in a fruitful rivalry made all the nuclei compete one with another until their growth joined them together. The part of the "hinge" is more difficult to perceive, but is easily demonstrated by the material accumulated in economic history. This seaboard had from the inception of the United States the possibility and the responsibility of serving both as an oceanic façade for relations with abroad and as a springboard for the settlement and development of the continent inland. At different periods of American history the main weight of the northeastern interests oscillated from sea trade to continental development and back again; in New England one of these oscillations in the beginning of the nineteenth century was defined as the period when the main interest shifted "from the wharf to the waterfall." Whether the general trends of the American economy threw the door open towards the outside or closed it to turn the main endeavors inland, the hinge remained fixed at the string of eastern cities which, alone in the country, extending from Boston to Washington, had the authority, the capital, and the skill to elaborate such policies and put them into application.

Virginia remained aloof from this remarkable economic system functioning from the falls of the Potomac northwards. She did not participate in the extraordinary prosperity and power thus enjoyed by the urban centers of the northeast, except through the careers made by many Virginians in these cities. However, in this century, especially with the boom of World War I, the areas that were to form Megalopolis became more and more crowded. At the mid-century, the crowding was an undisputable fact which will be evident from a look at the density of population by 1950 in the vast area stretching from southern New Hampshire to Fairfax County (see map, page 475). A mass of nearly thirty million people cannot live on a continuous Main Street; they need some spaces left green, some areas for industrial development, and various kinds of breathing areas. Megalopolis has obviously reached the saturation point from the Potomac to the Charles River. It shows, nevertheless, signs of growing further. In which direction can it expand?

In places there is room for urban or suburban expansion back of this enormous agglomeration to the west and northwest. In this direction, however, the advantages of the seaboard are lost and the topography rapidly becomes more hilly and therefore traffic more difficult. It should

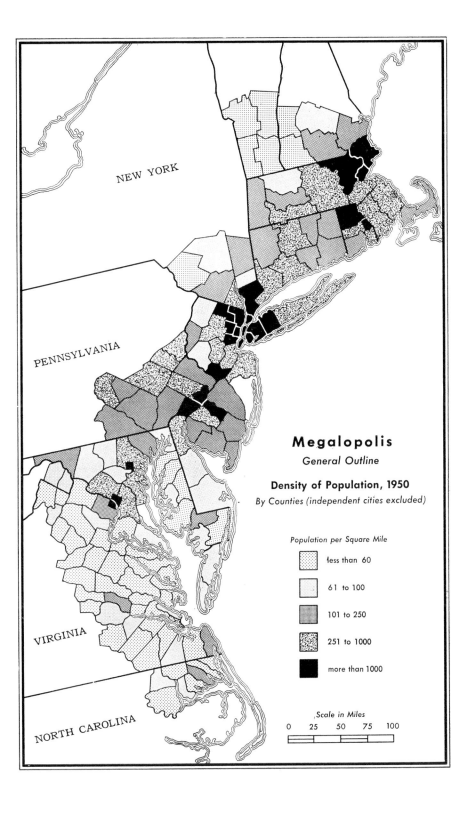

Megalopolis

General Outline

Density of Population, 1950

By Counties (independent cities excluded)

Population per Square Mile

	less than 60
	61 to 100
	101 to 250
	251 to 1000
	more than 1000

Scale in Miles

0 25 50 75 100

be added that in some cases inland expansion would make necessary more and different means of transportation; it might also come up against the barrier of publicly owned forests and parks, for instance, north of New York City, or it might come up against already heavily industrialized areas where residence is not so pleasant, such as the anthracite coal field of Pennsylvania back of the Delaware Bay area. Thus the logical directions for expansion remaining are rather towards the north or the south, along the coast of northern New England or the Tidewater of Virginia. In both cases there are vast areas as yet thinly populated.

The choice is obvious, and Megalopolis made it some time ago. The map of population increase in the intercensal period 1940–1950 (see page 477) shows that the progress northwards has been very slight, while southwards through Maryland and Virginia it has been substantial. This is due to several factors. On the one hand, even in the 1940's, the economy of New England did not seem to thrive and made less progress than was average for the nation, while Washington was expanding very fast. But more important was the fact that New England found itself situated at a dead end on the map of traffic and economic currents through the United States, while Virginia, at the gates of a developing South, was a major crossroads of rising importance. The contrast in the assets of the geographical positions at mid-century of northern New England and Virginia was striking. Virginia was bound to attract the expansion of Megalopolis; the increase in population shows that it did, even beyond the limits of Washington's metropolitan area. The importance of military installations, which are largely suburbs or satellites of the national capital, has kept down to some extent the apparent density of population between Washington and Fredericksburg and between this section of U. S. 1 and the Potomac, but the general trend is unmistakable.

Megalopolis has thus invaded northern Virginia and gives notice of proceeding even further. Where can it go in Virginia? Westward the Blue Ridge seems an obstacle which should limit the expansion of dense settlement. Moreover, the kind of outer suburbia that has been organized in parts of Loudoun and most of Fauquier Counties sets up a barrier protecting a semiagricultural type of settlement. Land is expensive here and it would require a great deal of money to pierce through such a barrier. If most of Loudoun County may be considered in 1954 as pertaining to the outer suburbs of Washington, and therefore to Megalopolis, a fact which may be recognized by the next census, the major expansion of residential sectors for people in lower-income brackets seems more likely to progress southwards, mainly on both sides of U. S. 1 and

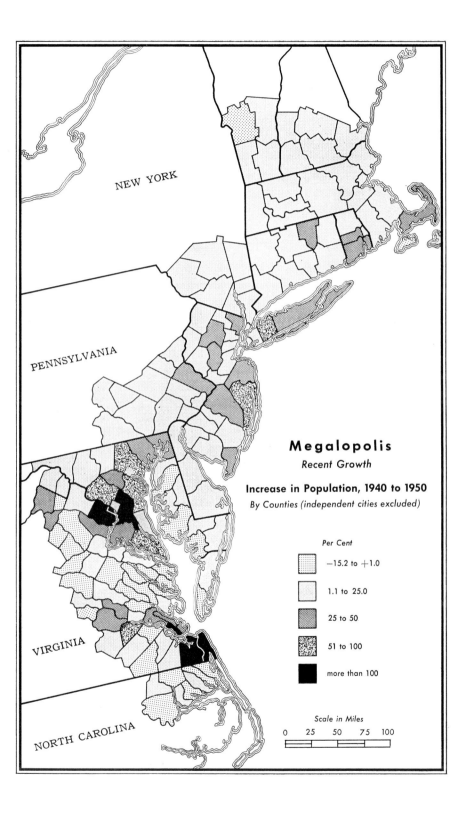

Megalopolis

Recent Growth

Increase in Population, 1940 to 1950

By Counties (independent cities excluded)

Per Cent

−15.2 to +1.0

1.1 to 25.0

25 to 50

51 to 100

more than 100

Scale in Miles

0   25   50   75   100

NEW YORK

PENNSYLVANIA

VIRGINIA

NORTH CAROLINA

its main tributaries. Some of this advance may follow also the banks of the Potomac, avoiding the spaces annexed by the military.

The maps of population increases in recent times (see pages 465 and 477) show how the three main metropolitan areas of the Virginia Tidewater give signs of expanding one towards the other. The tentacles have not joined yet. They may never do so completely, especially between Norfolk and Petersburg, where some excellent land supports rich farming. But it must be recognized that similar areas in New Jersey and Maryland have been gradually swallowed by the phenomenon of Megalopolis' tidal growth. It must be recognized that what is happening to northern Virginia and threatening much of the Tidewater is not a simple metropolitan growth explained entirely by the expansion of the national capital's role and size. It is a much bigger and deeper influence: it is the extension southwards of what could have been called "the Main Street of the Nation," already a "megalopolitan" system some 400 miles long.

Richmond and Norfolk have both greatly benefited by the overcrowding of the cities up north that might otherwise have attracted some of the functions that recently helped to build up these two Virginia cities. The ports of Hampton Roads would not have had the same stupendous expansion in the traffic of coal and the export of grain if in the peak periods caused by the two world wars all this traffic could have been handled by the port installations of the bigger cities northwards on the seaboard and by the rail network feeding these ports. Hampton Roads thus grew through a process of decentralization imposed by the recognition of the fact that New York, Philadelphia, the Delaware, and Baltimore had their hands full. Similarly Richmond attracted quite a bit of business—commercial, industrial, and federal services—in the attempt to somewhat decentralize Washington and Baltimore, which were too congested already. The proximity to Megalopolis has thus played a substantial part in the recent growth of these centers; it might have played an even bigger one if the Virginia cities had adopted a more aggressive attitude in terms of competition, for instance, in soliciting the heavier industries for which the gates of the Chesapeake offer the advantage of wider spaces available on land and water.

Thus Virginia offers a commendable geographical situation with good equipment in terms of roads, an abundant labor supply, and not many signs of crowding as yet along its fall line and along the James River. This is an invitation for the extension of Megalopolis therein, and it has not been overlooked. The future will tell whether the various suburban areas will finally consolidate, bringing a united and unique system of habitat to extend from the James to the shores where the Pilgrims landed, from one to the other of the two main birthplaces of America. Now that we have outlined the forces at play, we must review briefly the present state of the three main metropolitan areas of eastern Virginia and survey also other centers of urban development inland.

The suburbs of Washington in Virginia

According to the census of 1950, two counties and two independent cities —Fairfax and Arlington, Alexandria and Falls Church—were already included in the capital's metropolitan area. This ensemble encompassed 448 square miles of land, inhabited on April 1, 1950, by 303,000 persons of whom only 8 per cent were Negroes. The rural farm population of this area had fallen to the almost negligible figure of 7,873, all in Fairfax County. This total population had more than doubled from 1940 to 1950, and one-sixth of it lived in a different state or county in 1949, which is indicative of high mobility. It was a rather well-off and well-educated population, as 49.4 per cent of the families residing there in 1950 had an income of $5,000 or more in 1949, and as 61.8 per cent of the persons 25 years old and over had at least completed high school studies. Housing characteristics indicated a higher standard of living than in any other part of Virginia. The labor force was little employed in agriculture (only 1.5 per cent) or manufacturing (5.9 per cent); the major occupations were wholesale and retail trade, professional services, construction, transportation, and other public utilities.

A new independent city, which had been part of Fairfax County until 1948, appeared at Falls Church. Both Falls Church and Alexandria border on Arlington, which is the smallest of all the counties of Virginia and offers many of the features of urban territory. Arlington has an area of only 24 square miles, populated with an average density of 5,644 (higher than that of Falls Church). As the laws of Virginia authorize the annexation by an independent city of adjacent territory which has become fully urbanized and should therefore be placed under an administration separate from the usually rural unit of the county, Arlington is concerned that by gradual expansion of the cities of Alexandria and Falls Church it could be absorbed into these administrative units and lose all identity and even existence. Arlington has asked repeatedly to be transformed from a county into a city, which it is in many ways. Perhaps it is more of a suburb than a city, but a suburb of Washington, certainly not of Alexandria and even less of Falls Church. But the request of Arlington has not yet been granted.

Land use in Arlington is definitely of an urban character. It is an im-

Suburban development at Arlington
Virginia Chamber of Commerce

portant adjunct of the national capital, containing the capital's airport
(National Airport), the famous National Cemetery, many military establishments, and the whole complicated hub of highways by which Washington communicates with the area south of the Potomac. Four square
miles of territory there are directly managed by federal authorities. The
residents of Arlington County usually patronize the stores of downtown
Washington unless they go even farther away for shopping. It may be
said that the whole county belongs to the uptown of the urban system of
Washington, and some parts of the county may even claim to be a section
of downtown Washington beyond the Potomac. Although the calculation
is hard to make, it is quite possible that, particularly during periods of
peak military activity such as was the 1950–1951 period of the Korean
War, Arlington counts more people during office hours on weekdays than
at night, a basic characteristic of downtown areas.[4]

Arlington has been quite aware for at least a quarter of a century of the
fact that it belongs functionally to the capital's metropolitan area more

[4] An excellent study of Arlington, lavishly illustrated, was prepared for the County
Planning Commission by Homer Hoyt Associates, *Economic Survey of the Land Uses of
Arlington County, Va.*, September, 1951.

Arlington Ridge Road, looking toward Washington
Bureau of Public Roads, U. S. Department of Commerce

than to Virginia. It was the only county in Virginia to refuse to let the
state government take care of its system of secondary highways: this
unique county keeps the administration of its road financing well in
hand, fearing that some funds could be taken away from what it considers as its rightful share in the distribution of available funds for highways, if it were only a very small part of the vast commonwealth. The
traffic is indeed impressive in Arlington: to the two-way commuting resulting from its function both as a residential suburb and as a "downtown
section" must be added the huge transit traffic resulting from its location
at the southern entrance of the bridges across the Potomac to Washington. The amount of traffic appears quite enormous even on the major
primary highways (see maps pages 532–533). Although it is quite small,
Arlington ranks fifth among Virginia counties for the total vehicle-miles
per 24 hours, measuring by the intensity of traffic on rural primary highways in 1954; the figure was 495,458 vehicle-miles in Arlington; only four
other suburban, but much larger, counties had a higher figure.

In this respect Fairfax County led all the counties of Virginia in 1954,
a fact which emphasizes the intensity of traffic in Washington's metro-

politan area. The figure representing the county's vehicle-miles of travel in 1954 reached 1,059,014 according to official estimates,[5] almost double that of Norfolk County, the next on the list. The population of Fairfax grew more quickly than that of any other part of the metropolitan area in the 1940's. The number of its dwelling units almost trebled in the same decade. It was in that county again that most of the metropolitan area's expansion in Virginia developed in the early 1950's. The highway transportation problem thus created by the local commuting population as well as by transit in the Virginia section of Washington's suburbs has grown to threatening proportions in recent years, although some great drives were recently created to channel the intense flow during peak hours. A careful analysis of the situation made by a specialized engineering firm in 1953 concluded that immediate steps must be taken to accommodate the growing tide of traffic.[6] "Needless to say, the volume of highway transportation in the northern Virginia region far exceeds that of an isolated community of 367,000 persons since it is an integral part of the metropolitan area of more than 1,650,000." And it is much more than that, a fact which is dramatized by comparing the average daily traffic crossing the Potomac River between Virginia and Washington with that crossing the Hudson River between New Jersey and Manhattan during July, 1953: the daily average count gave 218,199 crossings over the Potomac as against 216,160 over the Hudson. The metropolitan area of Washington is, of course, less than one-tenth that of New York City. But these traffic figures are of a "megalopolitan" rather than only a metropolitan nature.

The old city of Alexandria is among the most congested sections of the metropolitan area at peak hours of traffic. Several major highways help the situation to some extent by skirting the town. One other has been suggested which would use a new proposed bridge over the Potomac and run around the built-up part of the area close to the expanse of railroad tracks and the marshalling yards. This would create on the edge of the town an area so well served by both rail and road and so close to large city markets that it could not help attracting some industries, at least of the lighter kind. Alexandria also has a seaport, but few steamers come to its wharves. The main traffic consists of the importation of newsprint from Sweden and Nova Scotia; occasionally some shipments of pulp and

[5] Commonwealth of Virginia, Department of Highways, 1954 Traffic Flow Map and Tabulation; see map on page 533. Statistics are from the tabulation. 1954 means year ending June 30, 1954.

[6] Wilbur Smith and Associates, *Highway Transportation in the Washington Metropolitan Area of Virginia*, New Haven, Conn., November, 1953—a beautifully illustrated report prepared for the State Highway Commission of Virginia.

Highway network near Washington, with the Pentagon in the background
Bureau of Public Roads, Department of Commerce

furniture land at the same wharf from Scandinavia. Another wharf handles sand and gravel, chiefly coastwise trade. Both serve the needs of the metropolitan area. It would not be accurate to call them an actual port. Both Alexandria first and later Washington were supposed when established to become great sea-trading centers; neither ever really was, although the wheat and flour trade kept Alexandria busy for a while. This city, too, shows all the usual signs of becoming a suburb. Its real downtown is across the Potomac. In 1954, four large new residential projects were coming into the picture within the city limits, and the Chamber of Commerce expected Alexandria to reach the 100,000 population mark by 1960.

The existence of a Northern Virginia Regional Planning Commission to coordinate the efforts towards a better solution of regional problems in transportation, zoning, policing, etc., shows the local sense of a need for integration. It is significant that, along with the two counties and two cities already recognized by the U. S. Bureau of the Census as participating in the metropolitan area, Loudoun County is also a member of the Northern Virginia regional body and that Prince William County has been on it at times. Thus the metropolitan area is expanding and slowly taking cognizance of its interests and problems as one unit within the commonwealth. It is a rather curious case, as the real nuclear section of this urban system is outside the state's borders and has expanded in other directions, too. As mentioned earlier, it would seem that expansions in other directions may be more difficult from now on than they will be within Virginia. Megalopolis is thus pushing ahead, with large military establishments serving as its advanced outposts inside Virginia, particularly along the fall line towards Richmond.

The Richmond-Petersburg-Hopewell metropolitan area

Virginia's capital has built on its own a substantial metropolitan area. By 1950 it encompassed officially Richmond City, and Henrico and Chesterfield Counties—an area of 734 square miles populated by 328,000 people. The three independent cities of Hopewell, Colonial Heights, and Petersburg are adjacent to Chesterfield County and should in our opinion be added in all fairness to the Richmond metropolitan area, thus bringing its population bulk to 380,000. The adjoining county of Prince George is still in large part rural, but its subdivision called "Bland," extending between Hopewell and Petersburg and next to Chesterfield, already showed in 1950, both by its density and its recent rhythm of growth, that it was entirely suburbanized. Such extensions of the Richmond metropolitan area may be actually so considered in 1960, as well as Hanover County to the north, parts of which along U. S. 1 are being rapidly invaded by metropolitan features.

This metropolitan area arose from the growth of two old Virginia towns, as such things went in Virginia—from the growth of Richmond and Petersburg since the beginning of the nineteenth century. Its main factors of development are definitely regional and rooted in Virginia. At the first census of 1790, Richmond had 3,761 inhabitants and Petersburg 2,828; there were only two other "cities" at that time in Virginia: Alexandria with 2,748 people and Norfolk with 2,959. All four towns were then of about equal size, although the state's capital had already gained the lead. Richmond's growth was a steady one, definitely more rapid throughout the nineteenth century than the increase in population of the other old Virginia towns. From 1790 to 1890 every intercensal period brought increases of at least 24 per cent; there was a lull in the 1890–1900 period when the city's population was augmented by only 4.5 per cent. In 1900 Richmond counted 85,050 inhabitants; then its growth was rapid again from 1900 to 1920, and slower since 1930, although the years 1940–1950 brought an increase of 19.3 per cent. In that period the city was already expanding into a metropolitan area with a rate of growth of 24.4 per cent.

Richmond was growing with Virginia, but faster than the commonwealth's total population. Its development, the main stages of which we mentioned in our brief historical review,[7] resulted largely from the need of Virginia to have a capital and an urban center. The city is well situated on the fall line and on the James River, located near the central section of the Tidewater, and at about equal distance from the other Piedmont centers that developed in the nineteenth century (see map, page 37). In cooperation with Lynchburg, Richmond endeavored to make the valley of the James a major thoroughfare of westward continental traffic. This enterprise did not succeed, and Richmond had to be resigned to a more modest and essentially regional role. When, in 1937, Richmond celebrated the two-hundredth anniversary of its foundation, it had become a large, modern American city like so many others, as Lewis Mattison remarked:

It is this highly mechanized and controlled condition of urban life, in which large numbers of people are immersed, and the strain of which some of them find increasingly hard to bear, that most powerfully molds our contemporary habits and customs. . . . Our own Richmond shares in this change, for though at times and by contrast it seems leisurely and sleepy, it is a city. . . . But it is Richmond's great good fortune that scenes and landmarks of many noble events in its past remain.[8]

The central part of Richmond, where stand such shrines as the State Capitol, designed by Jefferson, and the "White House of the Confederacy," has been increasingly overrun since 1940 by the rushing traffic of a growing industrial and commercial hub.

Richmond's metropolitan area had in 1950 an average density of only 447 persons per square mile. The addition of Hopewell and Petersburg would increase this density. But even as it was, it forms a curious comparison with the Virginia section of Washington's metropolitan area: in the Richmond area the families with an income of over $5,000 amount to only 25.3 per cent, and only 35.7 per cent of persons over 25 years of age have completed at least high school studies. Proportionately, the people in this metropolitan area are therefore about half as prosperous and as well educated as those in the southern tip of Megalopolis in Virginia. Its labor force employed in agriculture is very small indeed (1.5 per cent), but that working in manufactures is much more important (22.7 per cent) than in Washington suburbs. Here, too, however, the wholesale and re-

[7] See Chapter 2, especially pages 110–112.
[8] Lewis Mattison, *Richmond, Capital of Virginia: Approaches to Its History,* Richmond, 1938, Chapter III, p. 58.

The façade of the State Capitol at Richmond, designed by Thomas Jefferson, who modeled it after the Maison Carrée, a Roman building at Nîmes, France
Virginia Chamber of Commerce

tail trade appeared to be the first ranking category of employment, and the proportion of people in government service was relatively high. The expansion measured by the rate of building of new housing units was not as rapid.

In 1952 the industrial production of Richmond was estimated at 321 per cent of what it was in 1929. The principal industries by size of employment were cigarettes and other tobacco products, chemical products, including rayon and cellophane, food and kindred products, apparel and textile products, paper, iron and steel, printing and publishing. Thus the congregation of manufacturing concerns in Virginia's capital runs a variety of plants, creating a system with great elasticity in terms of employment: when tobacco experiences difficulties, paper mills may be able to absorb more workers, or iron and steel may expand. The largest single industrial unit was the impressive chemical plant of E. I. Du Pont de Nemours and Company. But if Hopewell were included in the Richmond area, its group of chemical and paper plants would probably make chemicals rank ahead of tobacco industries for the whole area.

In its present limits the Richmond metropolitan area depends very much on the cigarette market and has developed to a large extent owing to the popularity of cigarette smoking in this century. In 1952 Richmond's plants turned out the record number of 110,665 million cigarettes; all the major brands except Camels are produced in Richmond. And only the city of Winston-Salem, North Carolina, home of the Camel cigarette, can rival Richmond for the title of "cigarette capital of the world." In 1932 only 29 billion cigarettes were manufactured in Richmond. The rapid increase within twenty years gives an idea of the economic lift this industry has given the city and its suburbs. This increase in cigarette manufacture came, however, at the expense of other previously used types of tobacco products which required less handling. The volume of tobacco processed in Richmond went up only from 21.8 million pounds in 1932 to 26.5 in 1952; but the cigarette industry consumes much more than tobacco and flavoring materials. The cellophane and aluminum foil made in Richmond go to a large extent into cigarette wrapping; the manufacturing of filters, of the paper of which the packages are made and the printing of labels are partly done in Richmond or nearby. The tobacco industry is considered a relatively stable one, as tobacco consumers will almost always arrange to spend a little money for a smoke, whether for cigarettes, pipe tobacco, or another form of the "weed."

Besides the tobacco manufacturing function, the major role of Richmond is that of a trade center. As the population of Virginia grew more numerous and more prosperous in the recent quarter of a century, the trading role of Richmond expanded rapidly. The Chamber of Commerce claims that the city's retail trade area comprises 41 counties and 9 independent cities, i.e., a population of about one million people. The retail sales in the city went up from 66 million dollars in 1932 to 369 million in 1952. At that time the retail trade had started moving out of the city with the construction of large suburban shopping centers; Richmond was following in the usual path of American urban growth. But its downtown section still groups a number of large and small stores which attract shoppers from Charlottesville and Lynchburg, Norfolk and Newport News, Danville, and even Washington. Its trade area really stops to the north where Baltimore's trade area begins, and Washington's metropolitan area, though a large center of trading itself, may be regarded in some ways as a "twilight zone" between Richmond's and Baltimore's zones of influence. Many people in Washington's suburbs believe that their dollar goes farther in Richmond or Baltimore than it does in the national capital.

Richmond is also a major center of wholesale trade, handling a good deal of the produce of Virginia's Piedmont and of the Northern Necks. The total volume of trade in the city has risen from about 2 billion dollars in 1940 to over 7 in 1952. The harbor is also active, in spite of the disfavor in which seagoing ships nowadays hold river ports situated at the head of tidal estuaries. From 900,000 tons in 1935 the harbor tonnage rose to 2.4 million in 1951–1952. There was active trade with the West Indies and with Canada. Some transoceanic shipping also reached the city's wharves, although that kind of freight showed an increasing tendency to stop at Hampton Roads. The railroads employed about 5 per cent of Richmond's active labor force in early 1953, when government service (both state and federal) employed about 10 per cent. Thus the city had a manifold economy based on many varied activities and functions. No single industry employed such a high percentage of all employees as to be able to create a locally serious crisis by reducing its operations. Tobacco is the most critical industry, and it is, under ordinary circumstances, not likely to go through a sudden depression.

The traffic problem is quite grave in Richmond, as in any other city of this size, but it is perhaps somewhat worse than the population warrants. An impressive through-traffic crosses the city, especially along U. S. Route 1. Although an alternate route skirting the city's center has been devised, the approaches of Richmond and the downtown section are terribly crowded at peak traffic periods. The city's managers have tried to solve the problem insofar as possible by such special regulations as making almost all the streets one-way thoroughfares and applying strict rules about parking. Nevertheless, the city and its immediate suburbs are a difficult area greatly slowing up through-traffic; and the overabundance of this traffic increases the cost of maintenance of the city's roads. In fact, the bottleneck of north-south traffic extends along U. S. 1 as far as Petersburg and requires a solution on the scale of that for the metropolitan area. The possibility has been carefully investigated of building a new turnpike from the north of Richmond to the south of Petersburg to channel the through-traffic out of the congested parts of the metropolitan area. In 1954 the General Assembly and the Governor finally adopted the project in the face of stiff resistance from commercial interests along the old route of U. S. 1 who disliked the idea of losing some of the trade on this itinerary.

To fully study the traffic of the Richmond-Petersburg area the engineering firm in charge found it necessary to add to the metropolitan area the counties of Hanover, Prince George, and Dinwiddie, as well as the city of Hopewell. To the commercial traffic was thus added that generated by military establishments in the area, such as Fort Lee; moreover, the motor route from Washington to Norfolk goes through Richmond and Petersburg, branching out southeast only in the center of the latter town. The through-traffic consists to a large extent of trucks coming from or going to the rapidly developing South. This trucking movement, largely the result of Richmond's location at the gateway of the South facing Megalopolis, offers one more reason to expect a considerable lessening of congestion in the metropolitan area if larger vehicles in transit could take a toll road which would save them time.[9]

Petersburg and Hopewell are both at present reduced to the role of Richmond's suburbs; neither of them has an actual downtown in terms of business and its offices: this function is largely concentrated in Richmond. Petersburg, built on the falls of the Appomattox River, grew at a pace just slightly below Richmond's until 1860 when, with 18,266 inhabitants, it was about half the size of the capital. Then the long siege and the aftermath of the Civil War broke the city's impetus. Since then increase in population has been rather slow and irregular. The 1950 figure of 35,000 indicates a somewhat bolder progress since World War II, but this is largely a reflection of the rapid development of the adjacent metropolitan area. Petersburg still has some tobacco industries and warehouses and some leather and wood-using plants. It also has the Virginia State College for Negroes. It has a higher proportion of Negro population—42.2 per cent—while Richmond has 31.7 per cent and the Washington metropolitan area in Virginia 26.6 per cent. As an immediate consequence, Petersburg appears to be a poorer area than Richmond, only 14.2 per cent of its families having an income of $5,000 or more, with a less well-educated population, only 25.2 per cent of the adults having completed high school or more. The small independent city of Colonial Heights (with 6,000 inhabitants in 1950) is really a suburb of Petersburg, chiefly residential. Much more important is Hopewell, situated at some distance from Petersburg and closer to the James River's tidal section. Hopewell became a city only in 1920 with 1,397 inhabitants; in 1950 its population counted 10,219, slightly less than in 1930. The city is an agglomeration of impressive industrial plants belonging to such large firms as Allied Chemical and Dye Corporation, Celanese Corporation of America, Continental Can Company, and Hercules Powder Company, and in 1952 these plants employed almost as many workers together as there were inhabitants

[9] Wilbur Smith and Associates, *Toll Roads for the Richmond-Petersburg Area,* New Haven, Conn., July, 1953, a report prepared at the request of the Virginia State Highway Commission.

in the city of Hopewell. Most of these workers came from the adjacent counties, many of them from Chesterfield County, some from Charles City County across the James.

Thus Hopewell and Petersburg appear closely welded to the metropolitan area of Richmond. The triangular system thus established can be said to be already consolidated. There are many exchanges of people daily from one part of the area thus defined to another. Hopewell would not have developed the way it did without the proximity of the growing city up the James, and Petersburg is more and more a town complementing Richmond. Within the officially limited metropolitan area the Negro population is largely concentrated within the city itself. The proportion of Negroes in Henrico County is rather low: this is an area of expensive real estate, with some large industries and extensive suburban developments populated 90 per cent by Whites. The percentage of Negroes is somewhat higher in Chesterfield County; it is low again (about 14 per cent) in the new town of Hopewell, but it is quite high in Petersburg. There is no doubt that many of the Negroes who live in Petersburg are employed in the Richmond metropolitan area and some of them in Hopewell. However, the Richmond-Hopewell labor market has still greater openings for Negro manpower than could be filled by these residents alone. Many of the Negroes who come to work here have found it difficult and too expensive to live in town or within the metropolitan area. They have found it much easier to reside in a neighboring county, Charles City County, where the proportion of Negroes reaches the highest ratio in Virginia: 81 per cent in 1950. Such a concentration cannot be explained by local economics or history. Charles City County is sparsely populated (25 persons per square mile) and largely forested. Two-thirds of its population are registered as rural non-farm: they are families of commuters to Richmond or Hopewell; 35 per cent of this county's labor force were employed in manufacturing without any manufactures on the spot.

For many reasons that pertain to the generally scattered settlement, to labor policies, to the racial problem, and to the people's preference for a rural setting for their residences, the labor force of the metropolitan area of Richmond-Petersburg-Hopewell is even more widely scattered than it may appear on a map of densities. This definitely Virginian metropolitan growth has not been more concentrated or more rapid just because it followed a typical Virginia pattern. But it already forms an impressive urban system, a large industrial concentration, a big hub of traffic. Its development would go on, even if the very important cigarette industry were to undergo a period of lower sales. Richmond has a very profitable geographical location, and its development may be even faster once some of

West Main Street, Norfolk. *Library of Congress Photo by John Vachon*

the problems that hamper it are solved, such as that of congested thoroughfares.

Urban growth in the Hampton Roads area

Of all the cities in Virginia, Norfolk has had the most troubled history. The first township in the Old Dominion to take significant shape in colonial times, it was burnt during the Revolutionary War; the best situated, it would seem, of all the seaports of Virginia and of the Chesapeake—at the gates of both the Bay and the James River—it was the last important harbor to develop to considerable size. Its development has not been entirely within the bounds of or under the name of Norfolk. It moved partly into the neighboring cities of Portsmouth and South Norfolk, and partly across the James estuary into the conglomeration of Newport News–Hampton–Warwick. Thus the communities of the Hampton Roads area are still divided into several cities and two metropolitan areas, since the wide water space of Hampton Roads apparently cannot be included within a metropolitan system. However, we will consider the whole as one unit: these communities live and grow essentially owing to the sea and to the exceptional location and maritime facilities of the place.

Professor C. F. Marsh of the College of William and Mary, who directed an exhaustive survey of the Hampton Roads area during World War II, opens his study as follows:

> From the settlement of Jamestown in 1607 to the present, war has been a potent factor in shaping the lives of the people living along the shores of Hampton Roads. . . . The impact upon the region and its people, however, of the First and Second World Wars, though fought in distant lands and waters, was probably even sharper than the earlier campaigns. The building and repair of ships; the training, embarkation and debarkation of soldiers and sailors; and other war activities absorbed, especially in World War II, most of the existing human and other productive resources of the region, brought in thousands of migrants from other parts of the country, and necessitated the construction of vast military and industrial plants, public works, and housing.[10]

This study shows Virginia's preoccupation with the crowded and difficult cities arising within the commonwealth and founded upon large-scale sea trade, naval activities and related heavy industries. This urban growth was socially and economically very different from either the expansion of Washington's suburbs or the development of such cities as Richmond and Roanoke. The latter large urban centers belonged to a category of cities that one might describe as "genteel." Norfolk-Portsmouth and Newport News definitely did not: the quality of the people and the rhythm of growth were different. "Mars moulds a great city," wrote T. J. Wertenbaker of Norfolk's growth during World War I.[11] At present Mars appears to have moulded a vast urban and industrial area around Hampton Roads; and the communities that arose under this influence were marked with the toughness of war.

Norfolk grew irregularly and rather slowly until the Civil War. In 1860 its population was 14,620; by 1910 it had reached 67,452, but it jumped to 115,777 in 1920; by 1940 it had grown to 144,000, to jump again to 213,000 in 1950. In this case the increase in population of the city does not provide a sound measure of urban growth. The metropolitan area of Norfolk-Portsmouth encompassed by 1950 a total population of 446,200 persons, an increase of 72.3 per cent since 1940; the metropolitan area of these two cities included South Norfolk City and the counties of Norfolk and Princess Anne, an area of 667 square miles with an average density of 669 inhabitants per square mile. Of this total population, only 27.5 per cent were Negroes, a relatively low proportion for the southside Tidewater. Where the two counties extend southwards to the North Carolina line, some agriculture is still carried on in the rich soils of the

---

[10] Charles F. Marsh (editor), *The Hampton Roads Communities in World War II*, Chapel Hill, N. C., 1951, p. 3.
[11] Thomas J. Wertenbaker, *Norfolk: Historic Southern Port*, Durham, N. C., 1931.

A carrier and the liner *America* in the docks at Newport News
Virginia Chamber of Commerce Photo by Flournoy

Flatwoods between the Dismal Swamp and the seashore; 2.8 per cent of
the labor force were still employed in agriculture. Since 1950 the advance
of suburban residences southward has continued, but the metropolitan
area is also expanding to the northwest along the roads to Petersburg and
Richmond. Some day a solid line of urban occupation will unite Portsmouth and Suffolk; Norfolk will probably keep some agriculture within
its metropolitan area, especially as more and more Flatwoods soils are
drained and put under the plough.

Until the 1940 census, Newport News was included in the Norfolk
metropolitan area. In 1950 a new metropolitan area was created at the
tip of the historical peninsula between the James and York Rivers. Newport News had been recognized by the census as a city in its own right
only in 1890, when its population was 4,449. It grew then irregularly to
35,600 in 1920 and 42,358 in 1950. But that year the metropolitan area
of Hampton–Newport News–Warwick aggregated 143,227 inhabitants, a
growth of 69.5 per cent since 1940. The city of Warwick was created in
1952 out of the former Warwick County; at the same time the independent city of Hampton absorbed all of adjacent Elizabeth City County. The
metropolitan area thus defined borders on two counties being rapidly

suburbanized in those parts which are not under national monuments or military depots: York and James City Counties.

The constellation of towns around Hampton Roads and the adjoining counties forms a metropolitan system the total population of which was already close to 600,000 in 1950. At the end of that year, with the new naval activities resulting from the war in Korea, it certainly went above this mark. Hampton Roads is, therefore, the largest urban system in Virginia. It is largely dependent on federal policies, as the U. S. Navy is by far the greatest entrepreneur in the area, because of the personnel on its payroll, the importance of its yards, depots, and arsenals, the decisive part that war shipbuilding has had in recent years in the shipyards, and finally the expenditure on the spot of Navy personnel. But Norfolk is also a great commercial seaport. Like every large port, it has a whole section devoted to the kinds of trade that offer recreation to seamen. And on one of these streets, lined with bars and night clubs, it is significant to read on one of the doors the sign: "Merchant marine welcome, too."

In the Norfolk-Portsmouth area in 1950, out of the total resident employment (which does not include, of course, the military or the crews of ships calling in the port), about 16.5 per cent were employed in manufacturing, 23 per cent in trade, 11 per cent in transportation and communication, 7 per cent in professional services. In this area the mobility of the population was great as it had practically doubled within twenty years, but the average income was rather low (only 18.4 per cent of the families had incomes of more than $5,000). About 34 per cent of the adults had completed at least high school. In the metropolitan area of Newport News these standards of income and education were somewhat higher (19 per cent of the families, 37.9 per cent of the adults). Here 21.5 per cent of the total employment worked in manufactures. The greater importance of these industries in the peninsular section of the Hampton Roads area is due mainly to the gigantic shipyards of the Newport News Shipbuilding and Drydock Company, where so many fine and famous ships were built, including many gallant battleships, the superliner *United States,* holder of the blue ribbon on the North Atlantic, and the aircraft carriers *Midway, Coral Sea,* and *Forrestal.* Facing it on the other bank of the James, the Norfolk Naval Shipyard and two small private yards specialize in ship repairing, but also build some vessels. The number of persons employed in all these yards rose from 19,000 in January, 1940, to a record high of 76,300 in April, 1943, and declined thereafter. It is thus apparent that shipyard workers were second to none, unless to seamen, on the Hampton Roads scene during the war periods. Even in peacetime they are an important element in the community.

Shipyard workers at Newport News
Library of Congress Photo by John Vachon

The contracts awarded to the Hampton Roads yards in the past fifteen years amounted to a total of several billion dollars; the industry has thus been a source of prosperity to the whole area. It has been suffering recently from the seriously curtailed shipbuilding program, despite a few large orders from the navy. This curtailment has been felt in all large shipbuilding centers in the United States, and among them the Hampton Roads area is one of the leaders. The specialization here is perhaps more on the building and repairing of warships than it is in other principal centers; but merchant shipbuilding altogether has been reduced a great deal in the United States since 1952, and it is mainly contracts from the navy that keep the industry going.

Hampton Roads is also a great commercial seaport, one of the greatest on the East Coast. There are many different ways of estimating the rank of a seaport—by the tonnage of the ships that enter and clear, by the volume of merchandise loaded and unloaded, etc. The international custom is to consider foreign trade figures only, without taking account of coastwise traffic. The foreign water-borne commerce of the Hampton Roads ports ranked this seaport unit second only to New York in 1952 among the Atlantic ports of the United States. That year New York handled 33.8 million tons of goods in foreign commerce, Hampton Roads 26.2 million tons, Baltimore 21.3, Philadelphia 15.1, and Boston 5 million tons. The Hampton Roads total was split almost evenly between Norfolk (13.8) and Newport News (12.4); considering each of the two ports separately, they rank after Baltimore and Philadelphia. The figures for 1952 showed great progress since 1940, when Hampton Roads with a total of 4.4 million tons came after New York (24.4), Baltimore (9.5), and Philadelphia (7.1); only Newport News ranked even lower than Boston. This progress was largely due to an increase in outbound shipments.

If outbound and inbound trade are considered separately, Hampton Roads appears to be the typical exporter of heavy cargo. Ships come here riding high on the water and leave heavily loaded. In outbound shipments Hampton Roads is by far the leader of all other Atlantic coast ports, and each of its two components leads even New York in this respect—at least such was the situation in 1952, when Hampton Roads shipped out 23.1 million tons, while the corresponding figure for New York was 6.6, for Baltimore 6.5, for Philadelphia 2.8. The picture is quite reversed in terms of inbound trade: Hampton Roads received in 1952 a total of 3.1 million tons, ranking far below New York (27.1), Baltimore (14.7), Philadelphia (12.2), and even Boston (4.8). Most of the inbound shipments came to Norfolk (about 90 per cent), and Newport News imported even less than Charleston, S. C. This shows that Hampton Roads, in contrast to the great ports of Megalopolis to the north, is still mainly a wharf for the shipment of raw materials abroad, and among them coal is paramount.

Coal made up 22.4 out of the 23.1 million tons shipped out of Hampton Roads in 1952. Second in importance among exports came tobacco, of which about 200,000 tons were shipped. Thus the Hampton Roads ports appear to serve mainly as the shipping pier for the products of southern Virginia and of West Virginia, as the amount of coal shipped from West Virginia customarily exceeds the total amount of Virginia products shipped. Of these exports 80 per cent went in 1952 to Europe, 10 per cent to Asia (mainly Japan), and 8 per cent to Latin America. In 1940 the currents of traffic were different, as 31 per cent of the exports through Hampton Roads went to Europe and 58 per cent to Latin America. These changes reflect the evolution that occurred as a result of World War II in the world trade of coal. Western and southern Europe, which used to be importers mainly of British and German coal, turned to the United States, as Great Britain began to consume most of its coal and Germany has not been in a position to export much of the Ruhr coal until recently. By 1953, as the reconstruction of Europe became more

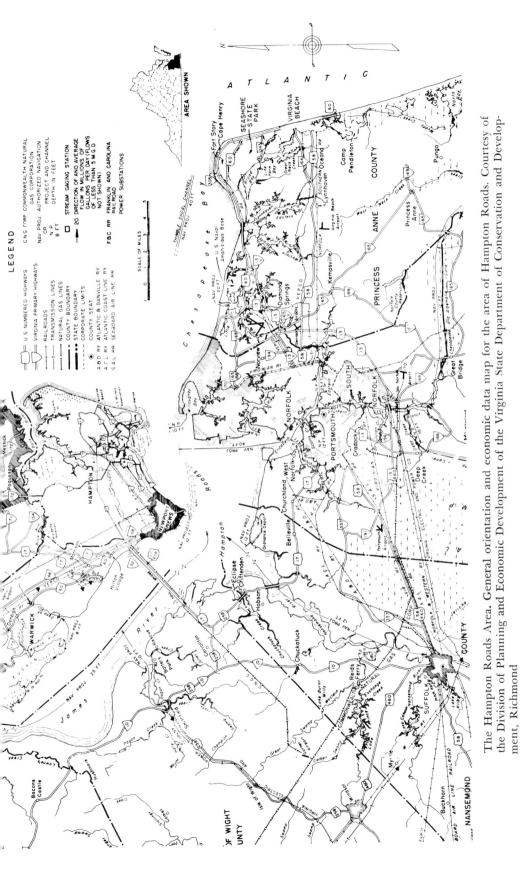

The Hampton Roads Area. General orientation and economic data map for the area of Hampton Roads. Courtesy of the Division of Planning and Economic Development of the Virginia State Department of Conservation and Development, Richmond

complete, the demand for American coal slackened. In that year, total exports declined by 9.7 million tons to a figure of 13.4. From 1952 to 1953 coal alone showed a loss of 10 million tons, slightly compensated for by gains in the shipments of grain and tobacco. This time Asia took one-fourth of the exports and Europe only about 40 per cent. In 1954 business showed a slight decline from the 1953 level. The endeavor of the ports and the related interests is to maintain if possible the 1953 level of coal shipments, and augment and diversify if possible the movement of general cargo. To be able to export and import a variety of goods in large quantities, a seaport must be the façade of a great consuming market and of a vast and diversified industrial area. Great harbor systems often start as specialized ports for the shipment or reception of one or two products; then as industries are built up in the area and a consumption market comes to depend on this harbor for supplies, more general cargo comes and leaves. Warehousing facilities, credit opportunities, and policies of steamship lines are all very important in the commercial upbuilding of the harbor, and Hampton Roads is still in the developing stage in this respect when compared with New York or Baltimore.

Foreign commerce does not represent all of the movement of ships and goods in Hampton Roads. Coastwise traffic is substantial, too, but not as impressive as foreign trade, again because it is too specialized: coastwise shipments are made up almost entirely of coal (about 10 million tons in each of the years 1951 and 1952). Of the coastwise receipts, 90 per cent were of petroleum products and the remaining one-tenth of phosphates and sulfur (both processed in the fertilizer plants at Norfolk), coal-tar products, and canned fruits and vegetables. As more industries are established in the vicinity of Hampton Roads, the goods handled by the port will develop in volume and variety. The fact that the movement of general cargo in foreign commerce exceeded 4 million tons in 1953 (of which more than one million was outbound) puts Hampton Roads in the class of important international ports on the world scale. It is too much to expect that this young maritime organization can easily outrank the veterans in the trade, better equipped and more closely linked to the outside by dense networks of steamship lines.

Hampton Roads already has an impressive array of mechanical and chemical industries aside from the shipyards. More are coming. In 1954, Standard Oil announced its decision to build a refinery near Norfolk, and the Pan American Refining Corporation started building a refinery in York County not far from Newport News. Thus a large new industry will come to the area and replace the coastwise receipts of refined petroleum products by receipts and imports of crude oil and possibly some ex-

Metropolitan growth has brought spreading slums in Newport News. *Library of Congress Photo by John Vachon*

ports of refined products. This industry will be added to the gradually expanding industries making fertilizers, gypsum and asphalt products, processing wood, producing brake shoes and car wheels, burlap and cotton bags, cement and mirrors, textiles and clothing. The Ford Motor Company has an assembly plant in Norfolk. Considering its natural endowment and its excellent geographical position, Hampton Roads is just at the beginning of its development as an industrial center and an industrial port. One of the many assets of the area is its excellent railroad connections with the interior. This has been achieved largely owing to three great coal carriers which organized this area for coal shipping. The Norfolk and Western Railway and the Virginian Railway Company dump coal at Norfolk, and the Chesapeake and Ohio Railway dumps it at Newport News. These railroads are themselves keenly interested in promoting the movement of general cargo through, to, and from Hampton Roads now that coal, their major freight, appears to be on the decline. Coal dumpings at Hampton Roads terminals have greatly varied in quantity from year to year recently. They reached a postwar low in 1950 of 12,120,975 long tons, rose to 36.6 million long tons the following year, to decrease to 29.7 in 1952 and 18.7 in 1953. Out of this total in 1953, 5 million tons were hauled in by the N. & W., 4.5 by the Virginian, and 9.2 by the C. & O., which made of Newport News the leading coal pier in the area. The figures for 1954 are expected to sink somewhat below the 1953 level. With the present trend of steel mills towards the coast, Norfolk offers, it would seem, an ideal position close to South American sources of ore, well supplied with coal and manpower, with a substantial consuming market on the spot and in the vicinity.

Hampton Roads can be considered, therefore, as a port and industrial group launched on a great career by wartime needs, but destined this time to remain a developing area even when the times of peace and of a declining coal market are threatening its prosperity. Its main asset is its great accessibility from all sides (the continent north, west, and south) by land as well as by sea. However, the facilities of access have to be carefully maintained as the flow of traffic in some channels increases. Here again arises the problem of adequately channeling traffic through the two metropolitan areas and between them. Bridges and tunnels have been built at considerable expense between Norfolk and Portsmouth and over the James. More of such works are needed. A road which will link advanced points on the south bank with Hampton and which will cross a section of Hampton Roads partly by tunnel and partly by bridge is being built at the cost of 95 million dollars. A good road system surrounds the Norfolk-Portsmouth area, another links the area of Newport News with that of Richmond and U. S. 1. Right in the back of the Newport News–Hampton–Warwick metropolitan area the national shrines, as they could be called, of Yorktown, Jamestown, and Williamsburg attract crowds of tourists who add to the highway crowding. Nevertheless, this area must be kept well serviced at all times for both commercial and strategic reasons. The new road crossing the mouth of the James by bridge and tunnel from Willoughby spit (Norfolk) to Old Point Comfort and Phoebus (Hampton) will effectuate a necessary link between the two banks of the magnificent roadstead. When this tremendous enterprise is completed it may be possible again to unite both metropolitan areas into one huge system, perhaps the ultimate southern tip of Megalopolis in the future.[12]

The population that has congregated in so short a time in this area comes from various parts of the country. Many of the shipyard workers came from southwestern Virginia and other parts of the Old Dominion; but many people engaged here in trade and, of course, the military came from all over the United States. Virginians have sometimes been resentful

[12] Our data comes from many publications by local organizations. See especially Hampton Roads Maritime Association, *The Ports of Greater Hampton Roads Annual, 1954,* Norfolk (annually published); Coverdale and Colpitts, *Report to the Virginia State Ports Authority,* New York, August 31, 1953; bulletins and releases of the Virginia State Ports Authority; *The Impact of Virginia Ports on the Economy of Virginia,* Charlottesville, Bureau of Population and Economic Research, 1954.

A row of houses in a Negro section of Portsmouth
Library of Congress Photo by John Vachon

of this invasion into the southern coastal plain. They had all the more reason to feel so as many of these "foreigners," civilian and military alike, were of the tougher kind of people who come first in the developing, frontierlike sections of the country. This was a shock to the mild-mannered Tidewater. Some Virginians voiced the opinion that the communities of Hampton Roads were no longer Virginian in terms of way of life; but more often the opinion was defended that this was one of the difficult episodes of the war and that with time the newcomers would be assimilated to Virginian ways and manners.

Rapidly growing metropolitan areas are bound to be small-scale melting pots with difficult community problems to solve. The area of northern Virginia which was converted into suburbs of Washington is one case of such growth in Virginia: but here most of the population is on a higher economic and educational level; northern Virginia is a problem in many ways, but a respectable one. Hampton Roads has had a quicker and less regular growth, involving the fluidity of more diversified, less well-educated social elements.

The Hampton Roads area, even before the war, was an area with a somewhat unstable social structure. The impingement of wartime conditions, including heavy increases in heterogeneous population, widespread inadequacy of social agencies, and changing behavior patterns, made the area even more unstable in this respect. In a sense, the glue of the society gave way.[13]

Such a conclusion is perhaps one that would worry a Virginian more than a Westerner. Nevertheless, this area did offer a number of troublesome problems.

After the wartime periods of intense activity and the subsequent business slumps, a widespread feeling of insecurity and pessimism as to the area's future has developed here more than in many other parts of the east coast and certainly more than in other parts of Virginia. This feeling results from awareness of the local economy's dependence on the navy and on coal: Washington's policies may change and drastically affect budget expenditure of the navy; the coal market shows definite signs of decline. Local endeavors to develop activities with local roots have made as yet little headway. For a great seaport, Hampton Roads lacks one factor symptomatic of stability and initiative: it has almost no locally owned steamship lines. Its traffic by land and by sea is entirely directed from the outside by interests with roots elsewhere. The various communities around Hampton Roads have also spent too much time and effort trying to cut down one another's enterprises, as some recent studies have pointed out successfully. The Virginia State Ports Authority and such organizations as the Hampton Roads Maritime Association have begun to work out a more cooperative arrangement. This is a problem area nowadays, and more surveys such as that directed by Dr. Charles F. Marsh could be of good help.

The Hampton Roads area is expanding in different directions and will probably continue to expand, since, despite some unstabilizing factors, it will retain the assets of its geographical position and of being less crowded than other major port areas of the northeastern coast. The recurrent labor trouble on the New York waterfront may also benefit Hampton Roads. The peninsular section will probably expand at an increasing pace, owing to both industrialization and travel trade. It is closer, too, to Richmond and Washington, and it has its back to a rather sparsely populated, largely wooded neck of land. The Norfolk-Portsmouth area is surrounded by both marshy lands and rich agricultural lands. The construction of the road across Hampton Roads from Hampton to Norfolk will therefore complete the welding together of the banks of the ports area and will bring Norfolk closer to Richmond and Washington via the historic peninsula. This should increase the chances that

[13] Charles F. Marsh (editor), *op. cit.*, p. 140.

this peninsula will be more densely settled and perhaps suburbanized in the future. Geography and history will thus combine to bring Jamestown closer to the modern capitals of the state and the nation.

The metropolitan area of Roanoke

No urban growth comparable to that on the Tidewater is found in Virginia west of the fall line. The only case worth separate study is that of Roanoke, at present a regional capital of western Virginia and a fairly recent town altogether.

Roanoke is a railroad town. It was created by the Norfolk and Western Railway near the point where this railroad's tracks penetrated inside the vast Appalachian realm. Later, the Virginian Railway came through it, too. The N. & W.'s headquarters are at Roanoke, occupying two large blocks of buildings close to the railroad station and to the large hotel also built by the company. This section is indeed the heart and the starting point of the city. Its business district has developed from there, but on the other side of the tracks.[14] The site of the settlement of Big Lick was selected by the railroad in 1881 for the junction of tracks from Norfolk, Richmond, and Lynchburg with the line being then built in the Shenandoah Valley.

Big Lick in 1881 so earnestly aspired to the status of an important railroad junction that its leading citizens handed the railroad $7,875 in cash as a consideration for choosing it. Also the town sold the railroad some 800 acres of bottom land for shops, engine house, transfer tracks, a hotel, and other structures. On June 27, 1881, the citizens even voted to change the name of the place. The size of the vote on that issue conveys the size of the community better than population figures could: fifty seven votes were cast for "Kimball" and seventeen for "Roenoke" (*sic*). "This has been done," one of the citizens wrote Kimball, "to give evidence of the high esteem and appreciation you enjoy in the hearts of these people on the account of the improvements you are projecting in their midst . . . and to show that our people hold no unkind feelings toward the people of the north." But Kimball, modest by nature, declined the honor, and the town became Roanoke.[15]

This beginning testifies to a lively tradition of economic development and social progress, probably even now felt in Roanoke more than in most of the other cities of Virginia.

[14] See R. E. Murphy and J. E. Vance, Jr., "A Comparative Study of Nine Central Business Districts," in *Economic Geography*, Vol. 30, No. 4, October, 1954, pp. 301–336.
[15] Joseph T. Lambie, *From Mine to Market: The History of Coal Transportation on the Norfolk and Western Railway*, New York, 1954, pp. 15–16. F. J. Kimball was head of the N. & W.

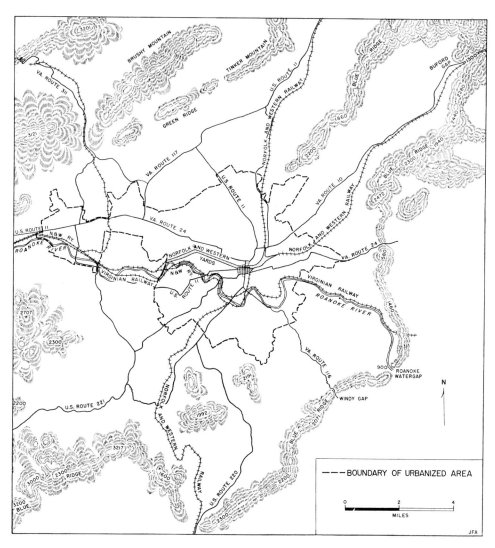

The Site of Roanoke
Courtesy of *Economic Geography*, Clark University, Worcester, Mass.

From about 700 people in 1881, Roanoke grew to 21,495 in 1900, 50,-
842 in 1920, and 91,921 in 1950. At this date its central sections were already quite congested and a whole metropolitan area had developed, including officially Roanoke County with its 303 square miles and 133,000
inhabitants in 1950. The urbanized area sends its tentacles beyond the
county's limits along U. S. 11. In terms of industrial grouping, areas that
are definitely satellites of Roanoke extend along U. S. 11 westward as far
as Radford on the New River. This area, however, is not entirely ur-

banized and suburbanized; parts of the counties thus concerned are still extremely rural at some distance from the main road. Within its standard metropolitan area Roanoke encloses a powerful industrial concentration. Being the principal hub of road and rail in western Virginia, Roanoke's function as a trade center is more important than its manufacturing function.

In 1950 the total employment in the Roanoke metropolitan area was divided between the various economic activities in approximately the same proportions as in the Richmond area: about one-fifth of the total was employed in each of the big three occupations—wholesale and retail trade, manufacturing, transportation and public utilities. It may be that a higher percentage of the workers within the area commuted from without than was the case in Richmond, but that would be hard to measure with precision. In the summer of 1953 the largest employer in Roanoke, and quite properly so, was the Norfolk and Western Railway with 7,800 persons, over one-tenth of the area's total employment; this number included employees in the large installations of the railroad and its engine shop. The second employer in importance was the American Viscose Corporation with 3,200 employees, followed by the Kenrose Manufacturing Company, producing wash dresses and employing 1,100 people. Other important plants employing more than 500 persons each were those of the American Bridge Division of U. S. Steel, the Appalachian Electric Power Company, the Johnson-Carper Furniture Company, the Roanoke Mills (knitted wear), the Yale and Towne Manufacturing Company (locks and hardware) in Salem, and the Burlington Mills Weaving Division in Vinton. This enumeration provides a summary of the diverse industries found in the group: chemicals, textiles, machinery, and wood-using industries congregate here, with perhaps more emphasis on steel structures and machinery than in any other place in Virginia except Newport News. The coming to Roanoke of a Koppers plant producing railroad ties and of a General Electric plant will further diversify and vitalize the industrial setup.

The average level of income and education is not particularly high in the Roanoke area. It is somewhat below that of Richmond's metropolitan area, although the latter is much bigger and has a much higher proportion of Negroes; the Negro population accounts for 26.6 per cent of the total in Richmond and for 13.6 per cent in the Roanoke area. As in the state capital, the Negroes are concentrated inside the city, the suburbs being largely closed to them. The fact that the population's level is not higher, although the proportion of the Negroes is much lower, provides one illustration among many of the fact that the poorer Whites in the hilly parts of Virginia are at least as much of an economic and social problem as the Negroes are. The common belief that the high percentage of Negroes in the population is at the center of the problem of the Southeast's relative backwardness, economically as well as culturally, is an oversimplification that distorts the truth. The poorer Whites of the western valleys and ridges are as much a problem, perhaps even more. The responsibility of the Whites in the general state of affairs is, of course, greater than that of the Negroes. Metropolitan growth and industrialization in these Appalachian parts is thus all the more important as a factor which should raise the economic and cultural level of these people and put an end to their isolation.

Roanoke has a reputation among Virginia cities for being more "Midwestern" than others. It has undertaken greater things industrially, it has showed more local initiative, it has made decisions and transacted business more rapidly than most Virginia cities. Roanokers often pride 'themselves on not being as slow—some may even say as sleepy—as their neighbors in Lynchburg, Danville, and Richmond. Just how far these differences are real is hard to ascertain and impossible to measure. But Roanoke has certainly grown quickly and shown a great appetite for business, from the establishing of the N. & W., with which all began, to the coming of the "silk mill" of American Viscose and more recently the General Electric plant. Such a difference from the usual Virginia tempo may well be explained by the youth of this city which was born during the economic renaissance of Virginia after the wounds of the Civil War had scarred over. Such dynamic qualities seem also becoming to a city created as a hub in the system of transportation and, therefore, more firmly linked with the outside than with the immediate surroundings. Roanoke benefited also from a very advantageous geographical position and from the abundance of labor in neighboring areas. Its rapid rise and dynamic reputation show the potentialities that southwestern Virginia can develop when given the opportunity.

Developing gradually into a regional capital, Roanoke claims that its trade area and its cultural influence (through newspapers) extends over a good part of southwestern Virginia, into the coalfield to the west, as far as Abingdon and Bristol to the southwest, and as far as Bedford and Martinsville in the Piedmont. For a city of its size, Roanoke has a business district unusually metropolitan in aspect; this is due partly to the dense population of surrounding rural counties and partly to the topography, as the next large cities, such as Lynchburg and Richmond, are some distance away and beyond the Blue Ridge. Between Roanoke and Lynchburg, however, the Blue Ridge is not so difficult to cross. In the final analysis, one must recognize that the vitality of Roanoke has been a decisive element in the part the city has played and will certainly continue to play in the future.[16]

The smaller cities of Virginia

The four metropolitan areas reviewed in this chapter are founded upon huge national or regional hubs of activity. Washington is developing out of the necessity of keeping together and directing the immense development of the American nation. The Hampton Roads area is based on its maritime position with respect to the present map of the United States. Richmond has inherited from the past the role of state capital and main crossroads of rail and road lines at the midpoint of the fall line in Virginia. Roanoke is the capital of the southwest, created as a rail hub at the contact of the Great Valley, the Blue Ridge, and the Piedmont. No other city in Virginia has a function comparable to these at present. The others are either strictly specialized and localized, or they carry on the tasks inherited from a past when they were better situated as crossroads on yesterday's map.

Lynchburg is in this fashion a crossroads of the past, situated at the contact of the Blue Ridge and the Piedmont, on the James River, and at the gates of the two more easily passable gaps across the Blue Ridge—the James water gap and the Montvale depression. But today the James no longer leads anywhere, and the Montvale road leads to Roanoke. Lynchburg is slowly being restricted in its radius as a central market by the rapid expansion of Roanoke on one side and of Richmond on the other.

Appearing in the census as a city of 4,600 inhabitants in 1830, Lynchburg grew slowly to 8,000 in 1850, lost during the 1850's, rose to 16,000 by 1880, 29,500 in 1910, 40,600 in 1930, and 47,700 in 1950. Now that suburbs are spreading around the city proper, the urbanized area has passed the 50,000 mark but is still far too modest to become the nucleus of a metropolitan area. There is small chance that growth will proceed more quickly in the foreseeable future. Lynchburg is, at any rate, a conservative city by all standards. It has succeeded, nevertheless, in maintaining an industrial and commercial role of some importance. About one-fifth of its employment is in trade and over one-third in manufacturing. The latter

[16] The best source on Roanoke's past development is the Virginia W.P.A. Writers' Program volume sponsored by the school boards of the city and the county in the *American Guide Series*, entitled *Roanoke: Story of County and City* (1942). Also see *Comprehensive City Plan, Roanoke, Virginia, 1928*, prepared by John Nolen, city planner of Cambridge, Mass., for the Roanoke City Planning and Zoning Commissions, and the *Roanoke Times* fiftieth anniversary edition, November 30, 1936.

A typical recent suburban development on the fringe of Danville
Virginia Chamber of Commerce

percentage is a high one, higher than in any of the other sizable Virginia cities with the exception of Danville. Lynchburg is located in the twilight zone between the Richmond and Roanoke marketing areas, but its industrial activities are on a solid foundation. In the field of manufacturing the major industries are quite diversified; to the usual combination in Virginia of chemicals, textiles and apparel, wood-using plants, and food and metal industries, Lynchburg adds a specialization in leather manufactures, owing particularly to the plants of the Craddock-Terry Shoe Corporation and of the Virginia Art Goods Studios. Iron products and clothing rank immediately after footwear in the city's principal productions. Cast-iron pipes made in Lynchburg are found in the mains of cities throughout the eastern United States. Tobacco has not been forgotten either, but the great days are definitely gone when Lynchburg was an important center of dark tobacco sales and the manufacture of plugs for chewing. Most of the industries are locally owned, and the whole economy of the city is closely controlled by a small number of local families. The community is rather homogeneous and without any fundamental conflicts. But the local people do not like much interference in their business from the outside; this attitude may well be responsible for the slower pace and smaller size of Lynchburg as against Roanoke, for instance.

Another town similar in its development, but with more spectacular achievements to boast, is Danville, the capital of the southern Piedmont and of the bright leaf tobacco belt, and the site of the great textile industry of Dan River Mills. Danville does not have any of Lynchburg's advantages of location. It is set in the tobacco realm, in the heart of the Old Belt, which lies in the southern part of Piedmont Virginia and the northern part of Piedmont North Carolina. It is still one of the leading tobacco markets in the country and in the world, and it processes large quantities of bright leaf before manufacturing. Such leading firms as the Liggett and Myers Tobacco Company, P. Lorillard Company, R. J. Reynolds Tobacco Company, and others have here large warehouses and plants of their leaf departments. There are also wood-processing plants that make veneer, plywood, and other wood products, and a plant building elevators. But the whole town's economy is dominated the year around by the vast mills of the Dan River Company, which are responsible for two-thirds of the city's total employment and explain the high proportion of it in manufacturing (37.7 per cent in 1950) and the lesser proportion in trade (21.5 per cent) despite the importance of tobacco. The old tobacco specialty takes over for a few weeks at the height of the sales season, when the easily recognizable special trucks crowd the approaches to and the downtown streets of the city; and a tobacco festival is held here. But all the year around textiles are the essential occupation of the place, drawing large numbers of workers from the surrounding countryside to the mills.

The third Piedmont city that must be mentioned has another specialty of its own: Charlottesville, located near another relatively easy pass across the Blue Ridge, is mainly the home of the University of Virginia and several state government services which have found it convenient to be located on the campus—the geological survey, the forest and water resources services, and others. Here the two leading occupations among employed persons are professional services and trade, each of them occupying about 22 per cent of the total population in 1950. The student body, which has rapidly expanded since 1940, forms the largest "occupation" group in town. Its present importance is partly responsible for the development of retail trade. Manufacturing is present, too, and employs about 13 per cent of the working population.

Charlottesville is a beautiful town. The campus of the University, the central buildings of which were designed by Jefferson and built under his personal supervision, is a renowned touristic site, as are Monticello, the restored home of Mr. Jefferson, and Ash Lawn, James Monroe's residence. The spirit of Jefferson seems to overshadow everything in this place, and his cult is certainly alive. Altogether Charlottesville counted 26,000 inhabitants in 1950, a relatively rapid growth since 1910, when it had only 6,700 residents. The expansion of the University and of the tourist trade is responsible for most of it. West of the city, on the approaches to the Blue Ridge and to the Shenandoah National Park, many beautiful and convenient sites have attracted wealthy new residents. These estates may be considered an extension of the northern Piedmont station-wagon farming area; farther away from Washington, they are in one of the more pleasant and well-organized sections of Virginia.

West of the Blue Ridge Virginia has hardly any city worth this name besides Roanoke. In the Great Valley a few small towns are scattered; none of them had reached 20,000 people by 1950. From north to south we find: Winchester (13,800), the capital of the apple orchard country; Staunton (19,900), with some growing industries and an active crossroads on U. S. Route 11; Waynesboro (12,300), with the large Du Pont rayon mill and new plants being built; Harrisonburg (10,800), capital of the poultry-raising country; Lexington (6,000), mainly a university town with both the Virginia Military Institute and Washington and Lee University; then to the southwest of Roanoke a string of small towns, county seats with a few industries in each, none of them grouping 10,000 inhabitants until Bristol is reached, astride the Tennessee border with a half in either state, the dividing line following the main street. Each of the two towns of Bristol, Virginia, and Bristol, Tennessee, has about 16,000 people, making a total of more than 30,000 in population and the first sizable trading and industrial center to be encountered southwest of Roanoke. Since 1953, new plants, mainly in the field of engineering, have been coming to the vicinity of various towns at the foot of the Blue Ridge. This promising new feature is to be observed at Roanoke, Lynchburg, Charlottesville, and Waynesboro.

Thus western Virginia, although quite industrialized, remains still a country of scattered settlement with a unique large city which developed owing to a railroad and the ambition of its inhabitants. On the whole, industrialization has not brought much urbanization west of the fall line. The metropolitan growth which is responsible for so much change in Virginia, statistically and perhaps otherwise, is as yet a phenomenon of eastern Virginia, chiefly of the Tidewater, with an extension in the very north of the Piedmont.

Consequences of urbanization

Now that about one-half of the Virginians live in "urban territory" and more than one-third of them within the limits of metropolitan areas, does this break away from the tradition of scattered settlement mean much else besides changes in statistics? These statistics would not be worth compiling if they were meaningless. We have already seen how much, as far back as 1700 and 1800, the pattern of settlement meant to the economy of Virginia, to the differences between her way of life and what was observed in New England and the Middle Atlantic areas. The scattering of habitat was a significant factor in determining the kind of life and society Virginia had. Today eastern Virginia is already being turned into an habitat area similar to those found to its north. Crowds of great cities have come to Virginia, and certainly they have come to stay.

Many problems have arisen therefrom—problems first in city government. In the rather strictly organized society of Virginia, with its firmly fixed hierarchy, it has seemed preferable to provide technical solutions to many problems; most of the Virginia cities are administered by city managers, and conservative Lynchburg claims to have been the first city in the United States to adopt this form of government. The downtown sections of Virginia cities were not built by people who expected them to grow rapidly. The growing traffic soon crowded them, and almost all of the major urbanized areas must face today the need of large-scale projects and expenditure to improve traffic conditions. For solving such problems the city manager type of government has proved quite efficient.

Metropolitan growth and crowding in some parts of the urbanized sections cause, however, other concerns than traffic alone. Slums develop, and community decisions must be made. This type of problem is relatively new to Virginia and not always easy to solve because of the local traditions of individualism, of resistance to collective action and to the recognition of community interests. These things might have been easier for Virginians if their neighbors had been the same families for some generations; to enter a compact with perfect strangers, with newcomers, appeared strange and undesirable. In the rapidly shifting and developing population of the metropolitan areas, neighbors are often "foreigners" or at least newcomers. The gregarious feeling of the Middle Western cities and of many cities in the northeast is a brand-new and as yet little-developed phenomenon in Virginia. Some of it, nevertheless, will probably be imposed upon the residents of large cities.

The growth of these urban or metropolitan areas means also greater needs in terms of schools, hospitals, and various other institutions; all these necessary improvements require money. Although federal funds help to meet such needs, they usually only match dollar for dollar the money provided by state funds; the tradition of economy in the government of the Old Dominion is being upset by the growing need for more buildings and more services as the cities grow. Local and state governments may tax the city people more if their income is higher. However, the young agglomerations of Virginia are not, with the exception of the better-paid Washington metropolitan area, regions of especially high income. And Virginians do not like paying taxes any more than other people do, perhaps even a little less than the average American.

The inhabitants of the metropolitan areas depend greatly on the expenditure of federal government funds for income payments to individuals as well as for the general level of business. This is particularly true of the areas around Washington and Hampton Roads. As military establishments develop or are maintained along the Tidewater between these two metropolitan areas, the trade of the whole coastal plain becomes more closely dependent on government expenditure. Eastern Virginia lives more and more on the assets, administered from afar, of her geographical position, rather than on local resources with their roots inside the state. This represents a great change from the traditional economy of the commonwealth, a change that has set its imprint on the Tidewater and northern Piedmont much more than on western Virginia. Even southern parts of the Piedmont and the rural southside coastal plain are feeling more and more the extent to which decisions made on a national scale in Washington affect their annual income: prices on tobacco, peanuts, and cotton are supported by these decisions and policies; even hay in time of drought is supplied partly by federal subsidy. Both Tidewater and Piedmont are thus realizing a little more every year that their actual economic well-being is a matter of national policy rather than of local decision.

Today the population of the metropolitan areas of Virginia is still by and large deeply rooted in the surrounding rural countryside; these people talk about farm matters and keep one foot on a farm. As time goes on, however, and unless the urban economy is seriously shattered by a major depression that nobody desires or really expects, the crowds of these great cities will eventually loosen their links with agriculture and the rural way of life. Such a change would be a great shock to Virginians; they do not believe it can happen. They rather expect the city dwellers of Virginia to remain loyal to the interests and traditions that have always belonged to a Virginia with a scattered settlement. Who knows? Perhaps with the present trend of large cities to expand into a semirural outer-suburbia, some of the old Virginia characteristics may be better preserved than they would have been in the agglomerated towns of the nineteenth-century type. It is too early to tell. But the growth of cities and metropolitan areas has injected new life into the bloodstream of the regional economy. Even the farms of Virginia would not have been enjoying so much prosperity if they had not had such rapidly developing large consumer markets close at hand.

Urban and metropolitan growth has been an essential feature of the American economy and also of the economies of most western nations in this century. It had to come to the South, and it has taken somewhat more impressive forms in Virginia than in the states to the south because of Virginia's geographical location so close to Megalopolis. It is in many ways a rejuvenation, or at least a way of avoiding the sclerosis of old age, for western peoples who no longer enjoy endless free land to settle and develop, but still refuse to renounce progress. To Virginia this metropolitan growth means even more than just staying young.

10. Breaking Partitions: Migrations, Roads, Schools

THE PREVALENT OPINION in Virginia is that things do not change much in the Old Dominion. However, a general consensus admits that there has been a great evolution in agriculture and that farming is much more prosperous than it used to be. There is also some slightly regretful acceptance of the fact that "foreigners," that is, Americans from other states, are coming to settle in increasing numbers in Virginia. Finally, Virginians speak with admiration of the new system of highways and of the amount of traffic on them, especially Virginians old enough to remember that thirty years ago moving around was rather difficult in Virginia and there was much less movement accordingly.

Breaking the traditional isolation

Migration is slowly changing the distribution of population within Virginia, and concentration into metropolitan areas is one of the main trends of the time; the growing proportion of in-migrants is another new feature, and it cannot help causing some social changes. The old society with its traditional stratification is slowly beginning to feel obsolete in the face of pressures which are not the result of the arrival of new, more or less pleasant neighbors, but which are the outcome of a deep evolution of the national economic system; in this system Virginia participates; she

U. S. Route 60 near Toano
Bureau of Public Roads, U. S. Department of Commerce

must accept these pressures, but cannot control them, whatever may be the personal influence of a few Virginians in Washington or New York.

The present network of good highways has broken up the isolation of the many small closed worlds that traditionally constituted Virginia. This was probably true to some extent of the whole Southeast, a land of plantations and strict social hierarchy resulting largely from the stability of the existing compartments of space. In the hilly Appalachians, the small valleys and "hollows" made another puzzle of closed spatial units, each of which also was a community, a society by itself, sharply differentiated from the next one. It is no wonder that the Great Valley of the Appalachians had such a reputation as a progressive and prosperous land amid the poor and conservative South: the Great Valley, aside from the quality of its soils and of its settlers, was an important thoroughfare that could not escape constant contact with the outside, that could not isolate itself and live in the past. The Valley people had to live in the present because other parts of the vast world forced it to. Living in the past almost always produces a way of life that contemporaries from more open areas call backward.

In every house or farm, the backyard is the part opposite the façade that looks toward the street and toward the traffic of the outside world. In the seventeenth century and the first half of the eighteenth, most of Virginia was on the Tidewater, directly accessible from the vast oceanic spaces and the lands overseas; it was entirely a great lively façade. For a while settlement progressed in the Piedmont along the rivers, then navigable by small craft with some portages. It was still a well-knit society. Then some settlers looking for cheap land and less control by the authorities went into the "backwoods" away from the arteries of traffic and the main valleys. The scattering that had characterized the long façade looking towards the outside world, mainly towards England, Scotland, and the West Indies, here became a scattering of isolated, locally rooted people who were cut off from the outside world. This situation was a great source of strength for the people of Virginia and of America for some time. Perhaps American nationalism and the will for independence would have been slower to develop without the settlement of the "backwoods." To break the system which had thus crystallized in the southeast, it needed the twentieth century marvel, the motorcar. B. Mitchell's well-known book *The Industrial Revolution in the South* showed skillfully how the Ford automobile gave to the scattered peoples of the southeast their first chance at coming back into the worldly circuit. Good highways were the next step: they opened the outside world to the isolated rural people; they opened the possibilities of trade, bringing the farm closer to the market and the delivery truck to the customer; they opened the labor supply to the factory. The improvement of the primary highways was a great change; the building of a good secondary highway system was a revolution, economically and culturally.

As the traditional isolation of the Virginians was broken up, they found themselves on the fringe of an advanced and onrushing world. Their neighbors were not just other people emancipated from rural isolation and stability; their neighbors were the people from Megalopolis, some of the most driving and advanced among the communities of the world. Inhabitants of the quaint, traditional counties of Virginia, whether on the Piedmont or in the hills, do not like New York; they blame many of their present problems on what appears to them as a monstrous and sinful structure. Not all of these pressures breaking up old partitions are due exclusively to outside action, and outsiders should not get the whole blame or the whole credit for what is happening. The improvement in means of transportation throughout the commonwealth is largely the state's achievement on its own initiative. The Secondary

U. S. Route 50, looking over an old stone arch bridge over Goose Creek near
Middleburg
Bureau of Public Roads, U. S. Department of Commerce

Road Act of 1932 is commonly known as the "Byrd Road Law," attaching
to this great step forward the name of Senator Harry F. Byrd and of his
administration as Governor of Virginia. Altogether, the Virginians did
not have to take from the outside more than they really wanted. If the
expansion of Megalopolis in the northern Piedmont and the growth of
the Hampton Roads metropolitan system have developed as an application of outside forces, Virginians are rather proud of the results achieved,
and rightly so, as they have their good share of responsibility for carrying
the evolution out and on.

The new patterns of movement of people and goods through the commonwealth are well worth some description, for they have rejuvenated
the regional economy and to some extent even the local society. A remarkable consequence of this evolution was the growth of the public
school system. Many new problems have also arisen in connection with
education, as newcomers asked for more changes in the schools and as
Virginians themselves recognized the greater part of education in the
modern world of which they were becoming more active members.

"The Negro goes north and the Yankee comes south"

The two main trends noticeable in recent times in the population of Virginia have been, besides a less rapid out-migration of White Virginians, the in-migration of Whites from other states, largely "Yankees" from the Northern or Western states, on the one hand, and the steady flow of Negroes out of the Old Dominion. Both trends worked in the same direction, making Virginia less a Southern state, at least insofar as statistical characteristics may be used to define this "Southern" quality.

It must be remarked that in 1870 only about one-half of the White Americans born in Virginia, the total number of which was 1,389,568, lived in Virginia; almost the entire White population of Virginia, numbering 659,230, was native born.[1] In 1900, out of 1.4 million Virginia-born Whites residing in the United States, 1.07 lived in Virginia; the total White population of the commonwealth stood then at 1.17 million people. In 1920, out of 1.77 million Virginia-born persons, 1.36 resided in their native state, where they formed still a vast majority of the total number of 1.58 million Whites. Finally, in 1950, the total number of Virginia-born residents of the United States had grown to 2.44 million: of these 1.82 were in Virginia, the White population of which had then reached 2.52 million. These figures show a double trend: on the one hand a greater percentage of Virginia-born Whites remains in Virginia in the twentieth century than in the nineteenth; this proportion was below 50 per cent in 1870, but close to 75 per cent in both 1920 and 1950; on the other hand the proportion of Virginia-born in the total White population of the Old Dominion has steadily decreased, from 94 per cent in 1870 to 73 per cent in 1950. Thus both the United States and Virginia have become less Virginian insofar as the birthplace of White residents is concerned.

Among the Whites living in Virginia without being born there in 1950, very few actually deserved the name of "Yankee" in the sense of having New England origins, as only 32,885 were natives of the New England states, and many were not even Northerners. They came from

---

[1] All these statistics are about the birth areas of Whites in Virginia. Data as to birthplace of Negroes in the nineteenth century and even more recently are too vague to be here taken into consideration. Moreover, the figures for Negroes, where available, may be confusing, as Virginia "exported" large numbers of Negro slaves to other states in the first half of the nineteenth century. For most of the figures in this section taken from census materials we are indebted to the study of population redistribution and economic growth in the United States directed by Professor Dorothy S. Thomas at the University of Pennsylvania. We have also used a paper on the demography of Virginia prepared by Mr. D. Matza under the direction of Professor Frank Notestein at Princeton University.

A laborer at the Chopawamsic recreational project
*Library of Congress Photo by Ar-
thur Rothstein*

many states: North Carolina (135,000), West Virginia (64,000), Pennsylvania (55,000), New York (43,000), Tennessee (32,000), Maryland (31,000),
Ohio (22,000). Some of these in-migrants may well claim Virginia ancestry, especially some of those born in West Virginia and Tennessee, but it
remains true that contingents from areas definitely northern in their
cultural features totalled hundreds of thousands of residents in Virginia.
New England, the Middle Atlantic states and the northern half of the
Midwest were represented in 1950 by some 250,000 people, about one-
tenth of the total White population of Virginia. These statistics reflect a
substantial change in the quality, family tradition, and cultural pattern of
the population of Virginia. There are good reasons to believe that both
trends—concentrating the Virginians in their home state and increasing
the proportion of Yankees in that state's White population—will continue through the 1950's.

The non-White population of Virginia was relatively stable in total
numbers from 1880, when it reached 631,000, to 1940, when it amounted
to 660,000 people. In 1950, a substantial increase was registered for the
intercensal period: the non-Whites then numbered 727,000 persons. The
rate of increase of the Negro population since 1870 has been much slower
than the rate of increase of the White population. The proportion of the
non-Whites in the total population of Virginia went down from 41.8 per

Construction of concrete pavement on the Shirley Memorial Highway
Bureau of Public Roads, U. S. Department of Commerce

cent in 1880 to 22.2 per cent in 1950. This percentage even decreased in
the 1940–1950 decade (being 24.7 per cent in 1940), despite the increase
in absolute numbers. As the Negro population has a natural rate of increase which is usually not inferior to that of the White population, the
relative decrease of their importance in Virginia must be attributed not
only to the in-migration of Whites but also, and perhaps equally, to the
out-migration of Negroes.

Of the Negro population of Virginia in 1950, only 610,000 or 83 per
cent were Virginia-born. Of those who had migrated into Virginia, the
majority came from further south: most of them were natives of North
Carolina (63,000), South Carolina (14,000), Georgia (5,000), Alabama
(3,000), etc. A few thousands had also been born in Maryland, the District
of Columbia and the Middle Atlantic states: the total for all this area
came up to 17,000 persons. Thus the Negro was not going exclusively
northwards, but the current in that direction was much more powerful
than the opposite one. This appears even more clearly when we consider
the statistics regarding Virginia-born non-Whites residing in other states.
The great majority went north and northeast: out of a total of 342,000
we find, in 1950, 42,000 in the District of Columbia, 44,000 in Maryland,

67,000 in Pennsylvania, 34,000 in New Jersey, 80,000 in New York State; some went westwards, as there were 11,000 in Ohio, 4,645 in Michigan, 3,170 in Illinois, and even 2,860 in California; a few trickled southwards: 11,000 in North Carolina, 2,155 in Florida. The predominating trend is, nevertheless, obviously northwards. The old saying applied to the whole South still holds good for Virginia—"the Negro goes north and the Yankee comes south."

Detailed figures concerning the mobility of population in 1949–1950, published in the 1950 Census, show in Virginia a predominant in-migration of White males and a predominant out-migration of Negro females. This double trend has made the Old Dominion the only state in the Union with more males than females, and increasingly so, in the total population. It would appear thus to have acquired a characteristic of frontier or pioneer countries; indeed, the recent rapid economic progress of Virginia has caused a male in-migration trend. The usual migration pattern in the United States has been that White men move ahead before their families, while, at least since 1890, women usually spearhead the movement of non-White people, largely because this movement is from rural to urban areas and women find employment more easily than men in lower income bracket work in the cities. These two trends, already general and traditional, apply fully to Virginia. Here the special importance of the military establishments and of the shipbuilding industry since 1930 may well be largely responsible for the striking predominance of men in the White in-migration.

The flow of Negroes from rural to urban areas has been a general feature of population movements in the United States. The trend has been quite clear in Virginia in terms of both internal migration within the state and interstate movements. Within most of the larger urban units of Megalopolis, such as New York City, Philadelphia, Baltimore, and Washington, the main growth of Negro residential sections has been in the city, and often close to downtown; the outer ring of suburbs has been for the most part reserved for White residences. To some extent there has been thus an exchange of populations between Virginia and the District of Columbia, more Negroes leaving the state for Washington and more Whites leaving the District for Arlington, Fairfax, and Alexandria. The same trend of concentration close to the downtown areas of the expanding Negro sections has been observed in the Richmond and Norfolk metropolitan areas. However, if Megalopolis has been a major attraction to the Negro migrants, one may wonder whether, with its present tendency to extend southwards and into Virginia, it will not bring more of the Virginia Negroes towards the urbanized areas of the Tidewater rather

Concrete paving at the intersection of Glebe Road and Arlington Boulevard in Arlington
Bureau of Public Roads, U. S. Department of Commerce

than carry them northward out of Virginia. Without the recent metropolitan growth, the out-migration of Negroes would probably have been much heavier. The main factors determining the movement of Negro people northward, and particularly to Megalopolis, may be summed up as higher wages and less discrimination; and these two features will probably remain for some time to come as reasons for attraction to the north.

As the proportion of Negroes in Virginia decreases, some of the tensions and attitudes resulting from cohabitation with a very large colored minority will probably evolve among the Whites. The race problem can certainly not be measured by statistical yardsticks. Old ideas and prejudices rooted in the education and in the tradition are an essential element in shaping the problem. Many White people in western Virginia, where the proportion of Negroes in the population has never been important, feel just as strongly as Tidewater conservatives about it. However, no better inducement to a favorable psychological change can be devised than a reduction in numerical proportion. On the other hand, as a result of recent migrations, there has been an increase in the proportion among the Whites of people who do not share the Southern mental-

Three levels of highway on the approaches to Washington
Bureau of Public Roads, U. S. Department of Commerce

ity and tradition in racial relations. These "Yankees" are not necessarily better disposed towards the Negroes than the traditional Virginian is. Many cases may be encountered that would even witness to the contrary. But the fact remains that some northern infiltration has developed within Virginia on a rather high level, that it has already affected some of the local leadership in several communities, and that various social changes are being advocated of a kind nobody heard much about in the Old Dominion before 1920. The question of race relations is only one, although a weighty one, among many others. The whole organization of society may slowly change as more people concentrate in the cities and as more leaders who may be northerners make places for themselves among the élite of many a city.

As one considers the detailed distribution by race, sex, and age of the net migration out of or into Virginia since the Civil War, one cannot help having the impression that some rejuvenation is occurring. From 1870 until 1930, as is well known, Virginia was losing people by outmigration, and the net result of the migratory movement for each intercensal period until 1930 showed a loss of native (i.e., American-born) Whites. Since 1930 the increase as a result of net migration has been ap-

U. S. 1 at the south end of Highway Bridge
Bureau of Public Roads, U. S. Department of Commerce

parent and was particularly important for 1940–1950, when 169,000 persons were thus added. It is interesting to note that in the 1930–1940 period there was already some increase; Virginia gained then in the age groups between 30 and 54, but lost in the age groups above 54 years. From 1940 to 1950 all age groups in both sexes gained, with the heaviest gains in the groups between 10 and 44 years insofar as men were concerned and between 20 and 39 for the women. The migrations affect, therefore, chiefly the population at the more active ages. Too often it is believed that White people come to Virginia chiefly to retire; the recent flow into the Old Dominion has had, on the contrary, a rejuvenating effect on the age pyramid.

The net migration for the Negro population has been steadily reducing the numbers of colored people in Virginia. Until 1890, more men than women were leaving. Since then there has been more reduction in the figures for women. This was particularly clear in the 1930–1940 intercensal period when the net out-migration was 10,479 men and 26,419 women. For the 1940–1950 period the net out-migration of women was almost double that of men. Curiously enough, this out-migration does not affect all ages equally, but takes out of Virginia mainly the age groups

Grade separation on the Pentagon network
Bureau of Public Roads, U. S. Department of Commerce

of 15 to 39 and of more than 65 years; the age groups between 40 and 60 still show an in-migration net result. Thus many older Negroes retire away from Virginia; this may be caused by two trends: either retirement to the region of origin, which is the deeper South in many families, or retirement close to the home of grown-up children who have migrated out and settled in another part of the country.

The net result of all these migrations makes Virginians, on the average, somewhat younger in 1950 than they were in 1930, or than they would have been had the pre-1930 trend continued. Newcomers have not moved to Virginia just to enjoy her climate and way of life. They have come to work and make a living; often they have come with small children, or at an age when they can have children. The population is becoming younger, and the problems of younger regions are coming to Virginia.

More and better highways

As the population picture evolves, the pattern of movement within the state is developing with the gradual improvement of the system of highways. We saw what crucial importance the highways have had in many

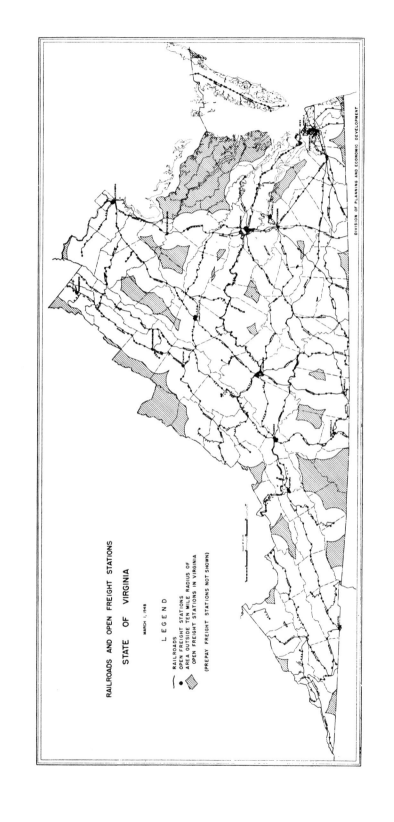

RAILROADS AND OPEN FREIGHT STATIONS

STATE OF VIRGINIA

MARCH 1, 1948

L E G E N D

RAILROADS
OPEN FREIGHT STATIONS
AREA OUTSIDE TEN MILE RADIUS OF
OPEN FREIGHT STATIONS IN VIRGINIA

(PREPAY FREIGHT STATIONS NOT SHOWN)

DIVISION OF PLANNING AND ECONOMIC DEVELOPMENT

fields: for industrialization and urbanization; for putting to real use the assets of the geographical location; for getting more trade into and through Virginia. As the population and the economy of the state grow, and as the activities of the southeast on one hand and of Megalopolis on the other develop more and more, Virginia's highways must expect an ever-rising flow of traffic.

How Virginia faced the motorcar era and built excellent networks of primary and secondary highways has already been related in this volume and commented upon many times.[2] The present distribution of traffic on the primary highways (see map, page 454) stresses the special importance of U. S. Routes 1 and 11, as well as the frequent tie-up in and around the main cities. Metropolitan growth forces constant reshaping of the system of main highways along the Tidewater. A transportation network constantly demands expansion unless the economy of the region concerned is sharply declining. As such is certainly not the case of the Old Dominion in this century, or of the neighboring states, the bettering of the means of transportation, and particularly of the highways, must remain a constant concern.

It may be interesting to compare at times the Virginia highways of the recent past with those of North Carolina. Both states extend from the eastern seaboard into the Appalachian folds; both are rapidly being industrialized, but are quite different in their ways and means of achieving results. North Carolina passed legislation in 1915 establishing a State Highway Commission and combining the efforts of state and counties in the construction of roads: Virginia had already done the same by 1906. In 1921, North Carolina decided to adopt a program of developing and paving 5,500 miles of major highways and sold a bond issue of 50 million dollars to finance it. This was for the time a bold and impressive investment in highway construction. In the 1920's it brought North Carolina an excellent highway network and the reputation of being the "good roads state." Virginia, meanwhile, had established a state highway system in 1918; to develop it, the pay-as-you-go financing policy was adopted in 1923. For some years the construction of highways proceeded more slowly in Virginia than in North Carolina. This lead, which North Carolina assumed in the 1920's, may be partly responsible for the quicker and earlier development of manufactures, particularly of textile mills, in North Carolina. Other factors, such as the earlier harnessing of water-power resources between the Appalachians and the fall line, concurred with the railroads to promote industrialization in North Carolina. In

[2] See Chapter 2, pp. 135–138 and also many references to the role of better highways throughout Part II.

The Washington-Richmond road (now U. S. 1) near Dumfries in 1919
Bureau of Public Roads, U. S. Department of Commerce

1931, the state took over the county roads and developed the secondary highways. Virginia followed in 1932, again at a somewhat slower pace, endeavoring to avoid indebtedness and paying for the highways through taxes rather than borrowing.

Both states were forced into further highway expansion by the surge of motor traffic after World War II. North Carolina finds now that the primary system which has been its pride has become more obsolete every year and that it is, in 1954, far short of the needs of traffic. The blueprint adopted in the early 1920's could not have foreseen the extraordinary development of the following thirty years. Virginia, having started slightly later and having constructed her roads at a slower pace, finds herself in a better position today, with wider and more modern major highways, with less congestion along the principal thoroughfares than in North Carolina, and with fewer problems of alignment in the sections of highways which need enlargement. Nevertheless, Virginia, with an immense travel trade, with a transit function even greater than that of the state to her south, and with more extensive metropolitan development, has more urgent need at present of such expensive undertakings as the pro-

The Washington-Richmond road near Dumfries in wet weather, 1919
Bureau of Public Roads, U. S. Department of Commerce

jected turnpike along U. S. 1 avoiding Richmond and Petersburg, and the bridge-tunnel road across Hampton Roads.

An excellent report prepared in 1954 by the Virginia Department of Highways sums up eloquently the present problems:

In the field of motor transport there has been tremendous expansion in recent years. The record of highway usage by freight-carrying vehicles confirms the fact that Virginia industry and agriculture are finding motor transportation an indispensable adjunct to their activities. In 1940 light and medium trucks averaged 1,167,690 vehicle-miles daily over the state's highways, but by 1952 daily travel of these vehicles had jumped to 2,368,972 miles, an increase of 103 per cent. Busses and tractor-trailers, big trucks used for interstate and intercity freight hauling, have shown an even more startling record of highway usage. In 1940 they averaged 347,369 vehicle-miles daily; by 1952 they were traveling 1,060,021 miles daily, an increase of 205 per cent. Not only do the state's highways tie water, rail, and air lines together, but they extend into rural areas where other means of transportation are not available. City streets today are crowded with the traffic that is essential to urban life; country roads reach into the most remote . . . corners of the state. Practically every family, regardless of social status or income group, has an automobile. In the ten year period from 1941 to 1951 the registration of passenger cars in Virginia increased by 306,949 vehicles (63 per

U. S. 1 near Dumfries, the same stretch of highway as it appeared in 1947
Bureau of Public Roads, U. S. Department of Commerce

cent), while the population of the state increased only 20 per cent. In 1951 there was a registered passenger car for every 4.3 persons in Virginia.[3]

The maps of intensity of traffic flow, published yearly by the Department of Highways, showed the increase of this intensity all over the state, but more on the Tidewater with its metropolitan growth than elsewhere. During World War II, when pleasure driving was restricted, statistics show that traffic in Virginia dipped: travel trade and tourism are so important in the Old Dominion that they affect even the whole mass of motor traffic. It has been estimated that tourists spend annually about half a billion dollars as they travel through Virginia. Many of these tourists come from outside the state, as some 3.4 million miles a day were driven on the rural primary system in 1952 by "foreign" passenger cars. This traffic contributes substantially to the upkeep of the highways through the tax on gasoline, besides the amount spent otherwise to the benefit of the state's retail trade and hotel industry.

[3] Virginia Department of Highways, *Virginia's Highway Needs,* 1954. The figures and data for North Carolina are largely taken from "North Carolina: Highways and Roads," ed. by James S. Burch, North Carolina State Highway Commission, Raleigh, N. C., 1953; and Capus Waynick, *North Carolina Roads and Their Builders,* Raleigh, 1952.

If the goal of the Highway Department has been for some thirty years "to get Virginia out of the mud," this aim has been almost completely attained. There are still a few roads left that would benefit by being hard-surfaced, but almost all of the present ones are passable in any kind of weather, and that was the main result to achieve. But now the goal could be changed to "getting highway tie-ups out of Virginia," and this is more difficult to plan in the face of rising needs. It is estimated that by 1965 there will be an increase of 78 per cent in the volume of traffic on Virginia roads as against 1952. A mounting number of deficiencies will become apparent each year on both the primary and secondary systems. Virginia must welcome such new developments, as they are a good measure of the commonwealth's increasing activity and swelling economy. But she must also be prepared to take care of the new problems, lest she lose many opportunities as a consequence of inadequate transport. As the present and future needs are evaluated in dollars and cents, they add up to an enormous amount of construction and expenditure. The report quoted above figured it out in 1954 as follows:

During the next twelve years highway needs will cost $1,375,166,000 to satisfy. Funds available will be $1,039,718,000. The difference between highway needs and available funds is 335,448,000 dollars, approximately 28 million a year. Unless this amount is made available for expenditure on Virginia's roads, the economic welfare and safety of the state will be gravely retarded.

To cover some of the huge expenditure now planned, Virginia may have to renounce the principle, strictly applied since 1923, of "pay-as-you-go" financing. A $95,000,000 bond issue, the biggest in Virginia's history, was floated during the Fall of 1954 to pay for the great bridge-tunnel road across Hampton Roads and its approaches. Also in 1954 the General Assembly passed legislation creating the Richmond-Petersburg Turnpike Authority to construct and operate a toll road in this metropolitan area and channel the through-traffic outside the crowded downtown sections of the cities, and an Old Dominion Turnpike Authority to construct and operate another toll road across western Virginia, linking the system of major southeastern highways with the already completed West Virginia Turnpike. The latter undertaking should improve the road links with the Midwest and the Great Lakes, especially as the West Virginia Turnpike must be connected with the Pennsylvania Turnpike, and it would increase the importance of Virginia's highway system as a hub in national transport. It was only in 1952 that the Virginia Highway Commission gained the authority to construct, maintain, and operate turnpike projects and to issue revenue bonds payable solely from tolls and other charges collected. The law provides that when funds are available for the

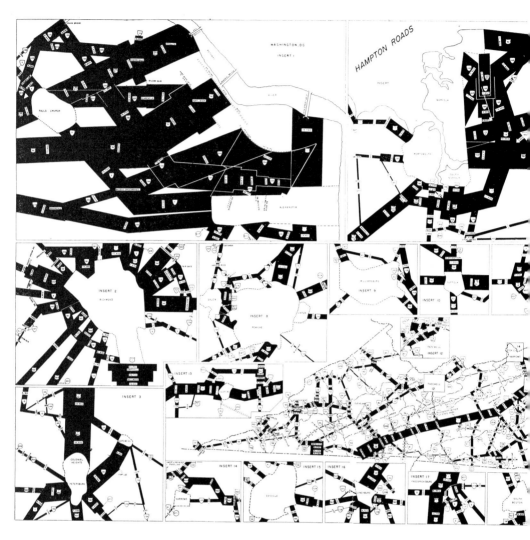

retirement of bonds issued for a specific highway project, the turnpike becomes a part of the state system, to be maintained by the Highway Commission free of tolls. Such problems are not peculiar to Virginia nowadays; many other parts of the United States and of other countries throughout the world are faced with the urgent need to expand road networks to accommodate the rising tide of motor traffic. It was wisely foreseen by the specialists of the steel market in America that by 1955 the domestic motorcar market would be saturated, with some sixty million cars on the road: every American family would have at least one car, and the roads would be so much travelled that at peak periods one would hardly be able to make any headway with one's car, especially

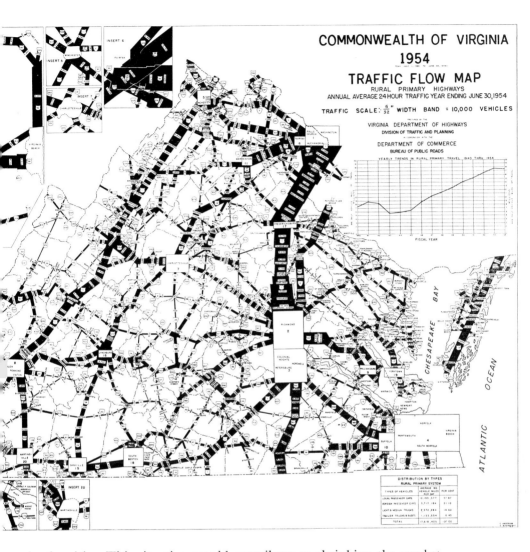

COMMONWEALTH OF VIRGINIA
1954
TRAFFIC FLOW MAP
RURAL PRIMARY HIGHWAYS
ANNUAL AVERAGE 24 HOUR TRAFFIC YEAR ENDING JUNE 30, 1954

TRAFFIC SCALE: $\frac{5}{32}$" WIDTH BAND = 10,000 VEHICLES

VIRGINIA DEPARTMENT OF HIGHWAYS
DIVISION OF TRAFFIC AND PLANNING

DEPARTMENT OF COMMERCE
BUREAU OF PUBLIC ROADS

in the cities. This situation would contribute to shrinking the market, which would then be limited to replacements instead of adding millions of cars annually to the existing number. The motorcar building industry is one of the major consumers of steel as well as other raw materials. A slump in its activities would therefore have unpleasant consequences for such basic industries as steel and rubber. To offset this the steel industry foresaw an indispensable expansion coming around 1955 of road construction and of such works as tunnels, bridges, overpasses, underpasses, and other fancies of engineering aimed at solving traffic tie-ups. By 1954 it was obvious that the country's economy needed these things imperatively and that the necessary funds would be made available. Virginia's

Trucks in Smithfield for the transportation of traditional Virginia hams

rejuvenated economy and her location on the nation's map made it especially important to avoid becoming one of the worst tie-ups in the country. It is certain that the necessary effort will be made and that the commonwealth's highways will be kept up to their users' expectations.

In the Southern states, the scattered settlement and recent industrialization made the highway system an essential and decisive tool for economic and social progress. How the highways affected the different states, according to their geographical location, the dates at which the major improvements took place, and the types of industries would be a subject well worth a detailed investigation. The findings of such an inquiry would be useful not only for general research about the economics of transportation and the location of industries, but also to state and local governments.

In Virginia the revolution caused by the advent of the motorcar and of good roads is still in progress. It has brought many closed worlds together, breaking partitions, opening new perspectives, and creating new problems. To some extent the crumbling local partitions were bound to give rise to difficulties. Some Virginians did not like having strangers around their countryside. Easier means of transportation and communication force upon any population, especially one as traditional as Virginia's, the building up of new social partitions to serve as barriers against a threatened invasion of the community's privacy. But Virginians are a hospitable people, and they could not hold out long against new neighbors and visitors.

The motorcar has done more than any other single factor to bring the Old Dominion into the booming circuit of the national economy. Social changes were bound to come as a result of the opening up of so many small isolated compartments of space. But the main partitions between people do not exist so much in the space that separates them as in the barriers of the mind. By making Virginia a more modern country, the roads and the rest of the economic changes created an increasing need for more and better schools. Such improvements involve also the need of large expenditure of public funds. It has been said in Virginia that there was a race between roads and schools for funds and that the roads were winning the race. This is necessarily only one aspect, and not the fundamental one, of an older and deeper problem. Education has always been treated in Virginia as being actually needed only for an upper stratum of society, and public schools have not been very popular here. The new evolution, however, may well force upon the commonwealth a revision of this attitude.

Virginia's tradition in education

From early witnesses such as Beverley and from the report on *The Present State of Virginia and the College* by Hartwell, Blair, and Chilton, it is apparent that as far back as 1700 there was not much interest among the leadership of the Old Dominion to provide extensive education facilities for the local people. The gentry on the plantations had private libraries and kept in touch with activities in the arts and letters, but through London. The élite of the Virginia gentlemen was educated in England, if possible at Oxford. If the College of William and Mary was one of the first established in the British American colonies, it was mainly because visitors from London found it necessary to have a good school in Virginia. New England was showing more interest and endeavor in this respect. The College at Williamsburg had some difficult times during the first half of the eighteenth century as a good deal of the money promised and of the endowment assigned officially by the Virginians did not materialize. William and Mary never developed into a major institution of learning as Harvard and Yale did. The indispensable basis of local support and enthusiasm was not there.

The same lukewarm attitude towards schools and public education

Yorktown Bridge across the
York River. *Virginia Chamber of Commerce*

was evidenced at the time of the Revolution and in early nineteenth century. There have always been a few persons in Virginia who were concerned about the education of the people. None of them has left on the
state a better mark than Mr. Jefferson. In the *Notes on Virginia* he offered a whole program for public education: it was an advanced blueprint for the time. Answering "Query XIV" on the administration of
justice and the description of the laws, Jefferson summarized the revision
of the whole code of laws of Virginia then being considered. Education
appears to have been one of the major concerns of the committee that
prepared a draft of the revised code at the request of the General Assembly: "Another object of the revisal," wrote Jefferson, "is to diffuse knowledge more generally through the mass of the people."

The ultimate result of the whole scheme of education would be the teaching all
the children of the State reading, writing and common arithmetic; turning out
ten annually, of superior genius, well taught in Greek, Latin, Geography, and
the higher branches of arithmetic; turning out ten others annually, of still
superior parts, who, to those branches of learning shall have added such of the
sciences as their genius shall have led them to; the furnishing to the wealthier
part of the people convenient schools at which their children may be educated
at their own expense. The general objects of this law are to provide an education adapted to the years, to the capacity, and the condition of every one, and
directed to their freedom and happiness.

Route 301 in Caroline County, with shoulder under construction
Virginia Department of Highways

Mr. Jefferson was already planning at the time of the Revolution a system of public education at three levels: the schools teaching the three "R's" to all the children; a set of secondary schools for selected students who would learn more mathematics, Greek, Latin, and Geography; and finally the university, for which it was suggested that the College of William and Mary "be enlarged . . . and extended to all the useful sciences." Besides the public schools, children of wealthier families could be taught, if they preferred, in private schools. Jefferson fought a long, almost lifelong, battle to have his scheme accepted by the commonwealth. It was half a century after the first proposals were put forth that the University of Virginia got under way in the 1820's. The experiment attempted under the auspices of both Benjamin Franklin and Thomas Jefferson to establish an academy at Richmond, the plans for which were drawn in Paris with the cooperation of many French scholars when the two great Americans were Ministers to France, did not make much headway. Jefferson succeeded in starting the University at Charlottesville because of his personal influence and his stubborn devotion to the project. He designed the famous central buildings and chose the first masters, most of whom came from Britain. He at last obtained a law granting the

Virginia Military Institute at Lexington. *Virginia Chamber of Commerce*

permanent financial support of the state to the University. As this institution grew and developed, other colleges were established in Virginia
chiefly under religious auspices by the different churches.

The Virginians remained, however, mainly interested in private
schools, and it took another stubborn fight led by Dr. W. H. Ruffner after
the Civil War to create a real system of free public schools.[4] Slowly this
system developed into a statewide network of schools. The results of this
educational setup have not always been as gratifying as may have been
the hope of the apostles who, like Jefferson, gallantly fought for it. The
statistics of the U. S. Bureau of the Census showed that in 1950 Virginia
often ranked at the bottom of the list among the states in terms of school
enrollment. Among the 48 states and the District of Columbia, Virginia's
rank was 46th in median number of years in school for persons 25 or over;
49th in per-cent enrollment for persons 5 to 24 years of age (not including
kindergarten); 47th in per-cent enrollment of persons 5 to 19; 40th in
per-cent enrollment for persons 7 to 13; 33rd in per-cent enrollment for
persons 14 and 15; 46th in per-cent enrollment for persons 16 and 17.
The most disturbing fact is that for the total enrollment among people

[4] Episodes in the history of the struggle for better education in Virginia have been
noted in Chapter 2, pp. 74–78, 113–117, and 129–130.

5 to 24 years of age, Virginia ranked last on the list; the state ranked in this respect 48th out of 49 in 1940 and dropped to the bottom of the scale during the 1940's. Altogether, the score is a rather disheartening one.

Reporting these figures from the publications of the 1950 Census, the *Newsletter* of the University of Virginia notes some "improvement"; in many respects, absolute figures for 1950 are better than those for 1940. "For each item listed in this summary the figure for 1950 is greater than or equal to the figure for 1940. A comparison of ranks, however, shows a lower rank in most instances for 1950. Obviously other states have also improved in respect to per cent of persons enrolled in school." [5] And other states have also, obviously, improved at a faster pace than Virginia did. Although a slight note of warning is sounded at the end of that issue of the *Newsletter* against being "unduly critical or pessimistic," one cannot help remarking the serenity with which the statement of facts is accepted by the University of Virginia. The commonwealth's tradition does not seem to call for worry on this score.

Growing concern for the schools

The traditional attitude does not solve all problems, nor does it satisfy everybody in the state. Concluding the summary of findings, the report to the Advisory Council on the Virginia Economy on Labor Resources and Labor Income in Virginia states:

Some objective piecemeal information on the education and trainability of Virginia workers appears unfavorable for Virginia. The number of years of schooling completed by persons 25 years old and older and the proportion of the young people ages 14 through 17 who are enrolled in school are less in Virginia than in the nation. Also the rate of rejection of young males by the armed forces on the basis of objective tests designed to estimate a man's ability to absorb training and perform effectively is twice as high in Virginia as in the nation." [6]

In 1944 the Virginia State Chamber of Commerce published a thoughtful report prepared by its committee on education concerning the opportunities for the improvement of the high schools. The recommendations of this report had a considerable influence on the commonwealth's policies with respect to high schools after World War II. Financial resources were provided to greatly improve the physical facilities of many high schools. As many of these were rebuilt, consolidation took place in order

[5] Richard A. Meade, "School Enrollment in Virginia," *The University of Virginia Newsletter*, Charlottesville, May 15, 1953.
[6] *Labor Resources and Labor Income in Virginia,* July, 1953, Vol. I, p. 7.

Shop of the Randolph Henry High School, where boys learn carpentry, welding, and repair of farm machinery
Library of Congress Photo by Philip Bonn

to avoid in certain rural areas a scattering which had made it impossible to provide suitable education at reasonable cost. It was found preferable to expand somewhat the network of school busses and make their routes longer in places, but concentrate the students from a wider area in a larger and better-equipped building.

As the physical plant of the school system was gradually improved, the second problem arose, which was not less important than that of the buildings and their equipment: the problem of the standing and quality of the teachers. The report of the State Chamber of Commerce had already drawn the attention of the authorities to the question of the instructional staff of high schools. Similar remarks could apply to the staff of the elementary schools. Better teachers could be had by better selection, fuller training, higher salaries, more bonuses, and a fuller employment during the year. The 1944 report recommended that "principals should be employed for twelve months a year and teachers for at least ten months a year." [7] Such a suggestion may surprise some northerners

[7] *Opportunities for the Improvement of High School Education in Virginia* (Education Document No. 2), Virginia State Chamber of Commerce, Richmond, 1944.

and city folk who are now used to considering teaching as a full-time and year-round occupation, with somewhat longer vacations than in other professions, but paid on a yearly basis. In many parts of Virginia, however, the tendency and the tradition have been to recruit teachers for elementary and secondary schools among people having some other means of subsistence for at least part of the year. In some counties such attitudes led to a preference for employing as teachers persons resident on farms, belonging therefore to farmers' families and thus more easily satisfied with the modest gains of the teaching profession. Such policies, however, do not always provide the best possible recruitment.

As the population of Virginia increased rapidly and the standards of education rose throughout the nation, the shortage of teachers became more acute in Virginia. The Annual Report of the State Superintendent of Public Instruction for 1951–1952 stated:

> The most valid measure of teacher shortage appears to be the number of uncertified teachers who are used on the basis of local permits or emergency teachers' licenses . . . approximately 11 per cent of the total number of teachers in the regular day schools have not qualified for regular certificates. . . . It is distressing to note that the number of uncertificated teachers is increasing again. Since the so-called "reserve" brought into use about 1943–1944 is still in use, the problem of where to turn for more teachers is growing very serious." [8]

Such problems exist in other states, too, but they are usually not so acute elsewhere. Virginia has, as we know, one of the lowest ratios of enrollment of children and youths in schools, and still has not prepared for the growth of the enrollment resulting from both population growth and average rise of standards in education. While it is usually considered in the United States that thirty students is the upper limit of a workable class, the same report of the Superintendent of Public Instruction revealed that in October, 1951, in the elementary schools of Virginia 63.7 per cent of the teachers employed were teaching classes of more than thirty pupils; 33 per cent had classes with more than thirty-five pupils. [9] A great deal can and must be done to improve the existing situation. It is essential that the proper authorities in the commonwealth show a growing concern in the matter.

This concern increases as one faces the projection of present trends into the future. The school-age population of Virginia is growing fast and will increase in numbers during the 1950's and the 1960's. This will be

---

[9] *Ibid.*, p. 29.

[8] *Eighty-first Annual Report of the Superintendent of Public Instruction: 1951–1952*, Richmond, Commonwealth of Virginia, 1952, quoted by R. O. Nelson and L. R. Stanley, "Teachers Shortage Problems in Virginia," *University of Virginia Newsletter*, Charlottesville, November 15, 1953.

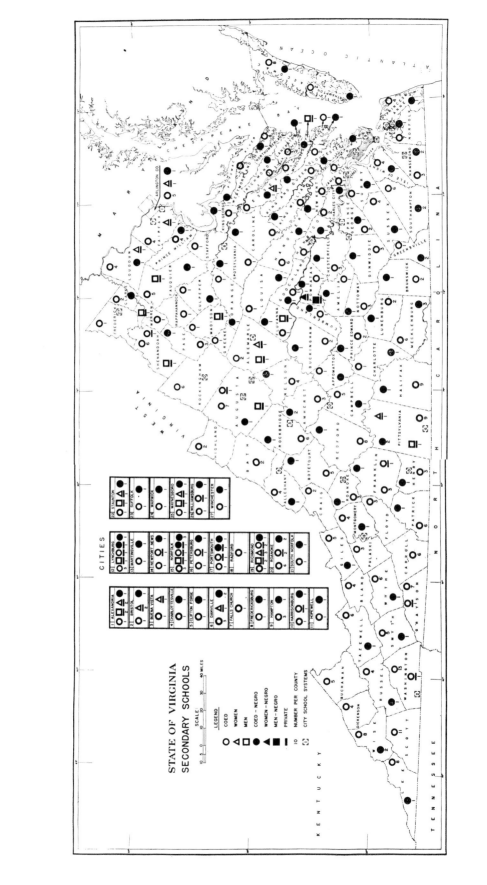

STATE OF VIRGINIA
SECONDARY SCHOOLS

Public school children reciting the Oath of Allegiance
Library of Congress Photo by John Vachon

the result of an increasing total population and of the rise in the average birth rate since World War II; but the growth of the school population will very likely be accelerated by a higher percentage of children going regularly to school. The rank of Virginia in the Union in this respect makes it a desirable and probable trend, especially as the urban population increases as against the rural; the smaller percentage of farm families ought to cause a corresponding decrease in the percentage of children dropping out of school. Stricter application of laws regarding child labor would also accelerate the growth of the school population. Present estimates of the future outlook for school enrollment, based on demographic trends alone, may well soon prove to fall far short of reality.[10] The report for 1952–1953 of the Superintendent of Public Instruction stated:

For the past four years public school enrollment has increased from 20,000 to 30,000 each year. If we are to maintain anything like the proper pupil-teacher ratio, this alone means from 700 to 1,000 more teachers each year. It means approximately the same number of classrooms. In planning for efficient administration of public education it is not a case of providing a given number of class-

[10] See estimates in *University of Virginia Newsletter,* November 15, 1953.

rooms for a given number of pupils taught by a specific number of teachers. There is no selection of pupils, there is no screening to fit the capacity. The public schools must do the best they can for all who come. Any failure due to inadequate facilities and an inadequate number of well-trained teachers impairs the efficiency of our citizenry. It is a loss to Virginia's children that can never be regained." [11]

The pressure on the public schools has been slightly lessened by the growth of private schools, some of them developed by the churches, especially the parochial Roman Catholic schools. Nevertheless, on the elementary and secondary level public school enrollment accounts for over 90 per cent of the total enrolled in all schools. The future education of Virginians depends thus essentially on the quality of their public school system.

On a higher level some pressures have also been felt in the colleges, demanding a great deal of expansion. The total college enrollment in Virginia colleges rose from 24,700 in 1940–1941 to a peak of 36,300 in 1948–1949 due to the G. I. Bill of Rights' allowance for the college education of veterans; it subsided to 28,200 in 1951–1952, reached 28,800 in 1953–1954 and is expected to reach 32,000 by 1960 and at least 42,000 by 1970.[12] At the college level, private institutions are taking care of about 35 to 40 per cent of the total enrollment. The majority of the students are still studying in state-supported colleges. Recent censuses showed that a college degree is more and more often held and needed by Americans. In the entire nation, 4.6 per cent of the population 25 years old and over had completed at least four years of college in 1940; this proportion had risen to 6.0 per cent by 1950. In Virginia the percentage was 4.4 in 1940, slightly below the national average, but 6.3 in 1950, somewhat above the national average. This progress is not a result of the expanded activities of Virginia's institutions of higher learning, but rather of the expansion of Washington's metropolitan area in Virginia, bringing in many new residents with a high average educational level.

As parents like their children to have an education at least equal to what they themselves received, one may safely predict that increased pressure will be brought to bear with regard to the public schools and colleges of Virginia for more and better education for an increasing number of students.

[11] Superintendent of Public Instruction, *Annual Report, 1952–1953,* Richmond, 1953, p. 26.
[12] See Lorin A. Thompson, "Recent Trends and Future Outlook of College Enrollment in Virginia," *The University of Virginia Newsletter,* Charlottesville, June 15, 1954.

The modern fight for the schools

The Office of the State Superintendent of Public Instruction must be well aware of the old divergencies of opinion in Virginia regarding the breadth of needs in education, and regarding the present struggle. One of its recent reports gives a look at the past and the future in these terms:

As we attempt to measure progress we may well occasionally look back into Virginia's history. What has been the philosophy of those who have led? What have been the influences that have finally brought many of Virginia's citizens to now believe that the unity and intensity of our educational system with its inspired purpose must become the great fact of the day in Virginia?

In the early days of Virginia's history Governor Berkeley, one of our Colonial Governors who served nearly thirty-six years, said in 1671, "I thank God there are no free schools or printing presses and I hope we shall not have them these hundred years; for learning has brought disobedience and heresy and sects into the world and printing has divulged them and libels against the best of Governments. God keeps us from both."

One hundred and forty-eight years later another Virginia Governor, Thomas Jefferson, with an extreme conflict of philosophy, stated, "Whenever the people are well informed they can be trusted with their own government. If a nation expects to be ignorant and free in a state of civilization, it expects what never was and never will be." The development of public education in Virginia may be considered by some to have been slow. As Virginia people have become more certain of their convictions their thinking is inspired by a burning desire for those things they have promised themselves and for even greater and loftier achievements.

Today, one hundred and thirty-three years after Thomas Jefferson, we have entered a third era in the struggle for the development of a strong program of public education in Virginia. [While] the traditions of the past [are] disappearing, the belief still remains in the minds of some that education should be limited to the few. Our leaders, however, manifested an increasing belief that in our Democratic system education is essential and when wisely administered is a sound investment.[13]

That the belief in the necessity of education for all is making progress in Virginia can be illustrated by many recent decisions and changes. The growing importance of the expenditures for the public schools in the commonwealth's budget is perhaps the best such illustration and the most significant in its consequences. Of the total expenditures for public free schools in Virginia in 1952–1953, 37 per cent came from state funds, 54.4 per cent from local funds, and 8.6 per cent from federal funds. The state funds come largely from taxation and other benefits of the commonwealth's government, which operates on the pay-as-you-go policy. But local funds, that is, mainly county and city funds, are obtained largely

[13] Superintendent of Public Instruction, *Annual Report, 1952–1953*, pp. 21–22.

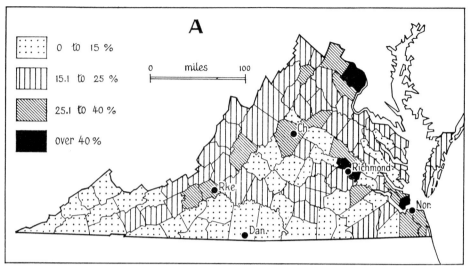

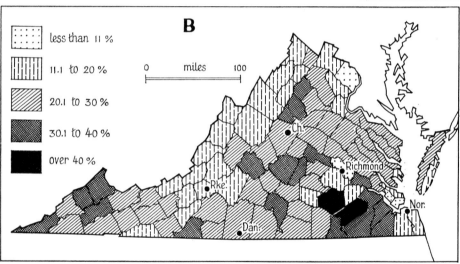

Education of Adults in Virginia, 1950

Map A shows the distribution by counties of the percentage of persons 25 years old and older having completed at least high school. Map B shows the distribution by counties of the percentage of persons 25 years old and older having completed less than five grades in school. This map indicates the extent of illiteracy among adults in Virginia. On both maps the cities are shown only for purposes of general orientation. Source: U. S. Bureau of the Census, *County and City Data Book, 1952*

by borrowing; the outstanding debt as a percentage of revenue has been increasing from year to year in Virginia, especially since 1947, faster than it did for the whole nation. But Virginians are beginning to admit that the betterment of education is a necessary and worthy investment. The expenditure for the public school system rose from 30 million dollars in 1939–1940 to 147 million in 1951–1952. Although the sum appears to be multiplied almost five times, as a per cent of income payments in the state it amounts only to a 26 per cent increase. As Virginia becomes richer, Virginians can and must afford more and better education. The expenditures for the public free schools in 1952–1953 reached a new high of 167.8 million dollars. In 1952, education costs ranked as the largest state government expenditure in Virginia, ahead of the highways.[14]

The public school system is administered by a state board of education which forms policies that the Superintendent of Public Instruction executes. But in the different counties and cities there are local boards deciding matters within the administrative division concerned. True, these county boards are not elected by the local people, but are appointed by judges who in turn are appointees from Richmond; hence the commonwealth's central administration controls also the local boards, and the result is a tendency to blame all the defects of the public schools and the slowness of progress on the state government and the political machine behind it. However, countries seldom keep for any prolonged time administrations of which the people disapprove. The lack of interest until recently on the part of the government of Virginia in the public schools was not so much the fault of any political organization as it was the result of a lack of interest on the part of the people and their leadership for improving these schools. As these opinions change gradually, the school system is being improved and expanded to better fit the needs of the people and of the time.

In many ways the administration of the public schools still bears the imprint of the recent predominance of rural areas and occupations in the life of the Old Dominion. As one looks at the list of the members of the State Board of Education, for instance, one finds there little representation of the metropolitan areas that account for over one-third of the total population. This is true of many other state committees, among them the Highway Commission. It has caused some protests from urban areas. As the population of Virginia becomes urban for a good half, and as metropolitan growth continues, pressure is bound to come from these areas that will gradually establish a more realistic balance between the interests from the various regions of the commonwealth. As more immigration flows into the Old Dominion, new people, coming from better

---

[14] *Virginia's Governmental Costs in Relation to Residents' Income,* Division of Planning and Economic Development, Department of Conservation and Development, Richmond, August, 1954.

educated regions of the country, will clamor for better schools; a hint of these forthcoming pressures was apparent in the recent political struggle concerning the school board of Arlington County.

It may be worth while in this connection to have a look at the distribution of educational levels throughout Virginia. The maps on page 546 show the distribution of relatively well-educated people (Map A, per cent of those having at least completed high school) and of what could be called illiterates (Map B, per cent of persons 25 years and older having completed less than five grades). Cities are not indicated according to the degree of education, but it is apparent from a look at the maps of the counties that the main concentrations of the better educated people are in the vicinity of cities; the effects of the proximity to Washington, Richmond, and Norfolk are particularly clear, as with the proximity to Roanoke and Charlottesville. On the whole, Virginia appears much better educated north of the James River than south of it, and the Great Valley also has a better rating than the central Piedmont and the whole southside area. Map B, that of illiteracy, provides a sort of "negative" version of Map A, but with greater detail in the distribution of the uneducated masses. One is not too surprised to find them in the central Piedmont, the southwestern triangle, and the southside coastal plain; in the latter the lower level of education corresponds to the greater percentage of Negroes. The illiteracy of the southwestern area is more directly due to the poor school system. The people of the coalfield area pay as little attention to schools, it seems, as they do to housing.

On the two maps, page 549, school enrollment is shown in 1950 as distributed among persons from 7 to 13 years of age (Map A) and among persons 14 to 17 years of age (Map B). These maps may give some indication as to present trends, to complement the picture of the other two maps previously analyzed. On Map A most of the Tidewater appears to be in a better condition than western Virginia and the southern Piedmont, but for the vicinity of Roanoke and the northern Shenandoah Valley. The influence of cities and of metropolitan growth seems undisputable in bringing about better school enrollment at an early age. Map B shows a more advanced stage, and percentages drop lower here; while the minimum is 87 per cent on Map A, it goes down to less than 66 per cent on Map B. The minima below 66 per cent on Map B are curiously scattered, but always correspond to some of the patches of worst illiteracy (as they appear on Map B of page 546). The Tidewater thus appears to be much more on its way to better education, although the southside in the tobacco and peanuts country still lags behind. Some mountain counties north and west of Roanoke give a much better impression here than

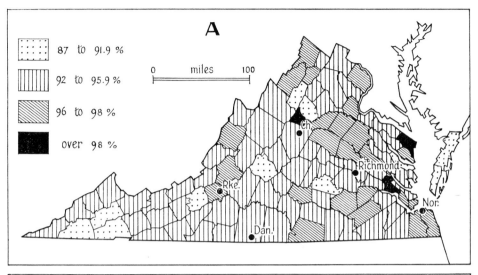

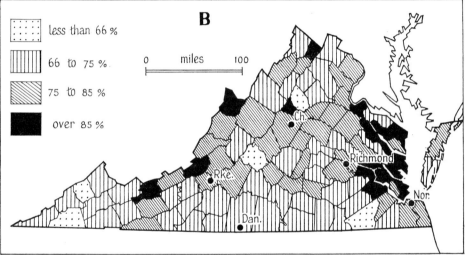

School Enrollment in Virginia, 1950
Map A shows the distribution by counties in Virginia of the school enrollment as
a per cent of the number of persons 7 to 13 years old. Map B shows the distribution of school enrollment as a per cent of the number of persons 14 to 17 years
old. Source: U. S. Bureau of the Census, *County and City Data Book, 1952*

on the maps of the education of adults, while the southwestern triangle
still offers little hope of serious improvement. Thus the comparison of
these four maps presents some regional details of the schooling situation
and shows current trends. The most obvious trend is the influence of
urbanization and industrialization in favor of better education, and this

Schoolhouse at Corbin Hollow, Shenandoah National Park
Library of Congress Photo by Arthur Rothstein

trend promises quicker progress in Virginia as the Old Dominion turns away from its traditional rural background.

To have better schools and more worthy teachers, Virginia must also give more attention to the institutions, and they are many in the state, training her teaching personnel. As the southwestern parts prove to be the more difficult parts in which to bring about improvement and possibly also the more promising for the future, since they offer a rich reservoir of potentially excellent elements, it might be wise to pay special attention to the schools in that area and to expand the means and influence of the Virginia Polytechnic Institute, the only large institution of higher learning close to the southwestern triangle. V.P.I. has probably already played an important part in bringing better education to the counties situated to the immediate northwest of Roanoke. It has the advantage of being the land-grant college of Virginia, the institution particularly interested in studying existing conditions in the commonwealth. As Virginians are brought into closer contact with a complicated and rapidly evolving world in which many counties of Virginia feel somewhat quaint and backward, more knowledge about the outside world is needed. Jefferson recognized this when he recommended that the better students of the schools he planned be trained in geography. But the knowledge of the vast world begins at home, by comparing what is *home* with the *neighborhood,* that is, the immediate environment different from home. Thus the study of the geography, economics, and sociology of Virginia and the neighboring states may be of great help in preparing coming generations to understand better their place in the vast changing world of which they are a part.

The school problem has recently taken on another aspect, which was to be expected. As in other Southern states, the schools in Virginia are separate for Whites and Negroes. It has often been claimed that the facilities are not equal for the two races and that the schools for Negro children are not so well equipped as those for the Whites. On the other hand, the Negro schools seem to have at least as good teachers on the whole as schools for Whites, and do not experience in Virginia as acute a teacher shortage as White schools do. In its decision made in the case of Plessy *versus* Ferguson in 1896, the Supreme Court of the United States held that segregation was not unconstitutional if equal facilities were provided for each race. This "separate but equal" doctrine was considered to be the law of the land until 1954, when on May 17th the Supreme Court announced that segregation in public education "is a denial of the equal protection of the laws."

The case that led in 1896 to the "separate but equal" doctrine involved transportation. This time, limiting itself to the field of public education, the Supreme Court set a new doctrine and called on all the states concerned to apply it in practice. "We conclude," said the 1954 decision, "that in the field of public education the doctrine 'separate but equal' has no place. Separate educational facilities are inherently unequal." This decision was laid down in answer to four cases on the matter brought to the Court by Negro plaintiffs against four states practicing segregation. Virginia was one of the four states directly involved. This momentous decision marks one of the major milestones in the history of education in the United States in general and more especially in the South.

It was generally admitted in 1954 that Virginia had made, particularly in the preceding thirty years, considerable efforts to offer Negroes better schools, with physical facilities and instructional staff quite equal in many cases to those enjoyed by Whites in the same locality. The backlog, however, was so considerable that by 1954 not all the Negro schools were just as good in terms of physical facilities as those of the Whites in the neighborhood. Perfect equality is hard to attain and even to evaluate with accuracy. Many of the schools for Negroes built around this time were indeed excellent; some localities clearly endeavored to be able to boast of this. The "separate but equal" doctrine was thus bearing fruit, but not without resistance and delay; full equality was probably not achieved even some fifty-odd years after the decision of 1896. The new decision likewise will take some time to bring about the results that may be logically expected from it. Virginia has shown great restraint in commenting and acting upon it. The plans for the schools in 1954–1955 have not been changed by the authorities: the schools continue as previously, applying the same segregation principles; plans for building separate facilities approved before the Supreme Court decision are being carried out.

Some Southern state governments have threatened to resist the application of the new doctrine by abandoning any public school system of their own. In practice it would mean that the existing public schools would be leased to private organizations. Public authorities would have no direct part in the operation or management of public education. Though some extremists may attempt such experiments locally, it seems hardly conceivable that the government of the Old Dominion would follow such a line. For the past thirty years it has been proud of the moderation and quiet wisdom of its policies. Virginia, moreover, abhors scandals and extreme outbreaks. Her leadership is socially too well educated to renounce public education officially as a matter of political protest. Virginia passed one of the strictest laws against lynchings to be found in the South, making everyone in the mob responsible for the action perpetrated. There have been no lynchings in Virginia for a long time. The commonwealth may be expected to act reasonably and calmly; but it may also be expected to resist stubbornly, particularly in its southern and eastern sections, any attempt at integration in practice.

Many ways may be used to avoid applying the new doctrine in public education. Pupils are assigned to schools according to place of residence. In the cities and small towns there is a clear-cut geographical segregation of the races: White and Negro people do not live in the same blocks and even not in the same sections of town. Districts can therefore be easily drawn in such a way as to send all the children from the White residential sections to schools different from those children living in the Negro sections go to. The delimitation is not as clear in rural areas; it might be handled there through a specially arranged routing of school busses. The matter may come to be complicated, however, in the case of small towns

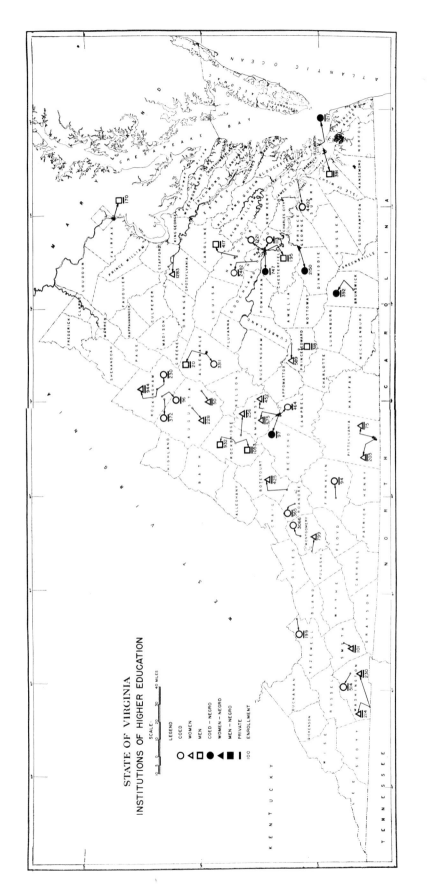

STATE OF VIRGINIA
INSTITUTIONS OF HIGHER EDUCATION

in areas with very few Negroes, where the present doctrine would hardly warrant the maintenance of separate facilities for a very small minority of the school-age population.

The resort to such subterfuges and to more debating in court appears to be unavoidable. Under maintained pressure, nevertheless, such arrangements will probably give way to rearrangements, locally to start with, then gradually in a more general fashion, bringing the situation closer to what the legislation requires. The problem of interracial relations in the nation and more particularly in the South was carefully reviewed in the early 1940's by Gunnar Myrdal and his team of researchers.[15] Little can be added to this exhaustive study, but a great deal of change has occurred since the publication of their report. In the last ten years the situation of the Negro in the United States and in the South has been greatly improved, both in the texts and in the facts. Virginia has not been bypassed by this evolution. Such legal decisions as the Supreme Court's decision against segregation in public education have done a great deal to accelerate the trend. It may well be expected to continue. It was significant that different churches in the South called for integration in education in 1954 after the new doctrine was announced by the Court.

In the summer of 1954, on a Sunday morning, we entered a small rural church in the intermountain region of the Blue Ridge in Virginia. We were directed then, it must be confessed, by the curiosity of the visitor from afar. The preacher spoke about segregation. He told his congregation in simple but poetic fashion that our world is a work of art to which the Creator wants all of us to contribute. But has anyone seen any great painting, any great work of art done in one single color? There are in fact always different colors, but disposed in such a way that they go together in harmony, that they do not clash. Perhaps our world is not better than it is, perhaps it is not more perfect as a work of art because we have attempted to make it in one color, to eliminate other colors insofar as possible. Then this should and could be remedied. None should be presumptuous enough to think that he alone and by himself can supply the solution that will be the remedy, but we must all think about it and work towards a better solution. Then the solution will come.

There is perhaps no better conclusion than this sermon, though inadequately rendered here, to a review of the present situation in the schools and of the social evolution of the Old Dominion.

[15] Gunnar Myrdal and Associates, *An American Dilemma: The Negro Problem and Modern Democracy*, New York, 1944, is a basic study of the question; see also Virginia Writers Project, W.P.A., *The Negro in Virginia*, New York, 1940 (sponsored by the Hampton Institute).

How much change?

At the mid-point of this century, it may be said that Virginia is again "at the crossroads." Unfortunately this expression can easily be applied to any region at any time. Every community is faced every moment with decisions to be made amidst constantly shifting conditions; and every decision that is made orients the community in some particular way. But Virginia around 1950 is and has been changing fast, and the existing conditions in the state and the surrounding areas make it easy to foresee more and more change. How much change? How extensive? It has not been the aim of this study to answer these questions. We have attempted to describe and explain to the best of our ability the forces at play.

Resistance to change, perhaps more than in other parts of the United States, is certainly characteristic of Virginia. This conservatism has often been explained as resulting from the local political system, from the "party machine" that controls the commonwealth's government. In his excellent analysis of Southern politics, Professor V. O. Key, Jr., started with the case of Virginia and called it a "political museum piece." [16] He pointed out how light the vote usually is in Virginia: in gubernatorial primaries the winning candidate rarely polls as much as ten per cent of the adult population, usually less than that. This proportion is among the lowest in the nation, considering that often in Virginia more people vote in the primaries than in the election proper. These numbers are kept low, we are told, by the poll tax, by many technical difficulties in the process of registration of the voters, by systematic challenging of the voters at the polls unless they are well known to the officials in charge. Such practices can decrease the number of voters, but they are efficient to achieve the aim of the "party machine" only insofar as this aim is tacitly accepted by the vast majority of the potential voters. It is our profound belief that no government can last long, and thirty years is a long time in these matters, unless it is acceptable to the majority of the governed. A people will not long retain an administration that they deeply dislike. Since the present "political machine" in Virginia came to power, with the reforms in the state's finances and the highway building program of Senator Harry F. Byrd, the people of the Old Dominion have enjoyed a period of economic change and rapid growth, even of rejuvenation. The cause of these changes largely transcended the state's boundaries; local politics have perhaps a limited part only in the responsibility

[16] See V. O. Key, Jr., *Southern Politics in State and Nation*, New York, 1949. A strong criticism of Virginia politics was made by William Manchester, "The Byrd Machine," *Harper's Magazine*, November, 1952.

for the evolution, and by the same token they should not be charged with the less encouraging features of the situation.

The roots of the forces at play reach deeper than the political parties. Resistance to change is a popular attitude among Virginians. Since they are slow to accept novelties, they benefit less quickly and sometimes less in the long run from new trends. They seem ready to accept the consequences of such belatedness. They know that they have been led and governed for a long time by an aristocracy: they usually feel it right and better to leave the matters of government to the same social group. One knows he does or does not "belong to the folks who vote" or to the "important folks" in general. And one finds it quite natural and endurable to belong or not to belong. The same beliefs and mental attitudes are also applicable to many economic matters and technical changes.

So the Virginian needs to be firmly convinced that some new thing or new capacity fits him. But as urbanization and industrialization come to the majority of the population, as more newcomers are added who do not feel the same way, as more education is attained by the average individual, new ideas and attitudes take shape. The old partitions show more and more cracks. This trend makes for change, although it cannot prevent new sets of partitions from arising. Such are the ways of human societies, constantly shifting, constantly endeavoring to reshape themselves, even in their efforts for self-preservation.

Conclusion

The Personality of Virginia

DEFINING the personality of a region and of its people is a difficult task. It can hardly be accomplished inside the framework of a brief description; but if the description or analysis is lengthened, many essential features are bound to fade amidst the mass of impressions accumulated. The study of a region should be a work of art. But the country itself is the work of art, created over a long period of time by the cooperation of many people, past and present, among themselves and with many physical and economic forces beyond easy control. Two works of art cannot be identical. Paintings of a person or of a landscape differ, depending on the moment, the light, the painter. We have not attempted here a portrait of Virginia, but rather an interpretation which the magnitude and complexity of our subject have sentenced in advance to be imperfect.

It is, however, quite obvious that Virginia stands out as a highly individual state in the nation, not only because of her past, but also because of her present; not only because of a set of economic features all her own, not duplicated elsewhere, but also because of a way of doing things that is Virginian and different from what can be expected from the neighbors.

A fixed, immobilized country is easier to define than one in flux. A region with a great past, having attained maximum development some time ago, is also easier to define than one rising at present to new and yet uncompleted heights of activity and prosperity. Virginia is today being rejuvenated by the industrial, agricultural, and metropolitan growths that have been so clearly developing since 1920.

The past and present of the Old Dominion testify both to the power of psychological isolation in shaping a region's behavior and to the inability of such mental attitudes to keep away indefinitely the pressures of the environing world. Examples to illustrate the state's resistance by isolation as well as the onrushing outside pressures to which she succumbs are abundantly scattered throughout the preceding chapters. It is perhaps the unique combination of these two trends in Virginia, one making for change, the other resisting it, that contributes to lend a special personality to the state.

The pressures making for change are many and varied. By far the chief among them resides in the present evolution of the whole American nation towards greater prosperity and higher standards in all fields, so sweeping in its effects that no part of the whole can avoid participating. Another factor of change is Virginia's geographical position at one of the important crossroads of this dynamic economic unit: Vermont, situated on the fringe, almost at a dead-end of the national territory, might keep some of the attitudes characteristic of isolation with more success than Virginia could, being in the center of things. The movement of industry southwards and its dispersal through the land, largely owing to the special quality of the regional labor supply and to the traditional pattern of scattered settlement, made things change in the depths of the commonwealth. The gradual encroachment of Megalopolis on Virginia and the rapidity of metropolitan growth in the Old Dominion meant more modifications, mainly in the eastern parts near the Tidewater. Finally, the modern techniques of transportation and communications, with the widespread use of the motorcar, radio, television, the development of tourism and travel, the commercialization of great historical monuments—this complex of features inherent to modern civilization added more incentives to change.

The resistance factors came from traditional characteristics of the people. The scattered settlement and the rural background still are two basic inheritances slowing down the modern dynamic economy founded on industrial and urban organization. To reach so many people scattered in so many places—in the woods, along the rivers, in the hollows between the ridges—takes more time and effort than to encompass and reorient teeming city crowds. The rural background itself generates stability, conservatism, cautiousness. And, in addition, the pride of a great past, of belonging to a state that had been the "Mother of Presidents" and of many other great leaders who did not live in the White House—this made Virginians more proud of their past than of their present and in-clined them to judge people according to their origin and past services rather than according to actual status. It is difficult to understand why and how Virginians adopted such attitudes and stuck to them stubbornly while cousins of theirs who went west to settle the wide open spaces be-yond the ridges turned into progressive and dynamic citizens, mainly preoccupied with problems of the present and of future progress. Geog-raphers have sometimes called upon the local "physical environment" to explain such differences of behavior. We know, however, that these be-havior patterns may change while the physical conditions of the environ-ment remain stable. Social evolution takes place among people who have not migrated. These differences appear to be determined by a slow proc-ess in which economic opportunity, family tradition and general educa-tion play decisive parts. The local physical conditions are only one aspect, and not always a major one, of economic opportunity.

The general pattern of education as received in the family circle and at school appears to be a more potent factor determining a community's general behavior than has been usually recognized, particularly in area studies. This pattern consists of so many and so subtle elements that they cannot be objectively measured and are seldom easily describable. Many features in the system of education, taking this term in its broadest sense, are quite similar from area to area, while the behavior of people differs from one area to another. The dissimilarities may be a better clue than the similarities in examining the ultimate result. Virginians are proud of their past. They delight in their nicknames, "Old Dominion" and "Cava-liers." It was because the colony was loyal to the Cavaliers' political party during the English civil war in the seventeenth century that Virginia was called the "Old Dominion." The Cavaliers were attached to the old regime, to the King, to an established political system and a social hier-archy. To a large extent Virginians have kept in their education the love of the past, the respect for established authority, and the traditional social hierarchy. They are individually less ambitious for great achieve-ment than are many people in the United States. They are less eager than the average American for widening the scope of economic oppor-tunity. Being satisfied with less, and enjoying their memories of greatness, they are happier perhaps than many people who seek more than they can reach.

Does this kind of happiness offer actual satisfaction? Perhaps psycho-logically it does, but in terms of strength, of the place it provides for the community among its neighbors, it is rather a weakness. Respecting the established hierarchy and the traditional order does not necessarily reinforce a country, especially when its neighbors are rapidly progressing in standard of living, in consumption and production, and in terms of relative power and prestige. Eventually the weaker region appears retarded and underdeveloped by comparison and is unable to resist the invasion by outside forces. Most of the economic and industrial development of Virginia in the twentieth century has been determined, financed, and managed from other parts in the United States, usually those north of Virginia. Whether this is advantageous or regrettable is for the Virginians to decide; however, if they should come to regret it, they could not change it without a long and strenuous endeavor.

The American nation has risen in a meteoric fashion to her present position of power and prosperity in the world. That a nation could so fully achieve world leadership less than 350 years after its first small foundations is almost unbelievable and certainly unprecedented in history. It would appear from history that the process usually takes more time. Perhaps, however, it is not always wise to look for precedents in our known past. No nation's history duplicates that of any other nation. And the pace of what can be done has been extraordinarily accelerated by the achievements of science and technology within the last hundred years.

In the rise of the United States many influences have come into play. The nation has been driven ahead by an immense endeavor towards progress and development, towards a bigger and better land and a bigger and better people; this endeavor has paid off handsomely. The titanic endeavor by means of which the North American continent was so rapidly settled and so well developed necessarily bestowed upon the nation as a whole some Promethean features which have come to be rooted in the common education of the people. Prometheus was, according to the Greek legend, an ancient hero, a Titan who endeavored to master some of the secrets of the gods and to achieve great advances for mankind by bringing him some of these secrets: he succeeded in bringing fire down to the earth and making it possible for men to use it. But Jupiter, to punish him for this achievement, chained him to the top of a mountain while a vulture daily consumed his liver. There are several versions of the myth of Prometheus, but its meaning is clear. Such tremendous drives, such titanic endeavors have their ransom in a feeling of constant dissatisfaction, in perpetual worries for still bigger and better results and for full and permanent security.

Such is the "Prometheism" of America. It has deep roots in the religious and social traditions which belong to New England, New York, and Pennsylvania. It was very nearly planned and expressed at the end of the eighteenth century in the discussions held by the American Philosophical Society in Philadelphia.

All peoples, of course, have some features that could be called Promethean. Legends similar to the ancient Greek one are found in the folklores of many another country. One may perhaps interpret some episodes of the Bible, such as Jacob's fight with the Angel, which left him lame, as expressing the same principle. However, the intensity and the quality of "Prometheism" vary greatly from people to people. None has demonstrated it in recent times with greater force and greater success than the Americans did. But there have been differences within the Union. Virginia has never been as Promethean in its attitude as the communities to its north. A few of her sons, among whom Jefferson is probably the most famous, have been deeply possessed by this aspect of American tradition, but most of the Virginia people and the Virginia aristocracy have remained aloof from it.

The Promethean endeavor is a magnificent but trying and burdensome experience. Perhaps it is because there is much less of it in the Old Dominion, in the Virginia mode of life, that so many Americans from elsewhere feel so great an attraction for this oasis of calm and quiet. Perhaps they hope that life in Virginia will offer them more relaxation and fuller satisfaction than they have known in other places. Perhaps it will. In this respect the Virginia way of life has a real mission: if it came to play a greater part within the American civilization it might mellow it somewhat. However, one wonders also whether the present would be a time well chosen for American endeavors to settle down and for the nation to relax. It may be safer for the future of Western civilization that Americans remain faithful to their Promethean traditions.

As for Virginia, the problem of her traditional way of life may well rest in the balance of the coming decades. More outsiders come to the Old Dominion, and few of them are attracted only by the charm and serenity of local life. Whether they will bring more of the usual American "Prometheism" to Virginia, or be assimilated to the local traditions, as most Virginians think they will not fail to be, we would not venture to forecast. Whatever the outcome, it may be safely assumed that in the forthcoming decades Virginia will play a greater part than earlier in this century.

Bibliographical Suggestions and Acknowledgments

Many people participate in the preparation of a volume of this kind. Vast amounts of material, printed and otherwise, are utilized for such a study. Most of our direct obligations to the work of others have been acknowledged in the footnotes in the preceding pages. It is not the purpose of this book to supply an exhaustive bibliography of Virginia and its problems. Such listings would unduly lengthen the present volume. Our intention is therefore to provide the interested reader with some indications as to materials for further reading or research. While making such bibliographical suggestions, we will mention the main sources of our own knowledge of Virginia as well as the principal persons and institutions that have generously helped us in our inquiry. The best way to proceed appears to be to acknowledge first the sources in the field of general information pertinent to this book, and refer the reader later to more specialized sources for each of our chapters.

I. General Information about Virginia

The geographer who attempts a regional study in the United States of an area the size of Virginia can easily be overwhelmed at first with the heaps of printed material available to him and with the immense quantity of unprinted material to which he can easily gain access. Once the necessary material is gathered, it seems easier to make ten volumes out of it than reduce it to one.

Our first bibliography on the subject was supplied by the Research Index of the American Geographical Society in New York, which kindly supplied us with a photostatic copy of all the cards in their file relating to Virginia and the neighboring areas. This basic source was complemented mainly by references from the indexes of the Library of Congress in Washington, the Virginia State Library in Richmond, and the Library of the University of Virginia in Charlottesville. We gathered more material, which related to the technical and economic aspects of our inquiry, from the library index and through the personal assistance of faculty members of the Virginia Polytechnic Institute in Blacksburg. A vast amount of data is available in Blacksburg on most of the questions covered by our study, either in the publications of the various departments and bureaus of V.P.I. or in mimeographed and manuscript form. This source is particularly important in the fields of agriculture and mining.

General data about Virginia has been summarized in one volume by an excellent team of the Virginia Writers' Project and published as *Virginia: A Guide to the Old Dominion* in the American Guide Series by the Oxford University Press, New York, in 1940. It still is a useful source for general background and historical information, although it mainly describes the commonwealth as it was by 1940. Pages 647 to 667 contain a helpful bibliography.

General data concerning the present social, economic, and regional status of Virginia can be found in many branches and departments of the commonwealth's government, mainly in Richmond, and of the University of Virginia in Charlottesville. We are especially indebted to the publications and mimeographed reports, many of which are quoted in the footnotes, of the Virginia Department of Conservation and Development (particularly of its Division of Planning and Economic Development, which works in close touch with the Advisory Council on the Virginia Economy in Richmond) and to the Bureau of Population and Economic Research, directed by Dr. Lorin A. Thompson, at the University of Virginia in Charlottesville. The staffs of both these institutions have helped us in different aspects of our research and made possible a rapid acquaintance with the commonwealth. Dr. Alfred C. Wolf of Harvard University made an interesting survey of federal payments in Virginia with the help of data from the U. S. Department of Commerce.

As the method of the geographer is largely a comparative one, and as data limited to the boundaries of Virginia could not satisfy us, we have constantly dug into the abundant statistics provided for the whole Union, for each city and county in detail, by many departments of the federal government and especially by the U. S. Bureau of the Census in Washington, D. C.; among the many publications of this bureau we have used most systematically the Census of Population and Housing for 1950, the *Statistical Abstract of the United States,* especially for 1953 and 1954, and the *County and City Data Book, 1952.* Special thanks are due to Dr. Clarence E. Batschelet, Chief of the Geography Division in the Bureau of the Census, for his untiring helpfulness in many cases.

Among periodicals, we have followed the economic evolution of Virginia in such publications as:

Virginia and the Virginia Record, Richmond (monthly);

The Virginia Economic Review, published quarterly by the Division of Planning and Economic Development of the Virginia Department of Conservation and Development, Richmond;

Federal Reserve Bank of Richmond Monthly Review;

Trends in Employment Hours and Earnings in Virginia, prepared and distributed by the Virginia Department of Labor and Industry, Richmond (monthly);

The University of Virginia Newsletter, published semimonthly by the Department of Rural Social Economics of the University of Virginia, in Charlottesville.

Among newspapers, we took our basic information from the daily *Richmond Times-Dispatch* and complemented it somewhat with the *Roanoke Times,* in which the emphasis more often was on events in western Virginia. The Washington, D. C., newspapers carry a good deal of information relating to the areas of northern Virginia close to the capital; and we have also often found useful data about events in Virginia in the *New York Times.*

In our quest for cartographic material we were often helped by the Map Division of the Library of Congress, by Professor Sidman Poole, director of the Virginia Geographical Institute in Charlottesville, and by the staff of the American Geographical Society in New York. In connection with historical maps we owe also a debt of gratitude to Melle Myriem Foncin, Curator of Maps at the Bibliothèque Nationale in Paris, who helped us find some old maps and supplied us with some of the reproductions used in this volume.

Finally, a great deal of the data which went into this volume was gathered in the field and did not come from written material. We conducted most of this field inquiry ourselves. We were greatly helped in it, however, by innumerable local people who received and directed us, but especially by a consultant on soils and agriculture, Professor Edward C. Higbee of Clark University, and by our assistants Mr. Theo F. Schearf, Mr. Robert T. Lester, and Mr. Leon François Hoffman. The maps were prepared by three distinguished cartographers, Miss Sylvie Rimbert, Miss Sara Love and Mr. J. Barbier. They all gave to their part in this study their best efforts and knowledge. Thanks are due also to Mrs. R. S. Mandelstam of Washington and Mrs. Jean Woltjen in Princeton for their devoted help in doing more than usual secretarial work.

II. Sources by Chapters

Chapter One

This being largely a general informative and introductory chapter, the sources of general data apply more particularly to it, with the addition of the sources quoted in the footnotes. Many of the titles mentioned below in connection with Chapter Three, can also be referred to for this descriptive chapter.

Chapter Two

Historical studies of Virginia are abundant, particularly on the first two centuries of Virginia history. There is a history of the commonwealth in one volume, with an important bibliography, by Matthew Page Andrews, *Virginia: The Old Dominion,* Doubleday, Doran, and Company, Garden City, N. Y., 1937. It tells the story up to the early 1930's, but is much more detailed for the period preceding the War Between the States. For all bibliographical research on old documents and texts, invaluable help can be obtained from the two volumes of the *Virginia Historical Index* by E. G. Swem, printed by the Stone Printing and Manufacturing Company, Roanoke, 1934.

We were fortunate in benefiting by the directions and kind advice of Professor Thomas Jefferson Wertenbaker of Princeton University in this part of our study. Many of Professor Wertenbaker's books on various aspects of Virginia's history are quoted in this and other chapters. Among the many classics describing the Old Dominion at the end of the seventeenth and during the eighteenth centuries, we have made abundant use particularly of Beverley's famous *Historie of Virginia* and of the less well known *The Present State of Virginia, and the College,* by Henry Hartwell, James Blair, and Edward Chilton, of which a new edition with an introduction by Hunter Dickinson Farish was published by Colonial Williamsburg, Inc., in Williamsburg, 1940. For a later period various sources were used, among which Thomas Jefferson's works, and particularly his *Notes on Virginia,* are of outstanding importance.

A great deal of interesting material, whether quoted directly or not, was found during a visit to the remarkable collections on American history of the Henry E. Huntington Library at San Marino, Calif., especially in the Brock Collection there. To the staff of this library we wish to express our sincere thanks for their gracious and efficient help as well as for the permission to quote from some of the documents and publications of the library. Professor George Boas of the Johns Hopkins University kindly gave us the great benefit of his assistance during our period of research at the Henry E. Huntington Library and helped us to understand various points in the history of education in Virginia and the elaboration of the Old Dominion's original tradition.

For the nineteenth and twentieth centuries, more varied and recent materials had to be used, as indicated in the footnotes. In many cases publications, both old and new, of the Bureau of the Census helped us to describe and understand the trends. Professor Frank Notestein of Princeton University kindly supervised the work of a graduate student of his in demography on a report retracing for the needs of our survey some details of the changes in the population of Virginia. Much was also derived from the good advice received from Professors Gilbert Chinard of Princeton and Sidney Ratner of Rutgers University.

Chapter Three

In this mainly descriptive chapter, the chief source of information was the field study of Virginia. There is no county or city in the commonwealth that was not visited, most of them several times, by the author. Data and impressions thus gathered in the field were interpreted in the light of the more objective knowledge derived from the study of the Censuses of Population, Housing, Agriculture and Manufactures, and from careful examination of maps—topographic, geological and economic—published by various official services.

We utilized also the report prepared by Professor Edward C. Higbee on the agricultural status and evolution of Virginia during his period of field study in the spring of 1953. Most of the sources used for Chapter One and listed in "General Information" were also helpful here. A great deal of the material used for Parts Two and Three of this volume contributed in some way to help us shape the general tableau sketched in this regional analysis of the commonwealth.

Chapter Four

Our study of forestry in Virginia results also from a considerable amount of fieldwork. We have been constantly helped and directed in it by the competent staff of the Virginia Forest Service and of the Federal Services administering forests in Virginia. Our sincere thanks are due to Mr. George W. Dean, the State Forester, and Mr. S. G. Hobart, the Chief of Forest Management, as well as to the Superintendent of the Shenandoah National Park and his staff in Luray, to the offices of the supervisors of the Jefferson National Forest in Roanoke and of the George Washington National Forest in Harrisonburg. The U. S. Forestry Service gave us every possible help through its staff in the Department of Agriculture in Washington, D. C., its Southeastern Forest Experiment Station in Asheville, N. C., and the branch of this station in Franklin, Va. Many of their publications have been quoted in footnotes in this chapter and much more was derived from long discussions with the staff either in the offices or in the field. Private companies helped us when we called on them, especially the Chesapeake Corporation in West Point, Va., and the West Virginia Pulp and Paper Company, in Covington, Va. Our special thanks are also due to Professor Hugh Raup, director of the Harvard Forest at Petersham, Mass., for discussing many important points with us and suggesting directions for research. Most of all in this chapter we are indebted to our consultant in forestry, Mr. Henri

Morel of the French National Forest Service, an international authority in matters of forest management.

The basic description of the Virginia forests and their problems as of the middle 1940's may be found in *Virginia Forest Resources and Industries* by Ronald B. Craig, U. S. Department of Agriculture, Miscellaneous Publ. No. 681, Washington, D. C., April, 1949. A new survey which should lead to a revised edition of this publication was in progress during 1954 but was not fully available at the time of the completion of our work. A good general scholarly description of the forests in and around Virginia is provided by E. Lucy Braun, *Deciduous Forests of Eastern North America*, Philadelphia, 1950. The well-known volume of the U. S. Department of Agriculture, *Trees, Yearbook of Agriculture, 1949*, remains another basic source of reference.

In the field of water conservation, we are greatly indebted to the directions given to us by Dr. Bernard Frank and Dr. Charles R. Hursh of the U. S. Forestry Service, as well as to the voluminous but always helpful report of the President's Commission on Water Policy. The staff of the Virginia Commission of Game and Inland Fisheries and several officials of the U. S. Fish and Wildlife Service helped us to better understand the problem of wildlife restoration and conservation.

Chapter Five

The *Census of Agriculture, 1950* was the basic statistical source for this chapter. Many publications by the U. S. Department of Agriculture and by the Virginia Agricultural Experiment Station (Blacksburg, Va.) were used to interpret and complement the statistics. The report on agriculture in Virginia by E. C. Higbee was most helpful here again. Most of the maps in this chapter, especially those commented upon early in the chapter, were drafted by Mr. Jean Barbier. We are also grateful to many members of the Faculty at the Virginia Polytechnic Institute and of the Virginia Department of Agriculture for their help and cooperation. A substantial number of farmers were interviewed during the fieldwork by the author, his consultants, and assistants.

Chapter Six

Publications of the U. S. Bureau of Mines in Washington, D. C., and of the Engineering Experiment Station at the Virginia Polytechnic Institute, in Blacksburg, supplied most of the material used in this chapter. Mr. Robert T. Lester prepared a special report on coal mining and marketing in Virginia for our purposes. A number of coal mine operators, miners, and union officials were interviewed in Virginia and in Washington. Special thanks are due to the management and staff of the Jewell

Ridge Coal Corporation, which kindly organized for us a special visit to their mines.

Some material was derived from the major railroad companies serving the coalfields, and much more from the library and staff of the Interstate Commerce Commission in Washington. The yearly publication by the U. S. Bureau of Mines, *Minerals Yearbook* (as a general source of reference) and the quite detailed report prepared for the Bureau of Mines by the Corps of Engineers, Department of the Army, and the firm of Ford, Bacon, and Davis, and entitled *The Synthetic Liquid Fuel Potential of Virginia,* Washington, D. C., April, 1951, may be considered as the two basic sources of information on the coal question.

Chapter Seven

The industrialization of the South has now been studied in many works. The classical study of Howard W. Odum, *Southern Regions of the United States,* Chapel Hill, N. C., 1936, still has an actual historical importance; it is well complemented by Broadus and G. S. Mitchell, *The Industrial Revolution in the South,* Baltimore, 1930, which put the emphasis on the labor problem. The present situation is described on the basis of statistics supplied by the U. S. Bureau of the Census, especially in the *Census of Manufactures, 1947,* adjusted by reference to *Trends in Employment Hours and Earnings in Virginia,* prepared monthly by the Virginia Department of Labor and Industry in Richmond, as well as to the annual survey supplied by the same department and the *Directory of Virginia Manufacturing and Mining, 1953–1954,* regularly published by the Virginia State Chamber of Commerce in Richmond. Many publications and reports of the Bureau of Labor Statistics, U. S. Department of Labor, Washington, have also been utilized and several of them have been quoted in footnotes.

In this field the author obtained invaluable help from the vast amount of knowledge gathered in the field of industrialization and connected problems by the Bureau of Economic and Population Research in Charlottesville and by the services of the Division of Planning and Economic Development in Richmond. Many of the publications of these two research organizations are quoted in our footnotes and we owe special gratitude to the personal help of many members of their staffs, particularly Dr. Lorin A. Thompson in Charlottesville and Dr. Edwin E. Holm, Jr., in Richmond. Many private industrial corporations helped us to better understand the industrial situation. Special thanks are due in this connection to the Dan River Mills in Danville, the American Viscose Corporation in Philadelphia, E. I. Dupont de Nemours and Company of Wilmington, Del., and to the directors of the Chambers of Commerce in many cities of Virginia, especially Richmond, Roanoke, Lynchburg, Danville, Alexandria, Charlottesville, Bristol, Norfolk, Portsmouth, and Newport News.

Mr. Edouard A. Seidler, who had specialized in labor relations at the University of California, made a helpful report on the industrial labor relations in Virginia, after a field survey, especially in the western part of the commonwealth. Reports prepared by the Virginia Department of Labor and Industry and by the Unemployment Compensation Commission of Virginia were quite helpful too.

Chapter Eight

On the problems regarding assets and liabilities of location, general data supplies the main source. This chapter has the functions both of an introduction and of a conclusion. We do not know of another work that studies in this general fashion the meaning of geographical location for that area or a neighboring one in terms of general economic opportunity rather than only for some specific aspect of marketing or plant location. Most of the sources quoted in the preceding chapters were indirectly utilized in some way for this one. For that reason we situated it at the end of Part II, discussing the use of resources in greater detail.

Chapter Nine

Most of the data on metropolitan growth in Virginia is provided by the detailed statistics available in the publications of the U. S. Bureau of the Census, and they can be interpreted mainly after careful field-work. Interviews with the research staffs of many chambers of commerce, and in a number of cities with the city manager, have put us on the track of the local problems as the responsible local people saw them. Certain counties and cities have recently had plans prepared for their redevelopment or zoning, and these we have utilized. The traffic problems are usually central in today's worries of local authorities. The whole question of the growing urbanization of Virginia encompasses much more than a purely local question and than the mosaic of traffic bottlenecks. Such studies as the one directed and edited by Dean Charles F. Marsh, *The Hampton Roads Communities in World War II*, Chapel Hill, N. C., 1951, are of great value for a wider view of all the questions and consequences involved. We were also helped by the survey of Roanoke and particularly of its Central Business District made in 1953 by a group of graduate students of Clark University under the direction of Professor Raymond E. Murphy. The maritime aspects of the urban development of the Tidewater are well surveyed and explained in the reports and publications of the Virginia State Port Authority, Norfolk, the research staff of which was most cooperative (see footnote, page 500). These questions, as well as those considered in Chapters Eight and Ten, are better understood in the light of a general examination of what happens along the whole area extending in the eastern United States from the Atlantic seaboard inland as far as the Appalachians.

Chapter Ten

This chapter, covering various aspects of Virginia's present evolution, has come out of the confrontation and study of material from a wide variety of sources. Publications of the U. S. Bureau of the Census are here again the foundation of most of our discussion. We were greatly helped in interpreting them, with regard to migrations, by the staff of the extensive and careful survey of population redistribution and economic growth conducted mainly on the basis of statistical data at the University of Pennsylvania, in Philadelphia, under the direction of Professors Simon Kuznets and Dorothy S. Thomas.

The Department of Highways of the Commonwealth of Virginia supplied us in its reports with abundant data as to roads and traffic. The staff of this department wholeheartedly cooperated with our research, offering enlightenment on many aspects of economic evolution seen from the highway engineer's standpoint. We were also helped in our comparative examination of the situation by the Highway Department of North Carolina in Raleigh.

In the field of education, many faculty members of the colleges and universities of Virginia gave us the benefit of their experience and knowledge. We talked also with many teachers in various parts of the state. The reports prepared by the Superintendent of Public Instruction and the State Chamber of Commerce in Richmond were often utilized for the related part of this chapter.

The reader has been spared the full bibliography of over one thousand items which we consulted in the study that led to this volume. He will nevertheless find the most important titles in the footnotes of the book, and these pages of bibliographical suggestions may direct interested readers to the sources where full information as to either bibliography or recent data may be found. We hope that the hundreds of Virginians and of public officials and academic persons who helped us in various ways during our work on this study throughout the United States will forgive us for not listing all their names. We feel almost embarrassed to acknowledge how much generous assistance we have received.

Index

Dismal Swamp, 30, 43; account of, 154; feeder ditch, *156;* forests of, 247, 272–273; proposed drainage, 247
Dismal Swamp Canal, 113
Dinwiddie, Robert, 83
District of Columbia, population growth, 456. *See also* Washington, D. C., metropolitan area
Doddridge, Joseph, quoted, 98
dogs, free-running, 288, 291, 298
Dosker, C. D., 258 n.
Douglas, Thomas W., 419 n.
drainage, around Dismal Swamp, 154; on Eastern Shore, 160; of Great Valley, 200, 205; of Piedmont, 168; projects, 247, 374
Drakes Mill, account of, 182–183
droughts, problems of, 332, 334, 373–374
Dublin, 214
Duffield, J. W., 271 n.
Dumfries, founded, 82; highways of 1919, *528, 529;* of 1947, *530*
du Pont, E. I., de Nemours Co., company labor union, 435–436; employment, 420; nylon, 419; rayon manufacture, 134, 214, *406, 411,* 417, 486, 510
Du Pont Rayon Co., 405, 408
Duveen, Denis Ian, 115 n.
dwelling units, 147 (M). *See also* housing

Eastern Shore, The, account of, 158–166; crops and livestock, 325–343 *passim;* climate, 23; food industries, 412 (M), 413; large farms, 369–370; marshland, 30; population density, 34; truck farming, 124, 159–162
eastern Virginia, differentiated from western, 11–12, 143–144, 226; early forests, 234; regional divisions and modes of life, 144–187; topography, 142, 144, 144–187. *See also* Piedmont; Tidewater region
Eavenson, E. N., 382 n.
economic data map, 497
economy, the, colonial, 66–68; before 1800, summarized, 91–92; and federal government, 457–460; and geographical location, 440–441; and metropolitan state areas, 471 (M), 472; and raw materials, 345; recent changes in, 463–464, 467–468; after the Revolution, 93–94; in 1750's, 88; of Shenandoah Valley, 208–210; of southern Blue Ridge, 199–200; of southern Piedmont, 186–187; of southeastern triangle, 223; and urbanization, 511–513; and War Between the States, 119–129
education, adults, 546 (M); cost of 545–547; current problems of, 539–544; early, 74–75, 535–538, 545; enrollment by age group, 539; in forestry, need for, 314; free schools established, 117 n.; higher, 551 (M); Jefferson and, 536–538, 545, 550–551; of Negroes, 129–130, 551–554; prior to 1860, 114–117; programs and problems, 545–554; teacher shortages, 116, 129, 540–541, 543; after War Between the States, 129–130
Edwards, A. D., 360 n.
Egerton, Sir John, 64
eggs, per-capita number of, 334–335

electronics industry, **213**
élite, development of, 88–93; education of, 74–75, 535; of northern Piedmont, 174; Elizabethan English, studies of, 189
elk, 287, 288, 290–291
Elk Knob, precipitation, 25
employment, in chemical industries, 416–417; in coal industry, 392–397; by federal government, 457; in manufacturing, 408–409, 410, 424, 426–427; nonagricultural, 140, 426; in pulp and paper industries, 259; in Richmond, 505; in shipyards, 422, 494; in tobacco manufacturing, 416; and unemployment compensation funds, 431; of women and children, 431–432; in wood-using industries, 231
England, coal problems of, 397–398; 17th-century, 76; forest history of, 306; settlement of Virginia, 55–68; timber needs of, 62, 230; and tobacco, 64–65
Erie Canal, 106
erosion. *See* geological erosion; soil erosion
excelsior manufacture, *258,* 259–260, *264*

Fairfax County, 174; county seat established, 82; forest area, 241; population, 1750's, 85; population growth, 85, 456; rural road, *167;* as suburb of Washington, 169–170, 479, 481–482
fall line, 19, 38, 39; importance of, 12–13, 144, 166
Falls Church, Negro population, 49; population, 169; as suburb of Washington, 169, 479
family income, 1950, 186
farm population, 317
Farm Security Administration, Ida Valley Farms, *14*
farmers, marginal subsistence, 360–363; standard of living of, 359 (M); and wildlife protection, 297
Farmer's Register, 101
farming. *See* agriculture; farmland and farms; plantation agriculture; tenant farming
farmland and farms, *281, 368;* area and numbers, 315, 316; average sizes, 317–318; commercial, 322–323; large, 367–371; marginal, and the Negro, 364–365; numbers of, 315; sizes, 317–318, 319 (M), 323, 360, 367; small, 358–367; with telephones, 366 (M); tenant-operated, 320–22; use of, 323–325; value of, 318–320, 319 (M); woodlot problems of, 280–286
Farmville, temperatures, 20
Farmville basin, coal in, 380, 382–383
Fauquier County, 174; agriculture, 172–173; copper, 377; large farms, 368, 369; railroad developments, 107; as suburb of Washington, 171–174
Fearnow, P. C., 293 n.
federal government. *See* United States
Fenneman, N. M., 19 n.
fertilizers, use of, 102
firewood, statistics on, 262
fish and fishing, *38,* 147, 287; catch, 449–450; licenses, 296; protection of, 291–292, 295–296. *See also* shellfish

Fisherman's Island waterfowl refuge, 294
Fiske, John, 55
Fitzhugh, William, 86, 373
Flannagan, Roy C., 112 n.
Flatwoods, 154, 157, 160
Florida, developments in, 460, 461; non-agricultural employment, 426
Floyd County, 191; account of, 197–199
Floyd Courthouse, 197
Fluvanna County, account of, 175–176
food industries, distribution of, 412 (M), 413, 422; metropolitan influence on, 459
forage crops, 330–334; distribution of, 333 (M)
forest areas, 240 (M), 241; of farmlands, 316–317; in pines, 244
forest fires, 245–246; control of, 232, 267–270, 276, 300, 310
forest management, problems of, 266–280; proposals for, 309–314; and wildlife program, 297
forestry, problems of, 280–283
forests, 28–29, 30–31, 230–314; of Allegheny Mountains, 217; of Blue Ridge, 193–195; climactic, 233; controlled burning of, 269–270; on Eastern Shore, 163–164; England's need for, 62, 230; history of, 233–239; and industrial needs, 254–266; of James peninsula, 153–154; of middle Piedmont, 175; of Northern Necks, 149; of southern coastal plain, 156; of southern Piedmont, 181; types of, 242 (M); water resources of, 298–305; and wildlife, 286–298. See also deforestation; lumbering; national forests and parks
Foster, Sir Augustus John, 95
fox hunting, 293
Franklin, Benjamin, 115, 537
Franklin, 158; pulp and paper industries, 260, 308
Franklin County, 197, 199; tobacco, 125
Frederick County, population, 1750's, 85; tenant farming, 320
Fredericksburg, 38, 39, 105; account of, 177; founded, 82; role of, 470; Washington's mother's house, 89
Freeman, Douglas Southall, quoted, 86, 88
French Huguenot settlers, 47, 71, 79
freight. See motor freight; railroad freight
From Mine to Market, etc., 389 n., 503 n.
Front Royal, 213, 214
frost, average number of days without, 24 (M); records of, 21–22
fruit growing, account of, 341–343; distribution of crops, 340 (M); in Shenandoah Valley, 209

Gage, Charles E., 356 n.
Galax, 197, 199; view of, 188
game. See wildlife
Garnet Peak, 231
Garnett, W. E., 360 n.
geographical location, importance of, 131, 140, 440–462; and manufacturing developments, 408; potentials of, 478–479
geological erosion, 15–19; in Great Valley, 202, 203
geological past, 15–19

geological structure, of Great Valley, 201–205, 215; of Piedmont, 168; of southwestern Virginia, 221
Georgia, nonagricultural employment, 426; population density, 33; tobacco growing, 93
German settlers, 47, 78, 79, 189
Gibson, W. L., Jr., 375 n.
Giles County, 216; account of, 219; diamonds, 376; elk, 291; limestone, 378
Gilliam, Sara K., 33 n., 122 n.; quoted, 34
Glasgow, 214; account of, 199
Gloucester County, population, 1750's, 85
Goochland County, account of, 175–176; cattle, 371; pulpwood glut, 281
Gordonsville, railroad connection, 107
Gould, E. V., Jr., 285 n.
Governor's Palace, Williamsburg, gateway, 86
grain reaper, invented, 102
grains, distribution of, 336 (M); growing of, 93–94, 97, 335, 337; storage problems, 337, 339. See also specific grains, e.g., corn, wheat
grasslands, cultivation, 371, 372–373, 374; and pasturage problems, 330–334
Grayson County, 191; account of, 197–199
Great Valley, The, 19, 39, 200–215; coal fields of, 380, 383; coal production, 383; crops and livestock, 325–343 passim; around 1800, 98; elevations, 187, 191, 205; forests, 253; importance of location, 451–455; large farms, 369; livestock after War Between the States, 125; manufacturing in, 411–416; 421–422; Negro population, 50; population, 1750's, 75; settlement of, 82–83, 189; small cities, 510; temperatures, 20; topography, 200–205; wheat growing, 94. See also Shenandoah Valley
Greene County, tobacco, 125
Greensville County, tenant farming, 322
ground water, 400–401
growing seasons, 21; driest, 26–27

habitat, of miners, 222; pattern of, 43; urban and rural, 39–45. See also settlement
Hakluyt, Richard, 62, 64
Halifax County, aerial view, 181; cattle in, 13; decline of farms, 177–178; farms, 180; hog killing, 145; tenant farming, 322, 353; tobacco, 125; tobacco farm, described, 354–356
Hamm, John E., 435 n.
Hampden-Sydney College, founded, 115
Hampton, 80
Hampton–Newport News–Warwick metropolitan area, 154; economic data, 497 (M); growth, 470, 491–503; manufacturing developments, 437; population, 40
Hampton Normal and Agricultural Institute, founded, 130
Hampton Roads, 144, 149; advantages of location, 447, 448, 449; economic data, 497 (M); employment, 424; growth of, 447, 478; as manufacturing center, 411, 415; Negro population, 49; population density, 34; as port, 495–498; railroad service, 124; shipbuilding, 422, 494–495;